THE HOVE INTERNATIONAL
BLUE BOOK
GUIDE PRICES FOR CLASSIC
AND COLLECTABLE CAMERAS

1992 – 1993

THE HOVE INTERNATIONAL

Blue Book

GUIDE PRICES FOR CLASSIC AND COLLECTABLE CAMERAS

1992 – 1993

Edited by
Douglas St Denny

HOVE FOTO BOOKS

The Hove International Blue Book
Guide Prices for Classic and Collectable Cameras
1992-1993

Third edition published March 1992 by
Hove Foto Books
34 Church Road
Hove, Sussex BN3 2GJ

British Library Cataloguing-in-Publication Data.
A catalogue record for this book is available from the British Library.
ISBN: 0 - 906447 - 50 - X

Vertrieb/Auslieferung in deutschsprachigen
Ländern ausschließlich durch:
Verlag Laterna magica Joachim F. Richter
ISBN: 3 - 87467 - 498 - 3

Design, and layout :
Wordpower Publishing   WIRE design studio
Herts AL6 9AG   Sussex BN1 4AP

Printed by Hartnolls Ltd
Cornwall PL31 1EG

Middle photograph on cover of
Kodak Beau Brownie cameras courtesy Brian Coe

Contents

Publisher's Note

THE HOVE INTERNATIONAL BLUE BOOK, like all price guides, indicates the possible price you may have to pay for an item.

You may consider the price of a particular camera to be too high, too low, or just right.

At the end of the day, only a willing seller and a willing buyer can determine the price at which a particular camera will change hands. At least with the aid of the *Blue Book* you have a basis to start from.

More makers and cameras are added to each edition of the *Blue Book.* This edition contains at least 25% more than that of 1990–91.

If you come across a camera which you think should be in the guide, the Publishers will be pleased to hear from you, ideally with a suitable illustration. After all, the *Blue Book* is for you, the Collector and Enthusiast.

D.R.G.

Foreword
ENGLISH

THIS 1992–93 EDITION of the *Blue Book,* now the *Hove International Blue Book*, is the biggest and best yet. Since publication of the second edition, more than 1,000 new listings have been added, with great care taken to add only those items which offer the most in terms of information or interest to the camera collector. It is not our wish to become a camera encyclopedia. We feel that the camera collecting public is better served with the *Blue Book* in its present form.

Some of the new items are "bread and butter" cameras, many described here for the first time. Others are obscure or rare, and add a touch of spice to the collecting market. You will find more accessories and lenses listed than ever before, many appearing only in the *Blue Book,* and no other guide. We have discovered that more and more, collectors are turning to accessories to fill out their collections, and knowing which accessories are available in the market place will also help collectors establish collecting goals.

New additions from Argentina, Brazil, Spain, Rumania, Czechoslovakia, and the USSR are often not described in any other price guide.

The new photos which appear in this edition were chosen for their information value and technical quality. We believe in the saying "one picture speaks a thousand words", and the clarity of the photographic reproductions you will find in the following pages sets a new standard for others to follow.

On a more personal level, making this newest edition of the *Blue Book* was a real joy. I had the pleasure of travelling to camera shows in the USA, Holland, France, England, Austria and Germany. I also visited museums and factories in France, Germany and Czechoslovakia. I even made a trip back to China to talk with collector friends, and look into the camera collecting movement there. All in all, I have been very busy working on the listings and prices which you will find in this book. I must say that it was a difficult job, the hardest edition yet, but also it was the most rewarding effort so far. Here is an example of what makes this book so personally fulfilling...

In Miami, Florida during the month of February, 1991, I attended the semi-annual two day camera fair.

I noticed a Clarus camera on a dealer's table (RU101). I stopped and picked it up. Though it looked like a Clarus, it wasn't really a Clarus after all. The name was Wescon. It had brown leather body covering, and was priced at $50. As I held it in my hands thinking that perhaps an offer of $40 might be accepted, I felt someone beside me. It was a world famous dealer in rare and speciality cameras whose table was just at the side. At that moment I knew that if I put the camera back down, I would have lost it. I told the owner that I would take the Wescon for $50, and fumbled with my wallet. The owner brought up a camera case, and told me that it went along with the deal. Inside was a flash reflector, but not just an ordinary flash reflector. Where every other flash reflector I had ever seen was chrome, this one was golden! In addition, the original instruction sheet lay in the bottom of the case. As I was packing my purchase up, the dealer at my side offered me a fast $25 profit. I turned him down.

The Wescon is now described in this edition (WC200) and nowhere else.

The story behind its discovery is one of the things that makes the *Blue Book* different from the other guides. The hunt, the find, the sharing of information, they never stop.

About the prices:

As with past editions, the prices you find here are real prices. Dealers buying for resale pay as little as possible for cameras. No collector wants to pay too much. Bidders at auction sometimes go a little overboard. Geography and emotions also play their part in establishing particular price. Sorting through these variables is often long and difficult.

No special formulae or computer programmes are used in figuring current prices. The best method is still commonsense and an open mind. Mailing lists, advertised prices, asking prices at shows, auction sale results, are looked at. Information on actual sales from around the world is reviewed. Opinions from every sort of collector and dealer are listened to.

Still, after everything is said and done, the final decision on what price is listed remains ours, mine and mine alone. You may not agree with some of them. If you don't, let the Publisher know, and tell them why. We will listen to everything you have to say.

Douglas St Denny

Introduction
ENGLISH

The *Blue Book* Goes International

WE ARE VERY PLEASED at Hove Foto Books to have been able to take over the publication of this 1992 – 1993 edition of the *Blue Book*. Our company was founded by a collector, who understands a collector's needs for detailed descriptions, good illustrations, dating information, history, model variations and all the other information that makes collecting such fun and such a challenging hobby. The *Blue Book* will be in good company with our other books on individual camera makes.

We believe that a camera collectors' price guide in the 1990s should quote prices in the major currencies in which cameras are traded internationally, especially for the rarer, more sought after items. While common, less expensive cameras are unlikely to be traded abroad, high-value rare, or fashionable, or quality marques are now traded, bought and fought for worldwide. Clearly, you are more likely to find a particularly desirable Eastman Kodak camera in the U.S.A., a Houghton-Butcher in the U.K., an early Canon in Japan, or a Zeiss in Germany. The Zeiss camera will probably be less expensive in Germany than in the U.S.A., whereas the reverse would apply to the Eastman Kodak. This has nothing to do with rates of exchange. An exchange rate quoted in, say June, might be considerably different in September or December, but the relative values of collectable cameras in the two countries will remain the same. A collector needs to know the actual value in his own country, and, if he trades internationally, in the other major markets.

Therefore prices in each country are determined by the market in each country. Prices from one country to another cannot be compared simply by multiplying by the current exchange rate. Other factors come into play with the less common items, such as availability, collecting fashions, and national characteristics. For example; in Japan original condition is all important and they will pay a premium for an outstanding example of a camera in perfect original condition: in the U.S.A. a first-class restoration, which may be rejected as unoriginal in Japan, is more likely to be regarded as desirable.

Previous editions of the *Blue Book* have given prices in U.S. Dollars, representing the Editor's judgement after taking soundings from correspondents in Germany, France, Belgium, England and the U.S.A. In this edition we are giving prices in U.S. Dollars, Pounds Sterling, Deutschmarks and French Francs, weighted to reflect, very broadly, the market conditions in the U.S.A., Britain, Germany and France. In the case of Leica cameras we are able differentiate prices between the different countries with a high degree of precision, due to our experience in producing the Hove *Leica International Price Guide,* now in its fifth edition.

The Current Market

Looking back on 1991 it has turned out to have been a year of traumatic events, from the Gulf war at the beginning to the disintegration of the Soviet Union at the end. Crisis and uncertainty in world events affect confidence and the markets which depend on it. As at the end of 1991 we have continuing recession in the U.K., still deepening recession in the U.S.A., the effects of German reunification on German inflation, and weakening of the French economy.

The camera collecting market has suffered in common with other antiques and fine art markets. Very high prices are no longer being achieved, although exceptionally sought-after items have proved exceptions to the trend. Generally speaking, the more common items in only average condition have tended to stick on dealer's shelves. The rare item, in fine condition, has still changed hands, but generally at a lower price than before. Now is the time for a collector to look carefully at the market and offer and buy selectively.

Advice to the Novice Collector

Originality

When buying, always go for the best possible condition of a camera. Originality must be the most important consideration if you are concerned about the future investment value of your collection. A restored camera, however well the restoration has been carried out, cannot be considered the same as an original; in many cases its value might be equivalent only to that of a similar model in a poorer condition, but original. On the other hand, many collectors want to see their prize exhibits in pristine condition and functioning perfectly.

Specialise

Collecting can be fun. Most collectors specialise in either a particular maker's products, or in a particular type of camera. Some may collect only folding cameras, or hand cameras, or reflex cameras, or Russian cameras, or Nikon or Kodak cameras. Others adopt a theme, perhaps to demonstrate the history of camera development, or different types of shutter, or sub-miniature cameras. Price can be another theme: some collect only cameras below a certain price, say $25. This makes it an inexpensive hobby and guards against the temptation to reach beyond one's means, but it can be just as interesting because the cheap mass-produced cameras are far more evocative of our social history than the exquisite hand-crafted machines that only few could afford when new. The possibilities are endless.

Fakes

Wherever an article has a high value and is keenly sought after by collectors, fakers are attracted by the possibilities of rich pickings. This applies as much to valuable cameras as to antiques. Faking has been a factor that collectors have needed to be aware of in the Leica world for many years now. The more involved you become in collecting and the more experience you gain, the easier it will be for you to determine the authenticity of the camera you are being offered. If you are buying from a reputable dealer you are on much safer ground. When buying at auction, you have the reassurance that by law in most countries the item being offered must be as described. Do not let the fear of fakes put you off collecting though; just be warned. There are collectors who actually collect fakes – so fakes can have a value of their own!

The Prices in this Guide

The *Blue Book* is a price GUIDE, which means what it says. The Editor has described in his *Foreword* how he arrived at the listed prices. You may think some are too high, or too low, but the purpose of this book is to give the collector a basis to work on. Some collectors may decide only to pay, say, up to 80% of the guide price. Others may be prepared to pay 110%, or even 120% of the guide price for a particularly desirable item they have been looking for. On the other hand, if selling to a dealer you would have to consider a substantially lower price, but again you have in this guide a basis for assessing his offer.

HOW TO USE THE BLUE BOOK

In looking at prices listed in this edition of *The Hove International Blue Book*, and comparing them to the value of those in your own collection, it is necessary to take the condition of each camera into account, because condition affects price.

Prices are also affected by the **rarity** of each camera. This latest edition of the *Blue Book* continues to give a rarity rating to each camera, on a scale from one to five stars, in which one star represents the commonest cameras and five stars the rarest. These ratings have been updated along with the prices.

The format of the *A to Z Camera Directory,* which forms the main part of the book, remains the same as before, except that the rarity and international price information is now given in a price bar at the bottom of each camera entry, except for lenses and accessories where the prices are given in U.S. $ only.

Condition

Prices listed in this book are for cameras in excellent condition. That means 80% to 100% original finish, similar to new, little used, no noticeable marring of wood or leather, little or no brassing, lens clean and clear, all mechanical parts in perfect working order.

For cameras in other states of condition, add or subtract from the listed prices as follows.

Mint condition: 100% original finish, everything perfect, in new condition in every respect. **Add** 10% to 25% to listed prices, but most cameras with a four- or five-star rarity can be worth an additional 100% or more than listed prices.

Very good condition: 60% original finish, item complete but wood or leather slightly scratched; scuffed or marred metal work, but no corrosion or pitmarks. Lens and viewfinder clean, shutter and other mechanical parts in working order, restorable with minimum effort and expense. **Deduct** 15% to 25% from listed prices.

Good condition: 45% original finish, minor wear on exposed surfaces, no broken major parts but may be in need of minor replacements, metal rusted or pitted in places but can be cleaned, leather scuffed andf/or aged, wood scratched, marred and may have minor cracks, but restorable. The lens will show use and the shutter may be in questionable mechanical condition, but repairable. Collectors are less and less interested in these cameras, and you might find you have a difficult time trading them off or selling them. **Deduct** 40% to 60% from listed price.

Fair condition: 25% original condition, well used and worn, in need of parts replacement and refinishing, leather cracked or missing, lens clouded or damaged, metal parts pitted and gears rounded, shutter inoperable, wood finish almost gone and in need of complete restoration. These cameras are usually sold for parts, to someone who has the same camera in better condition, but maybe needing a screw or a spring which can be salvaged from the fair camera. **Deduct** 60% to 85% from listed price.

Cameras with a four- or five-star rarity rating are often exceptions to the preceding rules. Restored cameras are usually less interesting to collectors than cameras in original condition; it can depend very much on the country and particular collecting speciality. Recently there have been a few "Luxus" gold-plated cameras of various makes coming onto the market. They are usually an attempt by a shrewd dealer to make a poor camera into something it is not. Few serious collectors will be willing to pay the money asked for such mutilations.

For usable cameras, such as the Leica M3 (EL134), or the Bessa II (VO105), needing repair, deduct the cost of repair from listed price. Be warned, though, that the repair of complex rangefinder or S.L.R. cameras can prove expensive. It can also be difficult to find a competent repairer.

Most collectors like to hear the shutter fire, particularly on the slowest speeds, but rarely require the mechanical perfection necessary for taking pictures. Pinhole leaks in the bellows of a plate camera, as long as the bellows themselves look good, should not affect a camera's price.

Rarity

Rarity indicates a camera's availability to the collector. The harder it is to find, the higher the rarity factor. The rarity factor is indicated by star ratings from 1* to 5*, as in previous editions. The ratings are defined as follows:

1* – Cameras with a **one-star** rating can be found easily. They are often seen as box lots at auctions or on market stalls. If a collector wants one, there are usually several to choose from. These cameras were mass-produced and were the most widely distributed. Most simple folding Kodak cameras and many box cameras fit into this category.

2* – Cameras with a **two-star** rarity are a little harder to find. They may have been made to a higher specification and sold originally for a higher price than the one-star rarity cameras. They are the bread and butter of the majority of camera collectors. If a collector wants one he may have to visit several flea markets, or attend a couple of camera fairs to find the model that would fit best into his collection. Most folding plate cameras, and cameras like the Zeiss Contina II camera (Z524/24) fit into this category.

3* – **Three-star** rarity cameras take a little more searching out. They are mostly found at camera fairs, or are offered for sale by dealers, but they do find their way onto market stalls, but one must be quite lucky to grab a three-star rarity camera. The Kodak Chevron (EK346) and the Foth-Flex (FO102) cameras are examples of three-star cameras.

4* – Some collectable cameras were made only in small quantities, or have not stood the test of time. These are **four-star** rarity cameras. Maybe they were not a commercial success, or maybe the manufacturer could not afford the investment to increase production. Maybe, like the Opema I (OP104), they just don't make it to the collector's marketplace very often. Specialist dealers are often the best place to look for these cameras, but don't expect to get the one you want first time.

5* – **Five-star** rarity cameras exist only in large private collections, or in museums. Occasionally a five-star rarity camera will be offered at auction, or by a specialist dealer. They are more likely to be traded privately across the world by fax or telephone. The Plastron Grey camera (WE100), and the Ben Akiba (LH100) cameras are examples of five-star rarity.

Leica Cameras and Accessories

Leica collecting is the most highly developed and specialised field of camera collecting. There are three main reasons for this. The Leica, although not the first to use 35mm cine film, was the first serious 35mm camera and it revolutionised photography. Leica users pioneered the real-life style of photography we are familiar with today. So it has immense historic significance. Secondly, its makers, Ernst Leitz, from the beginning saw it as a system camera. They developed interchangeable lenses and a myriad of accessories to expand its use into all types of photographic applications, so there are literally thousands of individual items, all beautifully engineered. Thirdly, and most significantly, there is more information available about the Leica than any other camera. This is because the archives of Ernst Leitz at Wetzlar survived the war, being neither destroyed nor looted.

A tremendous amount of research on the Leica has been carried out and published. Complete serial number lists are available, pinpointing the year of manufacture of each individual camera and lens. The history of many individual cameras is known, giving them a special value.

For the camera collector wanting to add some Leica examples to a general collection the *Blue Book* will provide adequate guidance, and furthermore place the Leica cameras in the context of cameras generally. The Leica specialist collector, however, needs much more detailed information and should turn to the Hove specialist Leica publications listed in the advertisement section of the book. In particular, the Hove *Leica International Price Guide* gives a finer division of rarity on a scale of 1 to 10 for cameras, lenses and accessories, necessary because of the many variations within individual models and the very limited production of some.

FURTHER INFORMATION

For fully detailed descriptions, illustrations and history of the following makes of camera, Hove Foto Books publish special books for collectors. Full details are give in the advertisement section of this book for the following:–
Leica cameras, lenses and accessories
Kodak cameras, including Retina cameras
Exakta cameras, with lenses and accessories
Minox cameras and history
Asahi Pentax and Pentax 35mm SLR cameras and lenses
Nikon rangefinder cameras and lenses
Canon rangefinder cameras and lenses

Abbreviations and codes
ENGLISH

CERTAIN ABBREVIATIONS and codes are used throughout the listings in this issue of *The Hove International Blue Book*. Here's how to read them...

(?): approximate.

*: one lens and shutter combination of several variations.

+: the "+" sign after a price indicates that in the editor's opinion the camera would sell for considerably more on today's market than it sold for when the price was originally figured.

BIM: built-in light meter.

C: Year of manufacture. The dates in the Zeiss section are precise; elsewhere the dates are approximate. A single date usually indicates the year the camera model first appeared.

CFPS: cloth focal-plane shutter.

Counterfeit: a camera, represented by the seller to the buyer as being historically accurate, but appearing to be of a make or model different from that which it really is. Counterfeit Leica cameras are usually Russian.

CRF: coupled rangefinder.

exp: exposure.

Fake: a camera which has been made to seem that which it is not, and which is represented by the seller to the buyer as original. A Leica "Luxus" which is really a re-worked Leica I(A) but found on a dealer's table at a show as a true "Luxus" would be called a fake. Beware of fakes, before making an expensive purchase, know all the facts about the camera and the seller. More and more "Fakes" are being made in Eastern Europe, and shipped into the West for the chance to turn a fast mark or pound.

FPS: focal plane shutter.

mfg: manufactured.

MFPS: metal focal-plane shutter.

NSR: no sales recorded.

Qty: quantity.

Replica: a camera, represented to the buyer by the seller as being non-historically accurate. Replica cameras are not sold to fool anybody. Leica "Luxus" cameras are sometimes made from Leica I(A) cameras, "Uhr" Leica cameras are indeed made by Leitz, and are faithful to the original, but alas......

RFR: rangefinder.

s: seconds.

Slr: single lens reflex.

Snr: serial number range.

VFR: viewfinder.

On cameras where more than one price is quoted for variations of the same type (e.g. chrome/black/military markings, etc) the value and rarity ratings apply to that of the basic camera in the section.

Camera codes

Every listing in the *The Hove International Blue Book,* with the exception of some Leitz accessories (the code used for these being the Leitz codeword), and most Zeiss cameras, (here, the Zeiss catalogue codes are used) has its own distinct code. It begins with two letters, and is followed by three numbers or, in the case of some Nikon accessories and Leitz lenses, four numbers.

These codes are generated whenever an item is added to the book. The letter/number combination is unique to each entry. Codes used to describe camera accessories have a zero following the two letter beginning.

Originally designed as a quick and easy method of finding a particular entry in the computer data base, these codes lend themselves to other applications as well.

When contributors write with updated information for the *The Hove International Blue Book,* they have only to reference the camera code, and the editor has all the information necessary to know which camera they are talking about.

Anyone needing a short and simple reference in future can use these codes accordingly, be they collectors, dealers, clubs or whatever.

As more and more collectors begin using home computers, these codes will become more valuable in setting up their own databases.

Vorwort
DEUTSCH

DIESES IST DIE 1992–93 Auflage des *Blue Book,* jetzt das *Hove International Blue Book;* es wurde erheblich erweitert und verbessert. Gegenüber der ersten Auflage sind über 1000 Exponate hinzugekommen. Dabei wurde besonders darauf geachtet, nur solche aufzunehmen, die für den Kamerasammler von besonderem Interesse sind. Wir haben uns bemüht, das Blue Book nicht zu einer Kameraenzyklopädie ausarten zu lassen. Wir meinen, daß es in seiner gegenwärtigen Form den Wünschen von Kamerasammlern am besten gerecht wird.

Manche der Exponate sind Kameras, die in großer Zahl gehandelt werden. Viele von ihnen sind hier zum ersten Mal beschrieben. Andere sind recht unbekannt und selten. Sie aufzuspüren, ist für den Sammler immer eine besondere Freude. Sie werden in diesem Blue Book auch mehr Zubehör und Objektive aufgelistet finden als anderswo. Es hat sich herausgestellt, daß immer mehr Sammler sich auch dem Zubehör zuwenden, um ihre Sammlungen zu vervollständigen. Die Kenntnis des Zubehörs, das auf dem Sammlermarkt erhältlich ist, wird es dem Sammler leichter machen, den gewünschten Umfang seiner Sammlung zu bestimmen.

Neu aufgenommen wurden Kameras aus Argentinien, Brasilien, Spanien, Rumänien, der Tschechoslowakei und der Sowjetunion, die in anderen Preisführern oft nicht zu finden sind.

Die Abbildungen in dieser neuen Auflage sollen ein Maximum an Information vermitteln. Deshalb wurde großer Wert auf ihre technische Qualität gelegt. Wir glauben an die größere Aussagekraft des Bildes gegenüber der detaillierten Wortbeschreibung. Die Klarheit der Fotos auf den folgenden Seiten wird Schule machen.

Für mich persönlich war die Herstellung dieser neusten Auflage eine große Freude. Ich hatte Gelegenheit, Kameraausstellungen in den USA, in Holland, Frankreich, England, Österreich und der Bundesrepublik und Kamerawerke und - museen in Frankreich, der Bundesrepublik Deutschland und der Tschechoslowakei zu besuchen. Ich fuhr auch nach China, um mit meinen Sammlerfreunden zu sprechen und einen Einblick in die Sammeltätigkeit dort zu gewinnen. Alles in allem hat mich die Arbeit an diesem Band ganz in Anspruch genommen. Dieses Projekt war bis jetzt das schwierigste, aber es hat mir auch große Befriedigung gebracht. Ich möchte es an einem Beispiel darlegen:

Im Februar 1991 war ich auf einer zweitägigen Kameraausstellung in Miami in Florida. Ich hatte mit französischen Freunden einen Verkaufstisch gemietet. Nach ereignisreichen Morgenstunden des ersten Tages bat ich einen amerikanischen Freund, auf die Waren aufzupassen, während ich mir die Beine vertreten und etwas trinken wollte. Als ich nach kurzer Zeit zurückkam, hatte ich einen Arm voller Kameras, mein Getränk aber irgendwo stehengelassen. Ich bat meinen Freund, noch einmal um ein paar Minuten und machte mich auf die Suche. Ich fand mein Getränk auf einem Tisch neben einer Agfa Memo. Mit der Flasche in der Hand eilte ich zu meinem Tisch zurück.

Da bemerkte ich auf einem Tisch eine wunderschön glänzende Clarus (RU101). Ich nahm sie in die Hand und betrachtete sie genauer. Sie sah einer Clarus täuschend ähnlich, entpuppte sich aber als eine Wescon. Das Gehäuse war in braunes Leder eingeschlagen, der Preis 50 Dollar. Ich überlegte noch, ob ich 40 Dollar bieten sollte, als jemand neben mir stand: ein weltbekannter Händler, dessen Fachbereich seltene und Spezialkameras ist. Ich wußte in diesem Moment, daß ich die Kamera verlieren würde, wenn ich sie wieder auf den Tisch zurücklegte. Ich zog meine Brieftasche und sagte dem Verkäufer, daß ich sie für 50 Dollar erstehen wollte. Darauf holte er noch die Tragetasche hervor, die dazugehörte und einen Blitzreflektor enthielt. Ich hatte bis jetzt nur verchromte Blitzreflektoren gesehen, aber dieser war vergoldet! Auch die ursprüngliche Gebrauchsanweisung lag noch in der Tasche. Als ich alles einwickelte, machte mir der Händler neben mir ein verlockendes Angebot von 25 Dollar Profit. Ich lehnte ab.

Meine Verwunderung ist immer noch groß, daß ich diese seltene und seltsame Kamera aufspüren konnte, nachdem Hunderte von Menschen im Verlauf von fünf Stunden an dem Tisch vorbeigegangen waren und alles in Augenschein genommen hatten. Eine Beschreibung der Wescon (WC200) ist nun in dieser Ausgabe und sonst nirgends zu finden.

Die Anekdote, wie ich in ihren Besitz gelangte, mag zeigen, in welchem Maß sich das Blue Book von anderen Preisführern unterscheidet. Suchen, finden, Information mitteilen...es gibt keinen Stillstand.

Die Preise betreffend

Wie in den ersten beiden Auflagen sind die Preise reelle Preise. Händler, die Kameras weiter verkaufen wollen, zahlen so wenig wie möglich. Kein Sammler will zuviel bezahlen. Bei Auktionen mögen die Preise manchmal zu sehr ansteigen. Auch der Ort, wo man kauft und das ganz persönliche Interesse spielen eine Rolle. Diese preislichen Schwankungen ins Gleichgewicht zu bringen, ist oft nicht leicht. Ich benutze keine besonderen Formeln oder Computerprogramme, um einen angemessenen Preis zu bestimmen. Ein klarer Verstand und offener Sinn sind immer noch die beste Methode. Ich ziehe auch Kataloge, Anzeigen und Preislisten heran und vergleiche die Preise auf Ausstellungen und Auktionen weltweit. Ich höre auch auf die Meinungen von Sammlern und Händlern, mit denen ich ins Gespräch komme.

Doch die Entscheidung, auf welchen Preis ich mich festlege, liegt allein bei mir. Wenn Sie hier und da anderer Meinung sind, setzen Sie sich bitte mit mir in Verbindung. Ich freue mich immer, von ihnen zu hören.

Douglas St Denny

Einführung
DEUTSCH

Das Blue Book wird international

WIR BEI Hove Foto Books und Laterna magica freuen uns, daß wir die Veröffentlichung dieser Auflage 1992 - 1993 des Blue Book übernehmen konnten. Unsere Firmen wurden von Sammlern gegründet, die volles Verständnis für die Wünsche der Sammler nach detaillierten Beschreibungen haben, nach guten Abbildungen, Datierungsinformationen, Geschichte, Modellvariationen und allen anderen Informationen, die das Sammeln zu einem solch erfreulichen und herausfordernden Hobby machen. Das Blue Book ist auch eine sinnvolle Ergänzung zu unseren anderen Büchern, die sich mit einzelnen Kameramodellen befassen.

Wir sind der Überzeugung, daß in den 90-ger Jahren ein Preisverzeichnis für Kamerasammler Preise in den Hauptwährungen angeben soll, in denen Kameras auf dem internationalen Markt gehandelt werden, besonders für die selteneren und sehr gefragten Stücke. Hochwertige, seltene oder Modekameras und Qualitätsmarken werden heute in der ganzen Welt gehandelt. Natürlich werden Sie eine besonders wünschenswerte Kamera von Eastman Kodak eher in den U.S.A. finden, eine Houghton-Butcher in Großbritannien, eine frühe Canon in Japan oder eine Zeiss in Deutschland. Höchstwahrscheinlich ist die Zeiss in Deutschland billiger als in den U.S.A. und umgekehrt die Eastman Kodak in Amerika. Dies hat nichts mit dem Währungskurs zu tun. Der Kurs im Juni kann zum Beispiel ganz anders als im September oder Dezember sein, der relative Wert von Sammlerkameras in den entsprechenden Ländern bleibt jedoch gleich. Der Sammler muß den tatsächlichen Wert im eigenen Land und, falls er international handelt, auf den anderen Hauptmärkten kennen.

Der Preis richtet sich jeweils nach dem Markt des einzelnen Landes. Die Preise von einem Land zum anderen lassen sich nicht einfach durch Multiplizieren mit dem gängigen Wechselkurs vergleichen. Bei weniger gebräuchlichen Artikeln spielen auch andere Faktoren eine Rolle - Verfügbarkeit, Sammeltrends oder nationale Eigenschaften. Beispielsweise ist in Japan der Originalzustand von größter Bedeutung, und die Japaner zahlen gerne für das hervorragende Exemplar einer Kamera in perfektem Originalzustand. In den U.S.A. legt man größeren Wert auf eine erstklassige Restaurierung, die in Japan als nicht original zurückgewiesen würde.

In früheren Auflagen des Blue Book wurden die Preise ausschließlich in U.S. Dollars angegeben. In dieser Auflage geben wir die Preise in U.S. Dollars, Pfund Sterling, Deutscher Mark und Französischen Francs an, wobei, sehr verallgemeinert, von den Markbedingungen in den U.S.A., Großbritannien, Deutschland und Frankreich ausgegangen wird. Was Leica-Kameras anbetrifft, konnten wir aufgrund unserer Erfahrung bei der Herausgabe des Hove Leica International Price Guide, jetzt in seiner fünften Auflage, zwischen den Preisen in den einzelnen Ländern mit großer Genauigkeit differenzieren.

Der Markt heute

Rückblickend auf 1991 stellt sich heraus, daß dies ein Jahr voller dramatischer Ereignisse war, angefangen mit dem Krieg am Golf bis hin zur Auflösung der Sowjetunion. Krisen und Unsicherheit in der Welt beeinflussen das Vertrauen und damit auch die Märkte, die darauf aufbauen. Zum Jahresende 1991 herrscht noch immer die Rezession in Großbritannien vor und eine sich vertiefende Rezession in den U.S.A.; wir erleben die Auswirkungen der deutschen Vereinigung und das Absinken der französchen Wirtschaft.

Wie andere Antiquitäten- und Kunstmärkte auch hat der Kamerasammlermarkt gelitten. Überhöhte Preise sind nicht mehr zu erzielen, obwohl einige äußerst gefragte Stücke die Ausnahme zur Regel darstellen. Allgemein gesprochen blieben jedoch gebräuchlichere Stücke in durchschnittlichem Zustand in den Händlerregallen liegen. Zwar wechselte die Seltenheit in ausgezeichnetem Zustand immer noch ihren Besitzer, aber meist zu einem geringeren Preis als zuvor. Der Sammler sollte sich jetzt den Markt genau ansehen und bei Angebot und Kauf wählerisch vorgehen.

Ratschläge für den Sammelneuling

Originalität

Streben Sie bei Ihrem Kauf immer den bestmöglichen Zustand einer Kamera an. Wenn Sie an einem zukünftigen Investitionswert Ihrer Sammlung interessiert sind, muß das wichtigste Kriterium immer die Originalität eines Stückes sein. Eine restaurierte Kamera, egal wie gut die Restaurierung durchgeführt wurde, wird nie als Original angesehen; oft ist ihr Wert nur so hoch wie der eines ähnlichen Modells in schlechterem Zustand, das aber ein Original ist. Andererseits erwarten viele Sammler, daß ihre Kamera unverdorben und voll funktionstüchtig ist.

Spezialität

Sammeln macht Spaß. Die meisten Sammler spezialisieren sich entweder auf die Produkte eines bestimmten Herstellers oder auf einen bestimmten Kameratyp. Manche sammeln Klappkameras, Handkameras, Reflexkameras, nur russische oder nur Nikon- oder Kodak-Kameras. Andere setzen sich ein Sammelthema, zum Beispiel die Entwicklungsgeschichte der Kamera, verschiedene Verschlußtypen oder Kleinstkameras. Der Preis selbst kann ein Sammelthema sein: manche Leute sammeln nur Kameras unter einem bestimmten Preis, zum Beispiel DM 100,—. Dadurch wird das Hobby relativ preiswert, und die Versuchung, die eigenen Finanzen zu übersteigen, ist gering. Dennoch kann dies genauso interessant sein, weil die billigen Massenkameras einen viel größeren Bezug zu unserer Sozialgeschichte darstellen als die exquisiten, handgefertigten Geräte, die sich nur wenige Leute neu leisten können. Den Sammelmöglichkeiten sind keine Grenzen gesetzt.

Fälschungen

Immer wenn ein Gegenstand einen großen Wert besitzt und von Sammlern hoch geschätzt wird, sind die Fälscher nicht weit. Das gilt für wertvolle Kameras wie für Antiquitäten. Auf Fälschungen muß der Leica-Sammler schon seit vielen Jahren gefaßt sein. Je mehr Sie sich in das Sammeln vertiefen und je erfahrener Sie werden, desto leichter werden Sie die Echtheit einer Ihnen angebotenen Kamera beurteilen können. Wenn Sie von einem ehrlichen Händler kaufen, gehen Sie wesentlich sicherer. Beim Kauf auf einer Versteigerung haben Sie die Gewißheit, daß in den meisten Ländern der Artikel nach dem Gesetz so sein muß, wie beschrieben. Lassen Sie sich von der Angst vor Fälschungen nicht die Freude am Sammeln verderben -

nur etwas Vorsicht sollten Sie walten lassen. Es gibt sogar Sammler, die Fälschungen sammeln, und damit haben auch Fälschungen ihren Wert!

Die Preise in diesem Buch

Das Blue Book ist ein Führer und sollte auch als solcher angesehen werden. Der Herausgeber hat in seinem Vorwort erklärt, wie er zu den Preisangaben gekommen ist. Vielleicht glauben Sie, daß einige zu hoch oder zu niedrig sind. Der Zweck dieses Buches ist jedoch, dem Sammler einen Anhaltspunkt zu liefern. Manche Sammler entschließen sich vielleicht, nur bis zu beispielsweise 80% des Richtpreises zu zahlen. Andere zahlen gerne 110% oder sogar 120% für ein besonders begehrenswertes Stück, nach dem sie schon lange gesucht haben. Andererseits ist beim Verkauf an einen Händler ein wesentlich geringerer Preis zu erwarten; aber dieses Buch gibt Ihnen wiederum eine Richtlinie, um das Angebot des Händlers zu beurteilen.

So benutzen Sie das Blue Book

Wenn Sie sich die Preisangaben in dieser Auflage des Hove International Blue Book ansehen und mit dem Wert der Artikel in Ihrer Sammlung vergleichen, müssen Sie unbedingt den Zustand der jeweiligen Kamera in Betracht ziehen, denn der Zustand macht den Preis ebenso wie der Kameratyp selbst.

Der Preis wird auch von der Seltenheit einer Kamera bestimmt. Diese neueste Auflage des Blue Book gibt Ihnen einen Seltenheitswert für jede Kamera an. Dieser wird durch eine Skala mit fünf Sternen ausgedrückt. Ein Stern für die gewöhnlichste und fünf Sterne für die seltenste Kamera. Diese Bewertungen wurden gleichzeitig mit den Preisen auf den neuesten Stand gebracht.

Für Objektive und Zubehör sind die Preisangaben allerdings nur in U.S. Dollars.

Zustand

Die Preisangaben in diesem Buch gelten nur für **Kameras in ausgezeichnetem** Zustand. Das bedeutet, 80% bis 100% der Originalausführung so gut wie neu, wenig benutzt, keine auffälligen Holz-

oder Lederkratzer, wenig oder kein Anlaufen, Objektiv sauber und klar, alle mechanischen Teile funktionieren einwandfrei.

Für andere Kamerazustände ist der Preis wie folgt zu berechnen:

Neuzustand: 100% der Originalausführung, alles tadellos, in jeder Hinsicht wie neu. Zu den Richtpreisen sind 10% bis 25% zu addieren. Die meisten Vier- oder Fünf-Sterne-Kameras können jedoch je nach Marktlage u.U. auch 100% oder mehr wert sein als angegeben.

Sehr guter Zustand: Mindestens 60% der Originalausführung, Artikel ist vollständig, jedoch mit leichten Holz- oder Lederkratzern; abgeriebene oder angelaufene Metallteile, jedoch kein Rost oder Lochfraß. Objektiv und Sucher sauber, Verschluß und andere Mechanikteile funktionsfähig, mit Mindestaufwand und -kosten restaurierbar. Von den Richtpreisen sind 15% bis 25% abzuziehen.

Guter Zustand: Mindestens 45% der Originalausführung, geringer Verschleiß auf freiliegenden Oberflächen, keine wesentlichen Teile kaputt, kleinere Reparaturen jedoch erforderlich; Metallteile mit Rost- oder Lochfraßstellen, aber zu reinigen; Leder verschlissen oder mürbe, Holz verkratzt, angelaufen und mit kleinen Rissen, aber reparierbar. Immer settener sind Sammler an diesen Kameras interessiert; und sie zu handeln oder zu verkaufen kann schwierig sein. Von den Richtpreisen sind 40% bis 60% abzuziehen.

Ansehnlicher Zustand: 25% der Originalausführung, gebraucht und verschlissen, Ersatzteile und Reparaturen notwendig; Leder gerissen oder fehlt; Objektiv milchig oder beschädigt; Metallteile verrostet und Mechanismus ausgeleiert; Verschluß nicht funktionsfähig; Holzteile fehlen weitgehend und müssen vollständig restauriert werden. Diese Kameras werden normalerweise für ihre Ersatzteile verkauft und zwar an Sammler, die eine gleiche Kamera in besserem Zustand besitzen und vielleicht eine Schraube oder eine Feder aus einer solchen Kamera benötigen. Von den Richtpreisen sind 60% bis 85% abzuziehen.

Kameras mit einem Seltenheitswert von vier oder fünf Sternen bilden meistens die Ausnahme zu den vorhergehenden Regeln. Restaurierte Kameras sind im allgemeinen für den Sammler weniger interessant als Kameras im Originalzustand; viel hängt von dem betreffenden Land und von besonderen Sammlerspezialitäten ab. Vor kurzem kamen einige vergoldete Luxuskameras verschiedener Marken auf den Markt. Meistens bedeutet das, daß ein schlauer Händler eine minderwertige Kamera in eine teure verwandelt hat. Kaum ein ernsthafter Sammler wird bereit sein, überhöhte Preise für solche "Verstümmelungen" zu zahlen.

Für eine gebrauchsfähige Kamera wie zum Beispiel die Leica M3 (EL134) oder die Bessa II (VO105), reparaturbedürftig, sind die Reparaturkosten von dem angegebenen Preis abzuziehen. Jedoch Vorsicht: die Reparatur einer komplizierten Meßsucher- oder Spiegelreflexkamera kann sich als sehr kostspielig herausstellen. Auch ist ein kompetenter Reparaturfachmann nicht immer leicht zu finden.

Die meisten Sammler hören gerne das Geräusch des Verschlusses, besonders bei langen Verschlußzeiten. Zum Fotografieren ist eine mechanische Perfektion jedoch selten erforderlich. Winzige Nadellöcher in der Harmonikamanschette einer Balgenkamera, solange der Balgen selbst noch in Ordnung ist, dürften keine Wirkung auf den Preis haben.

Seltenheit

Je schwieriger es ist, eine Kamera zu finden, desto höher liegt der Seltenheitswert. Der Seltenheitswert wird wie bei früheren Auflagen durch eine Sternskala von 1* bis 5* ausgedrückt. Die einzelnen Bewertungen sind wie folgt:

1* - Ein-Sterne-Kameras sind leicht zu finden. Sie erscheinen oft als Sammelposten auf Versteigerungen oder Flohmärkten. Der Sammler kann sich seine Kamera normalerweise unter mehreren aussuchen. Diese Kameras wurden als Massenware produziert und sind weit verbreitet. Die meisten Kodak Klappkameras und viele Boxkameras fallen in diese Gruppe.

2* - Zwei-Sterne-Kameras sind schon etwas schwieriger zu finden. Oft wurden sie nach einer höheren Spezifikation hergestellt und urspünglich teurer als Ein-Sterne-Kameras verkauft. Sie bilden das tägliche Brot für die meisten Kamerasammler. Wenn der Sammler eine bestimmte Kamera sucht, muß er oft mehrere Flohmärkte aufsuchen oder an Kameraausstellungen teilnehmen. Die meisten Klappkameras sowie Kameras wie die Zeiss Contina II (Z524/24) gehören in diese Gruppe.

3* - Nach Drei-Sterne-Kameras zu suchen, erfordert schon mehr Aufwand. Meist sind sie auf Kameraausstellungen zu finden, oder sie werden von einem Händler angeboten. Gelegentlich kann man eine Drei-Sterne-Kamera jedoch auch noch auf Marktständen aufstöbern. Dazu gehört aber eine Menge Glück und ein schnelles Reaktionsvermögen. Die Kodak Chevron (EK346) und die Foth-Flex (FO102) sind Beispiele dieser Gruppe.

4* - Einige Sammlerkameras wurden nur in kleinen Mengen hergestellt oder haben sich im Laufe der Zeit nicht bewährt. Das sind die Vier-Sterne-Kameras. Vielleicht versprachen sie keinen kommerziellen Erfolg oder der

Hersteller war finanziell nicht in der Lage, die Produktion zu steigern. Oder vielleicht, wie im Fall der Opema I (OP104), tauchen sie einfach nicht sehr oft auf dem Sammlermarkt auf. Spezialhändler sind in der Regel die besten Fundgruben für solche Kameras. Aber verlassen Sie sich nicht darauf, daß Sie Ihren Wunsch gleich beim ersten Mal erfüllt bekommen.

5* - Fünf-Sterne-Kameras finden sich nur in großen Privatsammlungen oder in Museen. Gelegentlich wird eine solche Kamera schon einmal auf einer Versteigerung oder von einem Spezialhändler angeboten. In der Regel werden Fünf-Sterne-Kameras in der ganzen Welt jedoch nur privat per Fax oder Telefon gehandelt. Beispiele dieser Gruppe sind die Plastron Grey (WE100) und die Ben Akiba (LH100).

Leica-Kameras und -Zubehör

Das Sammeln von Leica-Kameras ist weiter entwickelt und spezialisiert als jede andere Kamerasammelart. Dafür gibt es drei Gründe: Die Leica war zwar nicht die erste Kamera, die 35mm Kinofilme verwendete, sie war jedoch die erste ernsthafte Kleinbildkamera und veränderte die Fotografie von Grund auf. Leica-Benutzer galten als Pioniere in der lebensnahen Fotografie, wie wir sie kennen. Die Leica besitzt also eine unermeßlich hohe, historische Bedeutung. Zweitens sah Hersteller Ernst Leitz in ihr von Anfang an eine Systemkamera. Entwickelt wurden Wechselobjektive und eine Unzahl von Zubehörteilen, um die Verwendung dieser Kamera in allen Bereichen der Fotografie zu ermöglichen. Und so gibt es tausende von Einzelteilen, alle wunderschön ausgeführt. Zum Dritten, und wichtigsten, stehen mehr Informationen über die Leica als über jede andere Kamera zur Verfügung. Der Grund liegt darin, daß die Archive von Ernst Leitz in Wetzlar den Krieg überstanden und nie zerstört oder geplündert wurden.

Ein ungeheures Quantum an Forschungsarbeiten über die Leica ist durchgeführt und veröffentlicht worden. Vorhanden sind komplette Seriennummernlisten, die das Herstellungsjahr jeder einzelnen Kamera und jeden Objektivs festlegen. Von vielen einzelnen Kameras ist die Geschichte bekannt, was ihnen einen besonderen Wert verleiht.

Dem Kamerasammler, der seiner Sammlung ein paar Leica-Geräte zufügen will, gibt das Blue Book ausreichend Hilfestellung. Außerdem werden die Leica-Kameras in den Zusammenhang mit Kameras generell gestellt. Der Leica-Spezialsammler benötigt jedoch ausführlichere Informationen und sollte sich an die Leica-Spezialveröffentlichungen von Hove wenden, die im Anzeigenteil des Buches aufgeführt sind. Im Besonderen gibt der Hove Leica

International Price Guide eine genauere Aufteilung des Seltenheitswertes von 1 bis 10 für Kameras, Objektive und Zubehör. Die Notwendigkeit dafür liegt in den vielen Variationen innerhalb einzelner Modelle und der begrenzten Produktion von manchen Geräten.

WEITERE INFORMATIONEN

Die von Hove Foto Books herausgegebenen Spezialbücher geben detaillierte Beschreibungen, Abbildungen und die Geschichte der einzelner Kameramarken für Sammler. Weitere Einzelheiten über die folgenden Bücher finden Sie im Anzeigenteil dieses Buches:

Leica Kameras, Objektive und Zubehör
Kodak Kameras einschließlich Retin Kameras
Exakta Kameras mit Objektiven und Zubehör
Minox Kameras und ihre Geschichte
Asahi Pentax und pentax 35mm SLR Kameras und Objektive
Nikon Sucherkameras und Objektive
Canon Sucherkameras und Objektive

(Alle diese Bücher in englischer Sprache! Anfragen an: Verlag Laterna magica, Stridbeckstr. 48, D-8000 München 71, der die Anfragen gerne weiterleitet!)

Abkürzungen und Kennziffern
DEUTSCH

BEI DEN EINTRAGUNGEN im Hove International Blue Book wurden bestimmte Abkürzungen und Kennziffern verwendet, die wie folgt zu lesen sind ...

(?): ungefähr.

*: eine Blenden- und Verschlußkombination mit mehreren Variationen;

+: das "+" Zeichen nach der Preisangabe bedeutet, daß die Kamera nach Meinung des Herausgebers auf dem heutigen Markt für wesentlich mehr verkauft werden könnte als zur Zeit der ursprünglichen Preisfestsetzung;

BIM: eingebauter Belichtungsmesser (Built-In Lightmeter);

C: Herstellungsjahr. Die Daten im Kapitel Zeiss sind genaue Angaben; an anderen Stellen sind die Datenangaben ungefähr. Ein einzelnes Datum bedeutet normalerweise das erste Erscheinungsjahr der Kamera;

CFPS: Stoffschlitzverschluß (Cloth Focal-Plane Shutter);

Nachbildung: eine Kamera, die der Verkäufer dem Käufer als "historisch echt" vorstellt, die jedoch von einem anderen Hersteller ist. Leica-Nachbildungen sind meistens russischen Ursprungs;

CRF: Meßsucher (Coupled Range Finder);

Bel: Belichtung;

Fälschung: eine Kamera, die so aussehen soll, wie das Original, es jedoch nicht ist. Eine Leica "Luxus", in Wirklichkeit eine überarbeitete Leica I(A) wird auf dem Händlertisch oft als echte "Luxus" bezeichnet. Beim Kauf einer teuren Kamera sei vor Fälschungen gewarnt. Informieren Sie sich über alle Fakten der Kamera und auch über den Verkäufer. Immer mehr Fälschungen werden in Osteuropa hergestellt und für schnellen Profit in den Westen exportiert;

FPS: Schlitzverschluß (Focal Plane Shutter);

Hrst: Herstellung;

MFPS: Metallfolienschlitzverschluß (Metal Focal-Plane Shutter);

NSR: kein Verkauf verzeichnet (No Sales Recorded);

Mge: Menge;

Reprod: Reproduktion. Eine Kamera, die der Verkäufer dem Käufer als "nicht historisch echt" vorstellt. Kamerareproduktionen sollen niemanden irreführen. Manchmal wurden Leica-"Luxus"-Kameras aus Leica I(A) Kameras hergestellt, Leica-Kameras der Serie "Ur" wurden tatsächlich von Leitz produziert und sind orignialgetreu, allerdings ...

RFR: Entfernungsmesser (Rangefinder);

S: Sekunden;

SLR: Spiegelreflex (Single Lens Reflex);

Ser: Seriennummernbereich;

VFR: Sucher (Viewfinder).

Sind bei den Kameras mehrere Preise für Variationen des selben Typs (z.B. verchromt/schwarz/Militärausführung usw.) angegeben, beziehen sich Wert- und Seltenheitseinschätzung auf die Grundausführung des jeweiligen Artikels.

Kamera-Kennziffer

Jeder Eintrag im Hove International Blue Book, mit Ausnahme von einigen Leitz-Zubehörteilen (deren Kennziffer das Kennwort für Leitz ist) und fast allen Zeiss-Kameras (hier wurden die Kennziffern aus dem Zeiss-Katalog übernommen), hat seine eigene charakteristische Kennziffer. Sie beginnt mit zwei Buchstaben, gefolgt von drei oder, bei einigen Nikon-Zubehörteilen und Leitz-Objektiven, von vier Nummern.

Diese Kennziffern werden immer dann vergeben, wenn dem Buch ein Artikel zugefügt wird. Die Buchstaben/Nummern-Kombination bezieht sich dann nur auf diesen Eintrag. Die Kennziffern für Kamerazubehör haben eine Null nach den beiden Anfangsbuchstaben.

Ursprünglich als schnelle und leichte Suchmethode für einen bestimmten Eintrag in der Computer-Datenbank entwickelt, eignen sich diese Kennziffern auch gut für andere Anwendungen.

Wenn Leser Beiträge mit aktuellen Informationen für das Hove International Blue Book einschicken wollen, brauchen sie nur die Kamera-Kennziffer anzugeben und der Herausgeber weiß sofort, welche Kamera gemeint ist.

Jeder, der in Zukunft eine kurze und einfache Referenz benötigt, seien es Händler, Clubs oder private Sammler, kann diese Kennziffern entsprechend verwenden.

Seit mehr und mehr Sammler einen Heim-Computer besitzen, ist der Wert dieser Kennziffern für den Aufbau einer eigenen Datenbank von immer größerer Bedeutung.

Prologue

FRANÇAIS

CETTE EDITION 1992–93 du *Blue Book,* maintenant appelé le *Hove International Blue Book*, est la plus importante et à ce jour la meilleure de ce guide. A la seconde édition, c'est plus de 1000 descriptifs qui ont été ajoutés. Grand soin a été pris de n'ajouter que les informations qui présentent le plus d'intérêt pour les collectionneurs. Notre désir n'est pas de devenir une encyclopédie dans ce domaine. C'est sous sa forme actuelle que le *Blue Book* pourra rendre le plus de services au public des collectionneurs d'appareils photographiques : telle est notre conviction.

Certains des nouveaux éléments sont des appareils simples, beaucoup décrits ici pour la première fois. D'autres sont mal connus ou rares, ils apportent un peu de piment au marché de la collection. Vous trouverez davantage d'accessoires et d'objectifs répertoriés, beaucoup n' apparaissant que dans le *Blue Book.* Nous avons remarqué qu'un nombre grandissant de collectionneurs d'appareils photographiques se tourne vers les accessoires pour compléter leurs collections. Savoir quels sont les accessoires disponibles sur le marché pourra également aider les collectionneurs à se fixer des objectifs pour leurs collections.

Des descriptifs ajoutés en provenance d' Argentine, du Brésil, d'Espagne, de Roumanie, de Tchécoslovaquie et d'Union Soviétique ne figurent que rarement dans les autres guides des prix.

Les photos nouvellement incluses dans cette édition l'ont été en raison de leur valeur informative et de leur qualité technique. Nous croyons à la valeur de l'affirmation "une petite photo vaut une longue description". La netteté des reproductions photographiques que vous trouverez dans ce livre risque de faire école.

Sur un plan plus personnel, travailler à cette dernière édition du *Blue Book* a été un réel bonheur. J'ai eu le plaisir de voyager pour participer à des foires d'appareils photographiques anciens aux Etats-Unis, en Hollande, en France, en Angleterre, en Autriche et en Allemagne. J'ai également visité des musées et des usines en France, Allemagne et Tchécoslovaquie. Je suis même revenu en Chine pour parler avec mes amis collectionneurs et essayer de faire, pour ce pays, le point de l'évolution dans ce domaine. En fin de compte, j'ai été très occupé, à travailler sur les descriptifs et les prix que vous trouverez dans ce livre. Je dois dire que la tâche a été ardue, que ça a été l'édition la plus difficile à mettre au point, à ce jour, mais que ça a été, aussi, une épreuve très gratifiante. Voici un exemple de ce qui a contribué à rendre ce livre aussi enrichissant pour moi.

A Miami, en Floride, où je me trouvais au mois de février 1991, je participais à la foire semestrielle des appareils photographiques anciens, qui dure deux jours.

Juste avant d'arriver, je remarquai, sur la table d'un vendeur un appareil photographique Clarus (RU101). Il était beau, brillant, exactement le genre de choses à ramener avec moi en Europe. Je m'arrêtai et l'examinai. Il avait bien l'air d'un Clarus, mais, à y regarder de plus près, ce n'était pas un Clarus. Il portait le nom Wescon. Il était recouvert de cuir marron et coûtait 50$. Alors que je le tenais, réfléchissant aux chances de succès d'une offre de 40$, je sentis une présence derrière moi. C'était un vendeur mondialement connu dans le domaine des appareils photographiques rares et spéciaux, dont la table se trouvait juste à côté. Je sus, à ce moment précis, que reposer l'appareil photographique, c'était le perdre. J'informais le propriétaire que j'achetais le Wescon au prix indiqué et je fouillais dans mon portefeuille. Le propriétaire sortit, alors, une boîte et me dit que ça faisait partie du lot. A l'intérieur se trouvait un réflecteur de flash, mais pas n'importe quel réflecteur ! Alors que tous les réflecteurs de flash que j'avais vus jusqu'à ce jour étaient chromés, celui-ci était doré! De plus, au fond de la boîte, je découvrais le mode d'emploi original. Comme je remballais mon achat, le vendeur du stand d'à côté me fit une offre me garantissant un bénéfice rapide de 25$. Je refusai.

Le Wescon est à présent décrit dans cette édition (WC200) et nulle part ailleurs.

L'anecdote liée à sa découverte est une des choses qui font que le *Blue Book* est différent des autres guides. La chasse, la découverte, la mise en commun des informations...Ceci n'est jamais fini.

En ce qui concerne les prix

Comme dans les éditions précédentes, les prix que vous trouverez ici sont des prix réels. Les vendeurs, qui achètent pour revendre, paient le moins cher possible pour les appareils photographiques . Aucun collectionneur ne veut dépenser trop. Les enchérisseurs dans les ventes se laissent parfois entraîner. Géographie et émotions jouent aussi un rôle très important. De temps en temps il fut très dur de trouver un prix spécifique.

Aucune formule spéciale, aucun programme d'ordinateur n'a été utilisé pour dégager les prix actuels. Nous avons considéré les fichiers d'adresses, les prix affichés, ceux recueillis lors des foires. Les informations concernant les ventes réellement effectuées aux quatre coins du monde ont été revues. Nous avons écouté attentivement chaque collectionneur, chaque vendeur qui a bien voulu nous présenter son opinion.

Cependant, après que tout cela a été fait, la décision finale sur le prix qui sera enregistré nous revient à nous seuls. Peut-être n'êtes-vous pas d'accord avec certains d'entre eux. Dans ce cas, faites le nous savoir et dites nous pourquoi. Nous sommes à l'écoute de ce que vous avez à nous dire.

Et, pour vous, amis francophones du *Blue Book,* nous sommes heureux, pour cette nouvelle édition de vous saluer en français. Nous attendons vos remarques et suggestions.

Douglas St Denny

Introduction
FRANÇAIS

Le Blue Book à l'échelle internationale.

Nous sommes très heureux d'avoir pu racheter les droits de publication de cette édition 1992-93 du Blue Book. Notre maison, Hove Foto Books, a été fondée par un collectionneur qui comprend bien les besoins du collectionneur pour des descriptions détaillées, de bonnes illustrations, des dates, un historique et des détails concernant les variations sur un modèle particulier ainsi que toute autre sorte de petits faits qui font que collectionner est aussi bien un plaisir qu'un passe-temps qui présente un véritable challenge. Le Blue Book sera très bien complété tous nos autres ouvrages qui sont particulièrement consacrés aux différentes marques d'appareils de photographie.

Nous persons qu'un catalogue de prix des années 1990 doit offrir pour le collectionneur les prix en devises étrangères pour ces appareils-là qui sont vendus et revendus sur le marché international et tout specialement pour ce qui concerne les appareils rarissimes et ceux qui sont bien recherchés. Bien que les appareils moins chers, et généralement plus courants, ne se vendent généralement pas sur le marché mondial, les marques de qualité, les appareils rares de grande valeur ou simplement à la mode, sont maintenant vendus, achetés et même disputés aux quatre coins du monde. Evidemment il est plus probable que vous trouviez un appareil particulièrement recherché comme le Kodak Eastman aux Etats Unis, un Houghton-Butcher en Angleterre, un des premiers Canon au Japon ou un Zeiss en Allemagne. L'appareil Zeiss sera probablement moins cher en Allemagne qu'aux Etats Unis, alors que l'inverse sera vrai pour le Kodak Eastman. Ceci n'a rien a voir avec le taux d'échange. Le taux d'échange établi en juin dernier par exemple peut être très différent de celui du mois de septembre ou décembre suivant, mais la valeur des appareils collectables dans les deux pays restera comparable. Un collectionneur doit donc savoir reconnaître la valeur actuelle d'un appareil dans son propre pays ainsi que sa valeur, s'il marchande au niveau international, sur les principaux marchés extérieurs.

Les prix dans chaque pays sont donc déterminés par la situation interne à chaque pays. L'equivalence des prix d'un pays à un autre ne peut se trouver en multipliant par le taux d'échange. D'autres facteurs entrent en jeu pour les articles moins courants, comme leur disponibilité, les goûts et modes de collection, et caractéristiques nationales.. Par exemple, au Japon, la condition originale d'un appareil est d'une importance primaire, et ils iront même jusqu'à payer une prime pour un appareil en parfait état original. Par contre, aux Etats Unis, il est plus probable qu'un appareil restauré en état de premier order soit désirable, ce qui au Japon serait rejeté comme n'étant pas original.

Les éditions antérieures du Blue Book ont catalogué les prix en dollars d'après son éditeur americain, dont le jugement était basé sur des informations provenant de correspondants allemands, français, belges, anglais et americains. Dans la présente édition cependant, les prix vous sont donnés en dollar americain, livre sterling, mark allemand et franc francais, reflétant ainsi d'une manière générale les conditions de marché relatives à chaque pays. En ce qui concerne les appareils Leica nous sommes capables de vous fournir des prix très précis et spécifiques à chaque pays grâce à l'expertise acquise lors de la production du Hove Leica International Price Guide, maintenant à sa cinquieme édition.

Le marché actuel.

Faisant une retrospective de 1991, il se trouve que les évènements de l'année ont été traumatiques, l'année commençant avec la guerre du Golfe et se terminant sur la desintégration de l'Union Soviétique. De telles crises à l'échelle mondiale engendrent un climat d'insecurité qui se répercute sur la confiance et ce manque de confiance se fait ressentir sur les marchés dont ils en dépendent. Ainsi à la fin 1991 nous continuons de constater une baisse économique en Angleterre, une baisse des prix qui ne fait que s'aggraver aux Etats Unis, les effets de la réunification des deux Allemagnes sur l'inflation, et le taux de baisse de l'économie française.

Le marché de collection photographique, ainsi que ceux d'antiquités et d'objets d'art, ont également souffert. De très hauts prix ne sont plus réalisables, bien que des sommes payées pour des articles très recherchés fassent exception à la tendance générale. D'une manière générale les articles plus courants et de condition moyenne ont eu tendance à rester sur les étalages du revendeur. L'objet rare en très bonne condition a continué à changer de mains, mais généralement à un prix plus bas qu'auparavant. Il est donc maintenant temps pour le collectionneur de regarder très attentivement les cours de marché et d'acheter et vendre d'une manière sélective.

Conseils pour le collectionneur débutant.

Originalité.

Si vous êtes acheteur, choisissez toujours un appareil dont la condition est des meilleures. L'état original est une considération majeure si vous voulez investir pour l'avenir. Un appareil restauré, même si le travail de restauration est très bien exécuté, ne peut être vraiment comparable à un appareil d'origine; dans beaucoup de cas, sa valeur peut être identique seulement à celle d'un modèle original similaire mais de plus mauvaise condition. Par ailleurs plusieurs collectionneurs veulent seulement exhiber leurs appareils préférés en condition de jeunesse et en état de marché parfait.

Se spécialiser.

Collectionner peut donner beaucoup de satisfaction. La plupart des collectionneurs se spécialisent soit dans un produit de marque tout particulier, ou bien sur un type d'appareils photographiques. Certains collectionnent seulement des appareils pliants, ou portables, ou des appareils russes ou des Nikon ou Kodak. D'autres se consacrent à un thème, se portant sur l'histoire de l'évolution de la photographie ou sur différents types de fermoir ... ou sur les appareils miniatures. Le prix peut aussi être un thème, choisissant de collectionner seulement des appareils en dessous d'un certain prix, par exemple $25. Ceci a l'avantage de rendre ce passe-temps pas cher et offre une certaine protection contre la tentation de passer outre ses moyens financiers, mais ne manque en rien d'intérêt car les appareils photographiques qui sont actuellement fabriqués en série et peu chers sont en fait beaucoup plus évocatifs de notre histoire de société que les appareils faits main. Ces derniers, bien qu'exquis dans leur façon même d'être façonnés, ne sont en fait à la portee que de quelques uns d'entre nous. Les possiblités sont donc immenses.

Les copies.

Chaque fois qu'un objet a de la valeur et est recherché par les collectionneurs, les copieurs sont attirés par les possibilités de faire un profit rapide. Et ceci s'applique aussi bien à des appareils de valeur qu'aux objets d'antiquités. Ce copiage a été un facteur que les collectionneurs du Leica ont dû prendre conscience depuis maintenant quelques années. Plus vous vous engagez à collectionner, plus vous acquérez d'expérience, plus vous trouverez facile à juger l'originalité d'un appareil quelconque sur le champ même. Si vous achetez chez un revendeur de bonne renommée, vous êtes assuré d'une marchandise plus sûre. A la vente aux encheres vous avez l'assurance, dans la plupart des pays, d'une législation qui demande que la description reste fidèle à la marchandise qui vous est offerte. Mais ne laissez pas la peur du copiage et des copies vous dégoûter de collectionner; soyez simplement prudent. Il y a en fait des collectionneurs qui ne collectionnent que des copies - ainsi les copies peuvent elles aussi avoir leur propre valeur.

Les prix que vous trouverez dans ce guide.

Le Blue Book est tout simplement un guide des prix. L'éditeur a déjà explique dans le prologue comment il est arrivé à cataloguer ces prix. Vous pouvez très bien penser que certains sont trop hauts, ou trop bas, mais le but de ce livre est de donner au collectionneur des éléments de référence sur quoi se baser. Par exemple, certains collectionneurs peuvent décider de ne payer que 80% du prix mentionné dans ce livre. D'autres sont prêts à payer 110%, voire 120% du prix catalogué pour un article particulièrement recherché et désirable. Par contre, si vous voulez vendre à un marchand, vous devriez considérer un prix considérablement plus bas, mais ici encore ce quide vous offre sur quoi baser votre prix.

Comment utiliser le Blue Book.

Tenant compte des prix catalogués dans cette édition du Hove International Blue Book, et les comparant à la valeur des appareils photographiques que vous avez déjà collectionnés, il est nécessaire de prendre en considération l'état ou condition dans lequel votre appareil se trouve, car la condition joue sur le prix.

Les prix dépendent aussi de la rareté d'un appareil. Cette toute dernière édition du Blue Book continue de donner un indice de rareté, rangeant de 1 à 5 étoiles, à chaque appareil de photographie catalogué, une seule étoile représentant les appareils les plus courants et cinq étoiles les plus rares. Les indices ont été mis à jour ainsi que les prix.

Le format du directoire alphabétique des appareils photographiques, qui occupe une grande partie de ce livre, reste le même que dans les éditions antérieures, excepté pour l'indice de rareté et les prix internationaux que vous trouverez situer en fin de section sous forme de barre de prix, sauf pour les objectifs et accessoires dont le prix est indiqué uniquement en dollars américains.

Etat ou condition de l'appareil.

Les tarifs cités dans ce quide font référence à des appareils en condition excellente. Ceci veut dire que 80 à 100% du revêtement est original, comme neuf ou très peu utilisé sans aucune défiguration notable de la boiserie ou du cuir, sans ou très peu de frottements, l'objectif étant propre et clair, toutes les pièces mécaniques étant en parfait état de marche.

En ce qui concerne des appareils dont la condition est autre que celle décrite ci-dessus, veuillez bien ajouter ou soustraire au prix cité de la façon suivante.

Condition presque neuve.

100% du revêtement est original, en parfait état - comme neuf à tous points de vue - ajoutez 10-25% au prix cité bien que la plupart des appareils portant un indice de rareté de 4 à 5 étoiles peuvent être évaluée à 100% ou plus en dessus du prix catalogué.

Appareils en très bonne condition.

60% du revêtement est original; l'article est au complet bien que la boiserie ou cuir montre quelques rayures; la partie métallique est généralement défigurée ou éraflée mais sans evidence de corrosion ou marque. L'objectif et le viseur sont propres, l'obturateur et les autres pièces mécaniques en bon état de marche, peuvent être restitués à moindre effort et coût minime. A déduire 15-25% du prix catalogué.

Appareils en bonne condition.

45% du revêtement est intact, quelques signes d'usures sur les parties exposées. Peut être un besoin de remplacement de petites pièces mais il n'y a pas de grandes pièces cassées; la partie métallique peut être rouillee ou tachetee en certains endroits mais ceci peut être bien nettoyé; le cuir usagé et/ou age, la boiserie rayée, marquée et montrant quelques petites fissures qui sont réparables. L'objectif montre également quelques signes d'usage et l'état de marche de l'obturateur est suspect bien que réparable. Les collectionneurs sont de moins en moins intéressés par ces appareils et vous pourrez bien avoir du mal à les échanger ou à les vendre. A déduire 40-60% du prix catalogué.

Condition moyenne ou passable.
25% du revêtement est original; un appareil bien utilisé et usagé avec beaucoup de pièces à remplacer et restaurer, le cuir fissuré, cassé ou manquant, l'objectif voilé ou âbimé, le métal tacheté de partout, les engrenages arrondis, l'obturateur inopérable, la boiserie presque introuvable et à être entièrement restaurée. Ces appareils-ci sont généralement vendus pour leurs pièces détachées ou pièces de rechange à quelqu'un qui ayant un appareil semblable mais en meilleure condition a besoin d'une vis ou d'un ressort qui peut être récupéré d'un tel appareil. A déduire 60-85% du prix indiqué.

Les appareils portant un indice de rareté de 4 à 5 étoiles font souvent exception aux règles énoncees ci-dessus. Les appareils restaurés ont généralement moins d'intérêt pour les collectionneurs que les appareils originaux, mais cela dépend beaucoup du pays et de la spécialité particulière de la collection. Récemment quelques appareils plaqué or Luxus de maintes fabrications ont fait apparition sur le marché. Ceux-ci sont généralement une tentative par un marchand très astucieux, essayant de faire passer un appareil de qualité inférieure pour ce qu'il n'est pas en vérité. Peu de collectionneurs sérieux iraient jusqu'à payer les sommes demandées pour de tels appareils mutilés.

Pour des appareils usagés comme le Leica M3 (EL134) ou le Bessa II (VO105) en besoin de réparation, déduisez le coût des travaux à effectuer du prix catalogué. Mais faites bien attention car les réparations sur un télémètre très complexe ou sur les appareils à reflex monoculaire peuvent être très coûteuses. Il se peut aussi que vous ayez des difficultés à trouver un atelier de réparation compétent.

La plupart des collectionneurs ont plaisir à entendre le déclenchement de l'obturateur, particulièrement à petite vitesse, mais rarement s'attendent à une perfection mécanique necessaire pour effectuer de bonnes prises de vue. Des fuites dans les soufflets d'un appareil à plaque, pas plus grandes que des trous d'épingle, ne devraient pas modifier le prix de l'appareil à condition que les soufflets eux-mêmes soient en bonne condition.

Rareté.

L'indice de rareté indique le degré de difficulté que le collectionneur pourra rerencontrer pour trouver un appareil quelconque. Plus l'appareil est difficile à trouver, plus haut est l'indice de rareté. Cet indice, comme dans les éditions antérieures, est représenté par des étoiles en ordre de 1 à 5, chaque catégorie étant définie de la façon suivante :

1* Les appareils à une étoile peuvent être trouvés facilement. Ceux-ci sont souvent vendus soit dans des lots regroupés à la vente aux enchères ou sur les étalages de marché. Si un collectionneur désire en acheter un, il y en a généralement plusieurs exemplaires pour assister son choix. Ces appareils étaient fabriqués en série et distribués partout. Les appareils Kodak à chambre pliante les plus simples et beaucoup d'appareils en forme de boîte appartiennent à cette catégorie.

2* Les appareils à deux étoiles sont un peu plus difficiles à trouver. Ils ont été fabriqués à plus grande spécification et vendus à l'origine à un prix plus haut que les appareils à une étoile. Ces appareils font le gagne-pain de la plupart des collectionneurs. Et si le collectionneur désire en acheter un, il devra certainement visiter le marché aux puces plusieurs fois ou bien se rendre à deux ou trois foires photographiques pour trouver le modèle qui complèterait au mieux sa collection. La plupart des appareils à plaque pliante ainsi que le Zeiss Contina II (Z524/24) font partie de cette catégorie.

3* Les appareils à trois étoiles prennent quelque temps à trouver, principalement dans les foires ou bien en offre de vente chez les marchands. On peut parfois trouver un exemplaire sur les étalages de marché mais il faut avoir beaucoup de chance pour y trouver un appareil à trois étoiles. Le Kodak Chevron (EK346) et les appareils Foth-Flex (FO102) sont par exemple des appareils à trois étoiles.

4* Quelques appareils photographiques de collection ont seulement été fabriqués en petite quantité ou bien n'ont pas survécu à l'épreuve du temps. Ceux-ci sont des appareils à quatre étoiles. Peut-être n'ont-ils pas fait preuve d'un grand succés commercial ou que le fabriquant ne pouvait investir pour en accroître la production. Ou bien il se peut que comme pour l'Oppema I (OP104) ces appareils-là ne se rencontrent quère souvent sur le marché des collectionneurs. Les marchands spécialistes sont souvent le meilleur endroit où vous pourrez trouver de tels appareils, mais ne vous attendez surtout pas à trouver ce que vous désirez du premier coup.

5* Les appareils à cinq étoiles sont seulement trouvables dans de grandes collections privées ou bien dans les musées. De temps en temps un appareil à cinq étoiles sera offert à la vente aux enchères ou par un marchand spécialiste. Ces appareils sont probablement vendus entre collectionneurs privés des quatre coins du monde soit par fax or par téléphone. Les appareils Plastron Grey (WE100), le Ben Akiba (LH100) sont des exemples d'appareils à cinq étoiles.

Appareils Leica et accessoires.

La collection Leica est une des collections photographiques la plus développée et spécialisée. Il y a trois raisons pour cela. Le Leica , bien que n'étant pas le premier à utiliser le film de 35mm, était un des premiers appareils utilisant le 35mm d'une manière sérieuse, lui permettant ainsi de révolutioner totalement le monde photographique. Les premiers enthousiastes du Leica ont été les pionniers du style de photographie naturel, auquel nous sommes habitués aujourd'hui. Le Leica est donc d'un point de vue historique de grande importance. Deuxièmement, son inventeur/fabriquant, Ernst Leitz, à dès le début considéré le Leica comme un appareil à système. Ils développèrent des objectifs interchangeables ainsi qu'un grand nombre d'accessoires pour adapter son usage à tous genres d'applications photographiques. Ainsi donc il existe vraiment de milliers d'articles uniques, chacun étant admirablement machiné. Troisièmement, et peut-être un des points les plus importants, est que l'on a beaucoup plus d'informations au sujet du Leica que nous en avons à propos de quelque autre appareil photographique. Ceci est entièrement dû au fait que les archives de Ernst Leitz à Wetzlar ont entierement survécu à la guerre, n'ayant été ni détruites ni pillées.

Un nombre incroyable d'études et de recherches sur le Leica ont été faites et publiées. Ainsi des listes conplètes de numéros de série sont à notre disposition, indiquant exactement l'année de fabrication de chaque appareil et objectif. L'histoire individuelle de plusieurs appareils est ainsi connue, leur donnant une valeur spéciale et unique.

Pour le collectionneur voulant ajouter quelques modèles Leica à sa collection générale, le Blue Book lui fournira des conseils tout à fait suffisants et de plus placera le Leica dans le contexte d'autres appareils de photographie.

Cependant le collectionneur spécialiste du Leica a besoin de plus amples détails et devra donc consulter les publications de Hove spécialiste du Leica, qui sont catalogués dans la section publicité de ce livre. Tout particulièrement dans le Hove Leica International Price Guide vous trouverez un indice de rareté plus spécifique, passant de 1 à 10, les chambres, objectifs et accessoires, ceci étant nécessaire du fait d'un grand nombre de variations sur chaque modèle particulier et de leur production limitée.

Pour de plus amples informations.

Pour de plus amples détails, c'est-à-dire descriptions, illustrations et historiques des modèles énoncés ci-dessous, vous êtes invité à consulter les livres de Hove Foto Books qui sont publies tout spécialement pour le collectionneur. Veuillez donc vous reporter à la section publicité de ce livre pour les modèles suivants :

> Leica - chambres, objectifs et accessoires.
> Kodak - appareils, y compris les appareils Retina.
> Exakta - chambres avec objectifs et accessoires.
> Minox - appareils et leur historique.
> Asahi, Pentax, 35mm Pentax ainsi qu'à reflex monoculaire et objectifs.
> Nikon - appareils à mise au point avec télémètre et objectifs.
> Canon - appareils à mise au point avec télémètre et objectifs.

Tous ces livres sont publiés en Anglais, mais vous pouvez les obtenir chez:
La Photo Librarie
> 49 Avenue de Villiers
> 75017 Paris

Abréviations et codes
FRANÇAIS

Certaines abréviations et codes sont utilisés à travers toutes les catégories de cette edition du Hove International Blue Book. Leurs explications sont détaillées ci-dessous :

(?) approximatif

* combinaison d'objectif et obturateur à plusieurs variations

+ le signe "+" suivant un prix indique que, selon l'éditeur, l'appareil pourrait se vendre pour beaucoup plus sur le marché actuel comparé au prix de vente réalisé à l'origine.

BIM illuminomètre incorporé

C année de fabrication. Les dates dans la section Zeiss sont exactes. Partout autre part elles ne sont qu'approximatives. D'une manière générale une seule date indique l'année dans laquelle ce modèle-là a paru pour la première fois.

CFPS obturateur focal de voile

Contrefacon: un appareil, décrit pour le vendeur comme étant historiquement exact, mais dont l'apparence semble être d'une marque de fabrication ou modèle différent de ce qu'il est veritablement. Les contrefaçons Leica sont généralement d'origine russe.

CRF télémetre couplé.

exp pose

Trucage   un appareil qui a été fabriqué de façon telle à représenter ce qu'il n'est pas et qui est décrit par le vendeur comme étant un article original. Un Leica "Luxus" qui est en verité un Leica I(A) re-travaillé que l'on peut trouver sur l'étalage d'un revendeur à une exposition photographique comme étant un "Luxus" véritable pourrait être un article truqué. Faites bien attention au trucage avant de faire un achat coûteux; connaissez bien tous les détails concernant l'appareil que vous voulez acheter et renseignez-vous bien sur le vendeur. De plus en plus d'appareils truqués sont en fabrication en Europe de l'Est et sont ensuite exportés vers l'Ouest dans l'espoir de faire un profit rapide.

FPS   obturateur focal

mfg   fabriqué

MFPS   obturateur focal métallique

NSR   pas de vente à mentionner

Qty   quantité
Copie   un appareil photographique, décrit à l'acheteur par le vendeur comme n'étant pas historiquement exact. Les copies ne se vendent pas pour tromper. Les appareils Leica "Luxus" sont parfois fabriqués à partir d'appareils Leica I(A); Les Leica "Uhr" sont en fait fabriqués par Leitz et sont fidèles à l'original, mais hélas ...

RFR   télémètre

S   secondes

Slr   ordre des numéros de serie

Snr   reflex monoculaire

VFR   viseur

En ce qui concerne les appareils sur lesquels plusieurs prix sont mentionés pour tenir compte ainsi des variations sur un même type de modèle (par exemple, chrome/noir, avec marquage militaire etc...), la valeur et l'indice de rareté s'appliquent uniquement à l'appareil de base dans la catégorie concernée.

Codes pour les appareils de photographie

Chaque entrée, cataloguée dans le Hove International Blue Book, a son propre code unique, à l'exception de quelques accessoires Leitz (le code pour ceux-ci etant le code mis en usage par Leitz) et de la plupart des appareils photographiques Zeiss (leurs codes étant ceux du catalogue Zeiss). Le code comprend deux lettres suivies de trois chiffres ou dans le cas de quelques accessoires Nikon et objectifs Leitz de quatre chiffres.

Ces codes-ci sont donnés aussitôt qu'un article est ajouté au livre. La combinaison lettres/chiffres est donc unique à chaque entrée. Les codes utilisés pour décrire les accessoires d'appareils photographiques ont un zero qui précède les deux premières lettres.

Conçus à l'origine pour faciliter la recherche rapide d'une donnée spécifique sur un fichier d'ordinateur, ces codes-ci peuvent bien également servir à d'autres usages.

Lorsque des contributeurs nous écrivent, apportant des informations de dernière minute pour tenir à jour le Hove International Blue Book, ils n'ont qu'à simplement utiliser le code de référence pour permettre à l'éditeur de savoir exactement de quel appareil il s'agit.

De la même façon, n'importe qui aurait besoin d'une référence simple et courte peut utiliser ces mêmes codes, que ce soient des collectionneurs, vendeurs, clubs ou autres.

Comme de plus en plus de collectionneurs commencent à cataloguer leur collection sur ordinateur, ces codes deviendront certainement très utiles pour établir leur propre fichier.

Dating and identifying

ONE OF THE MOST important - and often difficult - aspects of camera collecting is the dating of a camera. There are, however, certain basic rules that can help in this direction. Here, then, are some tips that might help you in establishing a likely date of manufacture for some cameras.

In general...

First, some general rules that can help you narrow down the time period in which a camera was manufactured.

1. Red leather bellows on a folding drop bed camera indicate it was made before the First World War, but probably not before 1900.
2. Square corners on bellows were used before the turn of the century.
3. 35mm film cameras didn't really appear until after the Leica of 1926, though 35mm film was the standard for the moving picture industry.

Hidden codes

Some manufacturers used hidden codes to indicate the year of production of their products. For example, Kodak used a transliteration code for lenses made in the 1940s and 1950s that ran like this...

C A M E R O S I T Y
1 2 3 4 5 6 7 8 9 0

If you have a Kodak camera that you think is from this period, look carefully at the serial number around the lens. If it contains two letters in the beginning, such as *ER,* or *RY,* compare these letters to the code. You can see that *ER* stands for *45,* or 1945, while *RY* stands for *50* or 1950. Using this code, you can discover exactly which year your camera lens was made.

Though not quite as collectable as Kodak, Hasselblad uses a similar system on both its camera bodies and its film magazines that looks like this...

```
V  H  P  I C T U R E S
1  2  3  4 5 6 7  8 9 0
```

Consequently, a film magazine with *RC* in the serial number would have been made in 1985.

Some Chinese cameras have the date indicated as the number of years since liberation, which was 1949. For example, an East Wind 120 SLR with a serial number of 210036 on the lens would have been made in 1970 - i.e. 21 + 1949 = 1970.

Shutters

Cameras with shutters made by the Friedrich Deckel Company, of Munich, Germany, appear on many cameras right up into the 1950s.

The first of these shutters was called the Compound, and is so marked on the shutter, under the lens. This shutter first appeared on cameras beginning about 1905.

The next shutter was called the Compur, the name which was used for the life of the shutter. The original Compur used a small dial to set the shutter speeds. This dial was usually located at the 12 o'clock position, the cocking lever at 3 o'clock, and a dial marked *ZDM* or *ZBT* at 9 o'clock, as you face the camera. Often called the dial-set Compur, it was introduced in 1912.

The next Compur shutter moved the shutter speed setting to a ring concentric with the shutter housing. This shutter is known as the rim-set Compur and dates from 1929.

An increase in top speed from 1/250 second to 1/500 second came with the introduction of the Compur Rapid shutter in about 1935.

Lenses

Lens coating, with some rare exceptions, indicates that the lens was manufactured after 1945. Beware, however, of early lenses which were sent by their owners to be coated after coating came into vogue.

Zeiss lenses, like Deckel shutters, appeared on very many different manufacturers' cameras. Even some cameras made in Japan used the combination of Zeiss Lens/Compur Shutter, before Japanese lens production got off the ground. The list opposite should help in dating a Zeiss lens to approximately within a year of manufacture. This list isn't complete, and you may find numbers that don't appear here.

Zeiss Lens Serial Numbers:

Year	Range	Year	Range
1912	173400-200500	1928	903100-908150
1913	208500-249350	1929	919800-1016900
1914	249900-252700	1930	1020500-1239700
1915	282800-284500	1931	1239701-1365600
1916	285200-288100	1932	1365601-1389300
1917	289000-298150	1933	1436650-1456000
1918	298200-322750	1934	1500450-1590000
1919	322800-351600	1935	1615750-1752300
1920	375200-419800	1936	1774800-1942800
1921	433250-438350	1937	1950100-2220000
1922	438900-498000	1938	2268000-2528000
1923	561250-578300	1939	2528001-2651200
1924	631850-648500	1940	2652000-2678000
1925	652200-681751	1941	2678001-2790350
1926	686800-703200	1942	2799600- ?
1927	722200-798250		

Patent dates

Patent dates can give you an idea of when a camera was *not* made. When a patent date appears on a camera, you can be sure that the camera in question was not made before that date. Nothing, however, indicates that the camera was made one year after or twenty years after the patent was granted. It is not unusual for patents to be granted, and not be used in actual production for a number of years afterward.

Patent numbers can provide the same sort of information and, on the next page, the list by year might be helpful.

Film numbers

Another way to gauge the date after which a camera was made works with roll film cameras, which either have the film number marked inside the camera body, or which are found with an old roll of film inside. The list over the page will help you date a camera this way.

United States Patent numbers by year of issue

Year	Number	Year	Number	Year	Number
1850	6891	1882	251,685	1914	1,083,267
1851	7865	1883	269,820	1915	1,123,212
1852	8622	1884	291,016	1916	1,166,419
1853	9512	1885	310,163	1917	1,210,389
1854	10,358	1886	333,494	1918	1,251,458
1855	12,117	1887	355,291	1919	1,290,027
1856	14,009	1888	375,720	1920	1,326,899
1857	16,324	1889	395,305	1921	1,364,063
1858	19,010	1890	418,665	1922	1,401,948
1859	22,477	1891	443,987	1923	1,440,362
1860	26,642	1892	466,315	1924	1,478,996
1861	31,005	1893	488,976	1925	1,521,590
1862	34,045	1894	511,744	1926	1,568,040
1863	37,266	1895	531,619	1927	1,612,790
1864	41,047	1896	552,501	1928	1,654,521
1865	45,085	1897	574,369	1929	1,696,897
1866	51,784	1898	596,467	1930	1,742,818
1867	60,658	1899	616,871	1931	1,787,424
1868	72,959	1900	640,167	1932	1,839,190
1869	85,503	1901	664,827	1933	1,892,66
1870	98,460	1902	690,385	1934	1,941,449
1871	110,617	1903	717,521	1935	1,985,878
1872	122,304	1904	748,567	1936	2,026,516
1873	134,504	1905	778,834	1937	2,066,319
1874	146,010	1906	808,618	1938	2,014,004
1875	158,350	1907	839,799	1940	2,185,170
1876	171,641	1908	875,679	1941	2,227,418
1877	158,813	1909	908,436	1942	2,268,540
1878	198,733	1910	945,010	1943	2,307,007
1879	211,078	1911	980,178	1944	2,338.081
1880	223,211	1912	1,013,095	1945	2,366,154
1881	236,137	1913	1,049,326	1946	2,391,856

American Film Numbers by date of introduction

101: 1895	110: 1898	119: 1900	129: 1912
102: 1895	111: 1898	120: 1901	130: 1916
103: 1896	112: 1898	121: 1902	616: 1932
104: 1897	113: 1898	122: 1903	620: 1932
105: 1898	114: 1898	123: 1904	135: 1935
106: 1898	115: 1898	124: 1905	828: 1935*
107: 1898	116: 1899	126: 1906	126: 1963**
108: 1898	117: 1900	127: 1912	110: 1973***
109: 1898	118: 1900	128: 1912	

*also known as Bantam
**also known as Instamatic, not the same as 126 of 1906
***also known as Pocket Instamatic, not the same as 110 of 1898

Russian cameras

Many Russian cameras from the 1950s to the 1980s show the year of manufacture as the first two digits of the serial number: a Zorki 2-S camera with a serial number of 56083307, for example, was made in 1956.

It is often possible to tell if a Russian camera has its original lens simply by comparing the serial numbers. A 1956 camera with a 1968 lens would make you suspect that someone had swapped the original lens for a later one.

Russian cameras also offer a particular identification problem. The Cyrillic alphabet is very foreign to most of us. The Zorki 2-C camera is referred to by some as the Zorki 2-S because the transliteration for the Cyrillic C is the Roman S. In The *Hove International Blue Book*, we have tried to list such cameras with their Roman transliterations.

The list of serial numbers on the next page will help date a FED (Leica II copy).

Lens/shutter combinations

Many cameras were originally sold with one lens and shutter, and then sometime later, their owners updated one or both. It also happens that many

FED Serial Numbers

1934	31 - 4000	1947	176000 - 186000
1935	4000 -16000	1948	186000 - 203000
1936	16000 - 31000	1949	203000 - 221000
1937	31000 - 53000	1950	221000 - 248000
1938	53000 - 82000	1951	248000 - 289000
1939	82000 - 116000	1952	289000 - 341000
1940	116000 - 148000	1953	341000 - 424000
1941	148000 - 175000	1954	424000 - 560000
1942-45	No Camera Production	1955	560000 - 700000
1946	175000 - 176000		

cameras were available new with the option of several lens and shutter combinations, depending on the buyer's taste and purse.

Some cameras, therefore, have lens and shutters provided, not by the camera maker, but by the camera distributor. A French lens on a German camera could mean that it was originally sold in France.

Chinese cameras

Some Chinese cameras also have an indication of the year of production contained in the serial number, both of the lens and of the camera body. Sometimes this is seen simply as the first two digits being the year itself. 770020 on a Red Flag 20 camera shows that this camera was made in 1977. Incidently, this was the last year when the Red Flag 20 camera was produced.

Foca cameras

The list of Foca camera models on the next page, along with their dates of manufacture up until 1957, should help in identifying the year that a particular camera was produced, and also in distinguishing a PF2 from a PF2b, both of which have two stars marked on the body front.

Foca models and dates

Foca "PF1", one star
1946 16,001-20,300
1947 20.301-21,200
1948 60,001-61,300
1949 61,301-65,200
1950 65,201-67,700
       68,201-68,700
1951 67,701-68,200
       68,701-69,200
       69,701-69,999
       100,001-101,150
1952 69-201-69,700
       101,151-101,550
       160,001-161,000
1953 101,551-101,999

Foca "Standard" one star
1953 500.001-502,050
1954 502,051-503,150
1955 503,151-504,100
1956 504,101-505,300
1957 505,301-   ?

Foca "PF2" two stars
1946 10,001-15,999

Foca "PF2b" two stars*
1947 25,001-37,000
1948 37,001-46,600
1949 46,601-53,000
       54,401-55,350
1950 53,001-54,401
       55,351-56,000
1951 56.001-59,500
       125,000-150,000
1952 59,501-60,000
       90,001-92,700

1953 300,000-300,550
       92,701-94,999
1954 300,551-302,100
1955 302,101-303,700
1956 303,701-306,000
1957 306,001-   ?

Foca "PF3" three stars
1952 90,001-92,700
(taken from the PF2b list from the same year.)
1953 92,701-89.999
(taken from the PF2b list from the same year.)
       400,001-400,650
1954 400,651-402,400
1955 402,401-404,100
1956 404,101-406,400
1957 406,401-   ?

Foca Universel no stars
1949 70.001-74,800
1950 74,801-80,400
1951 80,401-84,650
1952 170,000-174,000
1953 84,651-86,900
1954 86,901-87,999
1955 200,501-201,250

Foca Universel "R" no stars
1955 200,001R-200,900R
1956 200,901R-203,300R
1957 203,301R-   ?

FOCASPORT
1955 10,001S-23,600S
1956 23,601S-48,500S
1957 48,501S-   ?

From 1947 until 1951, about 1200 PF3 cameras were made. These cameras used serial numbers taken from the "PF2b" list. They fall between two ranges, 25,000-59,999, and 125,000-150,000.

Nikon lens codes

Finally, not a dating aid as such, but interesting none the less is the code used by Nikon to indicate the number of lens elements in a Nikkor lens. This code was used into the mid-1970s. Remember that Nikon produced lenses for a number of cameras, not only their own.

Nikon codes

U	1 element		H	6 elements
B	2 elements		S	7 elements
T	3 elements		O	8 elements
Q	4 elements		N	9 elements
P	5 elements		D	10 elements

Wide-angle lenses usually did not have this coding. Instead, a *W,* indicating wideangle was engraved. The red *C* found on many Nikon lenses made before the end of the 1950s indicates that the lens was coated.

If you find your camera listed in the *Blue Book,* but have another lens or shutter on it, please let us know. We are always happy to receive new and useful information for future editions.

Identifying Leica Cameras

WE ARE INCLUDING in this 1992 – 1993 edition of the Blue Book a list of Leica camera and lens serial numbers, by kind permission of Leica Camera G.m.b.H. of Solms. This listing is essentially for use as a quick reference guide for the dating of a Leica camera or lens. The lists are in manufacturing batches. In a number of cases, particularly in the more recent post-war period, not all allocated numbers were used.

In the Leica screw period the individual batches were often much smaller than would be indicated by this quick reference list. You will often find individual cameras that are of a different model than that indicated in the list. For example, you might come across a Leica Standard with a serial number that indicates it should be one of a batch of 1000 Leica IIIa cameras. This is because, before the war, the Leitz company were willing to supply a special order camera to an individual customer: it would then be allotted a number from the current production batch. Leica Historica, the German Leica historical society, once published a screw camera listing that analysed production almost down to individual cameras by model and date and ran to 190 A4 pages of detail. This listing was compiled from the hand-written ledgers, which still exist in the factory, where every single camera produced was recorded, with its model type, date and destination.

Another anomaly that can arise with screw, and some M cameras, is caused by the Leitz policy, up to at least the end of the 1960s, of offering an upgrading service. Examples might be from Leica I to Leica II, or Leica II to Leica III or IIIa. After the war, flash synchronisation was also offered for earlier models. For these reasons you can see that an original Leica I could have been converted several times during its life, but it always retained its original serial number. This can be disappointing for the collector who comes into possession of a camera with the serial number of what should have been a valuable collector's item, but which has been converted into something much more up-to-date but far less valuable now!

Leitz also upgraded lenses for customers by changing the front ring on, say, an Elmax to a standard Elmar ring. Later they offered to change the aperture scale to the later type. They also coated earlier lenses. So it is quite possible to find an early unnumbered lens, that was not originally range-finder coupled, that has been converted to a later, coated specification.

For all the above reasons, use these serial number lists with caution. They are only a quick reference guide. The more detailed Leica publications from HOVE will give further help in identifying Leica cameras, lenses and accessories and act as guides into the fascinating Leica world.

List of Leica Serial Numbers up to 1988

This information reproduced by the kind permission of Leica Camera G.m.b.H.

Leica-No.	Model	Year
100 – 130	I	1923
131 – 1000	I	1925
1001 – 2445	I	1926
2446 – 5433	I	1926/27
5434 – 5700	I	1928
5700 – 6300	Compur	1926-29
6301 – 13100	I	1928
13101 – 13300	Compur	1929
13301 – 21478	I	1929
21479 – 21810	Compur	1930
21811 – 34450	I	1930
34451 – 34802	Compur	1930
34803 – 34817	I(Luxus)	1930
34818 – 60000	I	1930
60001 – 71199	I	1931
71200 – 101000	II	1.2.32
101001 – 106000	Standard	21.10.32
106001 – 107600	III	1933
107601 – 107757	III	1934
107758 – 108650	II	1934
108651 – 108700	III	1933
108701 – 109000	II	1933
109001 – 111550	III	1933
111551 – 111580	II Chrom	1933
111581 – 112000	III	1933
112001 – 112500	II Chrom	1933
112501 – 114400	III	1934
114401 – 114050	St Chrom	1933
114051 – 114052	Reporter	1933
114053 – 114400	III	1934
114401 – 115300	II Chrom	1933
115301 – 115650	III	1934
115651 – 115900	II Chrom	1934
115901 – 116000	St Chrom	1934
116001 – 123000	III Chrom	1933
123001 – 123580	Standard	1934
123581 – 124800	III Chrom	1933
124801 – 126200	III Chrom	24.11.33
126201 – 126800	III	
126801 – 137400	III	1934
137401 – 137625	Standard	1934
137626 – 138700	III Chrom	1934
138701 – 138950	St Chrom	1934
138951 – 139900	III Chrom	1934
139901 – 139950	Standard	1934
139951 – 140000	II	1934
140001 – 141500	III Chrom	1934
141501 – 141850	Standard	1934
141851 – 141900	II	1934
141901 – 142250	III Chrom	1934
142251 – 142350	II	1934
142351 – 142500	III	1934
142501 – 142700	I Standard	1934
142701 – 143425	III	1934
143426 – 143750	II Chrom	1934
143751 – 143900	Standard	1934
143901 – 144200	III	1934
144201 – 144400	II	1934
144401 – 144500	Standard	1934
144501 – 145600	III	1934
145601 – 145800	Standard	1934
145801 – 146200	III	1934
146201 – 146375	III	1934
146376 – 146675	III	1934
146676 – 146775	II	1934
146776 – 147000	III	1934
147001 – 147075	Standard	1934
147076 – 147175	II	1934
147176 – 147875	St Chrom	1934
147876 – 148025	II Chrom	1934
148026 – 148850	III Chrom	1934
148851 – 148950	II Chrom	1934
148951 – 149350	III Chrom	1935
149351 – 149450	St Chrom	1934/35
149451 – 149550	II Chrom	1934/35
149551 – 150000	III Chrom	1935
150001 – 150200	Reporter	1934-36
from 150125 with ¹/1000	Second	from 14.7.36

Leica-No.	Model	Year
150201 – 150850	III Chrom	1934/35
150851 – 151100	Standard	1935
151101 – 151225	III	1935
151226 – 151300	II	1935
151301 – 152500	III	1935
152501 – 152600	St Chrom	1935
152601 – 153175	III Chrom	1935
153176 – 153225	II	1935
153226 – 153550	III	1935
153551 – 153700	II	1935
153701 – 154150	III	1935
154151 – 154200	II	1935
154201 – 154800	III	1935
154801 – 154900	St Chrom	1935
154901 – 156200	III	1935
156201 – 156850	IIIa ¹/1000	1935
156851 – 157250	III	1935
157251 – 157400	II	1935
157401 – 158300	IIIa	1935
158301 – 158350	Standard	1935
158351 – 158400	II	1935
158401 – 158650	IIIa	1935
158651 – 159000	III	1935
159001 – 159200	IIIa	1935
159201 – 159350	Standard	1935
159351 – 159950	III	1935
159951 – 159625	IIIa	1935
159626 – 159675	III	1935
159676 – 160325	IIIa	1935
160326 – 160375	III	1935
160376 – 160450	I	1935
160451 – 160700	II	1935
160701 – 161150	I Standard	1935
161151 – 161450	II	1935
161451 – 161550	IIIa	1935
161551 – 161600	III	1935
161601 – 161800	IIIa	1935
161801 – 161950	III Chrom	1935
161951 – 162100	IIIa	1935
162101 – 162175	III	1935
162176 – 162350	IIIa	1935
162351 – 162400	III	1935
162401 – 162500	IIIa	1935
162501 – 162625	III	1935
162626 – 162675	IIIa	1935
162676 – 162750	III	1935
162751 – 162800	IIIa	1935
162801 – 162825	III	1935
162826 – 162925	IIIa	1935
162926 – 162975	III	1935
162976 – 163050	IIIa	1935
163051 – 163100	III	1935
163101 – 163225	IIIa	1935
163226 – 163250	III	1935
163251 – 163400	IIIa	1935
163401 – 163450	Standard	1935
163451 – 163550	IIIa	1935
163551 – 163775	III	1935
163776 – 163950	IIIa	1935
163951 – 164150	Standard	1935
164151 – 164275	IIIa	1935
164276 – 164675	III	1935
164676 – 164900	IIIa	1935
164901 – 165000	II	1935
165001 – 165100	III	1935
165101 – 165300	II	1935
165301 – 165500	Standard	1935
165501 – 165975	III	1935
165976 – 166075	IIIa	1935
166076 – 166600	III	1935
166601 – 166750	IIIa	1935
166751 – 166900	III	1935
166901 – 167050	IIIa	1935
167051 – 167175	III	1935
167176 – 167200	IIIa	1935
167201 – 167225	III	1935
167226 – 167700	IIIa	1935
167701 – 167750	III	1935

Leica-No.	Model	Year
167751 – 168000	Standard	1935
168001 – 168200	II	1935
168201 – 168250	III	1935
168251 – 168325	IIIa	1935
168326 – 168400	III	1935
168401 – 168500	IIIa	1935
168501 – 168600	III	1935
168601 – 168725	IIIa	1935
168726 – 168750	III	1935
168751 – 16885u	IIIa	1935
168851 – 169000	Standard	1935
169001 – 169200	III	1935
169201 – 169350	Standard	1935
169351 – 169450	II	1935
169451 – 169550	III	1935
169551 – 169650	II	1935
169651 – 170150	IIIa	1935
170151 – 170500	III	1935
170501 – 171300	IIIa	1935
171301 – 171550	II	1935
171551 – 171900	Standard	1935
171901 – 172250	IIIa	1935
172251 – 172300	III	1935
172301 – 172350	IIIa	1935
172351 – 172600	III	1935
172601 – 172800	II	1935
172801 – 173000	Standard	1935
173001 – 173125	IIIa	1935
173126 – 173176	III	1935
173177 – 173425	III	1935
173426 – 173475	III	1935
173476 – 173500	IIIa	1935
173501 – 173650	Standard	1935
173651 – 173675	III	1935
173676 – 173725	III	1935
173726 – 173825	III	1935
173826 – 173900	III	1935
173901 – 174025	IIIa	1935
174026 – 174075	III	1935
174076 – 174100	IIIa	1935
174101 – 174125	III	1935
174126 – 174150	IIIa	1935
174151 – 174400	III	1935
174401 – 174650	II	1935
174651 – 174675	IIIa	1935
174676 – 174750	III	1935
174751 – 174950	IIIa	1935
174951 – 175125	III	1935
175126 – 175200	IIIa	1935
175201 – 175350	III	1935
175351 – 175450	IIIa	1935
175451 – 175500	III	1935
175501 – 175700	Standard	1935
175701 – 175750	III	1935
175751 – 175850	IIIa	1935
175851 – 175900	III	1935
175901 – 176100	IIIa	1935
176101 – 176150	III	1935
176151 – 176250	IIIa	1935
176251 – 176300	III	1935
176301 – 176600	IIIa	1935
176601 – 177000	III	1935
177001 – 177400	IIIa	1935
177401 – 177550	III	1935
177551 – 177600	IIIa	1935
177601 – 177700	III	1955
177701 – 177800	Standard	1935
177801 – 177900	IIIa	1935
177901 – 178000	III	1935
178001 – 178100	III	1935
178101 – 178250	III	1935
178251 – 178550	IIIa	1935
178551 – 178600	III	1935
178601 – 179200	IIIa	1935
179201 – 179250	III	1935
179251 – 179500	IIIa	1935
179501 – 179575	II	1935
179576 – 179800	Standard	1935
179801 – 179900	II	1935

LEICA SERIAL NUMBERS

Leica-No.	Model	Year
179901 — 180100	IIIa	1935
180101 — 180400	III	1935
180401 — 180475	IIIa	1935
180476 — 180700	III	1935
180701 — 180800	Standard	1935
180801 — 181000	II	1935
181001 — 181450	IIIa	1935
181451 — 181550	III	1935
181551 — 181600	IIIa	1935
181601 — 181700	III	1935
181701 — 182000	IIIa	1935
182001 — 182050	III	1935
182051 — 182300	IIIa	1935
182301 — 182350	III	1935
182351 — 182500	IIIa	1935
182501 — 182700	Standard	1935
182701 — 182850	II	1935
182851 — 183500	IIIa	1935
183501 — 183600	II	1935
183601 — 183750	Standard	1935/36
183751 — 184400	IIIa	1936
184401 — 184450	III	1936
184451 — 184700	IIIa	1936
184701 — 184750	III	1936
184751 — 184800	IIIa	1936
184801 — 184950	III	1936
184951 — 185200	IIIa	1936
185201 — 185350	III	1936
185351 — 185500	II	1936
185501 — 185650	Standard	1936
185651 — 185700	III	1936
185701 — 185800	Standard	1936
185801 — 186100	IIIa	1936
186101 — 186200	III	1936
186201 — 186500	IIIa	1936
186501 — 186550	III	1936
186551 — 186800	IIIa	1936
186801 — 186900	III	1936
186901 — 186950	IIIa	1936
186951 — 187000	III	1936
187001 — 187100	IIIa	1936
187101 — 187200	III	1936
187201 — 187400	IIIa	1936
187401 — 187500	III	1936
187501 — 187650	II	1936
187651 — 187775	III	1936
187776 — 187785	IIIa	1936
187786 — 187850	III	1936
187851 — 188100	IIIa	1936
188101 — 188300	III	1936
188301 — 188600	Standard	1936
188601 — 188750	II	1936
188751 — 189300	IIIa	1936
189301 — 189475	III	1936
189476 — 189800	IIIa	1936
189801 — 189900	III	1936
189901 — 190200	IIIa	1936
190201 — 190500	III	1936
190501 — 190700	IIIa	1936
190701 — 190900	III	1936
190901 — 191100	IIIa	1936
191101 — 191200	III	1936
191201 — 191300	II	1936
191301 — 191350	IIIa	1936
191351 — 191500	III	1936
191501 — 191650	II	1936
191651 — 191750	Standard	1936
191751 — 191850	III	1936
191851 — 192100	IIIa	1936
192101 — 192400	III	1936
192401 — 192500	IIIa	1936
192501 — 192800	III	1936
192801 — 192950	II	1936
192951 — 193200	IIIa	1936
193201 — 193450	Standard	1936
193451 — 193500	IIIa	1936
193501 — 193600	III	1936
193601 — 194300	IIIa	1936
194301 — 194650	III	1936
194651 — 194850	II	1936
194851 — 194950	Standard	1936
194951 — 196200	IIIa	1936
196201 — 196300	III	1936
196301 — 196400	IIIa	1936
196401 — 196550	II	1936
196551 — 196750	Standard	1936
196751 — 197400	IIIa	1936
197401 — 197500	Standard	1936
197501 — 197550	IIIa	1936
197551 — 197800	III	1936
197801 — 198200	IIIa	1936
198201 — 198400	III	1936
198401 — 198800	IIIa	1936
198801 — 198900	III	1936
198901 — 199200	IIIa	1936
199201 — 199300	III	1936
199301 — 199500	IIIa	1936
199501 — 199600	III	1936
199601 — 199800	II	1936
199801 — 200100	IIIa	1936
200101 — 200200	III	1936
200201 — 200500	IIIa	1936
200501 — 200650	II	1936
200651 — 200750	Standard	1936
200751 — 201100	III	1936
201101 — 201200	III	1936
201201 — 201300	IIIa	1936
201301 — 201400	III	1936
201401 — 201600	IIIa	1936
201601 — 201700	Standard	1936
201701 — 202300	IIIa	1936
202301 — 202450	II	1936
202451 — 202600	IIIa	1936
202601 — 202700	III	1936
202701 — 202800	IIIa	1936
202801 — 202900	II	1936
202901 — 203100	IIIa	1936
203101 — 203300	III	1936
203301 — 203400	Standard	1936
203401 — 204100	IIIa	1936
204101 — 204200	III	1936
204201 — 204300	IIIa	1936
204301 — 204500	II	1936
204501 — 204600	III	1936
204601 — 204800	IIIa	1936
204801 — 205000	III	1936
205001 — 205100	IIIa	1936
205101 — 205300	III	1936
205301 — 205400	IIIa	1936
205401 — 205500	II	1936
205501 — 205700	Standard	1936
205701 — 207300	IIIa	1936
207301 — 207400	II	1936
207401 — 207600	Standard	1936
207601 — 207800	III	1936
207801 — 208000	IIIa	1936
208001 — 208300	III	1936
208301 — 208600	IIIa	1936
208601 — 208800	III	1936
208801 — 209000	IIIa	1936
209001 — 209600	III	1936
209601 — 209900	II	1936
209901 — 210100	IIIa	1936
210101 — 210200	III	1936
210201 — 210400	IIIa	1936
210401 — 210900	Standard	1936
210901 — 211000	III	1936
211001 — 211600	IIIa	1936
211601 — 211700	III	1936
211701 — 211800	IIIa	1936
211801 — 211900	II	1936
211901 — 212400	IIIa	1936
212401 — 212700	Standard	1936
212701 — 212800	IIIa	1936
212801 — 213200	III	1936
213201 — 213300	IIIa	1936
213301 — 213600	Standard	1936
213601 — 213700	II	1936
213701 — 214400	IIIa	1936
214401 — 214800	Standard	1936
214801 — 215300	IIIa	1936
215301 — 216000	III	1936
216001 — 216300	IIIa	1936
216301 — 216500	II	1936
216501 — 216800	IIIa	1936
216801 — 217000	III	1936
217001 — 217200	IIIa	1936
217201 — 217300	III	1936
217301 — 217500	Standard	1936
217501 — 217700	III	1937
217701 — 217900	II	1936/37
217901 — 218300	IIIa	1936/37
218301 — 218700	II	1936
218701 — 218800	III	1936
218801 — 219600	IIIa	1936
219601 — 219800	II	1936
219801 — 219900	IIIa	1936
219901 — 220000	III	1936
220001 — 220300	IIIa	1936
220301 — 220500	II	1937
220501 — 220600	IIIa	1936
220601 — 220700	III	1936
220701 — 220900	IIIa	1936
220901 — 221000	III	1936
221001 — 221300	IIIa	1936
221301 — 221400	III	1936
221401 — 222150	IIIa	1936
222151 — 222200	III	1936
222201 — 222300	IIIa	1936
222301 — 222700	Standard	1937
222701 — 223000	II	1937
223001 — 223300	III	1937
223301 — 223600	IIIa	1936
223601 — 223700	III	1936
223701 — 224600	IIIa	1936/37
224601 — 224800	Standard	1936/37
224801 — 224900	IIIa	1936/37
224901 — 225000	III	1936/37
225001 — 225200	IIIa	1936/37
225201 — 225300	III	1936/37
225301 — 225400	IIIa	1936/37
225401 — 225600	III	1936/37
225601 — 226300	IIIa	1936/37
226301 — 226400	III	1936/37
226401 — 227000	IIIa	1936/37
227001 — 227050	III	1936/37
227051 — 227600	IIIa	1936/37
227601 — 227650	III	1936/37
227651 — 231500	IIIa	1936/37
231501 — 231600	III	1936/37
231601 — 231800	IIIa	1936/37
231801 — 231900	III	1936/37
231901 — 232200	IIIa	1936/37
232201 — 232500	III	1936/37
232501 — 232800	IIIa	1936/37
232801 — 232900	III	1936/37
232901 — 233400	IIIa	1936/37
233401 — 233500	III	1936/37
233501 — 233700	Standard	1936/37
233701 — 233800	III	1936/37
233801 — 234000	IIIa	1936/37
234001 — 234100	II	1936/37
234101 — 234200	III	1936/37
234201 — 234500	IIIa	1936/37
234501 — 234600	III	1936/37
234601 — 235100	IIIa	1937
235101 — 235200	III	1937
235201 — 235800	III	1937
235801 — 235875	III	1937
235876 — 236200	IIIa	1937
236201 — 236300	III	1937
236301 — 236500	IIIa	1937
236501 — 236700	II	1937
236701 — 236800	IIIa	1937
236801 — 236900	III	1937
236901 — 237000	IIIa	1937
237001 — 237200	III	1937
237201 — 237500	IIIa	1937
237501 — 237600	III	1937
237601 — 238000	IIIa	1937
238001 — 238100	III	1937
238101 — 238500	IIIa	1937
238501 — 238600	III	1937
238601 — 238800	IIIa	1937
238801 — 238825	III	1937
238826 — 238900	IIIa	1937
238901 — 239000	III	1937
239001 — 239100	IIIa	1937
239101 — 239300	III	1937
239301 — 239400	III	1937
239401 — 239600	III	1937
239601 — 239700	IIIa	1937
239701 — 239800	III	1937
239801 — 240000	Standard	1937
240001 — 241000	IIIb	1937/38
241001 — 241100	IIIa	1937/38
241101 — 241300	III	1937/38
241301 — 241500	IIIa	1937/38

Leica-No.	Model	Year	Leica-No.	Model	Year	Leica-No.	Model	Year
241501 — 241700	II	1937/38	266001 — 266100	IIIa	1937	294901 — 295100	IIIa	1938
241701 — 241900	Standard	1937/38	266101 — 266200	III	1937	295101 — 295200	III	1938
241901 — 242000	II	1937/38	266201 — 266400	IIIa	1937	295201 — 295300	IIIa	1938
242001 — 243000	IIIb	1937/38	266401 — 266500	III	1937	295301 — 295400	Standard	1938
243001 — 243400	IIIa	1937/38	266501 — 266800	II	1937	295401 — 295500	III	1938
243401 — 243500	III	1937/38	266801 — 266900	IIIa	1937	295501 — 296000	IIIa	1938
243501 — 243800	II	1937/38	266901 — 267000	III	1937	296001 — 296200	II	1938
243801 — 244100	IIIa	1937/38	267001 — 267700	IIIa	1937	296201 — 296500	IIIa	1938
244101 — 244200	III	1937/38	267701 — 267800	III	1937	296501 — 296600	III	1938
244201 — 244400	Standard	1937/38	267801 — 267900	IIIa	1937	296691 — 296900	Standard	1938
244401 — 244600	III	1937/38	267901 — 268000	Standard		296901 — 297100	II	1938
244601 — 244800	IIIa	1937/38	268001 — 268100	IIIa	1937/38	297101 — 297200	IIIa	1938
244801 — 245000	Standard	1937/38	268101 — 268200	III	1938	297201 — 297400	III	1938
245001 — 245100	IIIa	1937/38	268201 — 268400	IIIa	1937	297401 — 297900	IIIa	1938
245101 — 245300	III	1937/38	268401 — 268500	III	1938	297901 — 298000	III	1938
245301 — 246200	IIIa	1937/38	268501 — 268700	IIIa	1938	298001 — 299000	IIIa	1938
246201 — 246300	III	1937/38	268701 — 268800	III	1938	299001 — 299200	III	1938
246301 — 246400	IIIa	1937/38	268801 — 269300	IIIa	1938	299201 — 299500	IIIa	1938
246401 — 246500	III	1937/38	269301 — 269400	III	1938	299501 — 299600	III	1938
246501 — 246700	II	1937/38	269401 — 269600	IIIa	1938	299601 — 299800	IIIa	1938
246701 — 247500	IIIa	1937/38	269601 — 269700	III	1938	299801 — 299900	III	1938
247501 — 247600	II	1937/38	269701 — 270100	IIIa	1938	299901 — 300000	Standard	1938
247601 — 248300	IIIa	1937/38	270101 — 270200	III	1938	300001 — 300100	Reporter	1938
248301 — 248400	II	1937/38	270201 — 270300	IIIa	1938	300101 — 300200	Standard	1938
248401 — 248600	Standard	1937/38	270301 — 270400	III	1938	300201 — 300300	II	1938
248601 — 248900	IIIa	1937	270401 — 271000	IIIa	1938	300301 — 300400	Standard	1938
248901 — 249000	III	1937	271001 — 271100	III	1938	300401 — 300700	IIIa	1938
249001 — 249200	IIIa	1937	271101 — 271600	Standard	1938	300701 — 300800	III	1938
249201 — 249400	II	1937	271601 — 271700	II	1938	300801 — 301000	IIIa	1938
249401 — 249500	III	1937	271701 — 271800	III	1938	301001 — 301100	III	1938
249501 — 249700	Standard	1937	271801 — 272300	IIIa	1938	301101 — 301400	IIIa	1938
249701 — 249800	IIIa	1937	272301 — 272400	II	1938	301401 — 301500	III	1938
249801 — 249900	III	1937	272401 — 274800	IIIa	1938	301501 — 301600	III	1938
249901 — 250300	IIIa	1937	274801 — 275200	III	1938	301601 — 201700	Standard	1938
250301 — 250400	III	1937	275201 — 275350	IIIa	1938	301701 — 301800	III	1938
250401 — 251200	IIIa	1937	275351 — 275650	II	1938	301801 — 301900	IIIa	1938
251201 — 251300	II	1937	275651 — 275675	IIIa	1938	301901 — 302000	III	1938
251301 — 251500	Standard	1937	275676 — 275700	III	1938	302001 — 302500	IIIa	1938
251501 — 251600	IIIa	1937	275701 — 275800	IIIa	1938	302501 — 302800	II	1938
251601 — 251800	II	1937	275801 — 276400	III	1938	302801 — 302900	III	1938
251801 — 252000	III	1937	276401 — 277000	IIIa	1938	302901 — 303200	IIIa	1938
252001 — 252200	II	1937	277001 — 277100	III	1938	303201 — 303300	III	1938
252201 — 252900	IIIa	1937	277101 — 277500	IIIa	1938	303301 — 303700	IIIa	1938
252901 — 253000	III	1937	277505 — 277900	Standard	1938	303701 — 303800	II	1938
253001 — 253200	IIIa	1937	277901 — 278100	II	1938	303801 — 303900	Standard	1938
253201 — 253400	III	1937	278101 — 278200	III	1938	303901 — 304400	IIIa	1938
253401 — 253500	IIIa	1937	278201 — 278500	IIIa	1938	304401 — 304500	III	1938
253501 — 253600	III	1937	278501 — 278525	III	1938	304501 — 304700	IIIa	1938
253601 — 253800	Standard	1937	278526 — 278550	IIIa	1938	304701 — 304800	III	1938
253801 — 254000	IIIa	1937	278551 — 278600	III	1938	304801 — 304900	IIIa	1938
254001 — 254200	III	1937	278601 — 278800	Standard	1938	304901 — 305000	III	1938
254201 — 254600	IIIa	1937	278801 — 279000	IIIa	1938	305001 — 305600	IIIa	1938
254601 — 254800	II	1937	279001 — 279200	III	1938	305601 — 305700	III	1938
254801 — 254900	III	1937	279201 — 279400	II	1938	305701 — 305800	Standard	1938
254901 — 266400	IIIa	1937	279401 — 280000	IIIa	1938	305801 — 306200	IIIa	1938
256401 — 256600	Standard	1937	280001 — 286500	IIIb	1938	306201 — 306300	III	1938
256601 — 256800	IIIa	1937	286501 — 286800	Standard	1938	306301 — 306500	II	1938
256801 — 256900	III	1937	286801 — 287000	III	1938	306501 — 306600	III	1938
256901 — 257400	IIIa	1937	287001 — 287200	IIIa	1938	306601 — 306800	IIIa	1938
257401 — 257525	III	1937	287201 — 287300	III	1938	306801 — 307000	III	1938
257526 — 257600	IIIa	1937	287307 — 287400	IIIa	1938	307001 — 307500	IIIa	1938
257601 — 257800	Standard	1937	287401 — 287600	II	1938	307501 — 308000	Standard	1938
257801 — 258200	III	1937	287601 — 288000	IIIa	1938	308001 — 308100	IIIa	1938
258201 — 259500	IIIa	1937	288001 — 290200	IIIb	1938/39	308101 — 308200	III	1938
259501 — 259800	II	1937	290201 — 290500	IIIa	1938	308201 — 308300	II	1938
259801 — 259900	Standard	1937	290501 — 290800	III	1938	308301 — 308500	Standard	1938
259901 — 260000	IIIa	1937	290801 — 291000	IIIa	1938	308501 — 308600	III	1938
260001 — 260100	Reporter	1937	291001 — 291200	Standard	1938	308601 — 308700	IIIa	1938
260101 — 260200	IIIa	1937	291201 — 291500	IIIa	1938	308701 — 308800	III	1938
260201 — 260600	III	1937	291501 — 291600	III	1938	308801 — 309000	IIIa	1938
260601 — 260800	IIIa	1937	291601 — 291800	IIIa	1938	309001 — 309200	Standard	1938
260801 — 260900	III	1937	291801 — 292000	Standard	1938	309201 — 309300	IIIa	1938
260901 — 261200	IIIa	1937	292001 — 292200	II	1938	309301 — 309400	III	1938
261201 — 261300	III	1937	292201 — 292400	Standard	1938	309401 — 309500	IIIa	1938
261301 — 261500	IIIa	1937	292401 — 292600	IIIa	1938	309501 — 309700	II	1938
261501 — 261600	III	1937	292601 — 292700	III	1938	309701 — 310000	IIIa	1938/39
261601 — 261800	IIIa	1937	292701 — 293000	IIIa	1938	310001 — 310200	III	1938/39
261801 — 262000	Standard	1937	293001 — 293100	III	1938	310201 — 310400	IIIa	1938/39
262001 — 262800	IIIa	1937	293101 — 293200	IIIa	1938	310401 — 310500	III	1938/39
262801 — 263000	III	1937	293201 — 293400	III	1938	310501 — 310600	IIIa	1939
263001 — 263600	IIIa	1937	293401 — 293500	II	1938	310601 — 311000	III	1938/39
263601 — 263900	II	1937	293501 — 293900	IIIa	1938	311001 — 311200	II	1938
263901 — 264000	III	1937	293901 — 294000	Standard	1938	311201 — 311400	IIIa	1939
264001 — 264800	IIIa	1937	294001 — 294600	IIIa	1939	311401 — 311700	III	1939
264801 — 265000	Standard	1937	294601 — 294800	II	1938	311701 — 311800	IIIa	1939
265001 — 266000	IIIb	1937	294801 — 294900	III	1938	311801 — 311900	III	1939

LEICA SERIAL NUMBERS

Leica-No.	Model	Year	Leica-No.	Model	Year	Leica-No.	Model	Year
311901 – 312000	IIIa	1939	333101 – 333300	IIIa	1939	524001 – 525000	IIIc	1950/51
312001 – 312200	Standard	1939	333301 – 333600	Standard	1939	525001 – 540000	IIIf	1950/51
312201 – 312400	IIIa	1939	333601 – 334000	IIIb	1939	540001 – 560000	IIIf	1951
312401 – 312500	III	1939	334001 – 334200	III	1939	560001 – 562800	Ic	1951
312501 – 312800	Standard	1939	334201 – 334400	IIIa	1939	562801 – 565000	If	1951
312801 – 313000	IIIa	1939	334401 – 334600	III	1939	565001 – 570000	IIIf	1951
313001 – 313100	III	1939	334601 – 335000	IIIa	1939	570001 – 575000	IIIf	1951/52
313101 – 313200	IIIa	1939	335001 – 337000	IIIb	1939/40	575001 – 580000	If*	1952/53
313201 – 313300	III	1939	337001 – 337200	II	1939	580001 – 610000	IIIf	1951/52
313301 – 313400	IIIa	1939	337201 – 337400	IIIa	1939	610001 – 611000	IIIf/ELC	1952
313401 – 313500	Standard	1939	337401 – 337500	III	1939	611001 – 615000	IIIf*	1952/53
313501 – 313600	III	1939	337501 – 337900	IIIa	1939	Leica with light weight shutter		
313601 – 314000	III	1939	337901 – 338100	II	1939	615001 – 650000	IIIf	1952/53
314001 – 314100	III	1939	338101 – 338200	IIIa	1939	650001 – 655000	If	1953
314101 – 314300	II	1939	338201 – 338600	III	1939	655001 – 673000	IIIf	1953
314301 – 314500	Standard	1939	338601 – 338900	IIIa	1939	673001 – 674999	If	1953/54
314501 – 314600	II	1939	338901 – 339000	III	1939	675000	IIIf	1953
314601 – 314700	III	1939	339001 – 340000	IIIb	1939/40	675001 – 680000	IIIf	1953/54
314701 – 314800	IIIa	1939	340001 – 340200	IIIa	1939	680001 – 682000	If	1954
314801 – 314900	III	1939	340201 – 340400	III	1939	682001 – 684000	If	1955
314901 – 315000	IIIa	1939	340401 – 340600	IIIa	1939	684001 – 685000	IIIf/ELC	1953
315001 – 315100	II	1939	340601 – 340700	III	1939	685001 – 699999	IIIf Vorl.	1954
315101 – 315400	IIIa	1939	340701 – 341000	IIIa	1939			
315401 – 315500	II	1939	341001 – 341300	II	1939/40	700000	M3	1954
315501 – 315700	IIIa	1939	341301 – 341500	Standard	1939	700001 – 710000	M3	1954
315701 – 315800	III	1939	341501 – 341700	III	1939	710001 – 711000	IIIf Vorl. ELC	1954
315801 – 316100	IIIa	1939	341701 – 341900	IIIa	1939	711001 – 713000	IIf	1954
316101 – 316400	III	1939	341901 – 342000	III	1939	713001 – 729000	IIIf Vorl.	1954
316401 – 316700	IIIa	1939	342001 – 342200	Standard	1939	729001 – 730000	IIIf Vorl. ELC	1954
316701 – 316900	Standard	1939	342201 – 342300	III	1939	730001 – 746450	M3	1955
316901 – 317000	II	1939	342301 – 342900	IIIa	1939	746451 – 746500	M3 ELC	1955
317001 – 318000	IIIb	1939	342901 – 343100	III	1939	746501 – 750000	M3	1955
318001 – 318200	IIIa	1939	343101 – 344000	IIIa	1939	750001 – 759700	M3	1955
318201 – 318300	II	1939	344001 – 348500	IIIb	1939/40	759701 – 760000	M3 ELC	1955
318301 – 318500	Standard	1939	348501 – 348600	Standard	1939/40	760001 – 762000	If	1955
318501 – 318800	II	1939	348601 – 349000	IIIb	1940	762001 – 765000	IIf	1955
318801 – 318900	IIIa	1939	349001 – 349050	Reporter	1940	765001 – 773000	IIIf Vorl.	1955
318901 – 319901	III	1939	349051 – 349300	Standard	1940	773001 – 774000	IIIf ELC	1955
319001 – 320000	IIIb	1939	349301 – 351100	IIIb	1940	774001 – 775000	IIIf	1955
320001 – 320200	II	1939	351101 – 351150	II	1940	775001 – 780000	M3	1955
320201 – 320400	III	1939	351151 – 352000	IIIb	1940	780001 – 780090	M3 ELC	1955
320401 – 320600	IIIa	1939	352001 – 352100	II	1940	780091 – 780100	If	1957
320601 – 320700	II	1939	352101 – 352150	Standard	1940	780101 – 787000	M3	1955
320701 – 321000	Standard	1939	352151 – 352300	II	1940	787001 – 789000	IIf	1955
321001 – 322000	IIIb	1939	352301 – 352500	Reporter	1940/41/42	789001 – 790000	If	1955
322001 – 322200	II	1939	352501 – 352900	II	1940/41/42	790001 – 799000	IIIf	1955
322201 – 322700	Standard	1939	352901 – 353600	Standard	1940/41/42	799001 – 799999	IIf	1956
322701 – 322800	IIIa	1939	353601 – 353800	Reporter	1942/43	800000 – 805000	M3	1955
322801 – 323000	III	1939	353801 – 354000	Standard	1942/47	805001 – 805100	M3 ELC	1955
323001 – 324000	IIIb	1939	354001 – 354050	IIIa	1941/47	805101 – 807500	M3	1955
324001 – 324100	Reporter	1939	354051 – 354075	IIIa	1941/46	807501 – 808500	If	1956
324101 – 324700	IIIa	1939	354076 – 354100	II	1947	808501 – 810000	IIIf	1956
324701 – 324800	III	1939	354101 – 354200	IIIa	1947	810001 – 815000	IIIf	1956
324801 – 325000	II	1939	354201 – 354400	II	1942/47	815001 – 816000	If	1956
325001 – 325200	IIIa	1939	354401 – 355000	IIIb	1946	816001 – 816900	M3	1956
325201 – 325275	III	1939	355001 – 355650	Standard	1947/48	816901 – 817000	M3 ELC	1956
325276 – 325300	IIIa	1939	355651 – 356500			817001 – 820500	M3	1956
325301 – 325400	I	1939	356501 – 356550	IIIa	1947/48	820501 – 821500	IIf	1956
325401 – 325600	IIIa	1939	356651 – 356700	II	1947/48	821501 – 822000	If	1956
325601 – 325800	III	1939	356701 – 357200	IIIa	1948/50	822001 – 822900	If	1956
325801 – 325900	IIIa	1939	357201 – 358500			822901 – 823000	IIIf kaltef.	1956
325901 – 326000	II	1939	358501 – 358650	II	1948	823001 – 823500	IIIf	1956
326001 – 327000	IIIb	1939	358651 – 360000			823501 – 823867	IIIf ELC	1956
327001 – 327200	II	1939	360001 – 360100	IIIa	1940/42	823868 – 825000	IIIf	1956
327201 – 327400	III	1939	360101 – 367000	IIIc	1940	825001 – 826000	IIIg	1956
327401 – 327500	IIIa	1939	367001 – 367325	IIIc	1941/44	826001 – 829750	IIIg	1956
327501 – 327600	III	1939	367326 – 367500	IIIc	1945	829751 – 829850	IIIf ELC	1956
327601 – 327800	IIIa	1939	367501 – 368800	IIIc	1940/41	829851 – 830000	M3 ELC	1956
327801 – 328000	Standard	1939	368801 – 368950	IIIc	1941	830001 – 837500	M3	1956
328001 – 329000	IIIb	1939	368951 – 369000	IIIc	1941	837501 – 837620	M3 ELC	1956
329001 – 329400	Standard	1939	369001 – 369050	IIIc	1941	837621 – 837720	IIIf ELC	1956
329401 – 329600	II	1939	369051 – 369450	IIIc	1941	837721 – 839620	M3	1956
329601 – 329800	IIIa	1939	369451 – 390000	IIIc	1941/42	839621 – 839700	M3 ELC	1956
329801 – 329900	III	1939	390001 – 397650	IIIc	1943/46	839701 – 840500	M3	1956
329901 – 330000	IIIa	1939	397651 – 399999			840501 – 840820	M3 ELC	1956
330001 – 330200	III	1939				840821 – 844780	M3	1956
330201 – 330300	II	1939	400000 – 440000	IIIc	1946/47	844781 – 845000	M3 ELC	1956
330301 – 330500	Standard	1939	440001 – 449999	IIc	1948/51	845001 – 845380	IIIg ELC	1956
330501 – 330700	III	1939	450000	IIIc	1949	845381 – 850900	IIIg	1956
330701 – 330800	IIIa	1939	450001 – 451000	IIc	1951	850901 – 851000	If	1956
330801 – 331000	Standard	1939	451001 – 455000	IIf	1951	851001 – 854000	M3	1956
331001 – 332000	IIIb	1939	455001 – 460000	Ic	1949/50	854001 – 858000	M3	1957
332001 – 332500	IIIa	1939	460001 – 465000	IIIc	1948/49	858001 – 861600	IIIg	1957
332501 – 332600	III	1939	465001 – 480000	IIIc	1949	861601 – 862000	IIIg ELC	1957
332601 – 333000	IIIa	1939	480001 – 495000	IIIc	1949/50	MP- 1 – 11	MP	1956
333001 – 333100	III	1939	495001 – 520000	IIIc	1950	862001 – 866620	M3	1957
			520001 – 524000	Ic	1950/51			

THE HOVE INTERNATIONAL BLUE BOOK

Leica-No.	Model	Year
866621 – 867000	M3 ELC	1957
867001 – 871200	IIIg	1957
871201 – 872000	IIIg ELC	1957
872001 – 877000	M3	1957
877001 – 882000	IIIg	1957
882001 – 886700	M3	1957
MP- 13 – 150	MP schw. l.	1957
MP-151 – 450	MP chrom	1957
886701 – 887000	M3 ELC	1957
887001 – 888000	Ig	1957
888001 – 893000	IIIg	1957
893001 – 894000	M3	1957
894001 – 894570	M3 ELC	1957
894571 – 898000	M3	1957
898001 – 903000	M3	1957
903001 – 903300	M3 ELC	1957
903301 – 907000	IIIg	1957
907001 – 910000	Ig	1957
910001 – 910500	M3	1957
910501 – 910600	M3 oliv. l.	1957
910601 – 915000	M3	1957
915001 – 915200	M3	1957
915201 – 916000	M3	1957
916001 – 919250	M3	1958
919251 – 920500	M3	1958
920501 – 920520	M3	1958
920521 – 924400	M3	1958
924401 – 924500	M3 ELC	1958
924501 – 924568	Ig	1958
924569 – 924588	Ig	1958
924589 – 926000	Ig	1958
926001 – 926200	M2	1957
926201 – 926700	Ig	1958
926701 – 928922	M3	1959
928923 – 929000	Postk.	1958
929001 – 931000	M2	1958
931001 – 933000	M2	1958
933001 – 934000	IIIg	1958
934001 – 934200	IIIg ELC	1958
934201 – 935000	IIIg	1958
935001 – 935512	MP2	1958
935513 – 937500	M2	1958
937501 – 937620	M2	1958
937621 – 937650	M2 ELC	1958
937651 – 940000	M2	1958
940001 – 942900	M2	1958
942901 – 943000	M2 ELC	1958
943001 – 944000	IIIg	1958
944001 – 946000	M2	1958
946001 – 946300	M2	1958
946301 – 946400	M2 ELC	1958
946401 – 946900	M2	1958
946901 – 947000	M2 ELC	1968
947001 – 948000	M2	1958
948001 – 948500	IIIg	1958
948501 – 948600	M2 ELC	1958
948601 – 949100	M2 schw. l.	1958
949101 – 949400	M2 Vorl.	1958
949401 – 950000	M2	1959
950001 – 950300	M1	1959
950301 – 951900	M3	1959
951901 – 952000	M3 ELC	1959
952001 – 952015	MP2	1959
952016 – 952500	M1	1959
952501 – 954800	M3	1959
954801 – 954900	M3 ELC	1959
954901 – 955000	M3 ELC	1959
955001 – 956500	IIIg	1959
956501 – 957000	M1	1959
957001 – 959400	M3	1959
959401 – 959500	M3 schw. l.	1959
959501 – 960200	M2 Vorl.	1959
960201 – 960500	M2	1960
960501 – 961500	M2	1959
961501 – 961700	M3 ELC	1959
961701 – 966500	M3	1959
966501 – 967500	M1	1959
967501 – 968350	M2	1959
968351 – 968500	M3 ELC	1959
968501 – 970000	IIIg	1959
970001 – 971500	M2	1959
971501 – 972000	IIIg	1959
972001 – 974700	M3	1959
974701 – 975000	M3 ELC	1959
975001 – 975800	M2	1959
975801 – 976100	M2 Vorl.	1960

Leica-No.	Model	Year
976101 – 976500	M2	1959
976501 – 979500	M3	1959
979501 – 980450	M1	1959
980451 – 980500	M1 oliv. l.	1960
980501 – 982000	IIIg	1959
982001 – 982150	M2 Vorl.	1960
982151 – 982900	M2	1959
982901 – 983500	M2 Vorl.	1959
983501 – 984000	M2	1959
984001 – 984200	M3 ELC	1959
984201 – 987000	M3	1959
987001 – 987200	M3 ELC	1960
987201 – 987300	M2 ELC	1960
987301 – 987600	Ig	1960
987601 – 987900	IIIg	1960
987901 – 988025	IIIg schw. l.	1960
988026 – 988350	IIIg	1960
988351 – 988650	M2	1960
988651 – 989250	M2 Vorl.	1960
989251 – 989650	M2 Vorl.	1960
989651 – 989800	M2	1960
989801 – 990500	M2 Vorl.	1960
990501 – 990750	M2 schw. l.	1960
990751 – 993500	M3	1960
993501 – 993750	M3 schw. l.	1960
993751 – 995000	M2	1960
995001 – 995100	M2 ELC	1960
995101 – 995400	M2 Vorl.	1960
995401 – 996000	M2	1960
996001 – 998000	M3	1960
998001 – 998300	M3 ELC	1960
998301 – 1000000	M3	1960
1000001 – 1003700	M3	1960
1003701 – 1004000	M3 ELC	1960
1004001 – 1005100	M2 VW	1960
1005101 – 1005350	M2 VW	1960
1005351 – 1005450	M2 ELC	1960
1005451 – 1005750	M2	1960
1005771 – 1007000	M2	1960
1007001 – 1011000	M3	1960
1011001 – 1014000	M2	1960
1014001 – 1014300	M3 ELC	1960
1014301 – 1017000	M3	1960
1017001 – 1017500	M1	1961
1017501 – 1017900	M2	1961
1017901 – 1018000	M2 ELC	1961
1018001 – 1020100	M2	1961
1020101 – 1020200	M2 ELC	1961
1020201 – 1022000	M2	1961
1022001 – 1022700	M3	1961
1022701 – 1023000	M3 ELC	1961
1023001 – 1027800	M3	1961
1027801 – 1028000	M3 ELC	1961
1028001 – 1028600	M1	1961
1028601 – 1031800	M2	1961
1031801 – 1032000	M2 schw. l.	1961
1032001 – 1035400	M3	1961
1035401 – 1035925	M1	1961
1036001 – 1026050	M2 ELC	1961
1036051 – 1036350	M3 ELC	1961
1036351 – 1037950	M2	1961
1037951 – 1038000	M2 ELC	1962
1038001 – 1038800	M3	1961
1038801 – 1039000	M3 schw. l.	1961
1039001 – 1040000	M3	1961
1040001 – 1040066	M1	1962
1040067 – 1040068	M3	1962
1040069 – 1040070	M1	1961
1040071 –	M3	1961
1040072 – 1040094	M1	1961
1040095 – 1040096	M3	1962
1040097 – 1040600	M1	1961
1040601 – 1043000	M3	1961
1043001 – 1043800	M2	1962
1043801 – 1044000	M2 schw. l.	1962
1044001 – 1046000	M3 schw. l.	1962
1046001 – 1046500	M1	1962
1046501 – 1048000	M3	1962
1047801 – 1048000	M3 ELC	1962
1048001 – 1050000	M2	1962
1050001 – 1050500	M1	1962
1050501 – 1053100	M2	1962
1053101 – 1053250	M2 lack.	1962
1053251 – 1054900	M2	1962

Leica-No.	Model	Year
1054901 – 1055000	M2 ELC	1962
1055001 – 1059849	M3	1962
1059850 – 1059999	M3 lack.	1962
1060000 –	M3	1962
1060001 – 1060500	M1	1962
1060501 – 1061700	M2	1962
1061701 – 1061800	M2 ELC	1962
1061801 – 1063000	M2	1962
1063001 – 1065000	M3	1962
1065001 – 1065200	M3 ELC	1962
1065201 – 1067500	M3	1962
1067501 – 1067870	M1	1963
1067871 – 1068000	Postk.	1963
1068001 – 1070000	M2	1963
1070001 – 1074000	M3	1963
1074001 – 1074500	M1	1963
1074501 – 1077000	M2	1963
1077001 – 1080000	M3	1963
1080001 – 1085000	Leicaflex	1964/65
1085001 – 1085450	M1	1963
1085451 – 1085500	M1	1963
1085501 – 1088000	M2	1963
1088001 – 1091000	M3	1963
1091001 – 1091300	M1	1964
1091301 – 1093500	M2	1964
1093501 – 1093750	M2 lack.	1964
1093751 – 1093800	M2 ELC	1964
1093801 – 1097700	M3	1964
1097701 – 1097850	M3 lack	1964
1097851 – 1098000	M3 ELC	1964
1098001 – 1098100	M1	1964
1098184 – 1098300	M1	1964
1098301 – 1099800	M2	1964
1099801 – 1099900	M2 ELC	1964
1099901 – 1100000	M2	1964
1100001 – 1102000	M3	1964
1102001 – 1102500	M1	1964
1102501 – 1102800	MD	1964
1102801 – 1102900	M1	1964
1102901 – 1103000	M3	1965
1103001 – 1104900	M2	1965
1104901 – 1105000	M2 ELC	1965
1105001 – 1106900	M3	1965
1106901 – 1107000	M3 ELC	1965
1107001 – 1109000	M2	1965
1109001 – 1110500	M3	1965
1110501 – 1112000	M3	1965
1112001 – 1114975	M2	1965
1114976 – 1115000	Postk.	1965
1115001 – 1128000	Leicaflex	1965
1128001 – 1128400	MD	1965
1128401 – 1130000	M3	1965
1130001 – 1130300	M2 lack.	1965
1130301 – 1132900	M2	1965
1132901 – 1133000	M2 ELC	1965
1133001 – 1134000	M3	1965
1134001 – 1134150	M3 lack.	1965
1134151 – 1135000	M3	1965
1135001 – 1135100	M3 ELC	1965
1135101 – 1136000	M3	1965
1136001 – 1136500	MD	1965
1136501 – 1137000	MD	1966
1137001 – 1138900	M2	1966
1138901 – 1139000	M2 ELC	1966
1139001 – 1140900	M3	1966
1140901 – 1141000	M3 ELC	1966
1141001 – 1141896	MD	1966
1141897 – 1141968	Postk.	1966
1141969 – 1142000	Postk. 24 x 27	1966
1142001 – 1145000	M2	1966
1145001 – 1155000	Leicaflex	1966
1155001 – 1157590	M3	1966
1157591 – 1157600	M3 lack.	1966
1157601 – 1158995	M3	1966
1159001 – 1160200	MDa	1966
1160201 – 1160820	MD	1966
1160821 – 1161420	MDa	1966
1161421 – 1163770	M2	1966
1163771 – 1164046	M2 Motor	1966
1164047 – 1164845	M2	1966
1164846 – 1164865	M3	1966
1164866 – 1164940	Postk. 24 x 36	1967
1164941 – 1165000	M2	1967
1165001 – 1173000	Leicaflex	1967

Leica-No.	Model	Year
1173001 – 1173250	Leicaflex SL	1968
1173251 – 1174700	Leicaflex	1968
1174701 – 1175000	Leicaflex SL	1968
1175001 – 1178000	M4	1967
1178001 – 1178100	M4 ELC	1967
1178101 – 1185000	M4	1967
1185001 – 1185150	M4 Motor	1968
1185151 – 1185290	M4 lack.	1968
1185291 – 1185300	Postk. 24 x 27	1968
1185301 – 1195000	M4	1968/69
1195001 – 1205000	Leicaflex SL	1968
1205001 – 1206736	MDa	1968/69
1206737 – 1206891	M4 Motor	1969
1206892 – 1206941	Postk. 24 x 36	1969
1206942 – 1206961	Postk. 24 x 27	1969
1207000	M2 Lack.	1968
1207001 – 1207480	M4 lack.	1968/69
1207481 – 1215000	M4	1968/69
1215001 – 1225000	Leicaflex SL	1969
1225001 – 1225800	M4 lack.	1969
1225801 – 1235000	M4	1969
1235001 – 1245000	Leicaflex SL	1969/70
1245001 – 1246200	MDa	1969
1246201 – 1248100	M4 lack.	1969/70
1248101 – 1248200	M4 Motor	1969
1248201 – 1250200	M2R	1969/70
1250201 – 1254650	M4	1970
1254651 – 1255000	MDa	1970
1255001 – 1265000	Leicaflex SL	1970
1265001 – 1266000	MDa	1970
1266001 – 1266100	M4 lack.	1970/71
1266101 – 1266131	M4 olivegr.	1970
1266132 – 1267100	M4 lack.	1970
1267101 – 1267500	M4 Motor	1970
1267501 – 1273921	M4	1970/71
1273922 – 1273925	Postk.24x27	1971
1273926 – 1274000	Postk.24x36	1971
1274001 – 1274100	M4 Motor	1971
1274101 – 1275000	MD a	1971
1275001 – 1285000	Leicaflex SL	1971
1285001 – 1286200	MD a	1971
1286201 – 1286700	M4 lack.	1971
1286701 – 1286760	Postk.24x27	1972
1286761 – 1287000	unbelegt	
1287001 – 1287050	M5 Nullserie	1971
1287051 – 1287250	M5 hell	1971
1287251 – 1288000	M5 schwarz	1971
1288001 – 1289000	M5 hell	1971
1288901 – 1291400	M5 schwarz	1971/72
1291401 – 1293000	M5 hell	1971/72
1293001 – 1293672	MD a	1971/72
1293673 – 1293770	MDa Blitzsp.	1972
1293771 – 1293877	M4-KE 7	1972
1293776 – 1293877	MDa Blitzsp.	1972
1293878 – 1294000	Postk.24x27	1972
1294001 – 1294500	M5 hell	1972
1294501 – 1295000	M4-KE 7	1972
1295001 – 1296500	LeicaflexSL	1972
1296501 – 1300000	M5 schwarz	1972
1300001 – 1335000	CL	1973/74
1335001 – 1336990	Leicaflex SL	1972

Leica-No.	Model	Year
1336991 – 1337110	LeicaflexSLmot	1972
1337111 – 1338220	LeicaflexSL	1972
1338221 – 1338300	LeicaflexSLmot	1972
1338301 – 1339870	LeicaflexSL	1972
1339871 – 1339900	LeicaflexSLmot	1972
1339901 – 1341450	LeicaflexSL	1972
1341451 – 1341470	LeicaflexSLmot	1972
1341471 – 1342020	LeicaflexSL	1973
1342021 – 1342050	LeicaflexSLmot	1973
1342051 – 1342900	LeicaflexSL	1973
1342901 – 1343000	LeicaflexSLmot	1973
1343001 – 1344400	LeicaflexSL	
1344401 – 1344500	LeicaflexSLmot	1973
1344501 – 1345000	LeicaflexSL	1973
1345001 – 1347000	M5 hell	1972
1347001 – 1354000	M5 schwarz	1972
1354001 – 1355000	M5 hell	1972
1355001 – 1356500	M5 hell	1973
1356501 – 1360000	M5 schwarz	1973
1360001 – 1361500	MD a	1973/74
1361501 – 1363000	M5 hell	1973/74
1363001 – 1365000	M5 schwarz	1973
1365001 – 1365380	LeicaflexSL	1973
1365381 – 1365470	LeicaflexSLmot	1973
1365471 – 1366990	LeicaflexSL	1973
1366991 – 1367090	LeicaflexSLmot	1973
1367091 – 1367950	LeicaflexSL	1973
1367951 – 1368020	LeicaflexSLmot	1973
1368021 – 1368850	LeicaflexSL	1973
1368851 – 1368900	LeicaflexSLmot	1973
1368901 – 1369800	LeicaflexSL	1973
1369801 – 1369875	LeicaflexSL2 (Nullserie)	1974
1369876 – 1370700	LeicaflexSL	1973
1370701 – 1372440	LeicaflexSL	1974
1372441 – 1372630	LeicaflexSLmot	1974
1372631 – 1374000	LeicaflexSL	1974
1374001 – 1375000	LeicaflexSL	1974
1375001 – 1378000	M5 schwarz	1973/74
1378001 – 1379000	M5 hell	1973/74
1379001 – 1380000	MD a	1974
1380001 – 1381650	M4 schwarz	1974
1381651 – 1382600	M4 schwarz (Leitz Canada-Gravur)	1974
1382601 – 1383000	M5 hell	1974/75
1383001 – 1384000	M5 schwarz	1974/75
1384001 – 1384600	M4 schwarz	1974
1384601 – 1385000	MD a	1974/75
1385001 – 1386000	LeicaflexSL2	1974/75
1386001 – 1386100	LeicaflexSL2	1975
1386101 – 1386600	LeicaflexSL2	1974/75
1386601 – 1386700	LeicaflxSL2 mot	1975
1386701 – 1387450	LeicaflexSL2	1974/75
1387451 – 1387500	LeicaflxSL2 mot	1975
1387501 – 1391760	LeicaflexSL2	1974/75
1391761 – 1392000	LeicaflxSL2 mot	1975
1392001 – 1393420	LeicaflexSL2	1975
1393421 – 1393510	LeicaflxSL2 mot	1975
1393511 – 1394300	LeicaflexSL2	1975
1394301 – 1394600	LeicaflxSL2 mot	1975
1394601 – 1395000	LeicaflexSL2	1975

Leica-No.	Model	Year
1395001 – 1410000	CL	1974/75
1410001 – 1412550	MD a	1975//6
1412551 – 1413350	M4 schwarz (Leitz Canada-Gravur)	1975
1413351 – 1415000	M4 schwarz	1975
1415001 – 1415140	LeicaflexSL2	1975
1415141 – 1415230	LeicaflxSL2 mot	1975
1415231 – 1421000	LeicaflexSL2	1975
1421001 – 1421150	LeicaflxSL2 mot	1975
1421151 – 1425000	LeicaflexSL2	1975
1425001 – 1440000	CL	1975/76
1440001 – 1443000	LeicaflexSL2	1975/76
1443001 – 1443170	M4 schwarz	1975
1443501 – 1446000	LeicaflexSL2	1976
1446001 – 1446100	R3 hell LW	1976
1446101 – 1447100	R3 hell LP	1976
1447101 – 1449000	R3 schw. LP	1976/77
1449001 – 1450500	R3 schw. LW	1976
1450501 – 1450900	R3 hell LW	1977
1450901 – 1468000	R3 schw. LP	1977/78
1468001 – 1470000	R3 oliv LP	1977/78
1470001 – 1479000	R3 schw. LP	1977/78
1479001 – 1480000	R3 hell LP	1978
1480001 – 1482000	M4-2	1978
1482001 – 1485000	R3 oliv LP	1978
1485001 – 1491000	R3 schw. LP	1978
1491001 – 1492250	R3 hell LP	1978
1492251 – 1502000	R3 mot LP	1978
1502001 – 1508000	M4-2	1978/79
1508001 – 1523750	R3 mot LP	1979
1523751 – 1523850	R3 schw. LP	1979
1523851 – 1524850	R3 gold LP	1979
1524851 – 1525350	R3 hell LP	1979
1525351 – 1527200	M4-2	1979
1527201 – 1527700	M4-2 gold	1979/80
1527701 – 1528150	M4-2	1980
1528151 – 1528650	M4-2 gold	1980
1528651 – 1533350	M4-2	1980
1533351 – 1543350	R4 schw.	1980/81
1543351 – 1545350	M4-P	1980/81
1545351 – 1546350	MD-2	1980/81
1546351 – 1552350	M4-P	1981
1552351 - 1552884	M4-P	1981
1552531 - 1562350	R4 schw'z	1981
1562351 - 1564350	M4-P	1982
1564351 - 1574350	R4 schw'z	1981/82
1574351 - 1576350	R4 hell	1982
1576351 - 1586350	R4 schw'z	1982
1586351 - 1590350	M4-P	1982
1590351 - 1590550	R4 schw'z	1982
1590551 - 1592550	R4 hell	1982
1592551 - 1602550	R4 schw'z	1982
1602551 - 1604550	R4 hell	1982
1604551 - 1606550	M4-P	1982/3
1606551 - 1616550	R4 schw'z	1983
1616551 - 1618550	R4 hell	1983
1618551 - 1620550	M4-P hell	1983
1620551 - 1622550	M4-P	1983/84
1622551 - 1632550	R4 schw'z	1983
1632551 - 1636550	R4s	1983
1636551 - 1637550	M4-P hell	1983
1637551 - 1642550	R4s	1983
1642551 - 1643750	M4-P	1984
1643751 - 1648750	R4s	1984
1648751 - 1649250	MD-2	1985
1649251 - 1651250	M4-P	1984/85
1651251 - 1652250	R4 Gold	1984/85
1652251 - 1657250	R4s	1984/85
1657251 - 1659250	M6	1984/85
1659251 - 1664250	R4 schw'z	1984/85
1664251 - 1664350	MD-2	1984/85
1664351 - 1665350	R4 hell	1984/85
1665351 - 1669350	M6	1985
1669351 - 1674350	R4	1985/86
1674351 - 1678350	M6	1985
1678351 - 1682350	M6	1985
1682351 - 1682950	M6 hell	1986
1682951 - 1687950	R4s-2	1985/86
1687951 - 1691950	M6	1986
1691951 - 1692950	M4-P	1986

KEY

Blitsp.	Motorised MDa
ELC	E. Leitz, Canada
Hell	Silver-chrome
Kaltef.	Winterised
Lack	Paint
LP	Leitz, Portugal
LW	Leitz, Wetzlar
Null Serie	Pre-Production model
Postk	Post Camera
Schw'z	Black chrome
Schw. 1	Black paint
St.	Standard
Unbel't	Not issued
Vorl.	Delayed action

Note: Spaces in 'M' camera list relate to military camera production.

List of Leica Lens Numbers

Year	From	To	Year	From	To
1933	156 001	195 000	1961	1 827 001	1 913 000
1934	195 001	236 000	1962	1 913 001	1 967 100
1935	236 001	284 600	1963	1 967 101	2 015 700
1936	284 601	345 000	1964	2 015 701	2 077 500
1937	345 001	416 500	1965	2 077 501	2 156 300
1938	416 501	490 000	1966	2 156 301	2 236 500
1939	490 001	538 500	1967	2 236 501	2 254 400
1940	538 501	565 000	1968	2 254 401	2 312 750
1941	565 001	582 290	1969	2 312 751	2 384 700
1942	582 295	593 000	1970	2 384 701	2 468 500
1943	593 001	594 880	1971	2 468 501	2 503 100
1944	594 881	595 000	1972	2 503 101	2 556 500
1945	595 001	601 000	1973	2 556 501	2 663 400
1946	601 001	633 000	1974	2 663 401	2 731 900
1947	633 001	647 000	1975	2 731 901	2 761 100
1948	647 001	682 000	1976	2 761 101	2 809 400
1949	682 001	765 000	1977	2 809 401	2 880 600
			1978	2 880 601	2 967 200
1950	765 001	840 000	1979	2 967 201	3 013 600
1951	840 001	950 000	1980	3 013 601	3 087 000
1952	950 001	1 051 000	1981	3 087 001	3 160 500
1953	1 051 001	1 124 000	1982	3 160 501	3 249 100
1954	1 124 001	1 236 000	1983	3 249 101	3 294 900
1955	1 236 001	1 333 000	1984	3 294 901	3 346 200
1956	1 333 001	1 459 000	1985	3 346 201	3 383 200
1957	1 459 001	1 548 000	1986	3 383 201	3 422 890
1958	1 548 001	1 645 300	1987	3 422 891	3 455 870
1959	1 645 301	1 717 000	1988	3 455 871	
1960	1 717 001	1 827 000			

Note: These numbers are allocated at the beginning of each year and this does not neccessarily mean that they are all used in that year. Some may not be used until the next year, or even later.

IDENTIFICATION NOTES

IDENTIFICATION NOTES

Museums for collectors

BELGIUM
Museum Voor Fotografie, Waalse Kaai 47 Antwerpen, Belgium, B-2000
A wide view on the world of photography, yesterday, today and tomor-row. Open 10:00-5:00pm, except Mondays. Contact Roger Coenen at (03) 2162211.

CZECHOSLOVAKIA
National Museum of Technology, Holesovice, Kostelni 42, Prague - 7, Czechoslovakia Telephone (2) 373651.

FRANCE
Musée Français de la Photographie, 78 rue de Paris, PO Box 03-Bievres, France 91570. *Cameras, photographs, accessories, and documentation.* Open everyday from 10:00-12:00 and 2:00-6:00, holidays included. Contact André Fage, Conservateur en Chef at (6941)1060
Musée National des Techniques, Conservatoire National des Arts et Métiers, 270 Rue Saint-Martin, Paris, France, 75003. *Cameras from 1850 to present day. Microphotography by Dagron for carrier pigeons, stereo cameras and spy cameras, motion study photography by Marey and Muybridge.* Open 10:00-5:30 Tuesday- Saturday. Contact Mr. Jaques Foiret at (1) 402-72220 or 402-72371.

GERMANY
Agfa-Gevaert Foto Historama, Bischofsgartenstrasse-1, Köln, West Germany, D-5000. Contact Dr. Bodo von Dewitz, Director, at (0221) 2212411.
Deutsches Museum, Museuminsel, Munich, West Germany
Leica Museum/Leica Academy, Schützenstrasse, Wetzlar/Lahn, Hessen, West Germany, D-6330. *Leica Cameras and accessories.* Open 8:00-5:00pm Contact K.H. Welcker at (06441) 29-2333.

Muenchner Stadt Museum, St Jakobsplatz, Munich, West Germany.
Optisches Museum Oberkochen, Am Ölweiher 15, PO Box 1369,
Oberkochen, Baden-Würtemberg, West Germany, D-7082. *Historical
and modern eyeglasses, telescopes, binoculars, surveying instruments,
cameras and microscopes.* Open 10:00-1:00pm and 2:00-4:00pm
Monday-Friday, 9:00-12:00 Sunday. Closed Saturdays and holidays.
Telephone (07364) 202878.

ITALY
Museo Nationale del Cinema, Palazzo Chiablese, piazza San Giovanni,
2, Turin, Italy, 10122. *Photograph and camera collections, "Cinema
Massimo" magazine, vintage film and magic lantern shows.* Contact for
Camera collections, Ms. Donata Pesenti; Photograph collections, Ms.
Marica Marcellino, at (011) 5661148 or 5661387.

JAPAN
Japan Camera Inspection Museum, Tokyo, Japan.
Pentax Gallery, 21-20, 3-Chome, Nishiazabu, Minato-ku, Tokyo, Japan
106. *A large display of photographica from the beginning of photography
to present day.* Open 10:00-5:00. Monday-Saturday, free admission.
Contact Mr. Shuichi Sakai, Curator, at (03) 401-2186 or 478-3071.

SOUTH AFRICA
Bensusan Musuem of Photography, 17 Empire Rd., Parktown, South
Africa.

UK
Barnes Museum of Cinematography, 44 Fore Street, St. Ives, Cornwall,
England.
Buckingham Movie Museum, Printers Mews, Market Hill, Buckingham,
England.
Fenton Photography Museum, Port Erin, Isle of Wight, England.
Fox Talbot Museum of Photography, Lacock Near Chippenham, Wilt-
shire, England, SN15 2LG. *Fox Talbot collection,* Open 11:00-6:00 pm
everyday except Good Friday, March 1st to November 5th Telephone
(024973) 459.
Medina Camera Museum, Golden Hill Fort, Freshwater, Isle of Man,
England.
Museum of the History of Science, Broad Street, Oxford, England, OX1
3AZ. *Cameras and photographic accessories, early and experimental
photographs, Specimens of scientific interest, (early Colour).* Open 10:30-

1:00pm and 2:00-4:00pm, Monday-Friday, except bank holidays, and Easter and Christmas weeks. Telephone (0865)277280.

National Museum of Photography, Film, and Television, Princes View, Bradford, West Yorkshire, England, BD5 0TR, Kodak Museum newly opened, *Interactive and Theatrical reconstruction in museum displays on the past, present and future of photography and television. Changing special exhibitions.* Open 11:00-6:00 Tuesday-Sunday, Contact Roger Taylor at (0274) 727488.

Science Museum, Exhibition Rd., South Kensington, London, England, SW7 2DD. *Photographic and Cinematographic equipment and photographs from 1835 to present day.* Open 10:00-6:00 Monday-Saturday, 11:00-6:00 Sundays. Contact Mr. J.P. Ward at (01) 938-8000.

The Royal Photographic Society, The Octagon, Milsom Street, Bath, England BA1 1DN. *Comprehensive collection of cameras photographs from the very beginning of photography.* Open 9:30-5:15 pm, Contact Mrs. P. Roberts, or Miss K. Rouse at (0225) 62841 ext. 212.

Woodspring Museum, Burlington Street, Weston-super-Mare, Avon, England BS23 1PR. *A good cross section of the progress of photography since the 1890s. Of special interest is a Bertsh "Chambre Automatique" from about 1861. Photo accessories are also on display.* Free admission. Open 10:00-5:00, Monday-Saturday, open Bank holidays except Good Friday, Christmas and New Year. Telephone (0934) 621028.

Woolstaplers Hall Museum, High Street, Chipping Campden, Gloucestershire, England, GL55 6HB. *Projectors, plate cameras, Kodak cameras, Contax cameras and other photographic paraphenalia.* Open 11:00-6:00 daily from April 1st to October 31st. Contact Mrs. J. Griffiths, Curator at (03) 86 840289.

The British Photographic Museum, Bowden House, Totnes, South Devon, England, TQ9 7PW. *Camera collection on display, gift shop and Tea Room available.* Contact Christopher or Belinda Petersen at (0803) 863664.

Royal Museum of Scotland, Chambers Street, Edinburgh, Scotland.

USA

California Academy of Science, Golden Gate Park, San Francisco, California, USA, 94118. *400 items late 19th and 20th century cameras and equipment.* Open 9:00-5:00 pm Monday-Friday Not yet on display. Contact Dr. Robert Sayers, Anthrology Dept. at 415-750-7163.

Chicago Historical Society, Clark Street at North Avenue, Chicago, Illinois, USA, 60614-6099. *Over 1,000,000 19th and 20th century photographs, mostly relating to Chicago history.* Open 9:30-4:00 Tuesday-Saturday, by appointment. Contact Larry A. Viskochil, Curator at (312) 642-4600.

Florida State Museum, Gainesville, FL, USA Gallery of Photographic History, 10010 Lanehart Road, Little Rock, Arkansas, USA, 72204. *Major photographic library, prints and equipment.* Open by appointment only. Contact Greer H. Lile at (501) 666-7409 or 455-0179.

Galloway House and Village, 336 Pioneer Rd., (PO Box 128), Fond du Lac , Wisconsin, USA, 54935. *Historic photo collection in a turn of the century village setting.* Open Daily 1:00-4:00 pm, Memorial Day through Labor Day. Contact Ray Thornton at (414) 922-6390.

Henry Ford Museum and Greenfield Village, PO Box 1970, 20900 Oakwood Blvd, Dearborn, MI, USA, 48121. *Small collection of cameras from 1890-1980.* Open 9:00-5:00pm daily except Christmas and Thanksgiving. Contact the Curator of Communications at (313) 271-1620 Jacksonville Museum, Courthouse Sq., Jacksonville, FL, USA.

Los Angeles County Museum of Natural History, 900 Exposition Blvd., Los Angeles, California USA, 90007. *Historical photographs concerning the growth and development of Los Angeles, and southern California. Includes Southwest Indians.* Open 1:00-4:00 pm Monday-Friday at the Seaver Center. Telephone (213) 744-3359.

National Museum of American History, Smithsonian Inst.,Washington, DC, USA, 20560 Part of the vast Smithsonian collection. Often called "America's attic". Open 10:00-5:30 pm, every day but Christmas Day. Contact Eugene Ostroff, Curator at 202-357-2059.

Patent Dept. Museum, Eastman Kodak, Kodak Park, Rochester, NY, USA Photography Collection, Harry Ransom Humanities Research Center, Box #7219, University of Texas at Austin, Auston, TX, USA, 78713-7219 *Materials relating to the entire history of photography, its growth and impact on world culture.* Open 9:00-5:00pm Monday-Friday, Appointments and reservations requested. Contact Roy Flukinger, Curator at (512) 471-9124.

Stonefield Village, Nelson Dewey State Park, Cassville, Wisconsin,USA, 53806. *Replica of 1890s Photographer's Shop.* Open 9:00-5:00 pm. Telephone (608) 725-5210.

The Antique Camera Museum, 1065 Jer Les Dr., Milford, OH, USA The International Museum of Photography at George Eastman House, 900 East Avenue, Rochester, New York, USA, 14607. *This collection covers the entire history of photography.* Contact Philip Condax, Curator at (716) 271-3361.

The Mattatuck Museum, 119 West Main St., Waterbury, CT, USA
The Museum of New Mexico, Photo Archives, 110 Washington Avenue,

PO Box 2087, Santa Fe, New Mexico, USA, 87504. 365,000. *Items: b/w original prints, film and glass negatives, covering History of the West and New Mexico, western occupations, China-Japan-India-Phillipines and more, 2,500 volume library dealing with the history of Photography.* Open 1:00-5:00 pm Monday-Friday. Telephone (505)-827-6472.

The California Museum of Photography, University of California, Riverside, CA, USA, 92521. *Keystone-Mast collection of Stereo cards and negatives, Mead Kibbey Zeiss collection, 120 seat Auditorium, "Bulletin" publication for members.* Moved from Univ. of California at Riverside, into new space in downtown Riverside. Contact Jane Fudge at (714) 784-FOTO.

Clubs for collectors

AUSTRALIA
Photographic Collectors Society, 10 Albert Jones Ct.,Eaglemont, Victoria, 3084, Australia Newsletter, published from time to time.
Sidney Stereo Camera Club, PO Box 465, Pymble, NS, 2073, Australia, For Stereo photographists, Bi-monthly newsletter, monthly membership meetings. Contact Judy Archer, Secretary.

BELGIUM
Photographica, Chausee de la Hulpe 382, Brussels, 1170, Belgium, Telephone (2) 673-8490.

CANADA
Photographic Historical Society of Metropolitan Toronto, PO Box 115, Postal Station "S", Toronto, Ontario, M5M 4L6, Canada, Telephone (416) 483-4185.
Western Canada Photographic Historical Association, PO Box 33742, Vancouver, British Columbia, V6J 4L6, Canada, Telephone (614)-873-2128.
The Photographic Historical Society of Canada, 10 Northolt Court, Islington, Ont.,M9A 3B1, Canada.

FRANCE
Club Niepce Lumiere, 35 Rue de la Mare a l'Ane, Montreuil, 93100, France.

GERMANY
Club Daguerre, Mohlenstrasse 5, Leverkusen, Hitdorf, D-5090, West Germany. (02173)-40080. Two news letters published four times a year. Annual membership meeting, more frequent regional meetings. About 450 members. Membership fees 100 Dm/year. Contact Klaus Storsberg.

Ihagee Historiker Gesellschaft, Charlottenburger Strasse 22A, Leverkusen, D-5090, West Germany.

Leica Historica, C/O Klaus Grothe, Bahnhof Str.53, D3252, Bad Münder 1, Germany, Membership 50DM/year includes 3-4 newsletters (Vidom) published each year, two annual meetings per year, usually at a location near Wetzlar, about 470 members.

HOLLAND

Dutch Society of Photographica Collectors, PO Box 4262, Haarlem, 2003EG, Netherlands. Illustrated magazine published four times a year. International camera shows twice a year, with more than 200 dealers, and 2,300 visitors. Regional meetings two or three times a year with 60 dealers. Postal auction four times a year. Museum outings several times each year. More than 1,100 members including 1,000 Dutch members, and more than 100 world wide members. Hfl 40 for Dutch membership, Hfl 47 for foreign membership, US$25.00 foreign. Contact Harry van Kohl, secretary.

Ihagee Historiker Gesellschaft, Tesselschadelaan 20, Hilversum, 1217LH, Netherlands.

UK

Ihagee Historical Association, c/o Teamwork, 11 Shelton St., London, WC2H 9JN, England, FAX (1) 379-0981.

Leica Historical Society,Greystoke, 8 Driffold, Sutton Coldfield, West Midlands, B73 6HE, England.

Magic Lantern Society of Great Britain, 'Prospect', High Street, Nutley, East Sussex TN22 3NH. UK subs, £15 for Journal and newsletter.

Photographic Collectors Club of Great Britain, Membership Secretary, 5 Station Industrial Estate, Prudhoe, Northumberland, NE42 6NP, England. Photographica World and Tailboard newsletter published quarterly. Meetings Regularly, all over Great Britain. Annual fair in May. About 1,000 members, £15 membership fee plus £3 joining fee for UK residents. Foreign membership available.

The Historical Group of the Royal Photographic Society, The Octagon, Milsom Street, Bath, Avon, BA1 1DN, England.

The Pen F Register, c/o 1 Sylvan Close, Hemel Hempstead, Hertfordshire, HP3 8DN, England.

The Stereoscopic Society, 195 Gilders Road, Chessington, Surrey, KT9 2EB, England. Quarterly magazine, monthly meetings from Sept-May. Membership fee £8/year. Contact H.P. Randall, General Secretary.

Third Dimension Society, 2, Davison Road, Darlington, Co. Durham, DL1 3DR, England. Telephone (0325) 59272, quarterly magazine. Membership fee £7/year, contact D.C. Wardle, Membership Secretary.
Club Rollei, Hôtel de France, St Saviors Road, Jersey, Channel Islands, U.K.Telephone (0534)73102. Journal published five times a year. Membership fee £10.00.

USA

American Photographical Historical Society, 520 West 44th Street, New York, NY,10036,USA, Telephone (212)-594-5056. Photographica magazine published four times a year. Eight membership meetings a year, and two camera shows annually. Over 400 members worldwide. Annual dues in the United States US$22.50. Foreign membership is available. Contact George Gilbert.
American Society of Camera Collectors, 4918 Alcove Avenue, North Hollywood, CA, 91670, USA, Telephone (213)-769-6160.
Atlanta Photographic Collectors Club, PO Box 98291, Atlanta, GA, 30345, USA.
Bay Area Photographic Association, 2538 34th Avenue, San Francisco, CA, 94116, USA, Telephone (415)-664-6498.
Chicago Photographic Collectors Society, PO Box 375, Winnetka, Ill, 60093, USA.
Club Daguerre-Darrah, 2562 Victoria, Witchita, KA, 67216, USA, Telephone (316)-265-0393.
Delaware Valley Photographic Association, PO Box 74, Delanco, NJ, 08075, USA.
Int'l Kodak Historical Society, PO Box 21, Flourtown, PA, 19031, USA.
Int'l Photographic Historical Organization, PO Box 16074, San Francisco, CA, 94116, USA, Telephone (415)-681-4356.
Leica Historical Society of America, 7611 Dornoch Lane, Dallas, TX, 75248, USA, (214) 387-5708. Viewfinder magazine and Leica Catalogue published four times a year. Annual membership meeting. More than 1,000 members. US$28.00 membership fee for the USA, Canada and Mexico,. All other countries, US$28.00 by surface mail, US$37.00 by airmail.
Michigan Photographic Historical Society, PO Box 202, Wayne, MI, 48184, USA, Telephone (313)-721-5126.
Midwest Photographic Historical Society, 19 Hazelnut Court, Florissant, MO, 63033, USA.
Miranda Club, PO Box 2001, Hammond, Indiana, 46323, USA, Contact Thomas Surovek.

National Stereoscopic Association, PO Box 14801, Columbus, OH, 43214, USA. Magazine published six times a year. Regional meetings and annual convention held in the US. More than 2200 members, worldwide. US$22 in the United States, US$32 foreign surface mail, and US$46 by airmail., US$22/year, foreign US$32 by surface, US$46 by air.

Nikon Historical Society, PO Box 3213, Munster, IN, 46321, USA. Telephone(708)-895-5319. The Nikon Journal is published four times a year. The Nikon Historical Society held its second convention in March of 1990. More than 150 members worldwide. Annual dues is US$25/year for the United States and Canada, Foreign membership is US$35/year, . Contact Robert Rotoloni.

Pennsylvania Photographic Historical Society, Inc., PO Box 862, Beaver Falls, PA, 15010, USA. Flash Pan newsletter five times a year. Five meetings are held annually. 40 regional members, US$10 annual dues, US$15 for family membership. No foreign membership is available at the present time. Membership fees are US$10/year, US$15 for family. Contact B.J. Tarr.

Photographic Collectors of Houston, 1201 McDuffie, #104, Houston, TX, 77019, USA.

Photographic Collectors of Tucson, PO Box 18646, Tucson, AR, 85731, USA. Telephone (602) 721-0478.

Photographic Historical Society of New England, Inc., PO Box 189, West Newton Branch, Boston, MA, 02165, USA. Telephone (617)-277-0207 Magazine, New England Journal of Photographic History, published four times a year. Monthly meetings held, except July and August. Over 450 members worldwide. Dues are US$18 for US and Canada, US$35 for foreign each year. Contact Jack Naylor.

Puget Sound Photographic Collectors Society, 10421 Delwood Dr. SW, Tacoma, WA, 98498, USA. Telephone (206)-582-4878, Membership fee US$10.00.

The Movie Machine Society, 50 Old Country Road, Hudsen, MA, 01749, USA, Quarterly Bulletin Sixteen Frames.

The Ohio Camera Collectors, PO Box 282, Columbus, OH, 43216, USA, Annual show Memorial Day weekend. Membership meeting on the first Saturday of each month, more than 100 members. contact John Durand (614) 885-3224.

The Photographic Historical Society, PO Box 9563, Rochester, NY, 14604, USA.

The Photographic Historical Society of the Western Reserve, PO Box 25663, Cleveland, OH, 44125, USA. Telephone (216)-382-6727. Membership meetings on the third Wednesday of each month, except August.

100 members. Contact William S. Nehez.

Tri-State Photographic Collectors Society, 8910 Cherry, Blue Ash, OH, 45242, USA. Telephone (513)-891-5266.

Western Photographic Collectors Assoc., PO Box 4294, Whittier, CA, 90607, USA. (213) 693-8421. Quarterly, 24 page Journal on coated stock. Membership meetings held monthly, plus two trade shows a year. 450 Members. Regular membership fee (receiving meeting notices) US$25, Corresponding US$20, Foreign US$30. Contact William P. Carroll.

Zeiss Historical Society, PO Box 631, Clifton, NJ, 07012, USA. (201)-472-1318.

Consultants

ALTHOUGH THIS IS the third modern edition of the *Blue Book,* let us not forget that Myron Wolf, the father of the original *Blue Book,* laid the groundwork. The results of his efforts, and the efforts of those who helped him, are still to be seen in its pages.

However, since the days when Myron Wolf first had the idea to make a price guide to collectable cameras, a new generation of collector/dealer has emerged. These people are every bit as dedicated and able as those who helped before. They took time and effort to make a contribution. They have every right to be proud of this book because, in fact, I wouldn't be able to do it without their help. It is their book as much as it is mine.

Some consultants still insist on not being named, but have my thanks nevertheless. Those I can thank in print include the following....

Japan
Michiaki Takayama

Holland
J.L. Korten
PF Lownds

France
Photo Beaumarchais
B. Ancelot
C. Baron
Dr. C. Heimfert
P.H. Pont/Foto Saga
J-L Princelle

Australia
Ian Carron
Adam Geschwind
John Moorhouse
Brian Woodward

Germany
Hans P. Rajner

USA
Lt.Col Bill Arps
Oscar Fricke
Robert Rotoloni
James Roy

Austria
Dr. H. Wiesler

Czechoslovakia
Milos Slany

China
Liu Bang
Jia Haining
Chen Shen

Yugoslavia
Prof. M. Kambic

UK
Michael Prichard
David Slade

Argentina
Dr. J.R. Garcia Menéndez

GENERAL NOTES

CAMERA DIRECTORY

**COLLECTABLE CAMERAS,
SPECIFICATIONS, PRICES, VALUES,
RARITY RATINGS AND
YEARS OF MANUFACTURE**

ACRO Scientific Products Company, Chicago, USA.

Acro R: (AC300); C1938, Bakelite RFR camera for 3 x 4cm frames on 127 roll film, f3.5 lens, Alphax shutter, built-in extinction meter, *un-coupled* RFR.

R3* $50	£26	DM82	FF256

Acro R

Acro IV: (AC301); as (AC300) but without extinction meter or RFR.

R3* $30	£16	DM49	FF153

ADAMS & CO., London, England.

Chapeau Photographique: (AD100); hat-type detective camera; patented by Jekeli and Horner, Switzerland; sold by Adams & Co. and Wachtl. C 1890. The hat must be removed from the head for picture taking; when it is worn, the plate holder folds out of the way. The version Adams & Co. sold came with a Rapid Rectilinear f11 lens and rotary shutter attached to the hat by bayonet mount. It used 8.5 x 11cm plates. Rare.

R5* NSR

Adams Deluxe Changeable Box Magazine Camera: (AD101); box magazine camera; pneumatic shutter to 1/1000 s; dark focusing red Russian leather bellows; could be used with Eastman-Walker roll holder; polished wood magazine holder. Same camera covered in red leather with 18 karat gold fittings, shutter and handle was made for Queen Victoria. C 1890's.

R4* $600	£315	DM989	FF3k

Adams Deluxe Changeable Box Magazine Camera

No. 1 Yale Photographic Outfit: (AD103); black paper covered cardboard box camera; 2" x 2" exp on plates. C 1890's.

R3* $95	£50	DM157	FF486

No. 5 Yale Stereo Detective: (AD104); leather covered camera; 7^{1}/2" Zeiss lenses; rack focusing; concealed bellows. Leather changing bag back. C 1890's.

R4* $800	£420	DM1.3k	FF4.1k

DeLuxe: (AD105); Spanish mahogany covered with sealskin. C 1899.

R4* $500	£262	DM824	FF2.6k

Minex: (AD106); 3^{1}/4" x 4^{1}/4" SLR camera. C 1910.

R4* $250	£131	DM412	FF1.3k

Minex Tropical: (AD107); 3^{1}/4" x 4^{1}/4" tropical SLR camera; CFPS 1/8-1/1000s. Teak wood construction with polished brass fittings. C 1930.

R4* $4k	£2.1k	DM6.6k	FF20.4k

Minex Tropical

Videx: (AD108); 3¹/₄" x 4¹/₄"SLR camera; Tessar 21cm f4.5 lens . C 1904.

| R3* $200 | £105 | DM330 | FF1k |

Idento: (AD109); 3¹/₄" x 4¹/₄" folding camera; Ross Homocentric 5" f5.3 lens. C 1908.

| R3* $200 | £105 | DM330 | FF1k |

ADOX KAMERAWERK, Wiesbaden, Germany.
(also Dr. C. Schleußner Fotowerk, Frankfort a/M, Germany)

Adox Adrette: (AK100); C 1939, 35mm camera with telescoping front; Schneider Radionar 50mm f2.9 lens; Compur Rapid shutter, 1-1/500 s, 36 exp, 24 x 36mm. This camera is identical to the Wirgin Edinex (WR107), and may be made by Wirgin.

| R2* $45 | £24 | DM74 | FF230 |

Adox Sport: (AK101); C1935-51, folding VFR camera for 6 x 9 or 6 x 4.5cm frames on 120 rollfilm, Anastigmat f6.3 or f4.5/105mm lens.

| R2* $30 | £16 | DM49 | FF153 |

Adox Sport O: (AK102); C1949, folding VFR camera for 6 x 9 or 6 x 4.5cm frames on 120 roll film, Radionar f4.5/10.5cm lens, Vario shutter, 1/25 - 1/100s, synch. Postwar version Sport.

| R2* $30 | £16 | DM49 | FF153 |

Adox Sport I: (AK103); C1950, as (AK102 but for Pronto shutter.

| R2* $30 | £16 | DM49 | FF153 |

Adox Sport II: (AK104); C1950, as (AK102) but for Prontor shutter.

| R2* $30 | £16 | DM49 | FF153 |

Adox Sport Ia: (AK105); C1952, folding VFR camera for 6 x 9cm or 6 x 6cm frames on 120 roll film, Cassar f4.5/105mm lens, Pronto shutter, synch. Differs from (AK101) by addition of new chromed top plate, double exposure prevention, and accessory shoe. Both formats visible in optical VFR.

| R2* $30 | £16 | DM49 | FF153 |

Adox Sport IIa: (AK106); C1952, as (AK105) but for Prontor S shutter.

| R2* $30 | £16 | DM49 | FF153 |

Adox Sport IIIa: (AK107); C1952, as (AK105) but for Prontor SV shutter.

| R2* $30 | £16 | DM49 | FF153 |

Adox Sport Rouge: (AK108); C1952, as (AK107), but with special red leatherette body covering, and red leather bellows.

| R4* $130 | £68 | DM214 | FF664 |

Adox Tempo: (AK109); C1935, folding vrf camera for 6 x 4.5cm frames on 120 roll film, many lens/shutter combinations including the top of the line Xenar f2.8/75mm lens in Compur Rapid shutter.

| R3* $50 | £26 | DM82 | FF256 |

Adox Trumpf: (AK110); C1932, folding VFR camera for 6 x 9 or 6 x 4.5 frames on rollfilm, Anastigmat f4.5/105mm lens, Vario shutter.

| R3* $25 | £13 | DM41 | FF128 |

Adox Trumpf II: (AK111); C1934, folding VFR camera for 6 x 9 or 6 x 4.5 frames on rollfilm, many lens/shutter combinations, typically Xenar f4.5/105mm lens, Compur Rapid shutter. Differs from (AK110) by the addition of body release, new film pressure plate, and better lens availability.

| R3* $30 | £16 | DM49 | FF153 |

Junka: (AK112); C1949, metal VFR camera for 3 x 4cm frames on special Schleußner/Junka film, f8/45mm lens, simple shutter.

| R3* $40 | £21 | DM66 | FF204 |

Adox 66: (AK113); C1950, black Bakelite TLR type box camera for 6 x 6cm frames on rollfilm, f8 lens, simple shutter, choice of three lenses with focusing from 1m to inf.

R1* $25	£13	DM41	FF128

Adox Blitz: (AK114); C1950, black Bakelite TLR type box camera for 6 x 6cm frames on roll film, f8 lens, simple shutter, basically the 66 camera (AK113) with provision for flash.

R2* $20	£10	DM33	FF102

Adox Golf: (AK115); C1952, folding VFR camera for 6 x 6 frames on roll film, Cassaren f4.5/75mm lens, Pronto shutter, accessory shoe, body release, knob wind.

R2* $25	£13	DM41	FF128

Adox Golf II: (AK116); C1952, folding VFR camera for 6 x 6 frames on roll film, as (AK115) but for Prontor S shutter.

R2* $25	£13	DM41	FF128

Adox Golf IV: (AK11); C1952, folding VFR camera for 6 x 6 frames on roll film, as (AK116) but for Cassar f3.5/75mm lens. No model III is known to exist.

R2* $25	£13	DM41	FF128

Adox Golf 63: (AK118); C1954, folding VFR camera for 6 x 6 frames on roll film, Adoxar f6.3/75mm lens, Vario shutter, accessory shoe, body release, knob wind. The cheapest version of the Adox Golf family.

R2* $20	£10	DM33	FF102

Adox Golf 63 S: (AK119); C1956, folding VFR camera for 6 x 6 frames on roll film, as (AK118) but for the addition of a selftimer.

R2* $25	£13	DM41	FF128

Adox Meß-Golf: (AK120); C1955, folding RFR camera for 6 x 6cm frames on roll film, CRF, Cassar f3.4 or 4.5/75mm lens, Pronto or Prontor S shutter, self timer, synch. Advertised as the "cheapest 6 x 6 RFR of the day!" 169DM for the f3.5 model.

R3* $75	£39	DM124	FF383

Adox 300: (AK121); C1956, 35mm RFR camera with *interchangeable film magazine backs*, each back having its own film counter and film reminder system, built-in light meter, Cassar f2.8/45mm lens and Synchro Compur MXV shutter with EV scale, or Xenar f2.8/45mm lens and Compur Rapid XV shutter with EV scale. Original price included *one* magazine, not three as is sometimes mentioned. Additional magazines were available for 56DM each.

R4* $250	£131	DM412	FF1.3k

Adox Golf IA: (AK122); C1963, 35mm VFR camera, (not to be confused with the folding roll film "Golf" series), Adoxon F2.8/45mm lens, Prontor 125 shutter.

R2* $10	£5	DM16	FF51

Adox Golf IA: (AK123); C1964, 35mm VFR camera, (not to be confused with the folding roll film "Golf" series), Adoxon F2.8/45mm lens, Prontor-matic shutter, built-in light meter, red greed diode light metering.

R2* $10	£5	DM16	FF51

Adox Golf IIIA: (AK124); C1954. 35mm VFR camera, (not to be confused with the folding roll film "Golf" series), Radionar L f2.8/45mm lens, Prontor 500 shutter, built-in light meter. The most expensive of the 35mm Golf series, using a rare earth glass lens.

R3* $25	£13	DM41	FF128

Adox Polo: (AK125); C1959. metal 35mm VFR camera, Adoxar f3.5/45mm lens, Pronto shutter.

R2* $15	£8	DM25	FF77

Adox Polo IS: (AK126); C1959, metal and plastic 35mm VFR camera, Radionar L f2.8/45mm lens, Pronto shutter.

R2* $15	£8	DM25	FF77

Adox Polo IB: (AK127); C1964, metal and plastic 35mm VFR camera, Adoxar f3.5/45mm lens, Prontor shutter.

R2* $15	£8	DM25	FF77

Adox Polomat: (AK128); C1959, 35mm VFR camera with built-in coupled light meter, Radionar L f2.8/45mm lens, Prontor LK shutter.

R2* $15	£8	DM25	FF77

Adox Polomat 1: (AK129); C1959, 35mm VFR camera with built-in coupled light meter, Radionar L f2.8/45mm lens, Prontor 500LK shutter, bright line parallax marking in the VFR.

R2* $20	£10	DM33	FF102

ADOX-A.F.I.O.M. A

Adox Polomat 2: (AK130); C1959, 35mm VFR camera with built-in coupled light meter visible in the VFR and on the top plate, Radionar L f2.8/45mm lens, Prontormat shutter.

R2* $15	£8	DM25	FF77

Adox Polomatic 2: (AK131); C1961, 35mm VFR camera with built-in coupled light meter, Radionar L f2.8/45mm lens, Prontor Lux shutter.

R2* $15	£8	DM25	FF77

Adox Polomatic 3: (AK132); C1961, 35mm VFR camera with built-in coupled light meter, Radionar L f2.8/45mm lens, Prontormat-S shutter.

R2* $15	£8	DM25	FF77

Adox Polomatic 3S: (AK133); C1961, 35mm VFR camera with built-in coupled light meter, Radionar L f2.8/45mm lens, Prontor-Matic shutter, lens opening visible in the VFR.

R2* $15	£8	DM25	FF77

L'AIGLON: (BB100); meniscus lens; single speed shutter; 8 exp, 12 x 14mm on special roll film. Mfd in France. C 1934.

R3* $150	£79	DM247	FF767

AIRES CAMERA INDUSTRY CO. Tokyo, Japan.

Aires 35-IIIL: (AR100); C1955, 35mm RFR camera, Coral f1.9 /45mm coated lens, Seikosha MXL 1-1/500 s, CRF.

R2* $50	£26	DM82	FF256

Aires 35-IIIL

Aires 35 IIIA: (AR102); C1957, 35mm RFR camera, similar to (AR100).

R2* $50	£26	DM82	FF256

Aires 35 IIIA

Aires 35-V: (AR105); C1960, 35mm RFR camera, interchangeable Coral f1.5/4.5cm lens, Seikosha MX shutter 1 - 1/400s, built-in light meter, CRF, bright line fields of view for 50mm and 100mm in VFR.

R3* $80	£42	DM132	FF409

Accessory lenses for Aires 35-V:
W Coral f3.2/35mm lens: (AR001); **$40**
Tele Coral f3.5/100mm lens: (AR002); **$60**

A.F. I. O.M., Pordenone, Italy.

Wega IIa: (PA100); 1950-51. Cfps, 1/20 -1/1000 sec, seperate Rfr/Vfr windows, flash synch. Screw mount Trixar F3.5/50mm lens.

R3* $650	£341	DM1.1k	FF3.3k

Wega IIa

Wega: (PA101); 1950. Cfps, 1/20 - 1/1000 sec, Vfr only, no Rfr, flash synch. Screw mount Trixar F3.5/50mm lens. Only

---

about 1000 cameras are thought to have been made.

R3* $500	£262	DM824	FF2.6k

Wega

AIR KING PRODUCTS COMPANY INC, New York.

Air King Camera Radio: (AK101); combination tube-type radio and plastic 120 roll film camera; finished in brown "lizard-skin".

R3* $175	£92	DM288	FF894

AIVAS AND CHAUVET, France.

Le Fin de Siecle: (AV100); Aplanat f8 lens; 9 x 12cm plates; magazine back. C 1892.

R4* $900	£472	DM1.5k	FF4.6k

Akeley Camera

AKELEY CAMERA, INC., New York.

Akeley Camera: (AC100); lightweight aluminium 35mm hand-cranked camera designed for wildlife photography; 230 degree FPS, rotates completely around camera between inner and outer cases. Weighs 43 pounds; for use by one person. Designed by Carl E. Akeley. C 1917. With tripod.

R4* $1.6k	£840	DM2.6k	FF8.2k

Charles ALIBERT, Paris, France.

Photo-Sac a Main: (CA100); lady's handbag detective camera; Rapid Rectilinear 150mm f12 lens; non-capping rotary shutter; single exp. 9 x 12cm on dry plates. C 1895.

R4* $3k+	£1.6k+	DM5k+	FF15.3k+

Photo-Sac a Main

ALPA - refer to PIGNONS, S.A.

ALSAPHOT
(Société Alsacienne d'Optique et de la Photographie),
France

Dauphin: (AP200); C1950, simple TLR camera for 6 x 6cm frames on roll film.

R3* $25	£13	DM41	FF128

Ajax: (AP201);, C1950, metal bodied VFR camera for 6 x 6cm frames on roll film, collapsible Alsar f3.5/75mm lens, Alsaphot shutter, 1 - 1/300s, accessory shoe.

R3* $30	£16	DM49	FF153

Cady: (AP202); C1950, metal bodied VFR camera for 6 x 6cm frames on roll film, collapsible Alsaphot Anastigmat f6.3/75mm lens, simple shutter, accessory shoe.

R3* $25	£13	DM41	FF128

D'Assas: (AP203); C1950, metal bodied VFR camera for 6 x 6cm frames on roll film, collapsible Boyer Topaz f4.5/75mm lens in Alsaphot shutter, 1/25 - 1/200s, tubular VFR, accessory shoe.

R3* $30	£16	DM49	FF153

Maine: (AP205); C1957, simple metal bodied 35mm VFR camera, knob advance, Berthiot f2.8/45mm lens in Alsaphot shutter, 1/25 - 1/200s, accessory shoe.

R2* $20	£10	DM33	FF102

Maine II: (AP206), C1960, as (AP205) but for lever advance instead of wind knob.

R2* $25	£13	DM41	FF128

Maine IIIa: (AP207); C1962, as (AP206), but for built-in light meter.

R2* $25	£13	DM41	FF128

Cyclope: (AP209); 1950-52, aluminium bodied VFR camera for 6 x 9cm frames on roll film, unique rigid construction using internal mirrors to lengthen the light path, eliminating the need for bellows, making a solid, compact camera. coated Boyer Saphir f4.5/105mm lens, Prontor II shutter to 1/175s, lens placement makes this camera hard to miss. Designed by Lucien Dodin, father of the split-image RFR, *about 1800 made*. Though very rare, one or two of these cameras show up at the annual camera fair at Bievre, France.

R3* $700	£367	DM1.2k	FF3.6k

Cyclope II: (AP210); 1953, as (AP209) but for Boyer Saphir f3.5/105mm lens, Prontor II shutter to 1/200s, and "Deluxe" finish, *only 200 made*, and these were made against the advice of Mr. Dodin, whose calculations showed that there was too much light fall-off with the lens wide opened at f3.5 for the mirror system to work well.

R4* $1k	£525	DM1.6k	FF5.1k

Alsaflex: (AP211); C1954, 35mm SLR camera for 24 x 24mm frames, compact body style through use of internal mirror system for focusing (similar to Pen F system), bayonette mount Boyer Saphir f2.8/50mm lens, rising lens panel, metal FPS, 1 - 1/2000s, (some tests made with 1/2400s or 1/2500s shutters),never put on the market, *only six cameras completed,* though unfinished bodies were sold off. The Kilfitt Mecaflex of 1953 is the only other known example of a 24 x 24mm SLR.

R5*	NSR		

ALTISSA KAMERAWERK,
Dresden, East Germany,
(post war continuation of Eho-Kamera-Fabrik GmbH, Emil Hofert, Dresden, Germany, see Eho listing for pre-war cameras)

NB, now that East Germany is no more, we can expect to see more and more of these cameras coming out to the market place, especially as former East Germans use their new wealth to buy modern, up-to-date equipment. This, of course will have an effect on the rarity and price of these items.

Altuca: (AL200); C1949, metal roll film camera for 6 x 6 frames, collapsible f3.5/75mm lens, simple three speed shutter.

R3* $40	£21	DM66	FF204

Altix II: (AL201); C1947 35mm VFR camera for 24 x 24mm frames, f3.5 35mm lens in simple btl shutter. Name written on the camera front. Interesting as a continuation of the pre-war Altissa, pleasing body style, quite rare.

R4* $50	£26	DM82	FF256

Altix III: (AL202);, 1950, 35mm VFR camera for 24 x 36mm frames, Meritar f2.9/50mm lens in simple btl shutter. The first "full frame" Altix.

R3* $45	£24	DM74	FF230

Altix IV: (AL203); C1951, 35mm VFR camera, now with accessory shoe and flash synch outlet, Trioplan f2.9/50mm lens in Cludor 1 - 1/200s or Vebur 1 - 1/250 shutter, with and without film reminder dial.

R3* $50	£26	DM82	FF256

Altix IV

Altix V: (AL204); C1957, 35mm VFR camera with interchangeable Trioplan f2.9 or CZ Jena f2.8/50mm lens in Tempor shutter, 1 - 1/250. The first Altix with interchangeable lens, quite rare.

R4* $60	£31	DM99	FF307

Altix n: (AL205); C1958, 35mm VFR camera, interchangeable CZ Jena f2.8 or Trioplan f2.9/50mm lens in Tempor shutter 1 - 1/250, new body style, The first Altix to be identified on the camera itself, "Altix-n" on the front or top of the camera.

R2* $45	£24	DM74	FF230

Altix-nb: (AL206); C1958, 35mm VFR camera, interchangeable CZ Jena f2.8 or Trioplan f2.9/50mm lens in Tempor shutter, as (AL205) but with the addition of uncoupled built-in light meter.

R2* $45	£24	DM74	FF230

Altissa: (AL207); C1957, all metal box camera for 6 x 6 frames on roll film, top mounted optical finder, simple shutter, Altissar Periscope f8 lens, not to be confused with the pre-war Altissa. This camera was copied by the Chinese and called the Xing Fu.

R2* $30	£16	DM49	FF153

Accessories for Altix Cameras
Primagon f4.5/35mm lens: (AL001), $30
Telefogar f3.5/90mm lens: (AL002); **$45**

AMERICAN ADVERTISING & RESEARCH CORP., Chicago, Illinois.

Cub: (AA100); plastic roll film box camera; meniscus lens and sector shutter; 828 roll film; side comes off to load. Later known as Scenex. Original cost was $.15—less than the cost of a roll of film; also given away as toothpaste premium. C 1950's.

R2* $15	£8	DM25	FF77

AMERICAN CAMERA MFG. CO. Northboro, Massachusetts.

Founded in 1895 by Thomas Blair, the American Camera Mfg. Co. marketed Buckeye Brand cameras, and also supplied them to E. & H. T. Anthony and Co. In 1896 the company was sold to George Eastman, who wanted control of the "front-roll system" patents.

No. 2 Buckeye: (AM100); box roll film camera; 4" x 5" exp on plates. Method of shutter tensioning and arrow in lens opening similar to Blair box cameras. C 1899.

R2* $75	£39	DM124	FF383

No. 1 Tourist Buckeye: (AM101); folding roll film camera; 3 1/2" x 3 1/2" exp on roll film. C 1895.

R3* $175	£92	DM288	FF894

AMERICAN OPTICAL CO.,
- refer to SCOVILL MFG. CO.

AMERICAN SAFETY-ANSCO [A]

AMERICAN SAFETY RAZOR CORP., CAMERA DIVISION, New York.

ASR Fotodisc: (AF100); two part camera consisting of film disc and lens mount; 32mm Rapodis-ASR lens; single speed shutter. 8 exp, 22 x 24mm on circular film, 10cm in diameter in special holder. C 1960.

R4* $450	£236	DM742	FF2.3k

ASR Fotodisc

ANSCO INC. (AGFA, G.A.F.), Binghamton, New York.

In 1902, E. & H. T. Anthony and Company merged with the Scovill and Adams Company, forming the Anthony and Scovill Company; in 1907, the company name was shortened to Ansco. In 1928 the company was merged with Agfa Products Inc. and Agfa Rawfilm Corp. of New York under the name of Agfa Ansco Corp. In 1939 the company name was changed to General Aniline & Film Corp., commonly referred to by its initials, G.A.F. Corp. For simplicity, German Agfa cameras are included in the following listing.

Anthony & Scovill Solograph Plate Camera: (AS100); 4" x 5" plate view camera; Scovill & Adams Co. lens and shutter; red bellows. C 1901.

R3* $125	£66	DM206	FF639

Anthony & Scovill Stereo Solograph: (AS101); 4" x 6" folding stereo camera; 4" x 6" exp on dry plates. C 1901.

R* $550	£289	DM907	FF2.8k

Anthony & Scovill Roll Film Camera: (AS102); Wollensak lens; wood interior with detailed engraving. Separate roll film back. C 1901. In 1907 this became the No. 8 Ansco.

R3* $170	£89	DM280	FF869

Anthony & Scovill Roll Film Camera

Anthony & Scovill 4" x 5" Box Camera: (AS103); no variable aperture control; red window; 6 or 12 exp, 4" x 5" on roll film. C 1902. In 1907 this became the No. 3 Ansco.

R3* $40	£21	DM66	FF204

Anthony & Scovill 4" x 5" Box Camera

Anthony & Scovill 3¹/₄" x 4¹/₄" Box Camera: (AS104); side variable aperture setting; dual vf; side shutter release; dual pushbutton rear opening; wood interior; 6 or 12 exp, 3¹/₄" x 4¹/₄". C 1903. In 1907 this became the No. 2 Ansco.

R2* $60	£31	DM99	FF307

Anthony & Scovill 3¹/₄" x 4¹/₄" Box Camera

Anthony & Scovill 3¹/₄" x 4¹/₄"' Box Camera: (AS105); key wind top shutter release; single top vf; rear slide back opening; wood interior; 6 or 12 exp, 3¹/₂" x 3¹/₂" on roll film. In 1902 this became the No. 1 Ansco.

R2* $60	£31	DM99	FF307

No. 4 Ansco Model D: (AS106); Wollensak lens; 3¹/₄" x 4¹/₄" exp on 118 roll film. C 1905.

R3* $45	£24	DM74	FF230

"Dollar" Box Camera: (AS107); 3¹/₂" x 2¹/₂" box camera. C 1910.

R2* $20	£10	DM33	FF102

No. 0 Buster Brown Camera: (AS108); small coloured box camera; red with gold trim.

R3* $25	£13	DM41	FF128

No. 3A Folding Buster Brown Camera: (AS109); Actuf shutter; 6 or 10 exp, 3¹/₄" x 5¹/₂".

R2* $40	£21	DM66	FF204

Ansco Folding Buster Brown, Junior Model A and Model B

No. 5 Ansco, Model C: (AS110); roll film camera; horizontal format; red bellows.

R2* $50	£26	DM82	FF256

Ansco Jr. Model A: (AS111); C 1912, 6 or 12 exp, 2¹/₄" x 4¹/₄".

R2* $65	£34	DM107	FF332

Ansco Jr. Model B: (AS112); C 1912, 6 or 12 exp, 2¹/₄" x 4¹/₄"

R2* $65	£34	DM107	FF332

No. 4 Ansco: (AS113); C1912, 6 or 12 exp, 3¹/₄" x 3¹/₄".

R2* $65	£34	DM107	FF332

No. 6 Ansco Model D: (AS114); C1912, 6 or 12 exp, 3¹/₄" x 4¹/₄"

R2* $65	£34	DM107	FF332

No. 0 Ansco: (AS115); C 1914, vest pocket camera; Ansco Anastigmat f6.3 or Modico Anastigmat f7.5 lens; 1⁵/₈ x 2¹/₂" exp; front pulls straight out.

R2* $60	£31	DM99	FF307

Vest Pocket Ansco No. 2: (AS116); C1914, 6 x 9cm roll film camera; Ansco Anastigmat lens; Bionic shutter; 8 exp, 6 x 9cm on 120 roll film.

R2* $35	£18	DM58	FF179

Vest Pocket Ansco No. 2

No. 1A Automatic Camera: (AS117); C1925, motor drive roll film camera; Ilex Anscomatic f7.9 lens; Ilex Semi-Automatic shutter 1/25-1/100 s; 2³/₄" x 4¹/₈" exp on D6 or D12 roll film. Spring wound motor automatically advances film after each exp at rate of approx 1 exp per sec.

R3* $250	£131	DM412	FF1.3k

No. 1A Automatic Camera

Agfa: (AS118); C 1930, folding roll film camera; Agfa-Anastigmat f7.7 lens; shutter 1/25-1/100 s. 8 exp, 6 x 9cm on B2 roll film.

R2* $25	£13	DM41	FF128

Ansco Readyset Camera: (AS120); C1926, 120 roll film folding camera; maroon leather, brass hardware.

R2* $65	£34	DM107	FF332

No. 1A Readyset Royal: (AS121); C 1926, 116 roll film folding camera; 116 Antar lens; Readyset shutter I, T; brown ostrich covering, matching brown bellows.

R2* $70	£37	DM115	FF358

No. 1A Readyset Special: (AS122); C 1926, 116 roll film folding camera; Antar lens; Readyset shutter I, T and B; dark reddish brown covering, brown bellows.

R2* $50	£26	DM82	FF256

No. 1 Readyset Royal: (AS123); C 1926, 120 roll film folding camera; 120 Antar lens and shutter; dark tone coloured sealskin covering, grey bellows.

R2* $95	£50	DM157	FF486

No. 1A Readyset Royal: (AS124); C 1926, 116 roll film folding camera; Wollensak Velostigmat f6.3 lens; shutter 1/10-1/100 s, I, T; brown ostrich covering, brown bellows.

R3* $75	£39	DM124	FF383

Photo-Vanity: (AS125); C1926, vanity-case type detective camera; containers for rouge, powder and lipstick; small Ansco box camera fitted; operates through exterior of case. 8 exp, 4 x 6.5cm on 127 roll film.

R4* $1.2k	£630	DM2k	FF6.1k

Memo (1927): (AS126); C1927, half-frame 35mm box camera; Ilex-Ansco Cinemat 40mm f6.3 lens; Ilex shutter 1/25-1/100 s. Rapid film shift mechanism.

R2* $110	£58	DM181	FF562

Memo

Official Boy Scout Memo Camera: (AS127); C 1927, wooden bodied, olive drab finish, miniature camera; 50 exp, 18 x 23mm on 35mm film.

R3* $175	£92	DM288	FF894

Billy I: (AS130); C 1928, folding VFR camera for 6 x 9cm frames on roll film, Igestar 105mm f8.8 lens; Agfa shutter 1/25-1/100s, squarish body ends make this camera easy to identify.

R3* $25	£13	DM41	FF128

Billy II: (AS160); C1930s, folding VFR camera for 6 x 9cm frames on roll film, Agfa Anastigmat f7.7 lens; Agfa shutter 1/25-1/100s.

R2* $15	£8	DM25	FF77

Billette F4.5: (AS161); C1930s, folding VFR camera for 6 x 9cm frames on roll film, either Oppar or Solinar Anastigmat f4.5 lens, Compur shutter, the top of the line "Billy".

R3* $20	£10	DM33	FF102

Billy Record 8.8: (AS162); C1930s, folding VFR camera for 6 x 9cm frames on roll film, Igestar f8.8/10cm lens, Automat shutter.

R2* $15	£8	DM25	FF77

Billy Record 7.7: (AS163); C1930s, folding VFR camera for 6 x 9cm frames on roll film, Igestar f7.7/10cm lens, Automat or Automat S shutter.

R2* $15	£8	DM25	FF77

Billy Record 6.3: (AS164); C1930s, folding VFR camera for 6 x 9cm frames on roll film, Igestar f6.3/10cm lens, Vario or Pronto S shutter.

R2* $15	£8	DM25	FF77

Billy Record 4.5: (AS165); C1930s, folding VFR camera for 6 x 9cm frames on roll film, Apolar f4.5/10.5cm lens, Prontor II-S shutter.

R2* $25	£13	DM41	FF128

Billy Compur: (AS166); C1935, folding VFR camera for 6 x 9cm frames on roll film, Apotar or Solinar f4.5/10.5cm lens, Compur or Compur Rapid shutter.

R2* $35	£18	DM58	FF179

Agfa Record I: (AS186); C1950s, folding VFR camera for 6 x 9cm frames on roll film, Agnar f6.3 or f4.5/105mm lens, Vario or Pronto shutter, with and without accessory shoe or body mounted shutter release.

R3* $20	£10	DM33	FF102

Agfa Record III: (AS187); C1950s folding RFR camera for 6 x 9cm frames on roll film, Solinar f4.5/105mm lens, Synchro Compur shutter, accessory shoe, built-in *un-cou-* *pled* RFR, body mounted shutter release

R3* $60	£31	DM99	FF307

Trolita: (AS167); C1938, plastic folding VFR camera for 6 x 9cm or 6 x 4.5fcm frames on roll film, Apotar f4.5/10.5cm lens, Compur or Prontor II shutter. Produced at the same time as the "Trolix: box camera (AS156) from "Trolit", a kind of thermo plastic.

R3* $55	£29	DM91	FF281

Standard 6 x 9: (AS168); C1930s, metal folding VFR camera for 6 x 9cm frames on roll film, marked "Standard" on the lens stand, Anastigmat f4.5 or 6.3/105mm lens, Automat shutter.

R3* $15	£8	DM25	FF77

Standard De Luxe: (AS132); C1930, 6 x 9cm folding camera; Agfa Anastigmat f6.3/105mm lens; 6 x 9cm plates.

R2* $75	£39	DM124	FF383

Ansco Memory Kit: (AS131); C1930, consists of No. 1 Readyset Royal camera in ostrich covering, instruction book, room for 4 rolls of film in walnut wood gift box.

R3* $175	£92	DM288	FF894

Agfa Ansco Readyset Moroccan Camera: (AS133); C1930's, 120 roll film folding camera; Antar lens; blue bellows, embossed blue Moroccan leather.

R3* $90	£47	DM148	FF460

Agfa Ansco Readyset Traveler: (AS134); Antar lenses; cloth covered in combination stripes, grey bellows; two models for 120 and 115 roll film. C 1930's.

R2* $35	£18	DM58	FF179

Ansco Vest Pocket Readyset 127 Camera: (AS135); Wollensak lens; 5 colours available; orange, blue, green, red and turquoise. C 1930's.

R2* $65	£34	DM107	FF332

Agfa Ansco View: (AS140); 5" x 7" view camera; Wollensak Verito Portrait lens. C 1939.

R3* $250	£131	DM412	FF1.3k

Memo (1940): (AS141); 35mm folding camera; Agfa Memar 50mm f3.5 lens; Ansco shutter 1/2-1/200 s. Rapid shift film mecha-

Agfa Ansco View

Memo

Automatic Reflex

nism. C 1940.

R2* $75	£39	DM124	FF383

Speedex: (AS142); C1940, 120 roll film folding camera; 85mm f4.5 lens; 12 exp, 2¹/₄" x 2¹/₄" on 120 roll film.

R2* $20	£10	DM33	FF102

Automatic Reflex (1949): (AS143); 2¹/₄" x 2¹/₄" TLR; Ansco Anastigmat 83mm f3.5 coated lens; Ansco shutter 1-1/400 s; 12 exp, 2¹/₄" x 2¹/₄" on 120 roll film. Eye-level focusing, built-in magnifying lens for critical focus. The Automatic Reflex was originally introduced in 1947 without flash synch. The 1949 version had factory installed flash synch for class F bulbs. 1947 version: **$150.** 1949 version:

R3* $175	£92	DM288	FF894

Isolar: (AS144); C1930s, Agfa Solinar 135mm f4.5 lens; Compur shutter; double extension bellows; ground glass back; 9 x 12cm plates.

R2* $35	£18	DM58	FF179

Optima IIIs: (AS145); 35mm camera; Colour Apotar 45mm f2.8 lens; Compur shutter.

R2* $35	£18	DM58	FF179

Karat 3.5: (AS137); C1937, 35mm folding VFR camera, Solinar f3.5/5cm lens, Compur Rapid shutter, 12 exposures on special Agfa cartridges, also available post-war as the "Agfa 12/3.5".

R3* $45	£24	DM74	FF230

Karat 4.5: (AS153); C1935, 35mm folding VFR camera, Agfa Oppar 5.5cm f4.5 lens, Vario shutter 1/25-1/125 s, 12 exposures on special Agfa cartridges.

R2* $35	£18	DM58	FF179

Karat 6.3: (AS154); C1934, 35mm folding VFR camera, Anastigmat-Igestar f6.3/5cm lens, Vario shutter, 1/25-1/100s,12 exposures on special Agfa cartridges.

R2* $35	£18	DM58	FF179

Karat 12/2.8: (AS173); C1946, folding RFR camera for 12 exposures on special Agfa cartridges, Xenar f2.8/50mm lens, Compur Rapid shutter, this camera became the Karat 36 of 1949 (AS146).

R3* $60	£31	DM99	FF307

Karat 36: (AS146); C 1949, 35mm folding RFR camera, Soligon, Heligon or Xenar

f2.8/50mm coated lens; Synchro-Compur shutter 1-1/500s, CRF. Used orthodox 35mm in normal cassettes.

R2* $75	£39	DM124	FF383

Karat 36

Karat IV; (AS151); C.1959, 35mm folding RFR camera; Agfa Solinar f2 or f2.8/50mm coated lens; prontor SVS shutter, 1 - 1/300s redesigned top plate, with centred accessory shoe.

R2* $75	£39	DM124	FF383

Agfa Silette: (AS189); C1957, metal 35mm VFR camera, Colour Apotar f2.8/45mm lens, Prontor SVS shutter, lever advance, top plate mounted shutter release, centred VFR and accessory shoe, also exists in off centre bright line finder.

R2* $20	£10	DM33	FF102

Agfa Ambi Silette: (AS207); C1950s, metal 35mm RFR camera with interchangeable Colour Solinar f2.8/50mm lens, Synchro Compur shutter, VFR with fields of view for 35mm, 50mm, and 90mm.

R3* $70	£37	DM115	FF358

Lenses for Ambi Silette:
Colour Ambion f4/35mm lens: (AS001); **$40**
Colour Telinear f4/90mm lens: (AS002); **$50**

Agfa Silette I: (AS190), C1962, metal 35mm VFR camera, Colour Agnar f2.8/45mm lens, Prontor 125 shutter, off-centre VFR and accessory shoe, front mounted shutter release, new square cornered design.

R2* $15	£8	DM25	FF77

Agfa Silette L: (AS191); C1957, metal 35mm VFR camera, Colour Solinar f2.8/

50mm lens, Compur Rapid shutter, built-in light meter, lever advance, top plate mounted shutter release, off centre VFR and accessory shoe.

R2* $25	£13	DM41	FF128

Agfa Silette L: (AS192), C1962, metal 35mm VFR camera, Colour Apotar f2.8/45mm lens, Prontor 125 shutter, built-in coupled light meter, off-centre VFR, centred accessory shoe, front mounted shutter release, new square cornered design.

R2* $15	£8	DM25	FF77

Agfa Silette SL: (AS208), C1957, metal 35mm VFR camera, Colour Solinar f2.8/50mm lens, Compur Rapid shutter, built-in light meter for match needle metering, lever advance, top plate mounted shutter release, off centre VFR and accessory shoe.

R2* $45	£24	DM74	FF230

Agfa Silette LK: (AS193); C1958, metal 35mm VFR camera, Colour Apotar f2.8/50mm lens, Prontor LK shutter, built-in coupled light meter, lever advance, top plate mounted shutter release, off centre VFR and accessory shoe.

R2* $30	£16	DM49	FF153

Agfa Super Silette: (AS194); C1959, metal 35mm RFR camera, Colour-Solinar f2.8/50mm or Soligon f2/50mm lens, Synchro Compur shutter, built-in light meter, CRF, off-centre VFR, centred accessory shoe, front mounted shutter release, new square cornered design.

R3* $35	£18	DM58	FF179

Agfa Super Silette LK: (AS195), C1960s, metal 35mm RFR camera, Colour Apotar f2.8/45mm lens, Prontor 125 shutter, built-in coupled light meter controls aperture, CRF, off-centre VFR, centred accessory shoe, front mounted shutter release, new square cornered design.

R2* $35	£18	DM58	FF179

Agfa Silette LK: (AS196), C1958, metal 35mm RFR camera, Colour Apotar f2.8/45mm lens, Prontor LK shutter, built-in coupled light meter, CRF, off-centre VFR and accessory shoe, top plate mounted shutter release.

R2* $35	£18	DM58	FF179

Agfa Silette Automatic: (AS197); C1958, metal 35mm RFR camera, Colour-Solinar f2.8/50mm lens, Prontor SLV shutter, built-in light meter for match needle metering, CRF, off-centre VFR and accessory shoe, top plate mounted shutter release.

R3* $30	£16	DM49	FF153

Agfa Silette F: (AS198), C1963, metal 35mm VFR camera, Colour Agnar f2.8/45mm lens, Prontor 125 shutter, flash for AG-1 bulbs, off-centre VFR , front mounted shutter release, square cornered design.

R2* $15	£8	DM25	FF77

Agfa Silette Rapid I: (AS199), C1965, metal 35mm VFR camera using special Agfa Rapid cassettes, Colour Agnar f2.8/45mm lens, Parator shutter, like (AS190).

R2* $15	£8	DM25	FF77

Agfa Silette F: (AS200), C1965, metal 35mm VFR camera using special Agfa Rapid cassettes, Colour Agnar f2.8/45mm lens, Parator shutter, built-in flash for AG-1 bulbs, like (AS198).

R2* $15	£8	DM25	FF77

Agfa Silette Rapid L: (AS201), C1962, metal 35mm VFR camera using special Agfa Rapid cassettes, , Colour Apotar f2.8/45mm lens, Prontor 250 shutter, built-in coupled light meter, like (AS192).

R2* $15	£8	DM25	FF77

Agfa Isola : (AS202); C1950s, horizontally styled metal VFR camera for 6 x 6cm frames on 120 roll film, collapsible Agnar f6.3/75mm lens, Singlo-2 shutter, body mounted shutter release.

R2* $10	£5	DM16	FF51

Agfa Isola I: (AS203); C1950s, horizontally styled metal VFR camera for 6 x 6cm frames on 120 roll film, collapsible meniscus lens and simple shutter, body mounted shutter release.

R2* $15	£8	DM25	FF77

Agfa Isoly I: (AS204); C1960s, metal VFR camera for *4 x 4cm frames on 120 roll film*, Achromat lens, simple shutter.

R2* $15	£8	DM25	FF77

Agfa Isoly II: (AS205); C1960s, metal VFR

camera for *4 x 4cm frames on 120 roll film*, Agnar f6.3/55mm lens, Single shutter.

R2* $10	£5	DM16	FF51

Agfa Isoly III: (AS206); C1960s, metal VFR camera for *4 x 4cm frames on 120 roll film*, Colour Apotar f3.9/60mm lens, Pronto shutter.

R2* $15	£8	DM25	FF77

Agfa-Box: (AS155); C1930s, metal box camera for 6 x 9cm frames on roll film, three position indicator for focusing.

R1* $15	£8	DM25	FF77

Agfa Trolix-Box: (AS156); C1938, plastic box camera for 6 x 9cm frames on roll film, meniscus lens, simple shutter, metal carrying handle, Produced at the same time as the Trolita folding camera, (AS167) from "Trolit", a kind of thermo plastic.

R3* $40	£21	DM66	FF204

Agfa Metalbox-45: (AS157); C1938, metal box camera for 6 x 9cm frames on roll film, meniscus lens, simple shutter.

R1* $10	£5	DM16	FF51

Agfa Cadet-A8: (AS158); C1937, metal box camera for 6 x 4.5cm frames on roll film, meniscus lens, simple shutter.

R2* $15	£8	DM25	FF77

Agfa Synchro-Box: (AS176); C1949, metal box camera for 6 x 9cm frames on 120 roll film, built-in yellow filter.

R1* $10	£5	DM16	FF51

Agfa Clack: (AS185); C1950s, horizontally styled metal VFR camera, 6 x 98cm frames on roll film, simple lens and shutter.

R2* $10	£5	DM16	FF51

Agfa Heli-Clack 9 x 12: (AS170); C1930s, folding plate camera for 9 x 12cm plates, Heliar f4.5/10.5cm lens, Compur shutter.

R3* $45	£24	DM74	FF230

Agfa Heli-Clack 6.5 x 9: (AS171); C1930's, horizontally styled folding plate camera for 6.5 x 9cm plates, Agfa Anastigmat f4.5/105mm lens, Agfa shutter.

R3* $65	£34	DM107	FF332

Agfa Isorette: (AS172); C1935, folding VFR

camera for 6 x 6cm or 6 x 4.5cm frames on roll film, many lens/shutter combinations, among which are Igestar f6.3/70mm lens, Vario shutter and Apotar f4.5/70mm lens, Compur shutter. Not to be confused with the post-war "Isolette" (AS179).

R3* $25	£13	DM41	FF128

Agfa Isolette 6 x 6: (AS179); C1949, folding VFR camera for 6 x 6cm frames on roll film, Apotar f4.5/85mm lens, Prontor shutter, centre mounted accessory shoe, body mounted shutter release.

R3* $20	£10	DM33	FF102

Agfa Isolette 4.5x6: (AS180); C1949, folding VFR camera for 6 x 4.5cm frames on roll film, Solinar f4.5/80mm lens, Compur Rapid shutter, body mounted shutter release.

R3* $45	£24	DM74	FF230

Agfa Isolette II: (AS181); C1950s, folding VFR camera for 6 x 6cm on roll film, Apotar f4.5/85mm lens, Prontor shutter, *new designed top plate*, body mounted release.

R2* $15	£8	DM25	FF77

Agfa Isolette III: (AS182); C1950s, folding RFR camera for 6 x 6cm frames on roll film, *un-coupled* RFR, Apotar or Solinar f4.5/85mm lens, Prontor or Synchro Compur shutter, body mounted shutter release.

R3* $65	£34	DM107	FF332

Agfa Isolette V: (AS183); C1950s, folding VFR camera for 6 x 6cm frames on roll film. Agnar f4.5/80mm lens, Vario shutter, *no body mounted shutter release, off-centre mounted accessory shoe.*

R3* $20	£10	DM33	FF102

Agfa Super Isolette: (AS184); C1950s, folding RFR camera for 6 x 6cm frames on roll film, *CRFR,* Solinar f3.5/85mm lens, Synchro Compur shutter, body mounted shutter release, no more ruby window, automatic frame counting.

R3* $55	£29	DM91	FF281

Isolette L: (AS136); C1950s, folding VFR camera for 6 x 6cm frames on roll film, or 24 x 36mm frames on special paperbacked Agfa film, Colour Apotar f4.5/85mm lens; Pronto shutter; built-in light meter.

R2* $45	£24	DM74	FF230

Agfa Solinette: (AS177); C1952, folding 35mmVFR camera, Apotar f3.5/5cm lens, Prontor SV shutter, accessory shoe.

R2* $20	£10	DM33	FF102

Agfa Super Solinette: (AS178); C1953, folding 35mm RFR camera, CRF, Solinar f3.5/50mm lens, Synchro Compur shutter, accessory shoe.

R3* $50	£26	DM82	FF256

Agfa Click-I: (AS174); C1959, plastic bodied horizontally styled box type camera, 6 x 6cm frames on 120 roll film, meniscus lens, simple shutter.

R1* $10	£5	DM16	FF51

Agfa Click-II: (AS175); C1959, plastic bodied horizontally styled box type camera, 6 x 6cm frames on 120 roll film, meniscus lens, simple shutter, built-in close-up lens, otherwise as (AS174).

R1* $10	£5	DM16	FF51

Memo Automatic (1964): (AS147); half-frame 35mm motor drive camera; Memar f2.8 coated lens; fixed shutter speed. Selenium photo-electric exp meter controls diaphragm for correct exp. Spring wound motor cycles 10-15 exp per wind at a rate of about 1 exp per s. Mfd. by Ricoh, Japan for G.A.F., New York. C 1964.

R2* $75	£39	DM124	FF383

Memo Automatic

Agfa Movex: (AS150); metal bodied 16mm movie camera; Agfa Kine Anastigmat 20mm f3.5 fixed lens; spring motor drive; 16mm film in 12m cassettes; first camera to simplify loading by using cassettes. C 1928.

R2* $150	£79	DM247	FF767

Agfa Movex 8: (AS152); 8mm movie camera, light and compact; Agfa Cine Anastigmat

12mm f2.8 lens; used pre-split 8mm film (single-8) loaded in special cassette. Apparently the first European mfr to use this system. C 1937.

R2* $40	£21	DM66	FF204

Agfa Movex 8

Agfa Movexoom: (AS148); 8mm movie camera; Agfa Variogon 9-30mm f1.8 zoom lens. Photo-electric exp meter coupled to diaphragm. Electric motor drive. C 1960.

R2* $50	£26	DM82	FF256

Agfa Movexoom

Ansco Risdon, Model A: (AS149); 16mm movie camera; Bausch & Lomb f3.5 lens, located behind the shutter; double-claw pull down with register pin (an unusual feature for inexpensive camera); 16mm spool load-

ing spring-wound motor drive; optical vf. C 1930. Mfg: Risdon Mfr. Co., Naugatuck, Connecticut; distributed by Agfa Ansco Corp., Binghamton, N.Y.

R3* $60	£31	DM99	FF307

Ansco Risdon, Model A
(see **Industria Argentina** *for Gevaert cameras made in South America)*

E. & H. T. ANTHONY & COMPANY, New York.

Edward Anthony opened his first daguerreotype studio in 1841, at 11 Park Row, New York City. In 1842, he and J. M. Edwards established a daguerreotype portrait studio in Washington D.C., where they photographed all the members of Congress, as well as many other prominent citizens.

In 1843 Anthony established the National Miniature Gallery at 247 Broadway, New York City, where he operated a studio and sold photographic equipment and supplies. The company name changed many times at this address: it was known as Edward Anthony and Howard Chilton from 1842 to 1843; as Anthony, Edwards & Chilton in 1843; as Anthony, Edwards & Co. from 1844 to 1845; Anthony, Edwards & Clark from 1844 to 1845; as Anthony Clark & Co. from 1845 to 1847; and as Edward Anthony from 1847 to 1862.

From 1849 to 1851, Edward Anthony operated his studio and manufactured equipment and supplies at 203, 205 and 207 Broadway and Fulton. During this time, Mathew Brady's studio was located in the same building at No. 207.

Anthony moved uptown in 1851, and opened his new office and warehouse at 308 Broadway. At the same time he also opened a factory at the Harlem River Depot, located at Centre Street and Franklin. The Anthony firm, at this time was one of the largest importers and manufacturers of photographic equipment and supplies in the United States.

Anthony's brother Henry joined the company in 1853. In 1860, they moved the offices and warehouse facilities to 501 Broadway. In 1862, the name of the company was changed to Edward & Henry T. Anthony and Company, and later to E. & H. T. Anthony and Company. In 1869, the firm moved to 591 Broadway. In 1880, E. & H. T. Anthony and Company became agents to sell dry plates for George Eastman; in 1888, they began marketing the world's first flexible base film.

The management of the company changed at this time, both Anthony brothers having died by 1888. In 1900, after 31 years at 591 Broadway, the company moved to a new building at 122-124 Fifth Ave.

In 1902, E. & H. T. Anthony and Company merged with the Scovill and Adams Company, forming the Anthony and Scovill Company; the manufacturing facilities were transferred to Binghamton, New York. In 1907, the company name was shortened to "Ansco".

Anthony Stereoscopic View—(Success Z Model): (EA100); 5" x 8" stereoscopic wet-plate view camera; rear focusing screw; Wright's patent metallic supports; mahogany finish, brass fittings. C 1870's. **NSR.**

Anthony 5" x 8" Wet and Dry Plate Holders: (EA101); black painted wood holders with carrying box. C 1870.

R?* \$?

Anthony 5" x 8" Wet and Dry Plate Holders

Anthony Stereoscopic View

Anthony 4 Gem Tube Carte de Visite Camera: (EA102); wet plate outfit with cherry wood stand; single early track. C 1860. With plate holder with glass corners, dipper, dipping tank and box of early colouring dyes.

R4* $4k	£2.1k	DM6.6k	FF20.4k

Anthony 4 Gem Tube Carte de Visite Camera

Anthony Victoria Ferrotype Camera: (EA103); four tube 5" x 7" multiple ferrotype camera; four Darlot lenses, 1, 2, 4 or 8 exp on a 5" x 7" plate. Patent perfection stand invented by L. H. Stoddard. C 1872.

R4* $2k	£1.1k	DM3.3k	FF10.2k

Anthony Nine Tube Ferrotype Wet Plate Camera: (EA104); 5" x 7" ferrotype wet plate camera; 9 gem size Darlot lenses; sliding back; holder shifts horizontally. 9 exp on a 5" x 7" plate. C 1872. Rare.

R5*	NSR

Anthony 8" x 10" Universal Portrait and Ferrotype Camera: (EA105); 4 Darlot Petzval 6½" f4 lenses; rubber bellows. 8" x 10" wet plate holder with glass corners specially fitted with 7" x 10" and 5" x 7" inserts: takes 1 or 4 exp on an 8" x 10" plate;

8 exp on a 7" x 10" plate; 4 or 8 exp on a 5" x 7" plate. C 1872.

R4* $2k	£1.1k	DM3.3k	FF10.2k

Anthony Climax 8" x 10" View and Portrait Camera: (EA106); Darlot stereo lenses in adjustable lens board; lever focusing screw; double swing back; revolving 5" x 7" back. Ivory label, multiple attachments, separate ground glass frame. Early elevating stand. C 1872; C 1890.

R4* $1.5k	£787	DM2.5k	FF7.7k

Anthony 4" x 5" View Camera: (EA107); early 4" x 5" view camera; nickel E. & A. lens; vertical format; rear focusing screw adjustment was used on late wet plate and early dry plate cameras. C 1881. Rare.

R5*	NSR

Anthony Equipment No. 2: (EA110); 5" x 7" view camera; Prosh triplex lens and shutter; double dry plate holder. Early model was finished in black ebony. C 1881. Rare.

R4* $550	£289	DM907	FF2.8k

Anthony Equipment No. 3: (EA111); 5" x 8" dry plate camera for single or stereo exp; pair of E & A single achromatic lenses; 5" x

Anthony Victoria Ferrotype Camera

8" double dry plate holder; black ebony construction. Inexpensive amateur line introduced in 1881. Original price $15 with tripod and case.

R4* $800	£420	DM1.3k	FF4.1k

Anthony 11" x 14" Novel View Plate Camera: (EA112); (preceded Patent Novellette); E. & A. Universal finder; key hole slots permitted bellows to revolve; single and double swing. 10 sizes: 4" x 5" to 18" x 22". Anthony unjointed wood tripod. Patent February 20, 1883. C 1876.

R3* $425	£223	DM701	FF2.2k

Anthony Novel View Plate Camera

Anthony 5" x 8" Novel View: (EA113); 5" x 8" view camera; Prosh Duplex lens and shutter; double swing. Early version of revolving back. 10 sizes: 4" x 5" to 18" x 22". C 1844.

R3* $300	£157	DM495	FF1.5k

Anthony 4" x 5" Patent Novellette View Camera: (EA114); 4" x 5" view camera; E.A. Rapid No. 1 lens; waterhouse stops; Anthony's drop shutter; solid wood bed. C 1887.

R4* $550	£289	DM907	FF2.8k

Anthony Patent Bijou 3$\frac{1}{4}$" x 4$\frac{1}{4}$" Camera: (EA115); 3$\frac{1}{4}$" x 4$\frac{1}{4}$" view camera; E. A. No. 1 Hemispherical lens; waterhouse stops. Available with or without swing back; polished mahogany with brass fittings. Smallest Anthony camera: dimensions, 5" x 5" x 3$\frac{1}{2}$"; weight, 14$\frac{1}{2}$ ounces. C 1884.

R4* $350	£184	DM577	FF1.8k

Anthony Patent Bijou Camera

Anthony English Style Compact Camera: (EA117); 5" x 8" compact view camera; reversible back; 16" bellows extension; telescopic bed for long focus lenses; folded size, 9$\frac{1}{8}$" x 9$\frac{1}{8}$" x 3$\frac{1}{8}$". 4 sizes: 5" x 7" to 8" x 10". C 1888.

R3* $350	£184	DM577	FF1.8k

Anthony Cooper Universal Enlarging Lantern: (EA120); used as an 8" x 10" enlarging camera, copying camera, portrait camera or magic lantern. The kerosene burner lamp and condensers were removed for daylight enlarging. Patent by Cooper & Lewis, 1887.

R4* $400	£210	DM659	FF2k

Anthony Penny Picture Camera: (EA121); 5" x 7" multiplying camera; 4 Darlot Gem tube lenses. Sliding back for multiple exp: takes 1, 2, 3, 4, 6, 12 or 24 exp on a 5" x 7" plate. Used for children's photos. Ivory label. Original price, $12. C 1880's. Rare.

R4*		NSR	

Anthony's Phantom Camera: (EA122); 8" x 10" view camera; revolving back using key hole slots. 5 sizes: 4$\frac{1}{4}$" x 6$\frac{1}{2}$" to 8" x 10". C 1888.

R4* $325	£171	DM536	FF1.7k

Anthony Vincent 8" x 10": (EA123); cone shaped Anthony single combination lens; reversible back; telescoping bed. 4 sizes:

Anthony Penny Picture Camera

Anthony Vincent 8" x 10"

5" x 7" to 8" x 10". C 1890.

R3* $400	£210	DM659	FF2k

Schmid's Patent Detective Camera—Original Model: (EA124); box-type detective camera. 6 sizes: 8 x 10.5cm; 10.5 x 12.5cm; 11.5 x 16.5cm; 12.5 x 20cm; 16.5 x 21.5cm; 20 x 25cm on plates. C 1882 non folding handle. First American camera designed to be hand held.

R5* $7.5k	£3.9k	DM12.4k	FF38.3k

Schmid's Patent Detective Camera

Schmid's Patent Detective Camera—Second Model: (EA125); 3¹/₄" x 4¹/₄" detective camera; E. Anthony Rapid Rectilinear 6¹/₂" f8 lens; interchangeable waterhouse stops; variable speed rotary shutter; brass handle that folds down. 6 sizes, 3¹/₄" x 4¹/₄" to 8" x 10". Patent 1883.

R5* $5k	£2.6k	DM8.2k	FF25.6k

Schmid's Patent Detective Camera—Third Camera: (EA126); 4" x 5" camera; removable back; side focusing lever; takes Eastman-Walker roll holder. C 1886.

R5* $4.5k	£2.4k	DM7.4k	FF23k

Schmid's Patent Detective Camera: (EA127); leather covered detective camera; Dallmeyer Rapid Rectilinear lens; takes Eastman-Walker roll holder. Several sizes: 3¹/₄" x 4¹/₄", 4" x 5" (larger sizes were made to order). C 1888. Patent 1883. Rare.

R5*		NSR	

Anthony Climax Detective Camera: (EA130); wood finish detective camera; lenses of varying focal length used without removing shutter. Camera could be fitted in patent satchel handbag. 4" x 5" exp (larger sizes made to order). Patent dates 1884, 1886, 1887.

R4* $1.4k	£735	DM2.3k	FF7.2k

Anthony Climax Detective Camera

Anthony's Climax Detective Camera: (EA131); leather covered detective camera; lenses of varying focal length; separate rear compartment was available with 5 double holders; 4" x 5" exp (larger sizes made to order). C 1888.

R4* $1.4k	£735	DM2.3k	FF7.2k

Anthony's Satchel Detective Camera: (EA132); satchel-type detective camera; Dallmeyer Rapid Rectilinear lens; guillotine shutter. A satchel covered in alligator skin contained a Climax Detective Camera. 4" x 5" exp on plates. C 1887.

R5* $20k+ £10.5k+ DM33k+ FF102.2k+

Anthony's Satchel Detective Camera

Anthony PDQ (Photography Done Quickly): (EA133); 4" x 5" detective camera; E & A single achromatic No. 1 lens, rotating stops; variable speed shutter and focusing; removable ground glass; reversible finder. Patent date 1884, 1887.

R4* $850 £446 DM1.4k FF4.3k

Anthony Magazine Camera: (EA134); 4" x 5" magazine camera; red interior bellows adjusted externally. 12 or 24 exp on plates or film. C 1888. Rare.

R5* NSR

Anthony Magazine Camera

Anthony Magazine Camera: (EA135); 4" x 5" magazine camera; double achromatic

lens; adjustable focusing. 12 or 24 exp, 4" x 5" on plates. C 1890. Rare.

R5* NSR

Anthony Lilliput Detective Camera: (EA136); detective camera in small leather handbag; 65mm f8 lens; covers a 60 degree angle; variable speed sector shutter; 6 exp, $2^{1}/_{2}$" x $2^{1}/_{2}$" on glass plates or film; camera measures 4" x 4" x 6". C 1889-1891.

R4* $2.75k £1.4k DM4.5k FF14.1k

Anthony Lilliput Detective Camera

Anthony School Outfit: (EA137); basic 4" x 5" camera; complete with chemicals, tripod and trays for the student to learn the

Anthony School Outfit

fundamentals of photography. Also sold as premium in the Youth Companion (by Perry Mason & Co., Boston, Mass.) as the Companion 4" x 5" Camera with special outfit. C 1890's.

R3* $350	£184	DM577	FF1.8k

Anthony Model Manhattan: (EA140); 5" x 8" mahogany view camera; single achromatic EA nickel plated lens; Anthony nonpareil shutter. Inexpensive model: lacks rising front; does not fold, has swings. 3 sizes: 4" x 5" to 5" x 8" and stereo. C 1886.

R3* $150-300	£79-157	DM247-495

Anthony Model 2B: (EA141); 5" x 8" view camera; Garland shutter; rising front; swing back; dark mahogany construction with brass fittings. 6 sizes: 4" x 5" to 8" x 10". C 1888.

R4* $250	£131	DM412	FF1.3k

Anthony Champion 8B: (EA142); 8" x 10" view camera; E & A cone shaped single achromatic No. 4 lens; swing back; back bed lock, folding bed with patent clamps (pat. February 20, 1888); mahogany finish with brass fitting; holder, case. C 1888.

R4* $275	£144	DM453	FF1.4k

Anthony Champion Model 5" x 8" Stereo Camera: (EA143); 5" x 8" stereo view camera; swing back; bed locks from rear; stereo patent lamp hooks. Patent November 11, 1884.

R4* $750	£394	DM1.2k	FF3.8k

Anthony Champion Model 5" x 7" View Camera: (EA144); 5" x 7" view camera; Darlot lens; rotating stops; swing back; patent clamp hooks; rear bed locks. 6 sizes and stereo format. Patent February 20, 1888.

R3* $275	£144	DM453	FF1.4k

Anthony Champion: (EA145); 5" x 8" view camera; E & A cone shaped single achromatic lens; patent clamp hooks; swing back; rear bed locks; patent spring back. 6 sizes: 4" x 5" to 8" x 10" and stereo. Patent date March 27, 1888.
Complete with original box.

R3* $300	£157	DM495	FF1.5k

Anthony Model NPA: (EA146); 5" x 8"

Anthony Champion Model 5" x 7" View Camera

Anthony Model NPA

stereo camera; EA wide angle nickel plated lens; rising front; patent swing back; patent clamp hooks; Anthony Climax tripod;

Anthony Universal finder. C 1888.
Complete outfit:

R4* $450	£236	DM742	FF2.3k

Anthony Patent Novellette View Camera: (EA147); 4" x 5" view camera; EA single achromatic lens; sliding bottom plate. Circassian walnut wood finish with nickel plated fittings. 4" x 5" and larger sizes. C 1890.

R3* $400	£210	DM659	FF2k

Anthony Patent Novellette View Camera: (EA150); 8" x 10" view camera; J. Dallmeyer R.R. lens; revolving bellows; E & A Universal finder; double swing back; patent clamp hooks; polished mahogany construction. 7 sizes: 4" x 5" to 11" x 14". Original price, $33. Patent February 20, 1888.

R4* $350	£184	DM577	FF1.8k

Anthony Patent Novellette View Camera

Anthony Patent Novellette Stereo Camera: (EA151); 5" x 8" stereo camera; pair of E & A cone shaped, single achromatic lenses; single swing; revolving bellows; patent clamp hooks. Patent February 20, 1888.

R4* $750	£394	DM1.2k	FF3.8k

Anthony Patent Novellette Stereo

Anthony Victor Camera: (EA152); Anthony single combination wide angle lens; rising front; single swing; double rack and pinion movement; patent swing back. Eclipse double plate holder. 6 sizes: 4" x 5" to 8" x 10". C 1888.

R4* $350	£184	DM577	FF1.8k

Anthony Fairy Camera: (EA153); 5" x 8" view camera; EA nickel lens; rack, cog wheel and pinion focusing; Anthony Universal wood finder; reversible back; key hole slots for revolving back; polished Circassian walnut wood. 6 sizes: 4" x 5" to 8" x 10". Early wood stand. C 1890.

R4* $350	£184	DM577	FF1.8k

Anthony Fairy Camera

Anthony Knickerbocker Camera: (EA154); 5" x 7" view camera; EA single achromatic nickel plate lens; reversible back single swing; back focus; nickel plated fittings. 4 sizes: 5" x 7" to 8" x 10". C 1891.

R3* $300	£157	DM495	FF1.5k

Anthony Normandie Camera: (EA155); 6¹/2" x 8¹/2" view camera; Darlot lens; back focus; revolving stops; single swing; reversible back. 9 sizes: 4" x 5" to 14" x 17". C 1890.

R4* $300	£157	DM495	FF1.5k

Anthony Normandie Camera

The Klondike Camera: (EA156); box plate camera; adjustable shutter speeds; adjustable diaphragm; dry plates, 3¹/₄" x 4¹/₄". C 1898.

R4* $125	£66	DM206	FF639

Climax Multiplying Camera: (EA157); 5" x 7" camera; single Darlot portrait tube; multiple exp on 5" x 7" plate. C 1901.

R4* $475	£249	DM783	FF2.4k

Anthony Climax Portrait Camera: (EA160); brass lens; double swing back; bed extends to 49". Anthony Automatic Cabinet Attachment: sliding ground glass replaced by plate holder. C 1888. Com-

Anthony Climax Portrait Camera

plete with No. 1 New York.
Camera and stand:

R2* $500	£262	DM824	FF2.6k

Anthony 4" x 5" Climax Enlarging Camera: (EA161); reducing or copying camera; reversible back; lens can be used inside or outside camera. 9 sizes: 4" x 5" to 20" x 24". C 1890.

R3* $300	£157	DM495	FF1.5k

Anthony Clifton View Camera: (EA162); Anthony drop shutter; double swing back and front; front and back focus; reversible back; red bellows. 6 sizes: 5" x 7" to 14" x 17". C 1901.

R4* $300	£157	DM495	FF1.5k

Anthony Lantern Slide Camera: (EA163); for copying negatives 4" x 5" or smaller on 3¹/₄" x 4¹/₄" plates. Revolving ground glass frame; folding extension bed. C 1888.

R4* $300	£157	DM495	FF1.5k

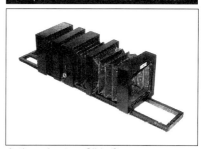

Anthony Lantern Slide Camera

Anthony View Camera: (EA164); 6¹/₂" x 8¹/₂" view camera; homocentric lens;

Anthony View Camera

Kolios shutter; nickel plated fittings. Ivory label marked: E. & H. T. Anthony, New York, Chicago. C 1900.

R3* $250	£131	DM412	FF1.3k

ANTHONY ACCESSORIES

Anthony CDV Albums: (EA001); 2 versions. C 1860's. **$25-$50 each.**

Anthony CDV Albums

Fuming box for albumen paper: (EA002); mahogany construction with lead lined drawers. Used ammonia to increase the speed of albumen paper (first suggested by H. T. Anthony in 1862).

R4* $400	£210	DM659	FF2k

Fuming box for albumen paper

Anthony Graphoscope: (EA003); viewer for photos and stereo cards. C 1870's.

R3* $300	£157	DM495	FF1.5k

Anthony Graphoscope: (EA004); viewer for photos and stereo cards. C 1870's.

R3* $300	£157	DM495	FF1.5k

Anthony Chemical Bottles: (EA005);

Anthony Graphoscope

Anthony Chemical Bottles

various labels. May be worth more to bottle collectors. C 1860-1890. **Each:**

R4*	$20-100	£10-52	DM33-165

Dry Plates: (EA006); distributed by E. & H.T. Anthony for the Eastman Dry Plate Co. C 1888.

R4* $25	£13	DM41	FF128

Anthony Ascot Lamp: (EA007); dark room lantern; uses kerosene; black enamel finish with detachable oil can. Original price, $.75. C 1900.

R2* $60	£31	DM99	FF307

Anthony Ascot Lamp

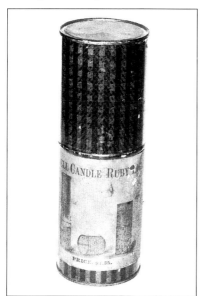

Anthony Tisdell Ruby Light

Anthony Tisdell Ruby Light: (EA010);
candle, ruby chimney. 6³/4" x 2¹/2". C 1888.

R4* $75	£39	DM124	FF383

Anthony's line of chemicals: (EA011);
contact printing and enlarging paper. C
1888. **Each:**

R3* $15-30	£8-16	DM25-49	FF77-153

**Anthony's Climax Kerosene Dark Room
Lantern:** (EA012); has three large illumi-
nating surfaces with reflector. C 1888.

R3* $80	£42	DM132	FF409

Anthony accessories: (EA013); Brighton
line; fibre trays; Success Print Mounter in 6"
and 12" sizes; Anthony improved printing
frames. C 1888-1895. **Each:**

R2* $10-30	£5-16	DM16-49	FF51-153

Anthony's Retouching Frame: (EA014);
for retouching negatives; has drawer for
brushes, stippling pencils and reflecting
mirror. C 1885.

R2* $45	£24	DM74	FF230

Anthony's Retouching Frame

Karl ARNOLD,
Marienberg, Germany.

Karma Flex 4 x 4 model II: (LU100);
C1932, SLR type for 4cm x 4cm frames on
roll film.Vidar or Victor or Regulyt f4.5/
60mm lens, guillotine shutter 1/25 -1/100 s.

R3* $350	£184	DM577	FF1.8k

Karma Flex 4 x 4 model I: (LU101); C1932,
TLR type box camera (fixed focus) for 4cm
x 4cm frames on roll film "Spezial" f9 lens,
simple shutter .

R3* $500	£262	DM824	FF2.6k

Karma Flex 6 x 6 model II: (LU102); C1932,
TLR for 6cm x 6cm frames on roll film, Victar

or Pololyt f3.5/75mm lens, CPFS to 1/500s.

R4* $375	£197	DM618	FF1.9k

Karma Flex 6 x 6 model I: (LU103); C1932, TLR type box camera (fixed focus) for 6cm x 6cm frames on roll film, "Spezial" f7.7 lens, simple shutter, waistlevel VFR convertible to eyelevel VFR.

R4* $190	£100	DM313	FF971

Karma: (LU104); C1932, RFR camera for 6cm x 6cm frames on roll film, Victar or Pololyt f3.5/75mm lens, CPFS to 1/500s, basically the bottom half of a Karma Flex 6 x 6 model II (LU102), with tubular VFR and uncoupled RFR.

R4* $275	£144	DM453	FF1.4k

APPARATE & KAMERABAU, Friedrichshafen, Germany.

Akarex I: (AP100); C1954, 35mm RFR camera, non-interchangeable Isco Westar f3.5/45mm lens in either Prontor, 1/25 - 1/200s or Prontor SVS 1 - 1/300s shutters, lever wind.

R3* $45	£24	DM74	FF230

Akarex I

Akarex III; (AP101); C1955 35mm RFR camera with interchangeable lens/VFR assemblies, Isco Westar F3.5/35mm or Schneider Xenon f2/50mm lens, Synchro Compur 1 - 500s shutter. Schneider 35mm and 90mm accessory lenses with attached finders were available, see (AP001) and (AP002).

R3* $55	£29	DM91	FF281

Akarette model "O"; (AP102); 1949-50, black metal bodied 35mm VFR camera with

interchangeable lens, Schneider Xenar f3.5/ 50mm, schneider Xenar f2.8/45mm or Schneider Xenon f2/50mm normal lens., behind the lens leaf shutter 1/25 - 1/200s, two viewfinders for fields of view corresponding to 35mm, 50mm, and 75mm, f4.5/ 35mm lens and f3.5/75mm lenses available, see (AP003) and (AP004).

R3* $85	£45	DM140	FF434

Akarette model II (AP103); 1950-54, metal bodied 35mm VFR camera with interchangeable lens, Schneider Xenar f3.5/50mm, schneider Xenar f2.8/45mm or Schneider Xenon f2/50mm normal lens., behind the lens leaf shutter 1/25 - 1/200s, two viewfinders for fields of view corresponding to 35mm, 50mm, and 75mm, selector lever on the front of the camera marked "50mm" and "75mm" allows blocking one of the VFR windows. f4.5/35mm lens, and f3.5/75mm lenses available, see (AP003) and (AP004). Much like the model "O" (AP102), with the addition of chrome trim, vrf selector lever and self timer.

R3* $75	£39	DM124	FF383

Akarelle: (AP104); 1954-55, metal bodied 35mm VFR camera with interchangeable lens, Schneider Xenar f3.5/50mm, Schneider Xenar f2.8/45mm or Schneider Xenon f2/50mm normal lens., Prontor S shutter 1/25 - 1/200s, two viewfinders for fields of view corresponding to 35mm, 50mm, and 90mm, selector lever on the front of the camera marked "50mm" and "90mm". f4.5/ 35mm lens, and f3.5/90mm lenses available, see (AP003) and (AP005). Much like the Akarette model II (AP102), with the addition of lever wind, front mounted strap lugs and 90mm field of view VFR. Late cameras have no selection lever, but rather fields marked in the VFR.

R3* $75	£39	DM124	FF383

Akarelle Automatic S: (AP105); C1960, 35mm VFR camera, non-interchangeable Isco Westanar f2.8/45mm lens, built-in lightmeter coupled to shutter, providing automatic exposure, speed selected indicated in the VFR.

R2* $45	£24	DM74	FF230

Akarelle V: (AP105); C1961, simple 35mm VFR camera, Arretar f2.8/45mm lens, Vario

ARNOLD-APPARATE & KAMERABAU-ARGUS A

Shutter, 1/25 - 1/200s

R2* $20	£10	DM33	FF102

Akarelle W: (AP107); C1963, 35mm VFR camera with interchangeable Colour-Wilon f2.8/50mm lens, Prontor SVS shutter, 1 - 1/300s, Lineogon f3.5/35mm WA accessory lens w/ shoe mount wide angle viewer available. (price is for camera with two lenses and WA VFR.)

R3* $80	£42	DM132	FF409

Arette-IB: (AP108); C1956, 35mm VFR camera with non interchangeable Westar or Xenar f2.8/45mm lens, Prontor SVS shutter, 1 - 1/300s, lever advance built-in light meter

R3* $45	£24	DM74	FF230

Arette IC: (AP109); C1957, 35mm camera with coupled RFR and non interchangeable Westar or Xenar f2.8/45mm lens, Prontor SVS shutter, 1 - 1/300s, lever advance like the Arette IB (AP105), but with CRF, new body style, and without built-in light meter.

R3* $45	£24	DM74	FF230

Arette ID: (AP110); C1957, 35mm camera with coupled RFR and non interchangeable Westar or Xenar f2.8/45mm lens, Prontor SVS shutter, 1 - 1/300s, lever advance like the Arette IC (AP106), but with built-in EV scale light meter.

R3* $55	£29	DM91	FF281

Arette-A: (AP111); C1957, 35mm VFR camera with non-interchangeable Arettar 2.8/45mm, Isconar f2.8/45mm lenses, Vario shutter, 1/25 - 1/200s or Prontor SVS shutter, 1 - 300s, 1:1 optical VFR so both eyes could be open when using the camera.

R3* $40	£21	DM66	FF204

Arette-BW: (AP112); C1959, 35mm *VFR* camera with interchangeable Schneider Xenon f2/50mm lens, Prontor SVS, 1 - 1/300s, field of view for 50mm and 90mm marked in VFR, built-in light meter. Late models (C1960), have the meter mounted in the front centre of the top plate, and Wilon f2.8/50mm lens. 90mm accessory lens available (see (AP006))

R3* $55	£29	DM91	FF281

Arette DN: (AP113); C1958, 35mm camera with coupled RFR and non interchangeable Westar or Xenar f2.8/45mm lens, Prontor SVS shutter, 1 - 1/300s, built-in EV scale light meter, lever advance Like the Arette ID (AP110), but lightmeter reading visible in the VFR.

R3* $45	£24	DM74	FF230

Schneider Xenagon f3.5/35mm lens and finder assembly: (AP001); **$50**
Schneider Tele-Xenar f3.5/90mm lens and finder assembly: (AP002); **$70**
Schneider Xenar f4.5/35mm lens: (AP003); **$45**
Schneider Tele-Xenar f3.5/75mm lens: (AP004); **$80**
Schneider Tele-Xenar f3.5/90mm lens: (AP005); **$110**
Telexon f5.6/90mm lens: (AP006); **$60**

Industria ARGENTINA, (SIAF)

Bislent: (IA100); C1950, Bakelite stereo VFR camera for 2.5 x 3.5cm single frames or stereo pairs vertically on 120 roll film, simple lens and shutters, each lens has its own release.

R4* $150	£79	DM247	FF767

Rex-Junior: (IA101); C1950, Bakelite VFR camera for 6 x 6cm frames on 120 or 620 film, Lujo f10/8.5cm lens, simple shutter, made under license from Gevaert.

R4* $50	£26	DM82	FF256

Rex: (IA102); C1950, Bakelite VFR camera for 6 x 9cm or 6 x 4.5cm on 120 or 620 film, Lujo f10/9.1cm lens, simple shutter.

R3* $40	£21	DM66	FF204

Gradosol: (IA103); as IA102 but for brand name.

R4* $60	£31	DM99	FF307

ARGUS INC., Ann Arbor, Michigan.

Argus K: (AI100); 35mm camera; Argus Anastigmat 50mm f4.5 lens; Ilex shutter 1/25-1/200 s. Extinction meter coupled to

ARGUS

Argus K

lens diaphragm. C 1939. This camera represents the only attempt to couple an extinction meter to the diaphragm of a 35mm camera.

R3* $110	£58	DM181	FF562

Argus A2B: (AI101); 35mm camera; Argus Anastigmat 50mm f4.5 lens; Argus shutter 1/25-1/50 s. C 1939-1950.

R2* $25	£13	DM41	FF128

Argus A2B

Argus A (gold coloured): (AI102); C1940, 35mm camera; Argus Anastigmat 50mm f4.5 lens; Argus shutter 1/25 - 1/50 s. This model was gold coloured to resemble the Leica I (A) Luxus.

R3* $100	£52	DM165	FF511

Argus A (gold coloured)

Argus C3: (AI103); C1940, 35mm RFR camera; Cintar Anastigmat 50mm f3.5 lens; Argus shutter 1/10-1/300 s, five rivets on the back hinge indicates pre-war production.

R1* $30	£16	DM49	FF153

Argus C3

Argus C3 Matchmatic: (AI104); 35mm RFR camera, add-on non-coupled Selenium meter. Two tone colour design.

R1* $30	£16	DM49	FF153

Argus Golden Shield:(AI111); as (AI104) but for chrome metal front plate, and "Golden Shield" emblem.

R2* $45	£24	DM74	FF230

Argus A3: (AI105); C1942, 35mm camera; Argus Anastigmatic 50mm f4 lens; Argus shutter 1/25-1/50 s. Built-in extinction exp meter.

R1* $25	£13	DM41	FF128

Argus C4: (AI106); C1951,35mm RFR camera; Cintar 50mm f2.8 coated lens; Argus shutter 1/10-1/300 s, CRF.

R1* $30	£16	DM49	FF153

Argus C4

Argus C44: (AI107); C1951, 35mm RFR camera, interchangeable Cintagon 50mm f2.8 coated lens, Argus shutter 1/25-1/300s, CRF.

R2* $45	£24	DM74	FF230

Argus C44

Accessories and lenses for C44:
35mm f4 wide angle lens: (AI001); **$30**
100mm f3.5 telephoto lens: (AI002); **$30**
VFR for 50mm, 35mm, and 100mm: (AI003); **$35**
light meter for C44: (AI004); **$10**

Argus Autronic 35: (AI110); Cintar 50mm f3.5 lens; synch shutter 1/30 - 1/500 s. Selenium photo-electric cell controlled exp. C 1960-1962.

R1* $45	£24	DM74	FF230

ARSENAL KIEV, Kiev, Ukraine, USSR.

Originally made with machinery removed from the Zeiss factory at the end of WWII, Kiev 35mm RFR cameras have been in production ever since. Like their Contax look-a-like relatives, they tend to have shutter problems which are very difficult to repair. For these cameras, at least, the first two digits of the snr give the year of production. As the Arsenal factory grew, other camera models came into production. Some cameras, especially the Kiev 88 are still available. They are included because of their origins and design, their relatively low price, and the fact that they are in many collections.

Kiev 2: (KV100); 1947?-55, Vertical mfps, 1 - 1/1250 sec, combined RFR/VFR windows, interchangeable Contax bayonet type mount, earliest cameras have lenses marked "3K" (maybe meaning Sonnar/Krasnogorsk) later cameras have f2.0/50mm Jupiter 8 lens.

R3* $125	£66	DM206	FF639

Kiev 2A: (KV101); 1947?-55, as (KV100) but for PC synch added, name written in Cyrilic and Latin letters.

R3* $125	£66	DM206	FF639

Kiev 3: (KV102); 1949-55, Vertical mfps, 1 - 1/1250 sec, combined RFR/VFR windows, interchangeable Contax bayonet type mount, f2.0/50mm Jupiter 8M lens uncoupled built-in meter located on the top of the camera body á la Contax III

R3* $125	£66	DM206	FF639

Kiev 3A: (KV103); 1956-58, Vertical mfps, 1 - 1/1250 sec, combined RFR/VFR windows, interchangeable Contax bayonet type mount, f2.0/50mm Jupiter 8 lens as the Kiev 3, but with PC synch added to the front of the camera body.

R2* $110	£58	DM181	FF562

Kiev 4: (KV104); 1957-79, Vertical mfps, 1 - 1/1250 sec, combined RFR/VFR windows, interchangeable Contax bayonet type mount, f2.0/50mm Jupiter 8M lens uncoupled built-in meter located on the top of the camera body as the Kiev 3 (but smaller and more sensitive), PC synch added to the front of the camera body. Redesigned camera back like post-war Contax, film memo.

R2* $110	£58	DM181	FF562

Kiev 4A: (KV105); 1958-?, Vertical mfps, 1 - 1/1250 sec, combined RFR/VFR windows, interchangeable Contax bayonet type mount, black f1.8/53mm Helios 103 lens as the Kiev 4, but with reduced top shutter speed and hot shoe in addition to the PC synch on the front of the camera body, no meter, black rewind and film advance knobs.

R2* $110	£58	DM181	FF562

Kiev 4AM: (KV106); 1978-81, Vertical mfps, 1 - 1/1000 sec, combined RFR/VFR windows, interchangeable Contax bayonet type mount, black f1.8/53mm Helios-103 lens as the Kiev 2A, but with reduced top shutter speed and hot shoe in addition to the PC synch on the front of the camera body, self timer, no meter, black rewind crank and film advance knob.

R2* $110	£58	DM181	FF562

Kiev 4M:(KV107); as Kiev4 AM, but for built-in uncoupled light meter

R2* $110	£58	DM181	FF562

"No Name" Kiev: (KV108); C1963, Vertical mfps, 1 - 1/1250 sec, combined RFR/VFR windows, Contax bayonet type mount. Often thought of as having been made at the post war Zeiss plant in East Germany, these cameras were really produced in the Soviet Union, concurrently with the Kiev 4A, for export to the West.

R4* $300	£157	DM495	FF1.5k

Kiev 5: (KV109); C1971, 35mm RFR camera, built-in lightmeter, interchangeable Jupitor-8M f2/50mm lens using Kiev/Contax mount, side mounted rewind crank, MFPS 1/2 - 1/1000s, made in limited numbers.

R4* $250	£131	DM412	FF1.3k

Kiev 35A: (KV110);C1985, black plastic 35mm VFR camera, copy of Minox 35GT.

R2* $70	£37	DM115	FF358

Accessories and lenses for Kiev 35mm RFR cameras

Jupitor-12 35mm f2.8: (KV001); in chrome **$90**
Jupitor-12 35mm f2.8: (KV002); in black **$80**
Jupitor-9 85mm f2.0: (KV003); in chrome **$80**
Jupitor-9 85mm f2.0: (KV004); in black **$70**
Jupitor-11 135mm f4 lens (copy of Zeiss Sonnar): (KV005); **$75**
Jupitor-11 135mm f4 lens (fat barrel): (KV006); **$100**
Kiev Stereo (copy of Zeiss Stereotar): (KV009); **$800**
3.5cm accessory VFR: (KV010); **$35**
8.5cm accessory VFR: (KV011); **$35**
(note: no 13.5cm finder was produced, and the only *turret type* finder made in the USSR was made by and for Zorki.)

Kiev-Vega: (KV111); C1965, subminiature camera for use with Minolta 16 cassettes, focusing f3.5/23mm Industar lens, shutter speeds 1/30, 1/60, & 1/200s. Grey or Brown.

R3* $65	£34	DM107	FF332

Kiev-30: (KV112); C1975, subminiature camera, as (KV111), but in black, often found in a complete set, including developing tank adapter and unused film. (for outfit add 50%).

R3* $50	£26	DM82	FF256

Kiev-30M: (KV113); C1989, subminiature camera as (KV112), but for stencilled name on the front.

R3* $50	£26	DM82	FF256

Kiev 30M 1949-89: (KV114); 1989, as Kiev 30M (KV113), but no name, engraved "Kiev 1949-1989" on back, Communist star with hammer and sickle engraved on front.

R4* $150	£79	DM247	FF767

Kiev 10 Automat: (KV115); C1965, 35mm SLR with interchangeable bayonet mount Helios f2/50mm lens, unique metal rotary focal plane shutter, 1/2 - 1/1000s, built-in non-TTL light meter, shutter speed preferred automatic to total manual operation, lever advance, bottom mounted rewind crank.

R4* $200	£105	DM330	FF1k

Lenses for Kiev 10:
20mm f4 lens: (KV020); **$80**
37mm f2.8 lens: (KV021); **$50**
85mm f2 lens:(KV022); **$100**

Kiev 6C: (KV116): C1970, SLR for 6cm x 6cm frames on 120 or 220 film, horizontally styled much like a large 35mm SLR, interchangeable Volna f2.8/80mm lens in Pentacon Six breech mount., CFPS 1 - 1/1000s, removable waist level finder.

R2* $200	£105	DM330	FF1k

Kiev 60: (KV117): C1980, SLR for 6cm x 6cm frames on 120 or 220 film, as (KV116) but for improved film transport and "more convenient shutter release button position", often found with the TTL metering prism, sometimes found in hard leather outfit case with lens hood, and accessory shoe.

R2* $200	£105	DM330	FF1k

Lenses for Kiev 6, 6C or 60

Zodiak-8b 30mm f3,5 wide angle lens: (KV030); **$225**

Mir-26b 45mm f3.5 wide angle lens: (KV031); **$125**

Mir-38b 65mm f3.5 wide angle lens: (KV032); **$100**

MC Vega-28b 120mm f2.8 telephoto lens: (KV033); **$90**

Kaleinar-3b 150mm f2.8 telephoto lans: (KV034); **$125**

MC Telear-5b 250mm f5.6 telephoto lens: (KV035); **$150**

Solyut: (KV120); C1965, 120 SLR for 6 x 6cm frames, copy of 1000F Hasselblad, f2.8/80mm lens in interchangeable mount, MFPS 1/2-1000s, interchangeable film backs, removable waistlevel finder, *non-automatic* lens aperture, usually found not working. *(note: because of patent infringement problems, Solyut cameras were made for domestic consumption only.)*

R3* $175	£92	DM288	FF894

Solyut S (C): (KV121): C1967, as (KV120) but for *semi-automatic aperture* à la Exakta.

R3* $175	£92	DM288	FF894

Kiev 80: (KV122); C1975, 120 SLR for 6cm x 6cm frames, interchangeable f2.8/80mm lens in bayonet mount, interchangeable backs, removable waist level finder, *automatic lens aperture,* MFPS 1/2 - 1/1000s, these cameras are famous for being unreliable, and not up to hard use.

R2* $150	£79	DM247	FF767

Zenith 80: (KV123); C1975, export version of the Kiev 80 (KV122) not very successful.

R3* $150	£79	DM247	FF767

Kiev 88: (KV124); C1984, as (KV122) but now with hot shoe synch, often found with the TTL metering prism, lens shade, extra film back in a hard leather case as a "Kiev 88TTL" outfit, MFPS 1/2 - 1/1000s, as with the preceding Kiev 120 SLRs, these cameras are famous for being unreliable, easily broken, hard to repair. (Still available *new* from a famous New York camera dealer, under another name, and at a much higher price than most collectors are willing to pay.) (complete "TTL" outfit adds 100%)

R2* $180	£94	DM297	FF920

Current Lenses for Zenith 80, Kiev 80 and 88

Zodiak-8B 30mm f3,5 wide angle lens: (KV040); **$250**

Mir-26B 45mm f3.5 wide angle lens: (KV041); **$125**

Mir-38B 65mm f3.5 wide angle lens: (KV042); **$100**

MC Vega-28B 120mm f2.8 telephoto lens: (KV043); **$90**

Kaleinar-3B 150mm f2.8 telephoto lans: (KV044); **$150**

MC Telear-5B 250mm f5.6 telephoto lens: (KV045); **$170**

ASAHI OPTICAL CO., Tokyo, Japan.

Asahiflex I: (AO100); 35mm SLR camera; Takumar 50mm f3.5 lens with interchangeable screw mount; CFPS 1/20-1/500s. C 1952. First Japanese 35mm SLR.

R* $350	£184
	DM577 FF1.8k

Asahiflex IIB: (AO101); 35mm SLR camera; Takumar 58mm f2.8 preset lens with interchangeable screw mount; CFPS 1/20-1/500 s. Waist-level vf and

Asahiflex I

eye-level optical vf. C 1954. First 35mm SLR with combined focusing and viewing to use instant-return mirror.

R3* $225	£118	DM371	FF1.2k

Pentax Auto 110: (AO120); C1976, SLR for 110 film, interchangeable f2.8/24mm normal lens, behind the lens automatic shutter, lever wind. (Prices 50% higher in Europe.)

R2* $75	£39	DM124	FF383

Accessories for the Pentax Auto 110:
f2.8/18mm wide angle lens: (AO001); **$40**
f2.8/50mm telephoto lens: (AO002); **$40**
auto winder: (AO007); **$30**

Pentax Auto 110 with auto winder fitted. Plus standard lens (on camera) wide-angle and telephoto.

AUSTRALIAN CAMERA MANUFACTURERS AUSTRALIA, A.C.M.A., Australia.

Sportshot: (AC200); C1938, VFR bakelite camera for 6 x 9cm on 120 or 620 film, curved film plane, Lentar f13.5 lens, simple shutter, base of camera marked "British made", but this was common practice for Australian-made products before WWII.

Available in black, brown, red, and green.

R3* $50	£26	DM82	FF256

Sportshot

AUTOMATIC RADIO MFG CO., Boston, Massachusetts.

Tom Thumb Camera Radio: (AU100); combination AM radio and detective camera; Maestar 57.5mm lens; reflex finder; 3 x 4cm exp on 127 film. C 1938.

R3* $200	£105	DM330	FF1k

Tom Thumb Camera Radio

B

BABY FLEX: (BB103); Sanko 20mm f3.5 lens; Peace Model 2 shutter 1/50-1/250; 10 exp, 13 x 14mm on special roll film. Mfd in Japan.

| R4* $750 | £394 | DM1.2k | FF3.8k |

A.H. BAIRD, Edinburgh, Scotland.

Baird Single Lens Stereo Camera: (AH100); Tessar 18cm f4.5 lens; rollerblind shutter; single or stereoscopic exposure by displacing the lensboard right, centred, or left. Mahogany tailboard with brass fittings.

| R4* $650 | £341 | DM1.1k | FF3.3k |

Max BALBRECK, J. JOUX, Paris, France.

L'Alethoscope: (MB100); stereo camera; Rapid Rectilinear lenses or Balbreck, Steinheil, Goerz, Zeiss Anastigmat; 5 speed guillotine shutter; changing magazine for 12 plates. C 1912. 2 sizes: 6 x 13cm, 45 x 107mm.

| R4* $250 | £131 | DM412 | FF1.3k |

B. & W. MANUFACTURING CO., Toronto, Canada.

Press King: (BM100); 4" x 5" press camera; Kodak Ektar 127mm f4.5 coated lens; Graphic MX shutter 1 - 1/400 s. 4" x 5" exp on cut film. C 1954.

| R4* $225 | £118 | DM371 | FF1.2k |

W. BAYER, Freital, Germany.

Bayerflex: (BA100); Anastigmat 75mm f3.5 lens, Pololyt Laak, Rathenow; FPS 1/25-1/500 s. C 1936.

| R3* $200 | £105 | DM330 | FF1k |

Ch. BAZIN et L. LEROY, Paris, France.

Le Stereocycle: (LL100); 6 x 13cm stereo camera; Koch Anastigmat 85mm f9 lens; guillotine shutter; 6 x 13cm plates; turning camera upside down activates plate changing mechanism. C 1898.

| R4* $400 | £210 | DM659 | FF2k |

BALDA WERKE, MAX BALDEWEG, Dresden, German (pre 1945), then: BALDA-KAMERAWERK-Bünde, Westfalen, West Germany.

Balda Roll-Box: (BW100); C1934, metal box camera for 6 x 9cm frames on roll film, simple lens and shutter.

| R2* $15 | £8 | DM25 | FF77 |

Balda Stahlbox: (BW101); C1936, metal box camera for 6 x 9cm frames on roll film, simple lens and I and B shutter. The name means "Steelbox".

| R2* $15 | £8 | DM25 | FF77 |

Balda Dreibild-Box: (BW102); C1935, box camera for 6 x 9cm, 6 x 6cm or 6 x 4.5cm frames on roll film, simple lens and shutter. The name means "Three picture box".

| R2* $20 | £10 | DM33 | FF102 |

Balda-Box: (BW103); C1935, metal box camera for 6 x 9cm frames on roll film.

| R3* $15 | £8 | DM25 | FF77 |

Balda Poka-Duplex: (BW104); C1934, box camera for 6 x 9cm or 6 x 4.5cm frames on roll film, simple "close" and "distant" focusing.

| R3* $20 | £10 | DM33 | FF102 |

BALDA

B

Balda Poka II: (BW105); metal box camera for 6 x 9cm frames on roll film, built-in close-up lens. Later cameras offered in red, blue,grey, green and beige, and with 6 x 6cm capacity (coloured camera adds 200% to the price).

R3* $20	£10	DM33	FF102

Balda Mickey Roll-Box: (BW106); C1936, simple box camera using 127 film for 6.5 x 4cm frames, advertized as the "camera for everyone", available in three models, Model "O" with meniscus lens, Model I with "better" lens and provision for cable release, and Model II, with simple focusing.

R3* $45	£24	DM74	FF230

Balda Frontbox: (BW107); C1934, metal box camera for 6 x 9cm frames on roll film, marked "Balda Frontbox" on the camera front, in different styles.

R2* $15	£8	DM25	FF77

Baldi: (BW108); C1930, folding camera for 3 x 4cm frames on 127 film, many 50mm lenses were available, including f2.9 Xenar, f3.5 Vidanar, and f4.5 Tessar, in various Compur shutters.

R2* $45	£24	DM74	FF230

Super Baldina (pre-war): (BW109); C1934 folding camera with coupled RFR for 24 x 36mm film, *many* 50mm lens were offered including f2.8 lensTessar and f2 Xenon, in various Compur shutters with either front element focusing or helicoid focusing mount. Early cameras have black top housings and shutter mounted shutter releases, while later cameras have chromed top housings and body mounted releases.

R2* $75	£39	DM124	FF383

Baldina (pre-war): (BW110); C1933, folding camera as (BW109), but without built-in RFR, late cameras have body mounted shutter release.

R2* $40	£21	DM66	FF204

Baldinette: (BW111); C1951, folding 35mm camera; Baldanar or radionar f2.8 or Baltar or Radionar f2.9 50mm lens; Prontor S, SV or Synchro Compur shutter.

R2* $35	£18	DM58	FF179

Super-Baldinette: (BW112); C 1951, fold-

Baldinette

ing 35mm camera with CRF, Ennit f2.8/50mm lens in Prontor SV shutter,or Heligon f2/50mm lens in Compur shutter. (add 50% for Heligon lens).

R3* $80	£42	DM132	FF409

Mess-Baldinette: (BW113); C1951, folding 35mm camera with *uncoupled* RFR, Baltar f2.9/5cm lens in Prontor shutter. This camera was intended as a less expensive alternative to the Super-Baldinette (BW112), but was priced only slightly higher than the Baldinette (BW111). Not sold in great quantities.

R3* $70	£37	DM115	FF358

Baldafix: (BW114); C1953, folding camera for 6 x 9, 6 x 6, or 6 x 4.5cm frames on rollfilm, non automatic frame counting, no double exposure prevention, Ennar f4.5/10.5cm lens in Pronto shutter.

R2* $45	£24	DM74	FF230

Baldalux: (BW115); C1953, folding camera for 6 x 9, 6 x 6, or 6 x 4.5cm frames on rollfilm, automatic frame counting, double exposure prevention, Radionar f4.5 or Trinar f3.5 10.5cm lenses in Synchro Compur or Prontor SV shutter. The higher priced alternative to the Baldifix (BW114).

R3* $60	£31	DM99	FF307

Baldax: (BW116); C1954, folding camera for 6 x 6cm frames on rollfilm, automatic frame counting, Ennagon f3.5/7.5cm lens or Radionar f2.9/8cm lens in Prontor Sv shutter.

R2* $45	£24	DM74	FF230

Super-Baldax: (BW117); C1959, folding camera for 6 x 6cm frames on rollfilm, automatic frame counting, CRF, Baldar f2.9/

8cm in Prontor SVS shutter or Ennit f2.8/ 8cm lens in Synchro Compur shutter.

R2* $80	£42	DM132	FF409

Super-Baldax

Baldalette: (BW118); C1949, folding 35mm camera with coated or uncoated Radionar f2.9/5cm lens in Pronto, Prontor or Compur Rapid shutter.

R3* $50	£26	DM82	FF256

Rigona (post war): (BW119); C1954, folding 35mm camera, Rigonar f3.5/50mm lens in Pronto shutter.

R3* $50	£26	DM82	FF256

Rigona (pre-war): (BW120); C1936, folding camera for 3 x 4cm frames on 127 rollfilm, Radionar f2.9/5cm or Vidanar f4.5/5cm lens in Prontor II or Vario shutter. Chrome top plate and body release were offerred as options. Found with film wind on the top, or on the bottom!

R3* $40	£21	DM66	FF204

Mess-Rigona: (BW121); C 1954, folding 35mm camera with *uncoupled* RFR, Rigonar f3.5/5cm lens in Pronto shutter.

R3* $65	£34	DM107	FF332

Baldix: (BW122); C1953, folding camera for 6 x 6 frames on 120 rollfilm, Ennagon f3.5 or Baltar f2.9 7.5cm lens in Prontor SVS shutter.

R2* $35	£18	DM58	FF179

Mess-Baldix: (BW123); C1954, folding camera for 6 x 6cm frames on 120 rollfilm,

uncoupled RFR, many lens and shutter combinations were listed in catalogues, but the Ennagon f3.5/7.5cm lens in Prontor SV shutter is most often seen.

R3* $70	£37	DM115	FF358

Jubilette: (BW124); C1934, folding 35mm camera with Baltar f3.5/5cm lens in Compur shutter.

R3* $50	£26	DM82	FF256

Venus: (BW125); C1935, aluminium bodied folding 6.5 x 9 sheet film with Zeiss Tessar or other lens in Compur shutter.

R2* $50	£26	DM82	FF256

Nizza: (BW126); C1935, aluminium bodied folding 9 x 12cm sheet film camera with Zeiss Tessar or other lens in Compur shutter. Like so many other cameras of the same kind and era.

R2* $50	£26	DM82	FF256

Juwella: (BW127); C1938, folding camera for 6 x 9 frames on rollfilm, Juwella Anastigmat f6.3 or f4.5/10.5cm lens in Balda or other shutter.

R2* $45	£24	DM74	FF230

Juwella II: (BW128); C1938, folding camera for 6 x 9 or 6 x 4.5 frames on rollfilm, Juwella Anastigmat f6.3 or f4.5/10.5cm lens in Balda, Pronto or other shutter, a*fs* (BW127) but for 6 x 4.5 format capability.

R2* $45	£24	DM74	FF230

Pontina: (BW129); C1936, folding camera for 6 x 9cm or 6 x 4.5cm frames on rollfilm, as with so many Balda cameras, the customer had a choice of several lens and shutter combinations, including Trioplan, Trinar, or Rarionar f4.5/10.5cm lens in Prontor I, Prontor II or Compur shutter.

R3* $50	£26	DM82	FF256

Baldaxette : (BW130); C1935, black folding camera for 6 x 4.5cm frames on rollfilm, CRF, automatic parallax correction, Trioplan, Radionar, Tessar, or Xenar 7.5cm lens in Compur shutter. Chrome model (marked Model -)brings 20% less.

R3* $90	£47	DM148	FF460

Baldaxette model-II: (BW131); C1935, chrome folding camera for 6 x 6cm frames

BALDA

B

on rollfilm, CRF, automatic parallax correction, Trioplan, Radionar, Tessar, or Xenar 7.5cm lens in Compur shutter.

R3* $75	£39	DM124	FF383

Super-Pontura: (BW132); C1939, folding camera for 6 x 9cm or 6 x 4.5cm frames on rollfilm, CRF, Trioplan f4.5 or f3.8/10.5cm lens or Tessar f4.5/10.5cm lens in Compur or Compur Rapid shutter. The lens assembly automatically returns to infinity when the camera is closed. The outbreak of War brought production to a standstill, and after 1945 no attempt was made to bring this camera back, few produced.

R4* NSR estimate $350	£184	DM577

Piccochic: (BW133); vest pocket camera; Vidanar 50mm f2.9 lens; Compur shutter; 16 exp, 3 x 4cm on 127 roll film.

R2* $60	£31	DM99	FF307

Piccochic

Baldina (post war): (BW134); C1954, 35mm VFR camera with interchangeable Baldinar,Xenon, Xenar, or Radionar 50mm lens in Pronto, Prontor, Compur-Rapid or Synchro-Compur shutter, Schneider 70mm Longar acessory lens available.

R2* $45	£24	DM74	FF230

Super-Baldina (post war): (BW135); C1954, 35mm camera with CRF and interchangeable Baldinar,Xenon, Xenar, or Radionar 50mm lens in Pronto, Prontor, Comnpur-Rapid or Synchro-Compur shutter, Schneider 70mm Longar acessory lens available.

R2* $85	£45	DM140	FF434

Baldixette: (BW136); C1960, metal VFR camera for 6 x 6cm frames in 120 roll film, front element focusing Baldar f9/7.2cm lens in collapsible tube mount, simple shutter.

R3* $20	£10	DM33	FF102

Baldixette

Baldessa: (BW137); C1957, 35mm VFR camera with Westanar f2.8/50mm lens in Prontor SVS shutter, top mounted shutter release, after 1964 the body style changed, and the shutter release was mounted on the front of the camera body.

R2* $20	£10	DM33	FF102

Baldessa

Baldessa I: (BW138); C1957, 35mm VFR camera with brightline finder, isconar f2.8/45mm lens in Pronto or Prontor SVS shutter.

R2* $20	£10	DM33	FF102

Baldessa Ia: (BW139); C1957, 35mm camera with CRF, Baldanar f2.8/45mm lens in Priontor SVS shutter.

R2* $30	£16	DM49	FF153

Baldessa Ib: (BW140); C1957, 35mm camera with CRF, and built-in light meter,

Baldanar f2.8/45mm lens in Priontor SVS shutter.

R2* $35	£18	DM58	FF179

Baldessa Ib

Baldessa F: (BW141); C1964, as (BW137) but for built-in AG-1 flash lamp holder.

R2* $20	£10	DM33	FF102

Baldessa LF: (BW142); C1964, as (BW141) but for built-in light meter.

R2* $20	£10	DM33	FF102

Baldessa LF

Baldessa RF/LK: (BW143); C1964, 35mm RFR camera, Westanar f2.8/45mm lens, Prontor shutter, CRF, but for built-in AG-1 flash lamp holder, built-in light meter with automatic aperture control.

R2* $25	£13	DM41	FF128

Baldessa F/LK: (BW144); C1964, as (BW143) but without CRF.

R2* $20	£10	DM33	FF102

Baldessa RF: (BW145); C1964, as (BW143) but without light meter.

R2* $20	£10	DM33	FF102

R. & J. BECK, LTD., London, England.

Frena: (BE100); box-type detective camera; Beck Achromatic single 4" f11 lens; rotating shutter 1/5-1/80 s; 50 exp, 6.5 x 9cm on sheet film in magazine. C 1897.

R3* $180	£94	DM297	FF920

Frena Deluxe: (BE101); box-type detective camera; 40 exp, 6.5 x 9cm on special sheet film. C 1897. Covered with brown calveshide, gilt metal-plated fittings.

R4* $650	£341	DM1.1k	FF3.3k

Alex BECKERS, New York.

Floor Model Stereopticon Viewer: (AB100); stereo viewer for paper and glass views; black walnut wood. Patent 1858. Rare.

R4* $1.5k	£787	DM2.5k	FF7.7k

Sweetheart Stereopticon Viewer

BECKERS-BELL & HOWELL

B

Sweetheart Stereopticon Viewer: (AB101); holds 144 stereo views; burled walnut finish. Patent dates: 1859, 1860, and 1870.

R4* $550	£289	DM907	FF2.8k

Kamera-Fabrik Woldemar BEIER, Freital, Germany.

Beier-Box model "O": (BE200); C1929, metal box camera for 6 x 9 frames on rollfilm

R3* $30	£16	DM49	FF153

Beier-Box model "I": (BE201); C1930, metal box camera for 6 x 9 frames on rollfilm, as (BE200) but with the addition of a wire frame finder and better lens.

R3* $30	£16	DM49	FF153

Beier-Box model "II": (BE202); C1930, metal box camera for 6 x 9 frames on rollfilm, as (BE201), but with the addition of a built-in close-up lens.

R3* $40	£21	DM66	FF204

Beira: (BE203); C1931,folding strut type camera for 36 exp, 24 x 36mm.on 1.6m of "normal movie film" Early cameras were without RFR, later cameras added a coupled RFR.Many lens and shutter combinations were offerred, among them Meyer Trioplan f2.9/50mm lens in Compur shutter 1-1/300 s and Leitz Elmar f3.5/50mm in Compur Rapid shutter, 1 - 1/500s, a Meyer Makro Plasmat f2.7/50mm lens was also offerred in catalogues of the day, but no cameras have been recently sold with this lens. In October 1990, one camera *without RFR* with Actinar f4.5/50mm lens failed to reach the minimum bid of $170, while a second example *with CRF* and Xenar 2.9/50mm lens made more than $350!; (coupled RFR adds %100, Elmar lens adds 100%, EST Makro Plasmat adds 100%).

R4* $140	£73	DM231	FF716

Beirette (pre-war); (BE204); C1938, folding 35mm VFR camera, Steinheil Cassar f2.9/5cm lens in Compur shutter, 1 - 1/200s.

R3* $50	£26	DM82	FF256

Beirette (post war): (BE205); C1965, simple metal 35mm camera from the East Ger-

man firm of VEB Beier.

R2* $15	£8	DM25	FF77

BELCA WERKE, Dresden, Germany.

Belplasca: (BK100); 35mm stereo camera; Tessar 37.5mm f3.5 lens; shutter 1-1/200 s. C 1955.

R3* $300	£157	DM495	FF1.5k

BELL & HOWELL INC., Chicago, Illinois.

Foton: (BH100); 35mm spring-wind motor drive camera; Taylor & Hobson-Cooke Amotal 50mm f2.2 coated lens with interchangeable screw mount; additional three lug bayonet mount for accessory telephoto lens. Mfps 1 - 1/1000 s; spring-wind motor drive advances film and cocks shutter at a maximum rate of 6 frames per s and cycles 9 - 15 exp per winding. C 1948. Cook Telephoto 216mm f5.6 coated lens, **$500**. Cook Telephoto 4" coated lens, **$225**. Prices higher in Japan.

R4* $750	£394	DM1.2k	FF3.8k

Foton

Stereo Vivid: (BH101); 35mm stereo camera; Steinheil Cassar or Rodenstock Tridar f3.5 lens; guillotine shutter 1/10-1/100 s, CRF. Taking the film under a roller reduced the inter-lens separation to 65mm. Originally by Three Dimension Co. C 1951.

R2* $225	£118	DM371	FF1.2k

Stereo Colourist: (BH102); 35mm stereo camera; Rodenstock Trinar f3.5 lens; Velio shutter 1/10-1/200 s, bulb, flash. Originally

BELL & HOWELL

by Three Dimension Co, and manufactured in Germany by Bodenseewerk Apparate und Maschinenbau G.m.b.H, Überlingen, Germany, and offered by them as the "Boden-Stereo", see (BO200) C 1952.

| R2* $140 | £73 | DM231 | FF716 |

Bell & Howell Auto Load Movie Camera: (BH103); 16mm movie camera; interchangeable Taylor & Hobson Super Comat 1" f1.9 lens; magazine load; 16 or 32 frames per s. C 1938.

| R2* $20 | £10 | DM33 | FF102 |

Bell & Howell Movie 252 Movie Camera: (BH104); simple 8mm movie camera for the beginner; Super Comat 10mm f2.3 lens, fixed focus; diaphragm settings: bright sun, hazy sun, light shade, cloudy dull.

| R2* $10 | £5 | DM16 | FF51 |

Bell & Howell Filmo Double Eight Movie Camera: (BH105); 8mm movie camera; Taylor & Hobson f2.5 lens; used double 8 film. C 1936.

| R2* $10 | £5 | DM16 | FF51 |

Bell & Howell Filmo Model 70 Movie Camera: (BH106); 16mm motion picture camera; Cooke Anastigmat f2.7 inter-

Bell & Howell Filmo Model 70

changeable lenses; focusing scale visible in vf; variable speeds. C 1923-1924. First amateur motion picture camera to offer governor controlled spring-wound motor drive in place of hand crank.

| R2* $50 | £26 | DM82 | FF256 |

Bell & Howell Filmo Model 75 Movie Camera: (BH107); 16mm movie camera; Taylor & Hobson 20mm f3.5 lens; 30m film pool; double claw pull-down; available in several colours. C 1932.

| R3* $150 | £79 | DM247 | FF767 |

Bell & Howell Filmo Model 75

Bell & Howell Filmo 141-A Movie Camera: (BH110); 16mm magazine movie camera.

| R2* $45 | £24 | DM74 | FF230 |

Bell & Howell Filmo 141-B Movie Camera: (BH111); 16mm movie camera; special cassette for film; 16 to 64 frames per s. C 1938.

| R2* $20 | £10 | DM33 | FF102 |

Bell & Howell Filmo "Straight-Eight" Model 127-A Movie Camera: (BH112); 8mm movie camera; interchangeable Anastigmat 12.5mm f3.5 lens; 4 speeds, 9, 16, 24 and 32 frames per s; first U.S. made camera to use pre-split single-8 film. C 1935.

| R2* $40 | £21 | DM66 | FF204 |

Bell & Howell Filmo Turret Movie Camera: (BH113); 8mm movie camera; triple lens holder for Taylor & Hobson 1/2", 1", 1 1/2" lenses; variable speeds from 16 to 64 frames per s. C 1938.

| R2* $50 | £26 | DM82 | FF256 |

BELL & HOWELL-BENZINI

B

Bell & Howell Model 10 Movie Camera: (BH114); 16mm movie camera, oval shaped body; no adjustments; Maltese Cross film drive mechanism. C 1930.

R2* $25	£13	DM41	FF128

Bell & Howell Model 172 Movie Camera: (BH115); 8mm magazine movie camera; Super Comat 1/2" f1.9 lens; variable speeds from 16 to 64 frames per s. C 1950.

R2* $10	£5	DM16	FF51

Bell & Howell 624EE Autoset Movie Camera: (BH116); 8mm movie camera; interchangeable lenses. C 1957.

R2* $15	£8	DM25	FF77

Bell & Howell 200EE Movie Camera: (BH117); 16mm movie camera; Super Comar 20mm f1.9 lens; selenium photoelectric exp meter coupled to lens diaphragm; 16 to 64 frames per s; first 16mm electric eye camera. C 1956.

R2* $30	£16	DM49	FF153

Bell & Howell 200EE Movie Camera

BELL CAMERA CO., Grinnell, Iowa.

Bell's Straight Working Panoram Camera: (BG100); horizontal format, folding bellows camera; 5 panoramic exp, 11 1/2" x 3 1/4" on roll film. C 1908.

R4* $500	£262	DM824	FF2.6k

BELL 14: (BB106); subminiature camera; 12 x 14mm exp on 16mm roll film. Mfg. in Japan. C 1960.

R3* $25	£13	DM41	FF128

H. BELLIENI & FILS, Nancy, France.

Jumelle Bellieni: (BF100); 9 x 14cm stereo camera; Zeiss Protar 135mm f8 lenses; pneumatic, circular 5 speed shutter. Magazine for 12 plates. C 1899.

R3* $250	£131	DM412	FF1.3k

Jumelle Bellieni: (BF101); 12.9 x 18cm stereo camera; Zeiss Protar 110mm f8 lenses; 6 speed rotating shutter; changing mechanism for 12.9 x 18cm plates. Panoramic setting; rising and sliding lens panel. C 1896.

R3* $200	£105	DM330	FF1k

Curt BENTZIN, Görlitz, Germany.

After 1945 the factory was "nationalized" and became the Optik-Primar-Kamera-Werke VEB . Cameras from this factory are located at the end of this listing, and are considered a continuation of the prewar production.

Primar Reflex 6.5 x 9: (CB100); "Spiegel Camera Reflex"C1920s, SLR for 6.5cm x 9cm plates, several lenses offered including Biotessar f4.5/13.5cm lens, self capping CFPS 1/5 - 1/1000s.

R3* $500	£262	DM824	FF2.6k

Primar Reflex 9 x 12: (CB103); "Spiegel Camera Reflex" C1920s, SLR for 9cm x 12cm plates, several lenses offered including Tessar f4.5/18cm lens, self capping CFPS 1/3 - 1/1000s.

R3* $500	£262	DM824	FF2.6k

Primar Reflex10 x 15: (CB104); "Spiegel Camera Reflex" C1920s, SLR for 10cm x 15cm plates, Tessar f4.5/21cm lens, self capping CFPS 1/3 - 1/1000s.

R3* $500	£262	DM824	FF2.6k

Primar Reflex 13 x 18: (CB105); "Spiegel Camera Reflex" C1920s, SLR for 13cm x 18cm plates, Tessar f4.5/25cm lens, self capping CFPS 1/4 - 1/1000s.

R3* $500	£262	DM824	FF2.6k

122   THE HOVE INTERNATIONAL BLUE BOOK

Primar Reflex 3¹/₄ x 4¹/₄: (CB109); **"Spiegel Camera Reflex"** C1920s, SLR for 3¹/₄inch x 4¹/₄ inch plates, Tessar f4.5/25cm lens, self capping CFPS 1/3 - 1/1000s.

R3* $500	£262	DM824	FF2.6k

Primarette: (CB101); C1920s, folding TLR camera 4cm x 6.5cm frames on roll film, several lenses offered including Trioplan f3.5/7.5cm lens, Compur shutter.

R4* $800	£420	DM1.3k	FF4.1k

Primar Folding Reflex 6.5 x 9: (CB106); **"Klapp Reflex Primar"** C1920s, folding SLR camera for 6.5 x 9cm plates several lenses offered including Biotessar f2.8/13.5cm lens, CFPS 1/5 - 1/1000 s.

R3* $175	£92	DM288	FF894

Primar Folding Reflex 9 x 12: (CB102); **"Klapp Reflex Primar"** C1920s, folding SLR camera for 9cm x 12cm plates several lenses offered including Tessar f4.5/18cm lens, CFPS 1/4 - 1/1000 s.

R3* $160	£84	DM264	FF818

Primar Folding Reflex 10 x 15: (CB107); **"Klapp Reflex Primar"** C1920s, folding SLR camera for 10 x 15cm plates, Tessar f2.8/13.5cm lens, CFPS 1/3 - 1/1000 s.

R3* $160	£84	DM264	FF818

Primar Folding Reflex 3¹/₄ x 4¹/₄: (CB108); **"Klapp Reflex Primar"** C1920s, folding SLR camera for 3 1/4inch x 4 1/4inch plates, Boitessar f2.8/16.5cm lens, CFPS 1/3 - 1/1000 s.

R3* $125	£66	DM206	FF639

Primar 6.5 x 9: (CB110); **"Fokal Primar"** C1920s, folding VFR camera for 6.5 x 9cm plates, several lenses offered including Doppel Plasm at f4/12cm lens, CFPS 1/8-1/1000 s.

R3* $125	£66	DM206	FF639

Primar 9 x 12: (CB111); **"Fokal Primar"** C1920s, folding VFR camera for 9cm x 12cm plates several lenses offered including Makro Plasmat f2.9/15cm lens, CFPS 1/5-1/1000 s.

R3* $125	£66	DM206	FF639

Primar 10 x 15: (CB112); **"Fokal Primar"** C1920s, folding VFR camera for 10 x 15cm plates, several lenses offered including Doppel Plasmat f4/18cm lens, CFPS 1/5-1/1000 s.

R3* $140	£73	DM231	FF716

Primar 13 x 18: (CB113); **"Fokal Primar"** C1920s, folding VFR camera for 13 x 18cm plates, several lenses offered including Doppel Plasmat f4/21cm lens, CFPS 1/4-1/1000 s.

R3* $170	£89	DM280	FF869

Night Primar: (CB114); **"Nacht Primar"** C1929, VFR camera for 6.5cm x 9cm plates, *Plasmat f1.9/9cm lens* , CFPS 8 - 1/1000s.

R4* NSR EST $1.2k	£630	DM2k	FF6.1k

Stereo Primar: (CB115); C1910, strut folding stereo VFR camera for 4.5cm x 10.7cm plates, Tessar f4.5/12cm lenses, CFPS 1 - 1/1000s.

R3* $325	£171	DM536	FF1.7k

Stereo reflex Primar: (CB116); C1915, strut folding stereo reflex camera for 4.5cm x 10.7cm plates, Anastigmat f6.8/9cm lenses, both lenses used for reflex viewing.

R4* NSR EST$900	£472	DM1.5k	FF4.6k

Plan Primar: (CB117); C1930s, folding VFR camera for 6.5cm x 9cm plates, several lens and shutters offered including front element focusing Trioplan f6.3/10.5 lens, Vario shutter.

R3* $45	£24	DM74	FF230

Horizontal Primar: (CB118); **"Quer Primar",** C1920s, horizontal folding VFR camera, *available with and without CFPS*, triple extension bellows, Tessar f3.5/13.5cm lens, Compur shutter, (CFPS adds 50%).

R3* $90	£47	DM148	FF460

Horizontal Primar Stereo: (CB119); **"Quer Primar",** C1920s, horizontal format folding stereo VFR camera, *available with and without CFPS*, triple extension bellows, Tessar f4.5/9cm lenses, Compur shutters, (CB118) with stereo lenses, (CFPS adds 50%).

R3* $300	£157	DM495	FF1.5k

Universal Square Primar 9 x 12: (CB120); **"Universal Quadrat Primar"** C1920s

B

folding drop bed VFR camera for 9cm x 12cm plates, *available with and without CFPS*, Plasmat f4/15cm lens, Compur shutter, (CFPS adds 25%).

R3* $85	£45	DM140	FF434

Universal Square Primar 10 x 15: (CB121); **"Universal Quadrat Primar"** C1920s folding drop bed VFR camera for 10cm x 15cm plates, *available with and without CFPS*, Satz Plasmat f4.5/17.3cm lens, Compur shutter, (CFPS adds 25%).

R3* $120	£63	DM198	FF613

Universal Square Primar 13 x 18: (CB122); **"Universal Quadrat Primar"** C1920s folding drop bed VFR camera for 13cm x 18cm plates, *available with and without CFPS*, Plasmat f4/21cm lens, Compur shutter, (CFPS adds 25%).

R3* $125	£66	DM206	FF639

Primarflex 6 x 6: (CB123); C1930s, SLR for 6cm x 6cm frames on 120 roll film, glass plates are also usable without further accessories, interchangeable Trioplan f2.8/10cm lens, CFPS 1 - 1/1000s. (often found with shutter problems.)

R3* $350	£184	DM577	FF1.8k

Optik Primar Kamera Werke, VEB Görlitz, East Germany.
Post-War successor to the Bentzin Factory

Primarflex II: (CB124); C1950, SLR for 6cm x 6cm frames on 120 roll film, interchangeable Trioplan f2.8/10cm lens, interchangeable VFR, same shutter problems as pre-war Primarflex.

R3* $200	£105	DM330	FF1k

Studio Primar: (CB125); C1950, SLR camera for 9cm x 12cm plates, specially reinforced lens standard and focusing rails in order to maintain "even the heaviest lenses" parallel to the film plane! CFPS 1-1/300s.

R4* $200	£105	DM330	FF1k

BERMPOHL, Germany.

Bermpohl Beam Splitting Camera:

(BN100); Meyer Plasmat 215mm f4 lens; Compound shutter 1-1/75 s, 9 x 12cm plate holders. Beams split by 2 semi-transparent mirrors. C 1935.

R4* $2.25k	£1.2k	DM3.7k	FF11.5k

BERNING-
(see ROBOT listing)

Adolphe BERTSCH, Paris, France.

Bertsch Developing Outfit: (BS100); miniature darkroom with chemicals for sensitizing and developing wet plates for Bertsch miniature cameras. C 1861.

R5*	NSR

Bertsch Developing Outfit

Chambre Automatique de Bertsch: (BS101); brass wet plate camera; Achromatic meniscus lens; lens cap controls exp. Single exp, $2^{1}/_2$" x $2^{1}/_2$" on wet collodion plate. C 1861. One of the first camera outfits to include materials necessary for the sensitizing and developing of wet plates.

R5* $6k	£3.1k	DM9.9k	FF30.7k

Stereo Chambre Automatique de Bertsch: (BS102); brass stereo version of

Bertsch's Chambre Automatique; paired Petzval stereoscopic objectives, lens cap controls exp. Measures 3³/₄" x 4¹/₂" x 6³/₈". Takes 2 exp, 2³/₈" on wet collodion plates. C 1860. This was one of the first camera outfits which included materials necessary for the sensitizing and developing of wet plates.

R5* $15k	£7.9k	DM24.7k	FF76.7k

Stereo Chambre Automatique de Bertsch

BIFLEX 35: (BB110); 35mm camera; Tritar 2cm f2.5 lens; 200 exp on 35mm roll film. Mfg. in Switzerland. C 1945. Possibly made for British intelligence.

R4* $1.25k	£656	DM2.1k	FF6.4k

Biflex 35

BINOCA: (BB111); subminiature binocular camera; camera is included in a 2.5 power binocular. Bicon 40mm f4.5 lens; variable speed shutter and bulb. 16mm film in cassette. Mfd in Japan. C 1951.
White:

R4* $750	£394	DM1.2k	FF3.8k

Red/Blue:

R4* $1k	£525	DM1.6k	FF5.1k

BLAIR CAMERA CO., Boston, Massachusetts.

In 1879, Thomas H. Blair founded the Blair Tourograph Co. in Connecticut. In 1881, he moved to Boston, Massachusetts, where he incorporated as the Blair Tourograph and Dry Plate Company; on March 5, 1886 the company name was changed to the Blair Camera Company.
The firm was purchased in 1899 by the Eastman Kodak Co; in 1907 the company assets were moved to Rochester, New York where, for a few years, some cameras were inscribed, "Blair, Division of the Eastman Kodak Co."

Baby Hawkeye: (BC100); roll film box camera; 2" x 2" exp on roll film. C 1897.

R4* $250	£131	DM412	FF1.3k

Blair 4" x 5" View Camera: (BC101); brass Dallmeyer No. 1 R.R. lens; front focus; tilting and reversible back; sliding bottom lock; mahogany with brass fittings. C 1880's.

R4* $250	£131	DM412	FF1.3k

Blair 4" x 5" View Camera

Blair's Improved Reversible Back Camera: (BC102); 5" x 7" view camera; rack and pinion front focusing; bed mfg. in 3 sections. Sizes: 4" x 5" to 8" x 10". C 1890's.

R4* $250	£131	DM412	FF1.3k

Detective and Combination Camera (first model): (BC103); 4" x 5" detective camera;

glass focusing; front shutter cocking; side shutter adjustments; oak finish, brass fittings. First model had removable knob for ground glass focusing. C 1888.

R4* $300	£157	DM495	FF1.5k

Detective and Combination Camera (second model): (BC104); 4" x 5" detective camera; removable rear panel for group glass focusing; counter on side for film or plates; oak finish, brass fittings; used with Eastman-Walker roll film holder. C 1890.

R4* Wood:$250	£131	DM412	FF1.3k
Leather:$325	£171	DM536	FF1.7k

Detective and Combination Camera (third model): (BC105); 4" x 5" detective camera; focusing and shutter release on top with Eastman-Walker roll holder; separate ground glass for critical focusing by removing rear panel; nickel or brass plated fittings, dark mahogany finish. C 1890's.

R4* Wood:$300	£157	DM495	FF1.5k
Leather:$300	£157	DM495	FF1.5k

English Compact View Camera: (BC106); 6^1/2" x 8^1/2" view camera; reversible back; double extension bellows; mahogany finish, brass fittings. 7 sizes: 3^1/4" x 4^1/4" to 10" x 12". C 1890's.

R3* $250	£131	DM412	FF1.3k

Folding Hawkeye: (BC107); 5" x 7" folding camera; Bausch & Lomb Rapid Rectilinear lens; Blair shutter. C 1890. 4" x 5"

R4* 4x5"size: $175	£92	DM288	FF894
5x7" size: $400	£210	DM659	FF2k

Hawkeye Detective Camera: (BC110); box-type detective camera. C 1890.

R3* Wood:$250	£131	DM412	FF1.3k
Leather:$275	£144	DM453	FF1.4k

Kamaret: (BC111); Rapid Rectilinear lens; double exp prevention; 2 speed guillotine shutter; for 100 exp, 4" x 5" without reloading. First camera to place film spools in front instead of to rear of camera. Original price $40. Distributed by E. & H.T. Anthony. C 1891.

R4* $550	£289	DM907	FF2.8k

Lucidograph: (BC112); 4" x 5" view camera; Pantagraph R.R. 5 ^{3}/4" lens. C 1885.

R4* $1k	£525	DM1.6k	FF5.1k

Lucidograph

No. 3 Combination Hawkeye: (BC113); 3^1/4" x 4^1/4"roll film and plate camera; roll holder lifts up for focusing—similar to No. 4 Screen Focus Kodak. C 1905.

R4* $375	£197	DM618	FF1.9k

No. 4 Weno Hawkeye: (BC114); 3^1/2" x 4^1/2" box camera. C 1900.

R2* $30	£16	DM49	FF153

No. 4 Combination Hawkeye: (BC115); 4" x 5" roll film and plate camera; roll holder lifts up for focusing—similar to No. 4 Screen Focus Kodak. C 1904.

R4* $400	£210	DM659	FF2k

Petite Kamarette: (BC116); miniature box roll film camera. Round exp, 3^1/2" diameter on roll film. C 1892.

R3* $550	£289	DM907	FF2.8k

Stereo Hawkeye Model No. 4: (BC117); roll film stereo camera; Bausch & Lomb Optical Co. Rapid Rectilinear lenses U.S. 4; shutter 1 - 1/100 s. Red bellows; leather covered body. C 1890's.

R4* $450	£236	DM742	FF2.3k

Tourist Hawkeye: (BC120); wooden folding roll film camera; 2 speed shutter; 3^1/2"x 3^1/2" exp on roll film or plates; exp counter at back.

R4* $190	£100	DM313	FF971

Tourist Hawkeye Special Camera: (BC121); 4" x 5" camera; Rapid Rectilinear Unicum shutter*. Sliding and rising front;

Tourist Hawkeye

fine focus; red bellows. C 1897.

R3* $225	£118	DM371	FF1.2k

Weno: (BC122); Rapid Rectilinear lens; Bausch & Lomb shutter; 9 x 18cm exp on roll film. C 1903.

R3* $175	£92	DM288	FF894

Weno Stereo Hawkeye: (BC123); folding roll film stereo camera; 3¹/₂" x 6" exp on roll film.

R4* $350	£184	DM577	FF1.8k

BLAND & CO., England.

Bland & Co. Wet Plate: (BB112); brass lens L.F. Colas; wet plate holder; ground glass screen. C 1850.

R4* $2.75k	£1.4k	DM4.5k	FF14.1k

Edmund BLOCH, Paris, France.

Photo-Cravate (Bloch's Detective Photo Scarf): (EB100); magazine camera concealed in cravate; periscopic lens, 25mm f16; single speed pneumatic shutter; 6 exp, 23mm diameter on dry plates. C 1890. The buyer had a choice of colours, styles, and patterns. Original cost of the complete outfit was 60 francs.

Le Physiographe: (EB101); monocular detective camera; Krauss Tessar 51mm

Photo-Cravate

Le Physiographe

f6.3 lens; 4.5 x 5cm exp on plates. C 1910.

R5* $1.2k	£630	DM2k	FF6.1k

Stereo Physiographe: (EB102); stereo binocular-type detective camera; Krauss Tessar 51mm f6.3 lenses; single speed

BLOCH-BOLSEY

rotating shutter; 45 x 107mm exp on plates.
C 1896.

R5* $2k+   £1.1k+ DM3.3k+   FF10.2k+

Leon BLOCH,
Paris, France.

Photo Bouquin: (LB100); stereo book-
type detective camera; achromatic lenses;
rotary shutter; central vf concealed in binding. 45 x 107mm exp on plates. The Photo
Bouquin was the only stereoscopic book
camera. C 1904.

R5* $5k+   £2.6k+ DM8.2k+ FF25.6k+

Physio Pocket: (LB101); monocular detective camera; Cooke Anastigmat f6.5 or
Tessar f6.3 or f4.5 lens; single speed cylindrical shutter. 4.5 x 6cm plates. C 1904.

R4* $2k+   £1.1k+ DM3.3k+   FF10.2k+

Bodenseewerk Aparate und
Maschinenbau GmbH,
Überlingen, Germany.

Boden-Stereo : (BH102); C1953,35mm
stereo camera; Rodenstock Trinar f3.5 lens;
Gauthier Velio shutter 1/10-1/200 s, bulb,
flash.The same camera as the Stereo-
Colourist, offered by Bell and Howell, but
under the manufacturer's own name.

R3* $190   £100   DM313   FF971

BOLSEY-DELMONICO CORP.
OF AMERICA, New York.

La Belle Pal: (BD100); 35mm rf camera;
Wollensak Anastigmat 44mm f4.5 coated
lens.

R3* $125   £66   DM206   FF639

Bolsey B: (BD 110); C1949 35mm RFR
camera, Wollensak f3.2/44mm lens, shutter 1/25-1/200 s, CRF.

R2* $25   £13   DM41   FF128

Bolsey B2: (BD101); C1949. 35mm RFR
camera, as (BD110) but with double exposure prevention, and flash synch, Wollensak
shutter 1/10 - 1/200.

R2* $30   £16   DM49   FF153

Bolsey B

Bolsey B2 (U.S. Army): (BD102); C1949.
similar to Model B2, except special plate on
top with U.S. Army engraving, and olive
drab paint.

R3* $175   £92   DM288   FF894

Bolsey B2 (U.S. Air Force): (BD103);
C1949, similar to Model B2, except special
plate on top with U.S.A.F. engraving.

R3* $175   £92   DM288   FF894

Bolsey C: (BD104); C1950, 35mm TLR;
Wollensak Anastigmat f3.2/44mm lens,
Wollensak Alphax shutter 1/10 - 1/200 s,
CRF. (prices much lower in the USA).

R3* $100   £52   DM165   FF511

Bolsey C

Bolsey C22 "Set-O-Matic": (BD105);
C1953, 35mm TLR, as (BD104) but with
"Set-O-Matic" flash calculator. (prices much
lower in the USA).

R2* $100   £52   DM165   FF511

BOLSEY-BOUMSEL

Bolsey 8: (BD106); 8mm still and motion picture camera; Bolsey-Elgeet 10mm f1.8 Navitar lens; rotary shutter 1/50-1/600 s. Special cassette holds 25 ft of 8mm film. Single exp stop mechanism, variable shutter speeds, automatic footage counter. C 1956.

R4* $250	£131	DM412	FF1.3k

Bolsey Jubilee: (BD107); 35mm rf camera; Bolsey-Steinheil Anastigmat 45mm f2.8 lens; Bolsey Gauthier Auto-Synchro shutter 1/10-1/200 s, CRF. C 1955.

R3* $45	£24	DM74	FF230

BOLTAVIT: (BB113); Boltar 40mm f7.7 lens; shutter 1/25-1/50-1/100 s; 12 exp, 25 x 25mm on 35mm roll film. Metal cast body. C 1936.

R3* $45	£24	DM74	FF230

BOND'S LTD., London, England.

Kinora Camera: (BL100); produced images using paper negatives for Kinora viewers; entire interior portion slides laterally for internal ground glass focus. C 1912.

R4* $600	£315	DM989	FF3.1k

BONIFORTI & BALLENO, Milano, Italy

Perseo: (PE100); C1948, 35mm RFR camera with coupled interchangeable f3.5 or Heligon f2/50mm lens, CFPS 1/20 - 1/1000s. front mounted shutter release, several variations exist with different shutter speed dials, film counters, and logo placements, in all around 200 units were produced.

R4* $2k	£1.1k	DM3.3k	FF10.2k,

Perseo

A. BOREUX, Basle, Switzerland.

Nana: (BX100); 45 x 107mm stereo camera; Suter 62mm f6.8 lenses; 6 speed guillotine shutter. Metal body covered with Morrocan leather. C 1913.

R4* $250	£131	DM412	FF1.3k

BOSTON CAMERA CO., Boston, Massachusetts.

Hawkeye Detective Camera: (BO100); box-type detective camera. C 1889.

R3* $350	£184	DM577	FF1.8k

Hawkeye Detective Camera

BOUMSEL, Paris, France.

Longchamp: (LC200); Pre WWII bakelite TLR for 3 x 4cm format on 127 film. Simple lens and single speed shutter. Probably made at the Norca factory for Boumsel. Also found in brown bakelite, from after the war. See (LC201) worth 200% more.

R2* $10	£5	DM16	FF51

Auteuil: (LC201); Brown bakelite, based on the Long Champ body (LC200), but with 50mm/f3.5 Topaz lens in a Gitzo shutter, or a 50mm/f3.5 FAP Anistigmat in a Rapid-Synchro shutter. A real sales flop, leftover bodies were made into Longchamp cameras. C.1948.

R4* $65	£34	DM107	FF332

Azur: (LC202); Folding roll film cameras for 6 x 9cm format. Available in several combi-

BRAUN

nations of lens and shutters, this camera is unique in that the roll film was loaded onto the camera back, instead of into the camera body C. 1948.

R3* $30	£16	DM49	FF153

Carl BRAUN CAMERAWERK, Nurnberg, Germany.

Paxette I: (CK100); C1950,35mm VFR camera, Pointar, Kataplast or Cassar f2.8/45mm lens, Prontor S shutter; built-in extinction meter, lever wind on early cameras.

R2* $30	£16	DM49	FF153

Paxette IM: (CK101}; C1951,35mm camera with uncoupled RFR, Cassar or Kataplast f2.8/45mm lens; Pronto or Prontor S shutter.

R2* $50	£26	DM82	FF256

Paxette II: (CK102); C1953, 35mm VFR cameras with interchangeable lenses, Cassar or Kata f2.8/45mm lens in Prontor S shutter, built-in extinction meter.

R3* $75	£39	DM124	FF383

Paxette IIM: (CK103); C1953, 35mm camera with *uncoupled* RFR, interchangeable Cassar or Kata f2.8/45mm lens; Pronto or Prontor S shutter.

R2* $90	£47	DM148	FF460

Super Paxette Ib: (CK104); 35mm camera with CFR; Kata f2.8/45mm lens; Pronto shutter.

R2* $60	£31	DM99	FF307

Super Paxette I: (CK105); 35mm camera with CFR, as (CK104) but for Prontor SVS shutter, Kata f2.8/45mm lens.

R2* $60 ₀	£31	DM99	FF307

Super Paxette IL: (CK106); C1958, 35mm camera with CRF and brightline finder, fixed f2.8/50mm Katagon lens in Pronto or Prontor SVS shutter.

R3* $50	£26	DM82	FF256

Super Paxette IIL: (CK107); C1958, 35mm camera with brightline finder and interchangeable Tessar, Cassarit, or Xenar f2.8/50mm lens or Quinon f2/50mm lens in Prontor SVS shutter. All Super Paxette II cameras have in common accessory lenses from 35mm to 200mm coupled with the RFR, and built-in fields of view for 35mm-135mm.

R3* $90	£47	DM148	FF460

Super Paxette II: (CK108); C1956, 35mm camera with coupled RFR; interchangeable Cassarit, Tessar, or Xenar f2.8/45mm lens in Prontor SVS shutter.

R3* $85	£45	DM140	FF434

Super Paxette IIB: (CK109); C1957, 35mm camera with coupled RFR; interchangeable Cassarit, Tessar, or Xenar f2.8/45mm lens in Prontor SVS shutter.

R3* $90	£47	DM148	FF460

Super Paxette IIBL: (CK110); C1958, 35mm camera with coupled RFR; interchangeable Cassarit, Tessar, or Xenar f2.8/45mm or Katagon f2.8/50mm lens in Prontor SVS shutter, built-in light meter.

R3* $100	£52	DM165	FF511

Paxette Automatic Reflex: (CK111); C1958, 35mm SLR with body mounted light meter coupled to interchangeable Ultralit f2.8/50mm lens, Synchro-Compur shutter 1 - 1/500s, several top styles and meter positions.

R3* $110	£58	DM181	FF562

Paxette Automatic Reflex IB: (CK112); C1958, 35mm SLR with body mounted light meter *not* coupled to *fix mounted* Cassarit f2.8/50mm lens, Synchro-Compur shutter 1 - 1/500s, lightmeter reading visible in the VFR.

R3* $80	£42	DM132	FF409

Paxette Automatic: (CK113); C1959, 35mm camera with CRF, VFR with fields of view for 35mm, 50mm, 85mm and 135mm, built-in light meter coupled to aperture and shutter speeds, interchangeable f2.8/50mm Colour-Ennit lens in Prontor-SLK shutter.

R3* $75	£39	DM124	FF383

Paxette Automatic I: (CK114); C1959, 35mm camera with CRF, built-in light meter coupled to aperture and shutter speeds, f2.8/50mm *non-interchangeable* Cassarit lens in Prontor-SLK shutter.

R2* $30	£16	DM49	FF153

Paxette Electromatic: (CK115); C1960, simple 35mm VFR camera with single speed shutter, and automatic aperture control, f5.6/45mm fixed focus lens.

R2* $25	£13	DM41	FF128

Paxette Electromatic IA: (CK116); C1961, 35mm VFR camera, automatic aperture control, *interchangeable* Trinar f2.8/40mm lens, field of view for accessory 75mm lens marked in VFR, special electronic flash offered as accessory.

R2* $55	£29	DM91	FF281

Paxette Electromatic III: (CK117): C1963, 35mm VFR camera with full automatic or manual control, Ultralit f2.8/40mm lens in Prontormatic shutter, 1 - 1/500s.

R2* $40	£21	DM66	FF204

Accessories for Paxette cameras:

optical VFR for 35mm and 85mm fields of view:(CK001); **$35**
optical VFR for 90mm field of view: (CK002); **$30**
optical VFR for 135mm field of view: (CK003); **$35**
optical VFR for 200mm field of view: (CK004); **$50**
Choroplast f4.5/35mm lens: (CK015); **$30**
Choro f3.5/38mm lens: (CK016); **$30**
Tele-Rotelar f4/75mm lens: (CK017); **$45**
Neoplast f5.6 85mm lens: (CK018); **$50**
Telexon f5.6/85mm lens: (CK019); **$40**
Telenar f3.8/90mm lens: (CK030); **$50**
Telexon f3.8/135mm lens: (CK031); **$65**
Telenar f5.6/135mm lens: (CK032); **$45**
Tele Ennalyt f4.5/200mm lens: (CK033); **$90**

Imperial Box 6 x6: (CK118); C1950, box camera for 6 x 6 frames on roll film, with and without synchro.

R2* $15	£8	DM25	FF77

Imperial Box 6 x 9: (CK119); C1950, box camera for 6 x 9 frames on roll film, with and without synchro.

R2* $15	£8	DM25	FF77

Nimco: (CK120); C1952, 6 x 6 box camera like (CK118) produced by Braun for other retail sellers.

R3* $20	£10	DM33	FF102

Norca I: (CK121); C1952, folding VFR camera for 6 x 9 frames on rollfilm, f8/105mm lens, Pronto shutter.

R2* $30	£16	DM49	FF153

Norca II: (CK122); C1952, folding VFR camera for 6 x 9 frames on rollfilm, F6.3 Gotar lens in Prontor-s shutter.

R2* $30	£16	DM49	FF153

Norca III: (CK123); C1952, folding VFR camera for 6 x 9 or 6 x 6 frames on rollfilm, f4.5 Gotar lens, Pronto shutter.

R2* $30	£16	DM49	FF153

Norca II Super: (CK124); C1953, folding RFR camera for 6 x 9 or 6 x 6 frames on roll film, f6.3/105mm Cassar lens, Prontor-s shutter.

R3* $65	£34	DM107	FF332

Norca IV Super: (CK124); C1953, folding RFR camera for 6 x 9 or 6 x 6 on roll film, f4.5/105mm Cassar lens, Prontor-s shutter.

R3* $85	£45	DM140	FF434

Paxina I: (CK125); C1952, metal VFR camera for 6 x 6 frames on roll film, simple f7.7 lens in two speed shutter, square telescoping front.

R3* $25	£13	DM41	FF128

Paxina II: (CK126); C1952, metal VFR camera for 6 x 6 frames on roll film, telescoping tube mounted Kata f3.5 or Steiner f3.5/75mm lens Vario shutter.

R2* $35	£18	DM58	FF179

Paxina 29: (CK127); C1953, metal VFR camera for 6 x 6 frames on roll film, telescoping tube mounted Steiner f2.9/75mm lens, Vario shutter.

R2* $30	£16	DM49	FF153

Gloriette: (CK128); C1954-57, 35mm VFR camera, lever advance, Cassar f2.8/45mm lens, Vario, Pronto or Prontor shutter, different top plate styles.

R2* $40	£21	DM66	FF204

Gloriette B: (CK129); C1955, 35mm VFR camera, lever advance, Cassar f2.8/45mm lens, Prontor-SVS shutter, built-in uncoupled light meter.

R3* $40	£21	DM66	FF204

B

Gloria: (CK130); C1958, metal RFR camera for 6 x 6 frames on rollfilm, *uncoupled* RFR, telescoping front, Praxar f2.9/75mm lens, Pronto or Prontor-SVS shutter.

| R3* $65 | £34 | DM107 | FF332 |

Colourette Super I: (CK131); 35mm camera CRF, lever advance, Cassar f2.8/45mm lens, Compur-Rapid shutter.

| R2* $35 | £18 | DM58 | FF179 |

Colourette Super IB: (CK132); C1956, 35mm camera CRF, lever advance, fixed mount Plastagon f2.8/45mm lens, Compur-Rapid shutter, Built-in light meter.

| R3* $40 | £21 | DM66 | FF204 |

Colourette Super IBL: (CK133); C1956, 35mm RFR camera, lever advance, fix mount Cassar, Culminar, Ysarex or Xenar f2.8/50mm lens, Synchro Compur shutter, built-in light meter.

| R3* $45 | £24 | DM74 | FF230 |

Colourette Super II: (CK134); 35mm camera CRF, lever advance, interchangeable Cassar, Culminar, Ysarex or Xenar f2.8/50mm lens, automatic depth of field indicator, Compur-Rapid shutter with EV values.

| R3* $80 | £42 | DM132 | FF409 |

Colourette Super IIB: (CK135); 35mm camera CRF, lever advance, interchangeable Cassar, Culminar, Ysarex or Xenar f2.8/50mm lens, automatic depth of field indicator, Compur-Rapid shutter with EV values, built-in light meter.

| R3* $90 | £47 | DM148 | FF460 |

Brins Patent Camera: (BB114); 30mm f3.5 lens; simple shutter. Circular exp, 25mm diameter; lens at rear permits use as monocular. Mfd in London, England. C 1891.

| R4* $4.5k+ | £2.4k+ | DM7.4k+ | FF23k+ |

A. BRIOIS,
Paris, France.

Le Revolver Thompson: (BI100); revolver-type detective camera; Petzval-type 40mm f2 lens; rotary shutter. 4 exp, 23mm diameter on circular wet collodion plates, 75mm

diameter. C 1862.

| R5* $30k | £15.7k | DM49.5k | FF153.3k |

BRISKIN CAMERA CORP.,
Santa Monica, California.

Briskin: (BP100); 8mm movie camera; magazine load. C 1960.

| R2* $25 | £13 | DM41 | FF128 |

Briskin

Andre BRIZET,
Paris, France.

Le Physioscope: (BZ100); 6 x 13cm stereo camera; Tessar Krauss 74mm f6.3 lenses; Stereo Compur shutter 1-1/150 s. Rising lens panel; changing magazine for 12 plates. C 1922.

| R4* $275 | £144 | DM453 | FF1.4k |

BROOKLYN CAMERA CO.,
Brooklyn, New York.

The Brooklyn Camera: (BR100); 1/4 plate view camera; non-folding bed; collapsible bellows. C 1885.

| R3* $200 | £105 | DM330 | FF1k |

Christian BRUNS, Munich, Germany.

Bruns Detective Camera: (CH100); 3^1/$_4$" x 4^1/$_4$" detective camera; 144mm f6.3 lens. Magazine holds 12 exp, 3^1/$_4$" x 4^1/$_4$. The camera has two vf: the first is a waist-level reflex viewer; the second consists of a separate bellows with ground glass, which is assembled on top of the camera—the camera lens slides upward and is positioned on the vf. C 1893.

| R5* $5k+ | £2.6k+ | DM8.2k+ | FF25.6k+ |

Bruns Detective Camera

BULLARD CAMERA CO., Springfield, Massachusetts.

Bullard Magazine Camera: (BU100); plate-loading magazine folding camera; eighteen 4" x 5" plates. C 1898.

| R4* $150 | £79 | DM247 | FF767 |

BURLEIGH BROOKS OPTICS, Hackensack, New Jersey.

Brooks Veriwide: (BV100); wide-angle panoram camera; Super-Angulon 47mm f8 coated lens; Synchro-Compur shutter 1-1/500 s; 8 exp, 6 x 9cm on 120 roll film. Users pay more than collectors for this.

| R2* $600 | £315 | DM989 | FF3.1k |

Brooks Veriwide

BUSCH CAMERA CO., Chicago, Illinois.

Busch Verascope F40: (BY100); 35mm stereo camera; Berthiot 40mm f3.5 coated lenses; CRF. Version of Richard Verascope F40 for U.S. market. C 1950.

| R4* $400 | £210 | DM659 | FF2k |

W. BUTCHER & CO., London, England.

Empire Cinematograph: (WB100); 35mm amateur movie camera; wooden bodied; hand cranked; daylight-loading.

| R3* $200 | £105 | DM330 | FF1k |

The Little Nipper: (WB101); Made by Hüttig; 2^1/$_2$" x 3^1/$_2$" exp on plates of film; reversing finder; lens cap. C 1900.

| R3* $110 | £58 | DM181 | FF562 |

Royal Mail Postage Stamp Camera: (WB102); 15 postage stamp size photographs on a single plate. C 1907.

| R4* $2.5k | £1.3k | DM4.1k | FF12.8k |

The Stereolette: (WB103); Made by Hüttig; 45 x 107mm stereo; meniscus lens; guillotine shutter; reflex viewer; spirit level; mahogany. 5 x 107mm exp on plates. C 1910.

| R4* $400 | £210 | DM659 | FF2k |

Watch Pocket Carbine, Tropical Model: (WB104); 120 roll film camera, Tessar 9cm/f4.5 lens, Dial-set Compur shutter, copper toned metal body, brown bellows.

| R3* $150 | £79 | DM247 | FF767 |

CADOT-CAILLON

A. CADOT,
Paris, France.

Scenographe Cadot: (CD100); 9 x 18cm stereo camera; Aplanatic 150mm f11 lenses; guillotine shutter. Rising front panel. C 1900.

R4* $350	£184	DM577	FF1.8k

E. CAILLON,
Paris, France.

Le Bioscope: (EC100); 45 x 107mm stereo camera; Berthiot Saphir f6.3 or f4.5 lenses; shutter 1/2-1/200 s. Leather covered; rising and falling front; panoramic movement. C 1915.

R4* $180	£94	DM297	FF920

Le Megascope: (EC101); 6 x 13cm stereo camera; Hermagis 85mm f6.3 lenses; guillotine shutter with variable speeds. Rising and falling front. Changing mechanism for 12 plates, 6 x 13cm. C 1915.

R3* $190	£100	DM313	FF971

Scopea: (EC102); 45 x 107mm stereo camera; Balbreck Rectilinear 54mm lenses; 5 speed guillotine shutter. C 1915.

R4* $180	£94	DM297	FF920

Calypso: (SP200); 1960, 35mm underwater camera; Som Berthiot 35mm f2.5 coated lens, interchangeable watertight bayonet mount; mfps 1/30-1/500s. This was the predecessor to the Nikonos underwater camera.

R4* $250	£131	DM412	FF1.3k

The Cameo: (BB115); 8 x 17cm folding stereo camera; Beck Symmetrical lenses.

Ground glass back. 8 x 17cm exp on plates. Mfd in Britain.

R3* $175	£92	DM288	FF894

Camera In a Shoe: (BB116); detective camera concealed in shoe heel; Tessar 25mm f2.7 lens; 16mm perforated film. Shutter tripped by pressing heel with other shoe. C 1929.

R5* NSR $2.5k+	£1.3k	DM4.1k	FF12.8k

Camera-Lite: (BB117); cigarette lighter-type detective camera; meniscus achromatic f8 lens. Similar to Echo 8, except has frame vf instead of reflex vf. C 1956.

R4* $350	£184	DM577	FF1.8k

Camera-Lite

Calypso

C

CAMERA PROJECTORS LTD., London, England.

Midas: (CP100); 9.5mm combination camera and projector; Taylor Hobson f2.5 lens. Two 3 volt batteries provided power for camera motor and projector bulb. The Midas was probably the first movie camera with electric motor drive. C 1933.

R3* $100	£52	DM165	FF511

THE CANADIAN CAMERA AND OPTICAL CO. LTD., Toronto, Canada.

Gem Glenco: (AN100); 4" x 5" folding plate camera; red bellows with brass fittings.

R4* $150	£79	DM247	FF767

CANDID CAMERA CORP. OF AMERICA.

Perfex 44: (CJ100); 35mm RFR camera; Anastigmat 50mm f3.5 or f2.8 lens, interchangeable screw mount; CFPS 1-1/250 s, B, synch. C 1939-1940.

R2* $80	£42	DM132	FF409

Perfex 44

Perfex Speed Candid: (CJ101); 35mm camera; Anastigmat 50mm f3.5 or f2.8 lens; CFPS 1/25-1/500 s; non-coupled RFR. C 1938-1939.

R2* $60	£31	DM99	FF307

CANON CAMERA CO., INC., Tokyo, Japan.

Note on Canon: Most of the cameras manufactured in Japan be-

tween 1947 and (late) 1951 were marked "Made in Occupied Japan", usually on the baseplate, rear door, or top cover.

Many cameras made after 1952 were marked with variations of the E-P symbol (usually within a diamond) which meant that the specific camera (or lens) was allocated for sale in the military post-exchange system. E-P markings are common—they do not designate any specific model of camera.

An earlier variation of the diamond marking encloses a series of Japanese characters that translate to "CPO" in English. This practice dates to 1947 (approximately).

A slightly later version encloses the English letters "CPO" within a diamond. Both of these markings are uncommon today; originally they designated cameras made for testing purposes. These cameras were supplied to the army of occupation and for early sale to military personnel.

Group 1: All cameras in this group have serial numbers below 45,000. The slowest instantaneous speed on the fast-speed dial is 1/20 s. All use 35mm film.

Kwanon: (CC101); only a few prototypes of various sorts were made between 1933 and 1935. At least two were later sold, but the only one known today is of questionable authenticity. The price for a verifiable Kwanon would be quite high if one were to be found.

R5*	NSR

Canon/NK Hansa: (CC103); Nikkor f3.5 lens in bayonet mount; CFPS 1/20-1/500 s. Pop-up vf; exp counter on front of body; top plate usually marked "Hansa" but sometimes not (if not the camera has sometimes been called "Canon Original"). This version was contemporaneously known simply as "the Canon Camera" and is distinguished by the engraved logo "Nippon Kogaku Tokyo" next to the serial number on its focusing mount, signifying that it was made under the su-

CANON

pervision of Nippon Kogaku at Seiki Kogaku Kenkyujo. It therefore can be considered the earliest of both Canon and Nikon lines. Mfd 10/1935-8/1937, qty est 400-500. $4000+ and greatly up depending on the presence of parts designed for earlier unmarked Kwanons which are usually found on only a few cameras among the range under approximately serial 300.

| R4* $4k+ | £2.1k+ | DM6.6k+ | FF20.4k+ |

Canon Hansa: (CC104); similar to (CC103) except for no "Nippon Kogaku Tokyo" engraving next to focusing mount serial number, signifying manufacture under Seiki Kogaku K. K. K. contol allowing reorganization and expansion of the company. Mfd 9/1937-6/1940, qty est 600-700.

| R4* $3k+ | £1.6k+ | DM5k+ | FF15.3k+ |

Canon Hansa

Canon S: (CC105); Nikkor f4.5, f3.5, f2.8 or f2 lens in bayonet mount; CFPS 1-1/500 s. Pop-up vf, CRF; lever operated slow-speed dial on front of body; exp counter under wind knob; serial no. on top plate. Qty 1600. C 1938-1944. This model shows several variations: in the slow-speed dial orientation, in the knob shape and markings and in the construction and markings of lens mounts. Some lenses may not fit all mounts. The earliest f2 lens with interior front diaphragm scale is the scarcest model; the f3.5 lens is the most common. With f3.5 lens, with f2.8 lens, with earliest interior-set f2 lens, with rimset f2,with these lenses $2500+, with Regno-Nikkor f2, $3000+.

| R4* $3k+ | £1.6k+ | DM5k+ | FF15.3k+ |

Canon NS: (CC106); similar to (CC105), except does not have slow-speed dial. Nikkor f4.5 or f3.5 lens. Qty est 100. C 1/1940-1942.

| R5* $2k+ | £1.1k+ | DM3.3k+ | FF10.2k+ |

Canon S

Canon J

Canon J: (CC107); Nikkor f4.5 or f3.5 lens in threaded mount similar to, but not identical to Leica mount; CFPS 1/20-1/500 s. No RFR. No body plate patch over slow-speed dial area; vf in Leica-type top plate with straight edge near rewind knob. Qty est 200. C 1/1939-1944.

| R5* $6k+ | £3.1k+ | DM9.9k+ | FF30.7k+ |

Canon JS: (CC108); similar to (CC107); except has front mounted slow-speed dial. (1-1/20 s). Qty est 50. C 1941-1945.

| R4* $5k+ | £2.6k+ | DM8.2k+ | FF25.6k+ |

Seiki X-Ray Camera: (CC111); 35mm X-Ray recording camera; Nikkor f2 or Serenar f1.5 lens in massive bayonet mount; exp by darkslide. Wind knob has spring loaded chain. Qty unknown, possibly several thousand. C 1939-1947.

| R4* $700 | £367 | DM1.2k | FF3.6k |

Canon X-Ray Camera: (CC113); similar to (CC111), except marked "X-Ray Canon 35" on top. Qty unknown. C 1947-1951.

| R4* $700 | £367 | DM1.2k | FF3.6k |

Canon S-I: (CC114); Nikkor f3.5 lens, postwar continuation of (CC105), and essentially identical to late wartime production;

most serials should be later than 12386 but are mixed. Qty 97. C 12/1945-11/1946.

R5* $1.5k+	£787+	DM2.5k+	FF7.7k+

Canon J-II: (CC115); Similar to (CC107) except the top cover resembles its Leica counterpart, curving around small rewind knob. Some have a metal patch over the slow-speed dial area. Nikkor or Serenar f3.5 lens in non-Leica type thread mount. Qty 525. C 1945-1946. With Nikkor lens, or Serenar lens.

R5* $3.5k+	£1.8k+	DM5.8k+	FF17.9k+

Canon J-II

Seiki Canon S-II: (CC116); Nikkor f3.5 or Seiki Kogaku Serenar f3.5 or f2 lenses. Interchangeable lens mount, almost all with semi-Leica screw thread but a few early ones with Canon J-thread or in-between mounts. CFPS 1-1/500 s. Combined vf-RFR without variable magnification. "Seiki Kogaku Tokyo" maker's name on top. Qty 2000, more with J-thread mount.

R4* $750	£394	DM1.2k	FF3.8k

Canon S-II: (CC117); Similar to (CC116), except all have "Canon Camera Co." logo and Nikkor or Canon Serenar lenses. Qty 5550. C 8/1947-1952.

R3* $450	£236	DM742	FF2.3k

Canon S-II

Canon CX-35: (CC118); Late version of Canon X-Ray Camera. Canon f1.5 lens in bayonet mount. Marked "CX-35" on top cover. Qty unknown, probably several thousand. C 1951-1957.

R4* $700	£367	DM1.2k	FF3.6k

Canon IIB: (CC119); Serenar f3.5 or f1.9 lens, CFPS 1-1/500 s. Combined vf-RFR with three-stage magnification. A few later (CC119) had flash synch rails. Qty 14,400. C 1/1949-7/1952. Without flash synch rail, $100-$175; more with synch rail.

R3* $275	£144	DM453	FF1.4k

Canon IIB

Group 2: All models in this group have serial numbers between 45,000 and 169,990. The slowest instantaneous speed on the fast-speed dial is 1/25 s. All have combined vf-RFR with three-stage magnification. Synched cameras all have side flash rail; they have no other flash outlet.

Canon 1950: (CC109); Serenar f1.9 lens, CFPS 1-1/1000 s; flashbulb rail synch. Can quickly be distinguished from later (CC120) by "Canon Camera Co. Ltd." maker's logo and serial between 50000 and 50199, and there are other differences. This version was briefly designated IIC by Canon, and most surviving examples have baseplates with "San Francisco" markings indicating sale (as model IIC or IVM) by C. R. Skinner in USA. Qty 50. Mfd 7/1950-10/1950.

R5* $2.5k	£1.3k	DM4.1k	FF12.8k

Canon IV: (CC120); Serenar f1.9 lens; CFPS 1-1/1000 s, flashbulb synch. Two piece vf magnification lever. Qty 1380. C 4/1951-4/1952. "Canon Camera Co. Inc." maker's logo.

R3* $325	£171	DM536	FF1.7k

Canon IIC: (CC121); Serenar f3.5 or f1.9 lens; CFPS 1-1/500 s, no synch. Two piece

CANON

magnification vf lever. Qty 800. C 3/1951-8/1951.

R4* $700	£367	DM1.2k	FF3.6k

Canon III: (CC122); Serenar f3.5 or f1.9 lens; CFPS 1-1/100 s, no synch. Two piece magnification lever. Qty 10,175. C 2/1951-12/1952.

R3* $300	£157	DM495	FF1.5k

Canon III

Canon IIIA: (CC123); Serenar f1.8 lens; CFPS 1-1/1000 s, no synch. One piece magnification lever. Film reminder in wind knob. There were several variations in the interior construction, the manufacturer's logo, and the engraving. Qty 9025. C 12/1951-9/1953.

R3* $300	£157	DM495	FF1.5k

Canon IIA: (CC124); CFPS 1/25-1/500 s, no synch. Slow-speed dial area covered by patch. Qty 99. Verify authenticity before paying premium price. C 3/1952-9/1952.

R5* $2k	£1.1k	DM3.3k	FF10.2k

Canon IIA

Canon IVF: (CC125); CFPS 1-1/1000s, flash bulb synch. One piece magnification lever; film reminder; built-up interior wall next to film supply chamber. Qty 6880 (including (CC126)). C 12/1951-1952.

R3* $275	£144	DM453	FF1.4k

Canon IVS: (CC126); Similar to (CC125), except has die-cast wall next to film supply chamber. Qty 6880 (including (CC125)). C 1952-5/1953.

R3* $250	£131	DM412	FF1.3k

Canon IVSB: (CC127); Canon f1.8 lens was standard (rather than Serenar); CFPS 1-1/1000 s, flashbulb synch, X synch at C 1/15 s setting on slow-speed dial. Slow-speed dial lock. Some (CC120), (CC125) and (CC126) bodies were updated by Canon agencies to (CC127) synch standards; these bodies show many variations. This model was often known overseas as IVS2, but IVSB is the factory designation. Qty 35,000. C 12/1952-3/1955.

R3* $250	£131	DM412	FF1.3k

Canon IVSB with 135mm f3.5 lens and 135mm finder

Canon IID: (CC128); CFPS 1-1/500 s, no synch. No film reminder; one piece magnification lever. Qty 21,700. C 8/1952-2/1955.

R3* $225	£118	DM371	FF1.2k

Canon IID1: (CC129); Similar to (CC128), except has film reminder in wind knob. Qty 2400. C 10/1952 - 6/1954.

R3* $250	£131	DM412	FF1.3k

Canon IID1 with later f1.2/50mm lens

Canon IIAF: (CC130); CFPS 1/25-1/500 s, flashbulb synch. Slow-speed dial area covered by patch. A poor counterfeit can be made by removing the slow-speed dial and patching that area of a (CC131). This is the scarcest Canon camera; buyers should authenticate any camera represented as a (CC130). This camera was never marketed in U.S. Qty 15. C 6/1953 - 8/1953.

R5* NSR $5k+	£2.6k	DM8.2k	FF25.6k

Canon IIF: (CC131); CFPS 1-1/500 s, flashbulb synch only. Some bodies are identified on the loading diagram inside the baseplate. Qty 12,000.
C 7/1953-3/1955.

R3* $250	£131	DM412	FF1.3k

Canon IIS: (CC132); CFPS 1-1/500 s, flashbulb synch and X synch at 1/15 s position on slow-speed dial. A few (CC131) cameras were updated to (CC132). Qty 1850. C 2/1954-3/1955.

R3* $325	£171	DM536	FF1.7k

Group 3: All models in this group have serial numbers between 170,000 and 235,000 (bottom loading) or between 500,001 and 599,900 (back loading), except as noted. All have combined vf-RFR with three-stage magnification. The slowest instantaneous speed on the fast speed dial is 1/30 s and all have front mounted slow-speed dials. The fast speed index is on top of the shaft in the centre of the dial and it rotates with the dial during winding and exp.

Canon IVSB2: (CC133); CFPS 1-1/1000 s, flashbulb synch, X synch on slow-speed dial at 1/15 s and on fast-speed dial at 1/45 s. Bottom loading. Qty 17,000. C 7/1954-7/1956, serial numbers between 120,000 and 230,000.

R3* $225	£118	DM371	FF1.2k

Canon IIS2: (CC134); Similar to (CC133), except CFPS 1-1/500 s. Qty 16,600. C 2/1955-7/1956.

R3* $225	£118	DM371	FF1.2k

Canon IID2: (CC135); Similar to (CC134), except no synch. Qty 16,200. C 1955-7/1956.

R3* $225	£118	DM371	FF1.2k

Canon IIF2: (CC136); Similar to (CC135) except only has flashbulb synch, no X synch. Qty 2420. C 6/1955-4/1956.

R3* $325	£171	DM536	FF1.7k

Canon VT: (CC138); Canon 50mm f1.2 lens and 35mm f1.8 lens were standard equipment on this camera, however the Canon 50mm f1.8 (black focusing ring) and 50mm f1.5 were also available. Identified on front of baseplate; backloading; baseplate trigger-wind film advance. Prototype models were often marked "Model V" (instead of "Model VT") and early advertising used that designation; at least four other minor variations exist. Qty 15,600. C 4/1956-2/1957.

R3* $275	£144	DM453	FF1.4k

Canon L2: (CC139); Identified on bottom of baseplate. Back loading; thumb-lever film advance. Qty 7,350. C 11/1956-12/1957.

R3* $300	£157	DM495	FF1.5k

Canon L1: (CC140); Identified on bottom of baseplate. No self-timer. Qty 8,000. C 2/1957-12/1957.

R3* Black: $700	£367	DM1.2k	FF3.6k
Chrome: $275	£144	DM453	FF1.4k

Canon L1

Canon VT-DeLuxe: (CC141); Identified on front of baseplate. Cloth shutter curtains; no baseplate magazine opening key. Qty 3500. C 2/1957-9/1957.

R3* Black: $750	£394	DM1.2k	FF3.8k
Chrome: $300	£157	DM495	FF1.5k

Canon VT-DeLuxe-Z: (CC110); similar to (CC141) but has baseplate magazine opening key. Qty 4875. C 4/1957-6/1958.

R3* Black: $750	£394	DM1.2k	FF3.8k
Chrome: $300	£157	DM495	FF1.5k

CANON

C

Canon VT-DeLuxe-M: (CC142); Identified "VT-DeLuxe" on front of baseplate and has original factory-installed metal shutter curtains; designated from the beginning as VT-DeLuxe-M in factory records. Qty 2550. C 1/1958-8/1958.

R4 * Black:$1k	£525	DM1.6k	FF5.1k
Chrome: $300	£157	DM495	FF1.5k

Canon L3: (CC143); Identified on bottom of baseplate. Qty 12,975.
C 10/1957-12/1958.

R3* $300	£157	DM495	FF1.5k

Canon VL: (CC144); metal FPS 1 - 1/1000 s, flashbulb and X synch. Backloading; thumb-lever film advance, self-timer (unlike (CC140)). No identification on body, although a few prototypes (C 1956) made to test the metal shutter design were probably marked "Model L1" on the baseplate. Qty 5450. C 12/1957-12/1958.

R3* $375	£197	DM618	FF1.9k

Canon VL

Canon VL2: (CC145); Similar to (CC144), except lacks 1/1000 s speed. Qty 8450. C 1/1958-12/1958.

R3* $300	£157	DM495	FF1.5k

Group 4: All models in this group have shutter speeds 1-1/1000 s on a single non-spinning top-mounted dial, metal shutter curtains, full synch, back-loading, and combined vf-RFR with projected frame lines.

Canon VI-T: (CC146); Identified on front of baseplate. Baseplate trigger wind; three-stage vf magnification; shutter speed dial notched for accessory exp meter. Qty 8175. C 6/1958-7/1960.

R3* Black: $750	£394	DM1.2k	FF3.8k
Chrome: $300	£157	DM495	FF1.5k

Canon VI-T

Canon VI-L: (CC147); Similar to (CC146), except thumb-lever film advance instead of baseplate trigger. This was the last Canon to lack model identification on body. Qty 10,350. C 6/1958-3/1961.
Very few were imported to the U.S.

R3* Black: $750	£394	DM1.2k	FF3.8k
Chrome: $325	£171	DM536	FF1.7k

Canon P: (CC148); Identified on top cover. Qty 88,000. C 12/1958-5/1961.

R3* Black: $600	£315	DM989	FF3.1k
Chrome: $250	£131	DM412	FF1.3k

Canon P

Canon 7: (CC149); Identified on top cover. Qty 138,000. C 6/1961-11/1964. The Canon 50mm f0.95 lens was introduced with this

Canon 7 with f0.95 lens

CANON

model which had a Leica-type thread mount with an outer bayonet flange. The Mirror Box 2 accessory housing was also introduced at this time; it accepted long focal length telephoto lenses. **(+$300 with 50mm f0.95 lens).**

R3* Black: $650	£341	DM1.1k	FF3.3k
Chrome: $325	£171	DM536	FF1.7k

Canon 7S: (CC150); Identifixed on top cover. Several variations with minor cosmetic differences exist; Canon 7 vf optics. Qty est 16,000. C 2/1965-8/1967. in Chrome **(+ $300 with 50mm f0.95 lens).** No black bodies known to date.

R3* $425	£223	DM701	FF2.2k

Canon 7sZ: (CC151); like (CC150) except has revised finder optics differentiated by adjustment port above second "n" in topside "Canon" logo. Qty est 4000. C 8/1967-9/1968.

R3* $425	£223	DM701	FF2.2k

Group 5: Early Canon SLR cameras. All are identified on the camera body.

Canonflex: (CC211); the first Canon SLR to be sold, with baseplate trigger wind, shutter to 1/1000 s, removable finder. Uses Canonmatic lenses. Qty 17,000. C 1/1959-7/1960.

R3* $150	£79	DM247	FF767

Canonflex RP: (CC212); fixed finder, Canomatic lenses. Qty 31,000. C 6/1960-1/1962.

R3* $150	£79	DM247	FF767

Canonflex R2000: (CC213); top speed 1/2000 s, Canomatic lenses. Qty 8800. C 6/1960-1/1962.

R3* $190	£100	DM313	FF971

Canonflex R2000

Canonflex RM: (CC214); built-in selenium meter, Canomatic lenses. Qty 72,000. C 2/1961-3/1964.

R3* $150	£79	DM247	FF767

Canonex: (CC222); leaf shutter, fixed lens. C 10/1963-5/1964.

R2* $75	£39	DM124	FF383

Canon FX: (CC231); CdS meter built-in FL lenses. This model did not have QL feature. C 4/1964-1966.

R2* $90	£47	DM148	FF460

Canon FP: (CC232); no meter, FL lenses, no QL. C 10/1964-3/1966.

R2* $90	£47	DM148	FF460

Canon Pellix: (CC233); 35mm SLR camera; Canon FL 50mm f1.8 lens, interchangeable breech-lock mount; mfps 1-1/1000 s, FP, M, X synch. Cds through-the-lens meter which measures the central 1/3 picture area and drops down out of the way during exp, stationary pellicle mirror splits light from the subject between the film and the vf, approximately 1/3 of an f stop less light falls on the film, the finder is about 1/3 less brilliant than comparable SLR cameras. C 1966.

R3* $170	£89	DM280	FF869

Canon Pellix

Canon screw mount (unless otherwise indicated) lenses for cameras: NB, lenses marked "Seiki Kogaku" should be for camera bodies also marked "Seiki Kogaku"
Serenar 28mm f3.5: (CC001); **$150**
Serenar 35mm f3.5: (CC002); **$125**
Serenar 35mm f3.2: (CC003); in Chrome, **$90**
Serenar 35mm f2.8: (CC004); **$175**

CANON-CARL ZEISS

C

Serenar 5cm f3.5: (CC005); **$200**
Serenar 50mm f3.5: (CC006); in Chrome **$65**
Serenar 5cm f2.0: (CC007); **$300**
Serenar 5cm f1.5: (CC008); **$350**
Serenar 50mm f1.8: (CC009); in Chrome **$60**
Serenar 85mm f2.0: (CC010); in Chrome **$110**
Serenar 85mm f1.9: (CC011); in Chrome **$150**
Serenar 100mm f4.0: (CC012); in Chrome, **$80**
Serenar in S-bayonet mount, 13.5cm f4.0: (CC013); **$500.00**
Serenar 13.5cm f4.0: (CC014); **$350**
Serenar 135mm f4.0: (CC015); in Chrome, **$75**
Serenar 20cm f4.0: (CC016); very rare, NSR **$2000?**
Canon Lens 25mm f3.5: (CC017); in Chrome, **$400.00** w/finder
Canon Lens 28mm f2.8: (CC018); in Chrome, **$125**
Canon Lens 28mm f3.5: (CC019); **$100**
Canon Lens 35mm f1.8: (CC020); in Black, **$130**
Canon Lens 35mm f1.5: (CC021); in Chrome, **$200**
Canon Lens 35mm f2.0: (CC022); n Black, **$150**
Canon Lens 35mm f3.5: (CC024); in Chrome, **$75**
Canon Lens 50mm f0.95: (CC025); in Black **$360**
Canon Lens 50mm f1.2: (CC026); in Black **$70**
Canon Lens 50mm f1.4: (CC027); in Black **$120**
Canon Lens 50mm f1.5: (CC028); in Chrome **$50**
Canon Lens 50mm f1.8: (CC029); in Black **$40**
Canon Lens 50mm f2.8: (CC030); in Black **$50**
Canon Lens (some marked Serenar) 85mm f1.5: (CC031);in Chrome, **$265**
Canon Lens 85mm f1.8: (CC032); in Black, **$140**
Canon Lens 85mm f2.0: (CC033); in Chrome, **$100**
Canon Lens 100mm f3.5: (CC034); in Black, **$80**
Canon Lens 100mm f2.0:(CC035); in Black, **$200**

Canon Lens: 135mm f3.5: (CC036); in Chrome, **$50.00,** in Black, **$80.00**
Canon Lens: (for use with Mirror Box 2), 135mm f2.5: (CC037); **$75**
Canon Lens (for use with Mirror Box), 200mm f3.5: (CC038); **$90**
Canon Lens (for use with Mirror Box), 400mm f4.5: (CC039); **$450**
Canon Lens (for use with Mirror box), 600mm f5.6: (CC040); **$600**
Canon Lens (with reflex housing), 800mm f8.0: (CC041); **$800**
Canon FL lens w/ mount converter B, 19mm f3.5: (CC042); **$500** w/finder

Canon Rangefinder accessories
Mirror Box 1 reflex housing: (CC043); **$115**

Mirror Box 2 reflex housing: (CC044); **$90**

Accessory finder, 28mm: (CC045); **$50**
VI-L Accessory light meter: (CC046); **$75**

Canon accessory Viewfinders
35mm: (CC050);   **$40**
85mm: (CC055);   **$55**
100mm: (CC058);   **$50**
135mm: (CC059);   **$35**

Mamiya Reflex with Canon lens: (CC221); special SLR combination sold briefly by Olden Camera, New York (about 1960). Body mfd by Mamiya with an Exakta lens mount—the standard lens was a Canon 50mm f1.9 (auto Exakta mount). This combination was unique in the U.S. (original price, $118.50); a curiosity item for Canon or Mamiya collectors.

| R4* $175 | £92 | DM288 | FF894 |

Carl Zeiss, Jena Germany

Noted as a lens manufacturer, the former East German Zeiss company actually made one camera. The Werra appeared in many different models between 1954 and 1966. All have in common the unique film

CARL ZEISS

> *advance/shutter arming ring around the lens and the metal/plastic lens shade with metal lens cap, which when reversed screws snugly onto the camera lens for storage. It should be noted that the price of a camera without the lens shade or screw-in lens cap is significantly lower!*

Werra: (CZ100); 1954-55, 35mm VFR camera with *olive green* body covering, f2.8/50mm coated Tessar in Compur Rapid shutter, 1 - 1/500s, knurled and knobbed aluminium film advance/shutter cocking ring, knob film rewind. (-75% without lens shade and/or screw in lens cap).

R3* $65	£34	DM107	FF332

Werra IA: (CZ101); 1956-60, 35mm VFR camera with *black* body covering, f2.8/50mm coated Tessar in Synchro Compur Rapid shutter, 1 - 1/500s, knurled and knobbed aluminium film advance/shutter cocking ring, knob film rewind. (-75% without lens shade and/or screw in lens cap).

R2* $45	£24	DM74	FF230

Werra IB: (CZ102); 1960-62, 35mm VFR camera with black body covering, f2.8/50mm coated Tessar in Synchro Compur Rapid shutter, 1 - 1/500s or Vebur 250 or Prestor RVS 500 shutters, after *1961 the RVS shutter indicated a top shutter speed of 1/750s* (putting this camera on the short list of cameras having leaf shutters with indicated speeds faster than 1/500s) *smooth covered* film advance/shutter cocking ring, knob film rewind, late cameras have a bright-line finder and round eye-piece. (-75% without lens shade and/or screw in lens cap, +50% for 1/750s shutter).

R3* $50	£26	DM82	FF256

Werra IC: (CZ103); 1962-64, 35mm VFR camera with black body covering, f2.8/50mm coated Tessar in Prestor RVS shutter 1-1/750s or Prestor RVS 500 shutter, smooth covered film advance/shutter cocking ring, *crank film rewind.* (-75% without lens shade and/or screw in lens cap).

R3* $50	£26	DM82	FF256

Werra IE: (CZ104); 19664-66, 35mm VFR camera with embossed black body cover-ing, f2.8/50mm coated Tessar in Prestor RVS shutter 1-1/750s or Prestor RVS 500 shutter, with *EV scale,* smooth covered film advance/shutter cocking ring, crank film rewind, re-designed rounder top plate, (-75% without lens shade and/or screw in lens cap).

R2* $50	£26	DM82	FF256

Werra II: (CZ105); 1960-64, 35mm VFR camera with black body covering, f2.8/50mm coated Tessar in Prestor RVS 500 shutter, 1 - 1/500s smooth covered film advance/shutter cocking ring, knob film rewind. *built-in selinium meter* with hinged cover and an exposure calculator on the camera back. (-75% without lens shade and/or screw in lens cap).

R3* $50	£26	DM82	FF256

Werra IIE: (CZ106); 1964, 35mm VFR camera with embossed black body cover-ing, f2.8/50mm coated Tessar in Prestor RVS 750 shutter, 1 - 1/750s smooth cov-ered film advance/shutter cocking ring, crank film rewind. built-in selinium meter as (CZ105), *but no exposure calculator* on the camera back, *accessory shoe*, re-designed rounder top plate, (-75% without lens shade and/or screw in lens cap).

R2* $50	£26	DM82	FF256

Werramat: (CZ107); 1961-64, 35mm VFR camera with embossed black body cover-ing, f2.8/50mm coated Tessar in RVS 500 shutter, 1 - 1/500s smooth covered film advance/shutter cocking ring, knob film re-wind. built-in selinium meter *without* hinged cover indicator needle visible in the VFR, *without* accessory shoe, streamlined lens housing (-75% without lens shade and/or screw in lens cap.)

R3* $70	£37	DM115	FF358

Werramat E: (CZ108); 1961-64, 35mm VFR camera with embossed black body covering, f2.8/50mm coated Tessar in RVS 500 shutter, 1 - 1/500s smooth covered film advance/shutter cocking ring, knob film re-wind. built-in selinium meter *without* hinged cover indicator needle visible in the VFR, *with* accessory shoe, streamlined lens hous-ing (-75% without lens shade and/or screw in lens cap.)

R3* $70	£37	DM115	FF358

CARL ZEISS-CARPENTIER

C

Werra III: (CZ109); 1959-64, 35mm camera with *coupled RFR* and *interchangeable lenses,* black body covering, bayonette mount f2.8/50mm Tessar in front of Prestor RVS shutter, 1 - 1/750s, crank rewind, field of view indicated for 35mm,50mm, and 100mm in the VFR.(-75% without lens shade and/or screw in lens cap.)

R3* $80	£42	DM132	FF409

Werra IIIE: (CZ110); 1964-66, 35mm camera with coupled RFR and interchangeable lenses, *rounder body style* with striated black body covering, bayonette mount f2.8/50mm Tessar in front of Prestor RVS shutter with EV scale, 1 - 1/750s, crank rewind, field of view indicated for 35mm,50mm, and 100mm in the VFR, as (CZ109) (-75% without lens shade and/or screw in lens cap.)

R3* $70	£37	DM115	FF358

Werra IV: (CZ111); 1959-62, 35mm camera with coupled RFR and interchangeable lenses, black body covering, bayonette mount f2.8/50mm Tessar in front of Prestor 500 shutter, 1 - 1/500s, crank rewind, field of view indicated for 35mm,50mm, and 100mm in the VFR, *built-in selenium meter with hinged cover.* (-75% without lens shade and/or screw in lens cap.)

R3* $80	£42	DM132	FF409

Werra V: (CZ112); 1959, 35mm camera with coupled RFR and interchangeable lenses, rounded body with black covering, bayonette mount f2.8/50mm Tessar with Prestor 500 shutter, 1 - 1/500s, crank rewind, field of view indicated for 35mm, 50mm, and 100mm in the VFR, built-in selenium meter with hinged cover. (-75% without lens shade and/or screw in lens cap.)

R3* $60	£31	DM99	FF307

Werramatic: (CZ113); 1961-64, 35mm camera with coupled RFR and interchangeable lenses, rounded body with black covering, bayonette mount f2.8/50mm Tessar in front of Prestor 500 shutter, 1 - 1/500s (after 1962, Prestor RVS 750 shutter, 1 - 1/750s), crank rewind, field of view indicated for 35mm,50mm, and 100mm in the VFR, built-in selenium meter *without* hinged cover. (-75% without lens shade and/or screw in lens cap, +50% for Prestor 750 shutter.)

R3* $50	£26	DM82	FF256

Werramatic E: (CZ114); 1964-66, 35mm camera with coupled RFR and interchangeable lenses, rounded body with black covering, bayonette mount f2.8/50mm Tessar in front of Prestor RVS 750 shutter with EV scale, 1 - 1/750s, crank rewind, field of view indicated for 35mm,50mm, and 100mm in the VFR, built-in selenium meter *without* hinged cover, accessory shoe, re-designed rounder top plate with new decoration, (-75% without lens shade and/or screw in lens cap.)

R3* $50	£26	DM82	FF256

Accessory Lenses for Werra cameras,

Flektogon f 2.8/35mm lens: (CZ001); **$70**
Cardinar f4/100mm lens: (CZ002); **$75**
Stereo attachment: (CZ003); **EST $150**

Jules CARPENTIER, Paris, France.

Jumelle Carpentier (4.5 x 6cm model): (JC100); binocular-type detective camera; Rectilinear lens or Zeiss Anastigmat lens. 12 exp, 4.5 x 6cm on plates. C 1892.

R2* $140	£73	DM231	FF716

Jumelle Carpentier (6.5 x 9cm model): (JC101); binocular-type detective camera; Zeiss Krauss Anastigmat lenses; 18 or 24 exp, 6.5 x 9cm on plates. C 1892.

R2* $140	£73	DM231	FF716

Carte-de-Visite Camera: (BB121); four lens wet-plate camera; 4 Petzval type 180mm f5

Carte-de-Visite Camera

lenses mfd by Alexis Millet, Paris, France. C 1860. Multiple lens camera for taking 4 portraits (cartes-de-visite) on a single wet-plate.

R5* NSR $5k+	£2.6k	DM8.2k	FF25.6k

C.D. CHINAGLIA DOMENICO, Belluno, Italy.

Kristall: (KI100); 1952. Cfps, 1/20 - 1/1000, Vfr only, no Rfr. flash synch, "E" for electrinic flash, "V" for bulbs. Screw mount Krinar F3.5/50mm, SOM Berthiot F2.8/50mm, or Schneider-Xenon F2.0/50mm lens. Less than 1000 cameras are thought to have been made.

R3* $400	£210	DM659	FF2k

Kristall

Kristal 2: (KI101); C1949, 35mm RFR camera with interchangeable Trixor, Trigon, Vistor, or Steiner f3.5/50mm lens, among others, CFPS 1/20 - 1/1000s, copy of Leica II.

Kristall 2a: (KI102); C1950, as Model 2s (KI103), but for internal synchro selector, (Identical to that of the Wega IIa).

R4* $500	£262	DM824	FF2.6k

Kristall 2a

Kristall 2s: (KI103); C1950, Cfps, 1/20 - 1/1000 sec, seperate Rfr/Vfr windows. Screw mount Steiner F3.5/50mm, SOM Berthiot F2.8/50mm, Schneider-Xenon F2.0/50mm, or Anastigmat Trixar F3.5/50mm lens. Both the top plate and the base plate are of polished steel, and are not chrome plated.

R4* $500	£262	DM824	FF2.6k

Kristall 3: (KI104); 1951. Cfps, 1 - 1/1000 sec, seperate Rfr/Vfr windows. Screw mount Steinar F3.5/50mm, SOM Berthiot F2.8/50mm, Schneider-Xenon F2.0/50mm, or Anastigmat Trixar F3.5/50mm lens. This model is the same as the 2, with slow speeds added.

R4* $550	£289	DM907	FF2.8k

Kristall 3s: (KI105); as (KI104) but for added PC synch on the front of the body.

R4* $550	£289	DM907	FF2.8k

Kristal 3s, type 2: (KI108); as (KI105), but for redesigned top plate, looking more like the Kristall 53 (KI106).

R4* $600	£315	DM989	FF3.1k

Kristall 53: (KI106); 1953. Cpfs, 1 - 1/1000 sec, seperate Rfr/Vfr windows, Vfr with fields of view for 28mm, 35mm, 50mm, 75mm, 90mm, and 105mm lenses. Screw mount Krinar F3.5/50mm, SOM Berthiot F2.8/50mm, or Schneider-Xenon F2.0/50mm lens. Less than 1000 cameras are thought to have been made.

R3* $600	£315	DM989	FF3.1k

Kristall 53 showing VFR selection lever.

Kristall R: (KI107); 1954. Cfps, 1/20 - 1/1000, combined Rfr/Vfr window with built-in orange filter to improve Rfr contrast, flash synch. Screw mount Krinar F3.5/50mm, SOM Berthiot F2.8/50mm, or Schneider-Xenon F2.0/50mm lens.

R4* $650	£341	DM1.1k	FF3.3k

CENTURY-CERTO KAMERAWERK

CENTURY CAMERA CO., Rochester, New York.

The Century Camera Co. was founded in 1900 by five former employees of the Rochester Optical Co.; the company was located at 65 Atlantic Avenue, Rochester, N.Y. In 1903 Eastman Kodak Co. bought controlling interest in the company. In 1907 the name was changed to Century Camera Div., Eastman Kodak Co.; in 1917 it became part of the Folmer-Century Div., of Eastman Kodak Co.

Century Enlarging & Reducing Camera: (CE100); 5" x 7" enlarging and reducing camera; extension bellows; lantern slide attachment. Polished wood finish, brass fittings. C 1890's.

R3* $175	£92	DM288	FF894

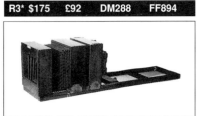

Century Enlarging & Reducing Camera

Century Grand Sr.: (CE101); 5" x 7" folding plate camera (top-of-the-line); Planatic Series III triple convertible lens. Red triple extension (24") bellows; front double sliding rack and pinion; back swings; dovetailed construction; covered with black cowhide. Sizes: 4" x 5" or 6 1/2" x 8 1/2" Original price, $45. C 1902.

R3* $200	£105	DM330	FF1k

Century Grand Sr.

Century Plate Camera: (CE102); 4" x 5" plate camera; Wollensak lens; Century shutter. Red bellows; brass fittings. C 1910.

R3* $140	£73	DM231	FF716

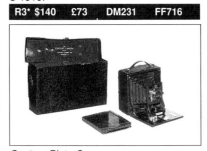

Century Plate Camera

Century Stereo Camera: (CE103); 5" x 7" folding plate stereo camera; stereo shutter 1-1/100 s. 5" x 7" exp on dry plates. C 1900's.

R4* $425	£223	DM701	FF2.2k

Century View Camera: (CE104); 5" x 7" view camera; rear focus; double extension bellows. Polished mahogany finish with brass fitting. Brass label: "Century Camera Co., Rochester, N.Y." Several sizes from 4" x 5" to 11" x 14". C 1900's.

R3* $250	£131	DM412	FF1.3k

Century View Camera

CERTO KAMERAWERK, Dresden, Germany.

Many models were around for years without great changes, note that dial set Compur shutters are found on cameras before 1928, afterwards, rimset Compur shutters were used. Sometimes this is the only differ-

CERTO KAMERAWERK

ence between identical camera models made ten years apart

Dolly Model A: (ER100); C1930, 3 x 4cm strut folding camera, front focusing Radionar f4.5/50mm lens, Compur shutter 1-1/300 s.

R2* $50	£26	DM82	FF256

Dolly Model B: (ER125); C1930, 3 x 4cm strut folding camera, *lever focusing* Radionar f2.9/50mm lens, Compur shutter 1-1/300 s.

R2* $50	£26	DM82	FF256

Dolly 4 x 6.5: (ER126); C1935, 4 x 6.5cm bed folding camera, Tessar f3.5/70mm lens, Compur shutter.

R2* $30	£16	DM49	FF153

SS Dolly Model A: (ER127); C1937, folding bed camera for 4.5 x 6cm or 6 x 6cm on 120 roll film , interchangeable Trioplan f2/75mm lens among others, Compur shutter.

R3* $50	£26	DM82	FF256

SS Dolly Model C: (ER128); C1937, folding bed camera as (ER127) but for use with either rollfilm *or plates,* interchangeable Xenar f2.8/75mm lens among others, Compur shutter.

R3* $60	£31	DM99	FF307

Super Sport Dolly Model A: (ER129); C1936, folding bed camera for 6 x 4.5cm or 6 x 6cm frames on 120 roll film, coupled RFR, after 1939 with built-in extinction meter, interchangeable Tessar f2.8/75mm lens among others, Compur shutter, early cameras are all black, later ones have a chromed top plate.

R2* $80	£42	DM132	FF409

Super Sport Dolly Model C: (ER130); C1936, as (ER129) but for *plates or rollfilm.*

R3* $100	£52	DM165	FF511

Dollina: (ER131); C1932, 35mm VFR strut bed folding camera for 24 x 36mm frames, many variations during production, early cameras lack body release and are more black than later versions, Cassar f2.9/50mm lens among others, Compur shutter.

R2* $30	£16	DM49	FF153

Dollina II: (ER132); C1933, 35mm RFR strut folding camera for 24 x 36mm frames,

CRF, Xenar f2/45mm lens among others, Compur shutter, available in either chrome or black.

R3* $60	£31	DM99	FF307

Dollina III: (ER133); C1936, 35mm folding RFR camera, CRF, new body style, Xenon f2.50mm lens among others, Compur or Compur Rapid shutter.

R3* $75	£39	DM124	FF383

Super Dollina: (ER102); C1937, 35mm RFR camera, Cassar f2.9/50mm lens among others, Compur or Compur Rapid shutter 1-1/500 s.

R2* $50	£26	DM82	FF256

Super Dollina

Super Dollina II: (ER103); C1950, 35mm RFR camera, CRF, *coated Jena Tessar* f2.8/50mm lens, Compur Rapid shutter 1-1/500 s, *PC synch connection.*

R3* $100	£52	DM165	FF511

Certo Super Six: (ER134); C1951, folding RFR camera for 6 x 6cm on 120 roll film, or 24 x 36mm on 35mm film with special adaptor, CRF, coated Jena Tessar f2.8/80mm lens, Synchro Compur shutter.

R3* $125	£66	DM206	FF639

Certo-phot: (ER135); C1955, all metal rollfilm camera for 6 x 6cm frames, simple focusing f8 lens, simple shutter 1/50s.

R2* $10	£5	DM16	FF51

Certo-matic: (ER136); C1960, as (ER135) but now with built-in uncoupled light meter.

R3* $15	£8	DM25	FF77

Certolob O: (ER104); C1925, leather bellows folding bed camera for 6.5 c 9cm film

C

CERTO KAMERAWERK

packs or plates, leather covered wooden body, Trioplan f4.5/105mm lens among others, Vario shutter.

| R2* $30 | £16 | DM49 | FF153 |

Certolob : (ER105); C1925, Xenar f2.9/105mm lens among others, Compur shutter, like (ER104) but with lens adjustments, and better finish.

| R2* $40 | £21 | DM66 | FF204 |

Certoruf 9 x 12: (ER106); C1925, leather bellows folding bed camera for 9 x 12cm film packs or plates, geared bed focusing Unofocal f4.5/135mm lens among others, Compur shutter, leather covered wooden body, waist lever finder mounted centrally on the front standard, double extension bellows.

| R2* $40 | £21 | DM66 | FF204 |

Certoruf 10 x 15cm: (ER107); C1925, as (ER106) but for 10 x 15cm plates or film packs. Xenar f4.5/165mm lens among others.

| R2* $40 | £21 | DM66 | FF204 |

Certorex: (ER108); C1925, leather bellows folding bed camera for 9 x 12cm film packs or plates, *lever focusing* Unofocal f4.5/135mm lens among others, Vario shutter, leather covered wooden body, waist lever finder mounted centrally on the front standard.

| R2* $40 | £21 | DM66 | FF204 |

Certotrop 6.5 x 9: (ER109); C1925, leather bellows folding bed camera for 6.5 x 9cm film packs or plates, *metal body*, geared bed focusing Trioplan f2.9/105mm lens, Compur shutter, *after 1930 with quick change lens/shutter mount.*

| R2* $45 | £24 | DM74 | FF230 |

Certotrop 9 x 12: (ER110); C1925, as (ER109) but for 9 x 12cm filmpacks or plates, Xenar f4.5/135mm lens among others, Compur shutter.

| R2* $45 | £24 | DM74 | FF230 |

Certotrop 10 x 15: (ER111); C1925, as (ER109) but for 10 x 15cm filmpacks or plates, Xenar f4.5/165mm lens among others, Compur shutter.

| R2* $45 | £24 | DM74 | FF230 |

Certoruhm: (ER112); C1925, like (ER106) but for "Quer" format, simply put, the camera has a square body with removable back allowing horizontal or vertical framing with our turning the whole camera, wooden body, drop bed for perspective control, Xenar f4.5/135mm lens among others, Compur shutter.

| R3* $45 | £24 | DM74 | FF230 |

Certochrom 9 x 12: (ER113); C1925, leather bellows folding bed camera for 9 x 12cm plates or filmpacks, drop bed, metal body, *interchangeable* Xenar f4.5/135mm lens among others, Compur shutter.

| R2* $40 | £21 | DM66 | FF204 |

Certochrom 10 x 15: (ER114); C1925, as (ER113) but for 10 x 15cm plates or filmpacks.

| R2* $40 | £21 | DM66 | FF204 |

Certoplat: (ER115); C1925, leather bellows folding bed camera for 9 x 12cm plates or filmpacks, specially made for use with Plasmat f4/15cm lens, Compur shutter, double extension bellows, otherwise as (ER106).

| R3* $60 | £31 | DM99 | FF307 |

Certokunst: (ER116); C1925, leather bellows folding bed camera for 9 x 12cm plates or filmpacks, interchangeable Xenar f4.5/135mm lens among others, drop bed, tilting lens standard, intended for architechtural or studio use.

| R3* $50 | £26 | DM82 | FF256 |

Certosport 9 x 12: (ER117); C1925, leather bellows folding bed camera for 9 x 12cm plates or filmpacks, Xenar f4.5/135mm lens among others, Compur shutter, like (ER106 but with wire frame finder.

| R2* $40 | £21 | DM66 | FF204 |

Certosport 6.5 x 9: (ER119); C1930, leather folding bed camera for 6.5 x 9cm filmpacks or plates, interchangeable Eurynar f4.5/105mm lens among others, Compur shutter, *metal body,* wire frame finder.

| R3* $50 | £26 | DM82 | FF256 |

Certonet O: (ER120); C1925, folding VFR camera for 6 x 9cm frames on roll film, Radionar f4.5/120mm lens, Vario shutter.

| R2* $25 | £13 | DM41 | FF128 |

Certonet XIV: (ER121); C1928, folding VFR camera for 6 x 9cm frames on roll film, Radionar f4.5/120mm lens, Vario shutter, *wire frame finder, bubble level* next to waist lever finder.

R2* $25	£13	DM41	FF128

Certonet XV: (ER122); C1927, folding VFR camera for 6 x 9cm frames on roll film, Radionar f4.5/120mm lens, Compur shutter, *wire frame finder.*

R2* $25	£13	DM41	FF128

Damen Kamera: (ER123); C1905, folding bed camera for 6 x 9cm plates, *in the form of an ornate ladies handbag. Beware of Eastern European forgeries!*

R5* NSR est$10k £5.2k DM16.5k FF51.1k

Doppel-Box: (ER101); C1935, Certomat lens; single speed shutter. 8 exp, 6 x 9cm or 16 exp, 4.5 x 6cm on 120 film. Format changed by turning dial.

R3* $65	£34	DM107	FF332

Certo-Box A: (ER124); C1930, metal box camera with fixed focus f11 lens, 6 x 9cm on roll film.

R2* $25	£13	DM41	FF128

W. I. CHADWICK,
Manchester, England.

Chadwick Detective Camera: (WI100); box-type. C 1890.

R4* $300	£157	DM495	FF1.5k

Chadwick Patent Stereoscopic Camera: (WI101); $1/4$ plate stereoscopic camera; single or stereo achromat lenses. Folding rectangular bellows; rotating waterhouse stops. Stereo exp on two 1/4 plates. C 1892.

R4* $600	£315	DM989	FF3.1k

J. T. CHAPMAN,
Manchester, England.

The British Detective Camera: (JT100); box-type detective camera; Wray lens (brass barrel) with waterhouse stops; Thornton Pickard string-set shutter. 2 1/4" x 3 1/4" exp on dry plates. C 1890.

R3* $275	£144	DM453	FF1.4k

CHARLIE THE TUNA: (BB122); toy plastic camera in shape of a tuna fish. 8 exp, 126 cartridge. C 1967.

R3* $65	£34	DM107	FF332

CHASE MAGAZINE CAMERA
Newburyport, Massachusetts.

Chase Magazine Camera: (CM100); box-type magazine camera. 12 exp, 4" x 5" loaded in a magazine. C 1899.

R3* $125	£66	DM206	FF639

Charles CHEVALIER,
Paris, France.

Chevalier Daguerreotype Camera: (AE100); collapsible daguerreotype camera; Photographs a verres combines 29cm f5.6 lens; lens cap controls exp. Single exp, 16.5 x 21.5cm on plates. C 1840. First collapsible daguerreotype camera.

R5* NSR $10k £5.2k DM16.5k FF51.1k

"Grand Photographe" Camera: (AE101); Photographes a verres combines lens; whole plate exp. Mercurizing box, plate, and reversing prism are inside camera. C 1841.

R5* NSR $7k £3.7k DM11.5k FF35.8k

Cheville Appareil: (BB123); ankle-strap detective camera; Goerz-Fournier Dogmar 62mm f4.5 lens; Compur shutter. Long flexible shutter release extends to pocket.

R5* NSR $5k £2.6k DM8.2k FF25.6k

Chevillon Drop-Plate Magazine Camera: (BB124); Rapid Rectilinear lens; rotating shutter. C 1905.

R3* $50	£26	DM82	FF256

CHICAGO CAMERA CO.,
Chicago, Illinois.

Photake Camera: (CG100); achromat 120mm f14 lens; guillotine shutter; 5 exp, 2" x 2" on dry plates. C 1896.

R4* $900	£472	DM1.5k	FF4.6k

CHICAGO FERROTYPE CO., Chicago, Illinois.

Mandelette Postcard Camera: (HI100); direct positive ferrotype camera. 2¼" x 3¼" direct positive exp on paper. C 1915.

| R3* $125 | £66 | DM206 | FF639 |

Mandel Photo Postcard Camera: (HI101); street camera. Direct positives, rectangular (2" x 3") or small circular images. C 1915.

| R3* $150 | £79 | DM247 | FF767 |

Wonder Automatic Cannon Photo Button Machine: (HI102); cannon-shaped street detective camera; round exp, 25mm diameter on ferrotype plates. C 1913. Produced button-size tintypes to insert in breast pins. The camera came complete with tripod, 300 plates, pins, and developing chemicals.

| R4* $750 | £394 | DM1.2k | FF3.8k |

Chiyoda Optical Company, Japan, see Minolta

CHIYOTAX CAMERA COMPANY, Japan.

(All cameras listed here were made under contract by the Reise Camera Company)

Chiyoca 35:(CD201); C1951, 35mm VFR camera with interchangeable rigid Hexar f3.5/50mm lens, CFPS 1/20 - 1/500s, Leica Standard copy.

| R4* $1k | £525 | DM1.6k | FF5.1k |

Chiyoca 35-1F: (CD202); C1952, as (CD201) but for added synch, collapsible Lena QC f3.5/50mm lens.

| R4* $1k | £525 | DM1.6k | FF5.1k |

Chiyoca IIF: (CD203); C1953, 35mm RFR camera with interchangeable screw mount Reise or Lena QC f3.5/50mm lens, CFPS 1/20 - 1/500s, copy of Leica II.

| R3* $900 | £472 | DM1.5k | FF4.6k |

Chiyotax IIIF: (CD200); 1954, 35mm RFR camera with screw mount Lena QC F3.5/5cm lens, 1 - 1/500 sec CFPS, seperate RFR/VFR windows, diopter adjustment, double male pin type flash synch, . Later cameras marked "Reise Camera Company", are identical to this earlier version, and are valued the same. Prices are higher in Japan.

| R3* $800 | £420 | DM1.3k | FF4.1k |

CINCINNATI CLOCK AND MFG. CO., Cincinnati, Ohio.

Cinclox Camera 16mm Model 3-S: (CI100); oval shaped 16mm movie camera; Cine Wollensak Velostigmat 1" f2.5 lens. Optical finder; footage indicator; variable speed mechanism; key wind operation. 1930.

| R2* $45 | £24 | DM74 | FF230 |

Cine 8 Emel: (BB125); 8mm movie camera; 3 lens turret for Berthiot 12.5, 116mm and 35mm lenses; 5 speeds from 8 to 64 frames per s. First 8mm camera with backwind capability. C 1935-1936.

| R3* $100 | £52 | DM165 | FF511 |

CIRO CAMERAS, INC., Delaware, Ohio.

Ciro 35R: (IR100); 35m RFR camera; Wollensak Anastigmat 50mm f4.5 coated lens; Alphax shutter 1/10-1/200 s, CRF. C 1950.

| R2* $25 | £13 | DM41 | FF128 |

Ciro 35S: (IR101); 35mm RFR camera; Wollensak Anastigmat 50mm f3.5 coated lens. C 1950.

| R2* $25 | £13 | DM41 | FF128 |

Ciro 35T: (IR102); 35mm RFR camera; Wollensak Anastigmat 50mm f2.8 coated lens; Rapax shutter 1-1/400 s. C 1950.

| R2* $30 | £16 | DM49 | FF153 |

Ciroflex A: (IR103); 2¼" x 2¼" TLR camera; Wollensak Velostigmat 85mm f3.5 lens; Alphax shutter 1/10-1/200 s. 12 exp, 2¼" x 2¼" on 120 roll film. C 1942.

| R2* $20 | £10 | DM33 | FF102 |

Ciroflex A

Ciroflex B: (IR104); 2¹/4" x 2¹/4" TLR camera. C 1948.

R2* $20	£10	DM33	FF102

Ciroflex C: (IR105); 2¹/4" x 2¹/4" TLR camera. C 1948.

R2* $20	£10	DM33	FF102

Ciroflex D: (IR106); 2¹/4" x 2¹/4" TLR camera. C 1950.

R*2 $25	£13	DM41	FF128

Ciroflex E: (IR107); 2¹/4" x 2¹/4" TLR camera. C 1950.

R2* $30	£16	DM49	FF153

Ciroflex F: (IR108); 2¹/4" x 2¹/4" TLR camera; Raptar f3.2 lens; Rapax shutter 1-1/400 s. 12 exp, 2¹/4" x 2¹/4" on 120 roll film. C 1950.

R2* $45	£24	DM74	FF230

Latimer CLARKE.

Latimer Clarke: (CL100); pantograph movement for sequential exp with single lens camera. C 1857.

R5* NSR $3.5k	£1.8k	DM5.8k	FF17.9k

CLARUS CAMERA MFG. CO., Minneapolis, Minnesota.

Clarus MS-35: (RU100); C 1950, 35mm RFR camera, Wollensak Velostigmat f2.8/ 50mm coated lens, CFPS 1/25-1/1000 s, CRF, first version with flash synch, and accessory shoe built-into the top plate. These cameras sell for 50% more in Europe.

R2* $75	£39	DM124	FF383

Clarus MS-35

CLARUS-CONLEY

C

Clarus MS-35: (RU101); C1954, as (RU100) but without flash synch, and with simple added on accessory shoe. This was an attempt to cut the cost of manufacturing the camera. Eventually, the Clarus Company went out of business, and the remaining camera parts *were probably* bought by the Wescon Company. (See the introduction of this edition a story about the Wescon camera.)

R2* $75	£39	DM124	FF383

Clement and Gilmer: (BB126); tailboard stereo camera. Mahogany finish with red bellows. Mfd in Paris, France.

R3* $180	£94	DM297	FF920

Le Clopic: (BB127); Zeiss Krauss 136mm f8 lens; shutter 2 - 1/2000 s. 6.5 x 9cm exp on plates. Mfd in Paris, France. C 1903.

R3* $275	£144	DM453	FF1.4k

Le Clopic Reporter: (BB130); 9 x 12cm camera; Berthiot Flor 135mm f4.5 lens; FPS 1/2-1/2000 s. Mfd in Paris, France. C 1903.

R3* $250	£131	DM412	FF1.3k

CLOSE & CONE,
New York, USA.

Quad Camera: (LO100); leather covered box camera; rotary wind shutter. 4 exp, 3½" x 3½" on plates. C 1896.

R3* $90	£47	DM148	FF460

Cluny: (LY100); box-type stereo camera; Protar 75mm f9 lenses; 3 speed guillotine shutter. Leather covered wooden body. Two models: 45 x 107mm and 6 x 13cm.

R4* $350	£184	DM577	FF1.8k

COMPCO,
USA

Compco Reflex II: (CQ100); C1950, metal and plastic TLR type box camera for 6 x 6cm frames on roll film, simple lens and shutter. (prices higher in Europe).

R2* $10	£5	DM16	FF51

Compco Reflex II

CONLEY CAMERA CO.,
Rochester, Minnesota.

Conley 4" x 5" Folding Plate Camera: (CY100); R.R. lens; Conley Safety shutter.

Conley 4" x 5" Folding Plate Camera

Polished wood interior with nickel plated fittings; red bellows. C 1900.

R3* $100	£52	DM165	FF511

Conley 5" x 7" Folding Plate Camera: (CY101); Gundlach Triple Convertible lens; double extension bellows; rear swings and tilts; shifting, rising and falling front. Polished mahogany with nickel plated fittings; red bellows. C 1890's.

R3* $150	£79	DM247	FF767

Conley Magazine Camera: (CY102); simple lens; rotary shutter. Twelve 4" x 5" exp on dry plates—drop plate changing mechanism. C 1904.

R3* $65	£34	DM107	FF332

Conley Postcard Camera: (CY103); 3 1/2" x 5" folding plate camera; Rapid Rectilinear lens; Klito shutter; vertical format; black bellows. Polished wood interior with nickel fittings. C 1905.

R3* $60	£31	DM99	FF307

Conley Stereoscopic Box Camera: (CY104); meniscus lenses; single speed shutter. Stereo exp on 5" x 7" dry plates. C 1906.

R4* $350	£184	DM577	FF1.8k

Kewpie No. 2: (CY105); side loading box camera; rotating waterhouse stops.

R3* $20	£10	DM33	FF102

CONTESSA NETTEL, Stuttgart, Germany.

Adoro Tropical Camera: (CN100); C 1925, 9 x 12cm tropical plate camera; Zeiss Tessar 15cm f4.5 lens; Compur shutter 1-1/150 s.

R4* $450	£236	DM742	FF2.3k

Clarissa Tropical: (CN102); C 1919, 4.5 x 6cm tropical plate camera; Hugo Meyer Trioplan 7.5mm f3.5 lens; CFPS 1/20-1/300

R4* $1k	£525	DM1.6k	FF5.1k

Citoskop: (CN103); C 1924, 45 x 107mm stereo camera; Tessar 65mm f4.5 lenses; Stereo Compur shutter, 1-1/300 s.

R4* $300	£157	DM495	FF1.5k

Contessa Nettel Sonnet: C 1921, (CN104);

Adoro Tropical Camera

Clarissa Tropical

Contessa Nettel Sonnet

4.5 x 6cm tropical camera; Tessar 7.5cm f4.5 lens; Compound shutter, 1-1/300 s.

R4* $800	£420	DM1.3k	FF4.1k

Deckrullo Tropical: (CN105); 9 x 12cm tropical plate camera; Tessar 120mm f4.5 lens; teak construction, partially covered with brown leather, light brown leather bellows.

R4* $850	£446	DM1.4k	FF4.3k

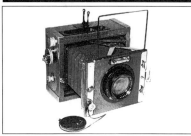

Deckrullo Tropical

Duchessa: (CN107); C 1926, 45 x 107mm folding stereo camera; Teronar f5.4 or Tessar f6.3 or f4.5 lenses; Compur shutter 1-1/250 s. 45 x 107mm exp on plates.

R4* $400	£210	DM659	FF2k

Ergo: (CN110); C 1924, monocular-type detective camera; Tessar 55mm f4.5 lens; Compur 1/25-1/100 s. 4.5 x 6cm exp on plates. Sold originally as the Argus by Contessa Nettel (see Nettel Kamerawerk listing); later sold as the Ergo by Zeiss Ikon.

R4* $1k+	£525+	DM1.6k+	FF5.1k+

Piccolette: (CN111); C 1920, 127 roll film folding camera; Carl Zeiss Series IIb 7.5cm f6.3 lens; Compur shutter 1-1/300 s. 8 exp, 4 x 6.5cm on 127 roll film.

R3* $70	£37	DM115	FF358

Westca: (CN112); C1914, all metal strut folding camera for 4.5 c 6cm plates, Aplanat f6.8/75mm lens.

R3* $150	£79	DM247	FF767

Atlanta: (CN113); C1915, plate camera for extra long (500mm or 800mm lens) for use as an aerial camera.CFPS, with either Aeroplast f6.8/500mm or f9/800mm lens.

NSR est $1k+	£525+	DM1.6k+	FF5.1k+

Pixie: (CN114); C1910, strut folding camera for 4 x 6cm frames on roll film, Tessar f6.3/70mm lens among others, various shutters.

R3* $90	£47	DM148	FF460

Recto: (CN115); C 1925, strut folding camera for 4.5 x 6cm plates or film packs, various lenses and shutters, waist level reflex finder.

R3* $125	£66	DM206	FF639

Nettix: (CN116); C1920, strut folding camera for 4.5 x 6cm plates or film packs, various lenses and shutters, wire frame finder.

R3* $100	£52	DM165	FF511

Fiduca 6.5 x 9: (CN117); C1920, metal bodied bed folding camera for 6.5 x 9cm plates or film packs, various lenses, Compur or Vario shutter.

R3* $40	£21	DM66	FF204

Fiduca 9 x 12: (CN118); C1920, metal bodied bed folding camera for 9 x 12cm plates or film packs, various lenses, Compur or Vario shutter.

R3* $45	£24	DM74	FF230

Alino:(CN119); C1920, metal bodied bed folding camera for 6.5 x 9cm plates or film packs, double extension bellows, various lenses and shutters.

R3* $60	£31	DM99	FF307

Piccolette

CONTESSA-CORFIELD

C

Suevia: (CN120); C1920, metal bodied bed folding camera for 6.5 x 9cm plates or film packs, various lenses and shutters, economy version.

| R3* $30 | £16 | DM49 | FF153 |

Taxo: (CN121); C1020, metal bodied bed folding camera for 9 x 12cm plates or film packs, various lenses and shutters, economy version.

| R2* $30 | £16 | DM49 | FF153 |

Tessco: (CN122); C1920, metal bodied bed folding camera for 9 x 12cm plates or film packs, double extension bellows, various lenses and shutters.

| R2* $40 | £21 | DM66 | FF204 |

Donata: (CN123); C1920, bed folding camera for 9 x 12cm plates or film packs, various lenses and shutters, double extension bellows.

| R2* $30 | £16 | DM49 | FF153 |

Adoro 9 x 12: (CN124); C1920, metal bodied folding bed camera for 9 x 12cm plates or film packs, various lenses and shutters, double extension bellows.

| R2* $40 | £21 | DM66 | FF204 |

Adoro 10 x 15: (CN125); C1920, metal bodied folding bed camera for 10 x 15cm plates or film packs, various lenses and shutters, double extension bellows.

| R2* $40 | £21 | DM66 | FF204 |

Onito 9 x 12: (CN126); C1920, folding bed camera for 9 x 12cm plates or film packs, various lenses and shutters, economy version.

| R2* $30 | £16 | DM49 | FF153 |

Onito 10 x 15: (CN127); C1920, folding bed camera for 10 x 15cm plates or film packs, various lenses and shutters, economy version.

| R2* $30 | £16 | DM49 | FF153 |

Altura 9 x 12: (CN128); C1920, folding bed camera for 9 x 12cm plates or film packs, various lenses and shutters.

| R2* $30 | £16 | DM49 | FF153 |

Altura 10 x 15: (CN128); C1920, folding bed camera for 10 x 15cm plates or film

packs, various lenses and shutters.

| R2* $30 | £16 | DM49 | FF153 |

Sonto: (CN129); C1920, folding bed camera for 13 x 18cm plates or filmpacks, various lenses and shutters, double extension bellows.

| R3* $45 | £24 | DM74 | FF230 |

Volupa: (CN130); C1920, folding bed camera for 10 x 15cm plates or filmpacks, double extension bellows, various lenses and shutters.

| R3* $40 | £21 | DM66 | FF204 |

Miroflex 6.5 x 9: (CN131); C1919, strut folding SLR for 6.5 x 9cm plates or filmpacks, Tessar f4.5/120mm lens among others, CFPS, later cameras are from Zeiss-Ikon are more often found.

| R4* $350 | £184 | DM577 | FF1.8k |

Miroflex 9 x 12: (CN132); C1919, strut folding SLR for 6.5 x 9cm plates or filmpacks, Tessar f4.5/135mm lens among others, CFPS, later cameras are from Zeiss-Ikon are more often found.

| R4* $300 | £157 | DM495 | FF1.5k |

CORFIELD, England.

Periflex 1: (CF100); 1953-58. Cfps, 1/30 - 1/1000 sec, reflex focusing using a small periscope which intercepts the aerial image before it reaches the film plane, interchangeable viewfinders, screw mount Lumax F1.9/50mm, F3.5/45mm or F2.8/50mm lens. Black top and bottom plates replaced by silver satin anodized finish in 1955.

| R2* $180 | £94 | DM297 | FF920 |

Periflex 1

CORFIELD

Corfield 66: (CF101); 1961. Cfps, 1/10 - 1/500 sec, Slr, interchangeable ground glass focusing, 6 X 6 on 120 roll film using film back, or sheet film holders, interchangeable finders, 4 element Lumax F3.5/95mm lens. About three hundred cameras were made before production was halted.

R4* $350	£184	DM577	FF1.8k

Corfield 66

Periflex Original: (CF102); 1953. Cfps, 1/30 - 1/1000 sec, reflex focusing using a small periscope which intercepts the aerial image before it reaches the film plane, interchangeable viewfinders, screw mount F3.5/50mm Lumar, front cell focusing, coated from 1954. Aluminium body, covered with light brown pigskin, black top and bottom plates. Glass pressure plate, sprocketless film advance.

R4* $650	£341	DM1.1k	FF3.3k

Periflex Original

Periflex 2: (CF103); 1958. Cfps, 1/30 - 1/500 sec, reflex focusing using a small periscope which intercepts the aerial image before it reaches the film plane, interchangeable viewfinders, screw mount Lumax F1.9/50mm, F3.5/45mm or F2.8/50mm lens. Simplified version of Periflex 3 with the EV scale and film reminder omitted. Introduced after the more expensive Periflex 3.

R2* $180	£94	DM297	FF920

Periflex 2

Periflex 3: (CF104); 1957. Cfps, 1 - 1/1000 sec, reflex focusing using a small periscope which decends automatically when the film is advanced, to intercept the aerial image from the centre of the frame before it reaches the film plane. Interchangeable viewfinders, screw mount F3.5, 2.8, or 1.9/50mm Lumax lenses, focusing to 9 inches.

R3* $250	£131	DM412	FF1.3k

Periflex 3

Periflex 3A: (CF105); 1959. Cfps, 1 - 1/1000 sec, lever wind, reflex focusing using a small periscope which decends automatically when the film is advanced, to intercept the aerial image from the centre of the frame before it reaches the film plane.

THE HOVE INTERNATIONAL BLUE BOOK

Interchangeable viewfinders, screw mount F3.5, 2.8, or 1.9/50mm Lumax lenses, focusing to 9 inches. Frame counter counts backward during rewind, showing number of frames rewound into the film cassette.

R3* $250	£131	DM412	FF1.3k

Periflex 3A

Periflex 3B: (CF106); 1960. Cfps, 1 - 1/1000 sec, lever wind, reflex focusing using a small periscope which decends automatically when the film is advanced, to intercept the aerial image from the centre of the frame before it reaches the film plane. Interchangeable viewfinders, screw mount F2.8 (four element), F2.4 (six element), f1.9 (six element) Lumax lenses. Distinguished by its three flash synch sockets, this camera represents the peak of the periflex range in features and complexity.

R3* $325	£171	DM536	FF1.7k

Periflex Gold Star: (CF107); 1961. Cfps, 1 - 1/300 sec using the same mechanism as the Prontor leaf shutter in order to give consistant and accurate exposure, lever wind, reflex focusing using a small periscope which decends automatically when

Periflex Gold Star

the film is advanced, to intercept the aerial image from the centre of the frame before it reaches the film plane. Interchangeable viewfinders, screw mount F2.8 (four element), F2.4 (six element), f1.9 (six element) Lumax lenses. Usually found in quite good working order, quite usable even today.

R2* $125	£66	DM206	FF639

Interplan: (CF108); 1960's. Cfps, 1 - 1/300 sec using the same mechanism as the Prontor leaf shutter in order to give consistant and accurate exposure, lever wind. Sold without lens, for use with Leica screw mount lenses (Interplan A), or Edixa/Pentax screw mount lenses (Interplan B), or Exakta bayonet (Interplan C). Based on the Periflex Gold Star, but simpler, without reflex focusing.

R3* $180	£94	DM297	FF920

Interplan

Maxim: (CF109); 1960's. Cfps, 1 - 1/300 sec using the same mechanism as the Prontor leaf shutter in order to give consistant and accurate exposure, lever wind. Similar to the Interplan, but with f3.5/45mm lens. Intended to be a low cost intro-

Maxim

duction to the Periflex system, this camera was never put into production. Of six prototypes made, only one is thought to still exist.

| R5* | NSR | | |

Lenses made for the Periflex system: 1950-60's

28mm, f3.5, Retro-Lumax, (CF001); 1959
35mm, f3.5, Retro-Lumax, (CF002); 1957
85mm, f1.5, Super Lumax, (CF003); 1960, rare
90mm, f2.8, Tele Lumax, (CF004); 1961, rare
95mm, f2.8, Lumax, (CF005); 1960
100mm, f4.0, Lumar, (CF006); 1956
135mm, f3.5, Tele Lumax, (CF007); 1958 (leather banded mount)
135mm, f3.5, Tele Lumax, (CF008); 1961 (diamond turned mount) rare
150mm, f3.5, Lumar, (CF009); 1954, only one known to exist
240mm, f4.5, Tele Lumax, (CF010); 1960, special viewfinder, rare
400mm, f4.5, Tele Lumax, (CF011); 1960, same Vfr as 240mm lens, rare

CORNU,
Paris, France.

Ontoflex: (CO100); TLR camera; Tessar 90mm f3.5 lens; Compur Rapid shutter 1-1/400 s. 6 x 9cm exp, horizontal or vertical format. C 1939.

| R4* $350 | £184 | DM577 | FF1.8k |

Ontoscope: (CO101); 35mm stereo camera; Berthiot 40mm f3.5 lenses; shutter 1-1/400 s. Pair of stereo exp, 24 x 30mm on 35mm film.

| R4* $300 | £157 | DM495 | FF1.5k |

Ontoscope: (CO102); 45 x 107mm stereo camera; Tessar 55mm f4.5 lenses; guillotine shutter 1/5-1/400 s. Changing magazine for 12 plates, 45 x 107mm. C 1925.

| R3* $200 | £105 | DM330 | FF1k |

Ontoscope: (CO103); 6 x 13cm stereo camera; Flor Berthiot 85mm f4.5 lenses; guillotine shutter 1/5-1/300 s. Panoramic settings; rising and falling front. C 1925.

| R3* $200 | £105 | DM330 | FF1k |

Reyna: (CO104); 1941, 35mm camera with cast aluminium body, 50mm/f3.5 Flor Berthiot or Saphir Boyer lens, Gitzo shutter 1/25-1/200s, no automatic stop when winding the film.

| R4* $100 | £52 | DM165 | FF511 |

Reyna II: (CO105); 1942, 35mm camera with cast aluminium body, 50mm/f3.5 Flor Berthiot lens, Vario Reyna shutter, 1/25-1/100s, In Black or shiny Brown. Like (CO104), with addition of automatic film stop.

| R3* $100 | £52 | DM165 | FF511 |

Ontobloc I: (CO106); 1946, 35mm camera with cast aluminium body, 50mm/f3.5 Saphir Boyer lens, Coronto shutter, 1-1/300s, owners of Reyna II cameras could have them fitted with the Coronto shutter by sending them back to the factory.

| R3* $75 | £39 | DM124 | FF383 |

Ontobloc II: (CO107); 35mm camera with cast aluminium body, 50mm/f3.5 Saphir Boyer lens, Coronto shutter, 1-1/300s, like (CO106), but with chrome top plate.

| R3* $75 | £39 | DM124 | FF383 |

Ontobloc III: (CO108); 35mm camera with cast aluminium body, 50mm/f2.8 Flor Berthiot lens, Coronto-Rapid shutter, 1-1/400s, like (C)107), but with faster shutter and lens.

| R3* $75 | £39 | DM124 | FF383 |

Week-End Bob: (CO109); 35mm camera with cast aluminium body, the same style as the Reyna cameras previously listed, but with simple shutter and lens. Grey body with gold coloured metal work.

| R3* $60 | £31 | DM99 | FF307 |

Fama-Flor: (CO110); 35mm camera with cast aluminium body, distributed by the Maillard company, Fama shutter 1-1/300s, 50mm/f2.8 lens in interchangeable mount. Built-in blind which protects the film from light when the lens/shutter are changed.

| R3* $125 | £66 | DM206 | FF639 |

Fama-Flor II: (CO111); 35mm camera with cast aluminium body, Like (CO110), but with built-in vrf adjustable for 35mm, 50mm, and 90mm fields of view. A 35mm/f3.5 wide angle lens and a 90mm/f4.5 Telephoto lens were available for this, and the Fama-Flor camera. A complete set, including both accessory lenses adds 200% to the price.

| R3* $125 | £66 | DM206 | FF639 |

CORONET,
Birmingham, England.

Coronet Cameo: (CT100); plastic subminiature camera; 8 x 13cm exp on 8mm roll film. C 1935.

| R2* $85 | £45 | DM140 | FF434 |

Coronet Cine 9.5mm: (CT101); 9.5mm movie camera; Coronet Anastigmat f3.9 lens; spring motor. C 1934.

| R2* $55 | £29 | DM91 | FF281 |

Coronet Midget: (CT102); sub-miniature novelty camera; made from bakelite, available in five colours. Taylor Hobson Meniscus f10 lens; single speed sector shutter 1/30 s. 6 exp on 15mm roll film in special cassette. C 1936.

R3* Black: $90	£47	DM148	FF460
Brown/Red/Green:$120-140			
Blue:	$250	£131	DM412 FF1.3k

Coronet "3D" Stereo Camera: (CT103); plastic stereo camera, available in different colours; meniscus lens; single speed shutter. 4 stereo pairs or 8 single exp, 4.5cm on 127 film. C 1954.

| R2* $55 | £29 | DM91 | FF281 |

Jean CROS, St. Etienne, France.

Reyna-Cross II: (CS100); 1942, 35mm camera with cast aluminium body, 50mm/f3.5 Flor Berthiot lens, Reyna/Cross shutter,1/25-1/200s. Like (CO105), but made in the "free" zone of France.

| R4* $100 | £52 | DM165 | FF511 |

Reyna Cross III: (CS101); 35mm camera with cast aluminium body, like (CS100), but now equipt with a 45mm/f2.9 lens, and Microméanic shutter, 1/25-1/200s.

| R4* $100 | £52 | DM165 | FF511 |

Coronet Midget

CROWN CAMERA CO.,
New York.

Crown Camera: (CR100); cardboard box camera; meniscus lens; simple shutter. 1¼" x 1½" exp on dry plates. C 1910.

| R3* $175 | £92 | DM288 | FF894 |

CURTIS COLOUR LAB.

Curtis Colour Scout: (CU100); 2¼" x 3¼" colour camera; Goerz Dogmar 7½" f4.5 lens; Compur shutter. C 1942.

| R5* $500 | £262 | DM824 | FF2.6k |

Cyclops: (BB131); binocular-type detective camera; Telesigmar f4.5 lens; shutter 1/25-1/100 s. 16mm film in special cassettes. Similar to Teleca Camera. Mfd in Japan. C 1950.

| R4* $750 | £394 | DM1.2k | FF3.8k |

THE DAGUERREOTYPE PROCESS

Louis Jacques Mande Daguerre (1787-1851) was experimenting with methods to chemically fix the camera obscura image as early as 1826. In 1829, Daguerre met Nicephore Niepce through a mutual friend, Charles Chevalier, the Parisian optician who supplied both of them with lenses. After three years of negotiation, the two men formed a partnership, and their collaboration nearly met with success when, in 1833, Niepce died. Daguerre continued to experiment, returning to earlier work with silver salts. He found that silver iodide was more sensitive to light than silver nitrate, but more importantly he discovered the latent image.

The daguerreotype process was disclosed before a joint meeting of the Academy of Sciences and the Academy of Fine Arts in Paris on August 19, 1839. A sheet of copper, plated with silver, was washed carefully in a solution of nitric acid to remove surface impurities. It was then polished with jeweller's rouge and a buffing stick. The sheet was immediately placed in a fuming box and exposed to the vapours of iodine crystals; the fumes combined chemically with the silver to form a thin layer of light-sensitive silver iodide. Sensitization of the plate was complete when a deep golden yellow was attained. Thus prepared, the sheet was ready to be placed in the camera obscura for an exposure of 3-30 minutes in full sunlight.

The latent image was developed by holding the silvered surface at a 45-degree angle over a heated iron cup, containing mercury, which was maintained at 110 degrees Fahrenheit by an alcohol lamp. The mercury fumes combined with the exposed silver iodide to form an image consisting of a mercury-silver amalgam. The unexposed silver iodide was removed in a solution of sodium thiosulfate. The image was then toned with gold chloride to make the mercury-silver amalgam chemically stable. The image remained delicate, however, and was protected with a mat and glass and was mounted in a decorative case.

Daguerre's original process required long exposures, making it suitable only for still lifes, landscapes, and architectural views. Within a year, however, other experimenters improved the process. Exposure times were greatly reduced by sensitizing the plate with silver iodide and silver bromide. This higher plate speed, coupled with the availability of new high-speed lenses, reduced exposures by skilled daguerreotypists to between one and sixty seconds, making portraiture possible.

Today, daguerreotypes are prized by collectors. Ordinary portraits sell for between $5 and $50 depending on the size, quality and beauty of the image. Daguerreotypes of famous people by an identified portraitist can sell for several thousand dollars. A self-portrait by Albert Sands Southworth (C 1848) was sold for $36,000 at Christie's East in New York on May 15, 1980. An occupational—that is, daguerreotypes of a worker with his tools—is especially valued. A 1/6th-plate or a 1/4-plate occupational usually will bring between $300 and $1,000. Outdoor scenes are rare and very desirable; they usually sell for between $500 and $1,500.

Daguerreotype Outfit. From the collection of the George Eastman House/International Museum of Photography.

Daguerreotype Outfit

Daguerrian Sensitizing Box: (BB135); American-style of sensitizing box using either iodine or bromine for preparing quarter, sixth or ninth daguerreotype plates. C 1845.

R5* $1.5k+ £787+ DM2.5k+ FF7.7k+

Daguerrian Sensitizing Box

Daguerreotype Posing Stand: (BB134); cast-iron fluted stand; original paint. C 1845.

R5* $1k+ £525+ DM1.6k+ FF5.1k+

Daguerreotype Camera: (BB136): 1/2 plate chamfered-box type daguerreotype camera; Petzval 6" lens. Adjustable focus: the rear section is locked in one of three

Daguerreotype Posing Stand

Daguerreotype Camera

positions with a knurled wooden bolt. Stand: maple wood and cast iron. Mfr unknown;

American construction. C 1848.

R5* Complete: $8k+	£4.2k+	DM13.2k+	
Stand alone: $1.2k	£630	DM2k	

Daguerreotype Camera: (BB137); 1/4 plate chamfered-box type daguerreotype camera. Mfr unknown; American construction. C 1845.

$7k+	£3.7k+	DM11.5k+	FF35.8k+

Daguerreotype Camera: (BB140); 1/4 plate chamfered-box type daguerreotype camera. Petzval-type lens. Mfr unknown; American construction. C 1848.

$7k+	£3.7k+	DM11.5k+	FF35.8k+

DAI-ICHI OPTICAL WORKS, Japan.

Chicon 35: (DI100);1954. Cfps, 1 - 1/500 sec, seperate Rfr/Vfr windows, diopter adjustment. Screw mount Hexanon F3.5/ 50mm lens. Made in very small quantities, this camera was the forerunner of the Honor cameras from Mejiro Optical Works. Very Rare.

R5* $1.7k	£892	DM2.8k	FF8.7k

Zenobia: (DI101); 1949-53. 16 exposures on 120 film, folding camera with between the lens shutter 1 - 1/500s, 75mm f3.5 Hesper Anastigmat lens.

R3* $30	£16	DM49	FF153

DALKA Industries Pty. Ltd., Australia.

Candid: (DK200); C1939, plastic VFR camera for 6 x 6cm on 120 or 620 film, simple lens and shutter, believed to be a very early

Candid

example of rigid polystyrene injection molding. very rare.

R4* $50	£26	DM82	FF256

J. H. DALLMEYER, London, England.

Dallmeyer Stereoscopic Wet-Plate Camera: (JH100); Petzval lens rarer than later Rapid Rectilinear; flap shutter; rack and pinion focusing; mahogany wood with brass fittings. C 1861.

R5* $7.5k+	£3.9k+	DM12.4k+	FF38.3k+

M. DAMOIZEAU, Paris, France.

Le Cyclographe a Foyer Fixe: (DA100); panoramic camera covers 360 degrees. Spring wound motor drives roll film in the opposite direction to camera rotation. 9 exp, 13 x 80mm. C 1893.

R5* $5k+	£2.6k+	DM8.2k+	FF25.6k+

J. B. DANCER, Manchester, England.

J. B. Dancer's Stereo Wet-Plate Camera: (JB100); C 1856. This camera was probably the first commercially produced stereo wet-plate camera.

R5* $12k+	£6.3k+	DM19.8k+	FF61.3k+

DANGELMAIER & CO, Reutlingen, Germany

This company changed names and address more than a few times in the 1950's and 60's, ending up in the mid 1970's as the Dacora/Weber company in Nürnberg. For simplicity all cameras are listed here, whether made in Reutlingen, Munich or Nürnberg.

Daco: (DK100); C1949, bakelite box camera for 6 x 6 frames on roll film, simple lens, two position focusing, three lens openings, f11,f16, and f 22, single speed shutter, no built-in handle!

R3* $40	£21	DM66	FF204

DANGELMAIER-DIAX

Daci Royal: (DK101); C1950, metal box camera for 6 x 6 frames on roll film, simple f9 lens, single speed shutter, synch connection.

R2* $15	£8	DM25	FF77

Daci Royal I: (DK102); C1950, metal box camera for 6 x 6 frames on roll film, simple f9 lens, single speed shutter, like (DK100) but without synch connection.

R2* $15	£8	DM25	FF77

Subita: (DK103); C1953, folding VFR camera for 6 x 6 frames on roll film, Astigmat f6.3/75mm lens, simple Singlo two speed shutter, *without* double exposure prevention or body release. A cheap version of the Dacora camera (DK104).

R2* $25	£13	DM41	FF128

Dacora: (DK104); C1953, folding VFR camera for 6 x 6 frames on roll film, Dacora f5.6/75mm lens, Vario shutter *without* double exposure prevention, or coated Dacora F3.5/75mm lens in Pronto or Prontor shutter *with* double exposure prevention!

R2* $30	£16	DM49	FF153

Dacora-Record: (DK105); C1954, folding camera for 6 x 6 frames on roll film, uncoupled RFR, lever film advance, Dignar f4.5/75mm lens or Ennar or Westar f3.5/75mm lens in Prontor-s or Prontor SVS shutter.

R3* $65	£34	DM107	FF332

Dacora-Record-Royal: (DK106); C1954, folding camera for 6 x 6 frames on roll film, *coupled RFR,* lever film advance, Dignar f4.5/75mm lens or Ennar or Westar f3.5/75mm lens in Prontor-S or Prontor SVS shutter.

R3* $80	£42	DM132	FF409

Dignette: (DK107); C1954-60, 35mm VFR camera, several body styles, several lens and shutter combinations, typically, Dignar f2.8/45mm lens in Vario shutter.

R2* $25	£13	DM41	FF128

Super Dignette: (DK108); C1955-60, 35mm VFR camera with built-in light meter, several body styles, several lens available, typically, Dignar f2.8/45mm lens in Vario or Pronto shutter.

R2* $25	£13	DM41	FF128

Digna 6 x 6: (DK109); C1954, metal VFR camera for 6 x 6 frames on roll film, several lens and shutter combinations available, typically Westar f2.9/75mm, Prontor shutter

R2* $25	£13	DM41	FF128

Digna I: (DK110); C1954, metal VFR camera for 6 x 6 frames on roll film, Achromat lens in single speed shutter, cheap version of the Digna 6 x6 (DK109).

R2* $15	£8	DM25	FF77

Colour Digna 6 x 6: (DK111); C1956, metal VFR camera for 6 x 6 frames on roll film, several lens and shutter combinations available, typically Achromat f4.5/75mm, Vario shutter, built-in extinction light meter.

R2* $25	£13	DM41	FF128

Dacora CC: (DK112); C1960, full automatic 35mm VFR camera, with manual possible, Ysarex f2.8/45mm lens, Prontormatic shutter.

R2* $25	£13	DM41	FF128

Dakora 66: (DK113); C1964, simple metal VFR camera for 6 x 6 frames on 120 roll film.

R2* $20	£10	DM33	FF102

Dakora 44: (DK114); C1964, simple metal VFR camera for 4 x 4 frames on 127 roll film.

R3* $25	£13	DM41	FF128

DIAX KAMERAWERK, Walter Voss, Ulm, Germany

Diax: (VS100); C1948-52, metal 35mm VFR camera, Xenar f2.8/4.5cm lens, Compur Rapid shutter.

R3* $40	£21	DM66	FF204

Diax

DIAX-DARLOT

Diax Ia: (VS101); C1950, metal 35mm VFR camera with three finders, one each for 35mm, 50mm, and 90mm fields of view, interchangeable Xenar f2.8/45mm, Xenon f2/50mm, Westar, or Isconar f3.5/50mm lens, Synchro Compur shutter.

R2* $60	£31	DM99	FF307

Diax II: (VS102); C1950, metal 35mm camera with *coupled* RFR, *non*-changeable Xenar f2.8, Xenon f2, or Heligon f2/45mm lens, Synchro Compur shutter.

R2* $60	£31	DM99	FF307

Diax IIa: (VS103); C1955, metal 35mm camera with coupled RFR, interchangeable Xenar f2.8/45mm, Xenon f2/50mm, Westar f3.5/50mm, or Isconar f3.5/50mm lens, Synchro Compur shutter. built-in finder for 90mm lens located next to 50mm combined RFR/VFR.

R2* $90	£47	DM148	FF460

Diax Ib: (VS104); C1956, metal 35mm VFR camera with three finders, one each for 35mm, 50mm, and 90mm fields of view, Westar f3.5, Isconar f3.5, Xenar f2.8 or Xenon f2/50mm lens, Synchro Compur shutter, lever advance, new body style compared with Diax Ia (VS101).

R3* $65	£34	DM107	FF332

Diax IIb: (VS105); C1956, 35mm camera with coupled RFR for all lenses from 35mm to 135mm, seperate VFR for 90mm lens located next to combined RFR/VFR, Isconar f3.5, Xenar f2.8 or Xenon f2/50mm lens, Synchro Compur shutter, lever advance, new body style compared with Diax IIa (VS103).

R2* $80	£42	DM132	FF409

Diaxette: (VS106); C1953, simple metal 35mm VFR camera, Cassar f2.8/45mm lens, Prontor shutter.

R3* $25	£13	DM41	FF128

Accessories for Diax cameras

Xenagon f3.5/35mm lens: (VS001); **$45**
Isconar f4.5/85mm lens: (VS002); **$60**
Tele-Xenar f3.5/90mm lens: (VS003); **$65**
Tele-Xenar f4/135mm lens: (VS004); **$70**

DAN 35: (BB141); Dan 40mm f4.5 lens; single speed shutter; 12 exp on special cassettes, 24 x 24mm exp. C 1950.

R3* $75	£39	DM124	FF383

Albert DARIER, Geneva, Switzerland.

L'Escopette de Darier: (DR100); gun-type detective camera; Steinheil Antiplanet 90mm f6 lens; spherical shutter 1/25-1/100 s. One of the first cameras to use Eastman roll film for 100 exp. 6.8 x 7.2cm. C 1888.

R5* $10k+	£5.2k+	DM16.5k+	FF51.1k+

Darling: (SI200); sub-miniature camera; 16mm film in special cassette.

R4* $450	£236	DM742	FF2.3k

Darling

A. DARLOT, Paris, France.

Le Rapide: (DQ100); Darlot rectilinear 135mm f8 lens; rotary between-the-lens shutter; 12 plates, 9 x 12cm in gravity-fed magazine. C 1887.

R4* $2.5k	£1.3k	DM4.1k	FF12.8k

L. F. DEARDORFF & SONS, Chicago, Illinois.

L. F. Deardorff & Sons View Camera: (DE100); 5" x 7" view camera; front and rear swings and tilts; double extension bellows. Seasoned mahogany wood with nickel plated fittings. C 1960. 4" x 5", 8" x 10". Users are willing to pay more than collectors.

R4* $1k	£525	DM1.6k	FF5.1k

Andre DEBRIE, Paris, France.

Sept: (DB100); half-frame 35mm still camera; movie camera, projector, contact printer. Berthiot Stylor 50mm f3.5 lens; rotary shutter 1/60 s—single exp and sequence settings. C 1923. Invented by Guiseppe Tartara. 250 exp on perforated 18 x 24mm film. Cartridge held 17' of film. Sold by Societe Francais Sept. First model—flat spring wound motor unit. Second model—

Sept first model

Sept second model

rounded (enlarged) spring wound motor unit.

R2* $225	£118	DM371	FF1.2k

Dekko: (BB143); 9.5mm movie camera; interchangeable lens mount; optical vf; speeds from 8 to 64 frames per s; bakelite body in Art Deco style. Mfd in England. C 1937.

R*3 $45	£24	DM74	FF230

DELAYE, Paris, France.

Le Prismac: (DL100); stereo camera; Kenngott Anastigmatic 54mm lenses; variable speed guillotine shutter. Takes 2 simultaneous exp through 90 degree prisms on roll film. C 1906.

R5* $2.5k+	£1.3k+	DM4.1k+	FF12.8k+

DEMARIE-LAPIERRE-MOLLIER, Paris, France

Dehel: (DH100); 1940, 6 x 9cm folding roll film camera with various lenses and shutters, among which the Manar 90mm/f3.5 and f4.5 use a slightly curved film plane and pressure plate.

R2* $25	£13	DM41	FF128

Dehel Primar: (DH101); 1940, 6 x 4.5cm roll film camera, with various lens and shutter combinations. Called "The soldiers camera" when first introduced in the Spring of 1940.

R2* $35	£18	DM58	FF179

Telka-III (Dehel Super): (DH102); 1948, 6 x 9cm folding roll film camera with CRF, 95mm/f3.5 Sagittar in Prontor shutter, speeds of 1-1/200s, early cameras have a black face plate on the shutter, while later ones have a chrome plate. Delivered with a test film taken with the camera at the factory to show the quality of the lens!

R2* $60	£31	DM99	FF307

Telka-IIIA: (DH103); 1951, 6 x 9cm folding roll film camera with CRF, 95mm/f3.5 Sagittar in Prontor SV shutter, speeds of 1-1/200s, bright yellow VFR windo to increase the contrast of the rangefinder image.

R3* $60	£31	DM99	FF307

Telka-IIIB: (DH104); 1952, 6 x 9cm folding roll film camera with CRF, 95mm/f3.5 Sagittar in Prontor SV shutter with "EV" markings, speeds of 1-1/300s, special adaptor for using Bantam 828 colour film.

R2* $90	£47	DM148	FF460

Telka-III "Professional": (DH105); 1953, 6 x 9cm folding roll film camera with CRF, 95mm/f3.5 Sagittar in Prontor SV shutter, speeds of 1-1/300s, entirely black for that "professional look".

R4* $150	£79	DM247	FF767

Telka-X: (DH106); 1950, 6 x 9cm folding roll film camera with simple lens and shutter, folding VFR, name marked on the shutter.

R2* $20	£10	DM33	FF102

Telka-XX: (DH107); 1951, 6 x 9cm folding roll film camera with 110mm/f4.5 Manar lens in Gitzo shutter. Early cameras have a folding VFR, while later ones have a top plate similar to the Telka-III without CRF.

R2* $30	£16	DM49	FF153

Telka-I: (DH108); 1954, 6 x 9cm folding roll film camera without CRF, 95mm/f3.5 Sagittar in Prontor shutter, speeds of 1-1/200s, essentially the same camera as the Telka-III, but without CRF.

R3* $35	£18	DM58	FF179

Summa: (DH109); 1953, 6 x 9cm folding roll film camera with simple lens and shutter, or 110mm/f4.5 Manar lens in Gitzo shutter, folding VFR, name marked on the shutter. The same camera as the Telka-X, and Telka-XX, but delivered for a company in Monte Carlo. The name was quickly dropped, as an Italian camera already had the registered rights to the name.

R3* $40	£21	DM66	FF204

Telka-II: (DH110); 1955, 6 x 4.5cm roll film camera, front focusing 75mm/f3.5 Manar lens, Prontor S shutter, speeds of 1 - 1/200s, folding VFR.

R3* $60	£31	DM99	FF307

Telka-Sport: (DH111); 1960, 6 x 4.5cm roll film camera, CRF 70mm/f3.5 Sagittar lens in an Atos shutter, speeds of 1-1/300s. Provided with adaptors for using Bantam 828 film. About 1000 cameras are said to have been made. The last camera made by Demarie-Lapierre-Mollier, a house which was originally founded in 1848.

R4* $175	£92	DM288	FF894

DETROLA CORP, Detroit, Michigan.

Detrola 400: (DC100); 35mm rf camera; Wollensak Velostigmat 50mm f3.5 lens, interchangeable screw mount; CFPS 1-1/500 s, CRF.

R3* $550	£289	DM907	FF2.8k

Detrola 400

Detrola A: (DC101); C1938, Bakelite VFR camera for 3 x 4cm frames on 127 film, fixed focus lens and shutter in collapsible tube mount. (prices less in the USA).

R2* $20	£10	DM33	FF102

Detrola B: (DC102); C1938, as (DC101) but with built-in extinction meter. (prices less in the USA).

R2* $25	£13	DM41	FF128

Detrola D: (DC103); C1938, as (DC102) but with f4.5 lens. (prices less in the USA).

R3* $25	£13	DM41	FF128

Detrola G

D

Detrola E: (DC104); C1938, as DC102) but with f3.5 lens. (prices less in the USA).

R3* $25	£13	DM41	FF128

Detrola G : (DC105); C1938, Bakelite VFR camera for 3 x 4cm frames on 127 film, Detrola f4.5/2" lens, shutter 1/25 - 1/200s, collapsible tube mount, helociod focusing. (prices less in the USA).

R2* $25	£13	DM41	FF128

DEVIN COLOURGRAPH CO., New York.

Devin One-Shot Colour Camera: (DW100); 6.5 x 9cm sheet film one-shot colour camera; Goerz Dogmar 5¹/2" f4.5 lens; Compur dial-set shutter 1-1/250 s, CRF. C 1940.

R5* $800+	£420+	DM1.3k+	FF4.1k+

Devin One-Shot Colour Camera

DEVRY CORPORATION, Chicago, Illinois.

Devry: (DV100); 16mm movie camera; Wollensak f1.9 lens; spring motor drive or hand crank, double claw film advance. C 1932. Distinguished by a table of exp times for the different temperate zones of the world; advises closing diaphragm one stop in tropical climates.

R2* $45	£24	DM74	FF230

QRS Kamra: (DV101); 35mm bakelite camera; Graf Anastigmat f7.7 lens; single shutter speed. 40 exp on 35mm film in special cassette. C 1928.

R3* $125	£66	DM206	FF639

QRS Kamra

QRS: (DV102); metal bodied 16mm movie camera; fixed lens; adjustable diaphragm (waterhouse stops). Spring wound motor drive. 100' of film. C 1930.

R3* $45	£24	DM74	FF230

E. DEYROLLE FILS, Paris, France.

Le Scenographe of Dr. Candeze: (ED100); landscape lens mounted on sliding panel—stereo pictures in two exp. 10 x 15cm on dry plates. C 1874.

R4* $4.5k+	£2.4k+	DM7.4k+	FF23k+

Dick Tracy Camera: (BB144); toy plastic camera; 127 roll film.

R2* $45	£24	DM74	FF230

Ditmar: (BB145); 9.5mm movie camera; Cinor Berthiot 25mm f1.8 lens; 2 speeds: 16 and 32 frames per s; non-coupled photo-electric cell; 15mm cassettes. Mfd in Austria. C 1939.

R3* $50	£26	DM82	FF256

Ditmar: (BB146); 8mm movie camera; f1.8 lens; photo-electric cell light meter, non-coupled; 2 speeds. Mfd in Austria. C 1938.

| R2* $50 | £26 | DM82 | FF256 |

Ditmar: (BB147); 8mm movie camera; one of the first European-made high quality cameras for 8mm format. 16 or 32 frames per s; diaphragm and counter visible in vf; spring motor drive could advance 11' of film on one winding; hand crank for backwinding; self-filming device. Mfd in Austria. C 1933.

| R3* $60 | £31 | DM99 | FF307 |

DOM-MARTIN,
Paris, France.

Dom-Martin: (DO100); press-type stereo camera; aluminium body. 2 sizes: 6 x 13cm, 8 x 16cm. C 1903.

| R4* $800 | £420 | DM1.3k | FF4.1k |

DORYU CAMERA CO.,
Japan.

Doryu-2: (DX100); pistol-type detective camera; Dorimar 17mm f2.5 lens; 3 speed shutter. 10 x 10mm exp on special 16mm

Doryu-2

film. bullet shaped Flash cartridges. C 1954. In 1955, an improved model was produced with a 15mm f2.2 lens and a faster shutter.

| R5* $7k+ | £3.7k+ | DM11.5k+ | FF35.8k+ |

Doryu flash cartridges: (DX001); Packages of six bullet shaped flash cartridges have recently made their way into the market. They would be of more value to a Doryu owner, who might be willing to pay above the going price for a package to try out in his camera!

| R3* $50 | £26 | DM82 | FF256 |

DOSSERT DETECTIVE
CAMERA CO.,
New York, New York.

Dossert Detective Camera: (DD100); 4" x 5" leather covered, box-type detective camera; 4" x 5" exp on dry plates; sliding panels to mask lens openings and ground glass opening. C 1890.

| R4* $900 | £472 | DM1.5k | FF4.6k |

007 Attache Case Camera: (BB150); toy camera; radio, coding device, and telescope in attache case.

| R4* $300 | £157 | DM495 | FF1.5k |

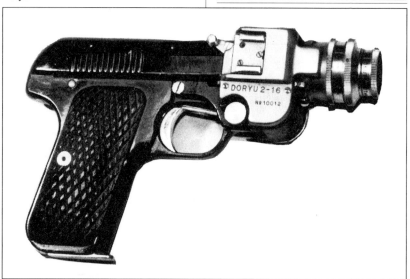

D

Dr. DOYER, M. GILLON, France.

La Diplide: (DY100); eye-level reflex camera; helicoid focusing to 0.5m. 6 x 13cm exp on roll film. C 1904.

R4* $500	£262
	DM824 FF2.6k

DUBRONI, Paris, France.

Dubroni Apparatus No. 1: (DU100); rigid bodied camera for in-camera processing of single wet collodion plate; "Lachenal Opticien" 60mm f3.5 lens; lens cap controls exp. Invented by Bourdin, Paris, France.

Dubroni Apparatus No. 1

(Dubroni is an anagram of Bourdin). Mfd by Maison Dubroni, Paris, France. C 1865. First model. Second model.

R5* $3.5k	£1.8k	DM5.8k	FF17.9k

Le Photographe de Poche: (DU101); 5 x 5cm plates; built-in bottles for developing chemicals. Box carries all accessories necessary for developing and printing. Patent: May 21, 1860.

R5* $10k+	£5.2k+	DM16.5k+	FF51.1k+

Le Photo Sport: (DU102); C1889, Darlot Planigraphe 210mm f9 lens; simple rotary shutter. 9 x 12cm plates.

R5* $2k+	£1.1k+	DM3.3k+	FF10.2k+

DUCATI, Milan, Italy.

Ducati: (DT100); C 1938, half-frame 35mm camera; Ducati Etar f3.5/35mm lens; CFPS 1/25-1/250 s.

R3* $250	£131	DM412	FF1.3k

Ducati (with rangefinder): (DT101); C1938, half-frame 35mm camera, Vitor f3.5/35mm lens; CFPS 1/20-1/500 s, CRF.

R3* $350	£184	DM577	FF1.8k

Ducati with and without rangefinder

DURST S.A., Switzerland.

Duca: (DZ100); 35mm camera; Ducar 50mm f11 lens; shutter, T and I. 12 exp, 24 x 36mm on Agfa Rapid cassettes. C 1946.

R3* $100	£52	DM165	FF511

E

EASTERN SPECIALTY MFG. CO., Boston, Massachusetts.

Springfield Union Camera: (EM100); plate brought into plane of focus by rotating block inside camera; 4 exp, 3¹/₂" x 3¹/₂" on dry plates. C 1899.

R4* $400	£210	DM659	FF2k

Albert EBNER & CO., Stuttgart, Germany.

Ebner: (EN100); plastic folding camera; Rodenstock-Trinar-Anastigmat 10.5cm f4.5 lens; Compur shutter 1-1/250 s; 8 exp, 2¹/₄" x 3¹/₄" on 120 roll film. C 1938.

R3* $150	£79	DM247	FF767

Ebner

Eder Patent Camera: (BB152); German folding plate camera; viewing lens and bel-

lows paired horizontally with taking lens; 6 x 6cm exp on plate or film.

R4* $750	£394	DM1.2k	FF3.8k

Thomas A. EDISON, INC.

Edison Home Kinetoscope: (TA100); home movie projector. Special 22mm film with 2 rows of perforations and 3 rows of images. The Thomas A. Edison company provided reduction prints of 35mm films produced for theatre use. C 1912.

R4* $500	£262	DM824	FF2.6k

Edison Kinetoscope: (TA101); peep show viewing device for 50' loops of 35mm film. Electric motor advanced film and rotated shutter; electric lamp illuminated film. C 1894. Very rare.

R5* NSR $5k+	£2.6k+	DM8.2k+	FF25.6k+

Edison Kinetoscope

EFICA S.R.L., Argentina.

Atlas: (EF100); C1950, metal box camera for 6 x 9cm frames on roll film, simple lens and shutter.

R4* $40	£21	DM66	FF204

EHO KAMERAFABRIK, Dresden, Germany.

After July 1939, known as the Amca Kamerawerk, Berthold Altman prop, Altmann lent the first three letters of his family name to Altissa, Altix, Altiflex and Altiscope line of cameras. See Altissa Kamerawerk for post-war cameras.

Altissa: (EH100); Simple fixed focus box camera design with I and B speed shutter. Large optical finder in top with some models having reflex viewing adds 100% to the price. Not to be confused with the post-war Altissa, though looking very similar!

| R2* $25 | £13 | DM41 | FF128 |

Altissa

Eho Box: (EH101); 1932-39, line of inexpensive box cameras in 6 x 6cm, 6 x 9cm, 6 x 4.5cm and 3 x 4cm formats with meniscus or better lenses, some with wire frame finders in addition to the typical waistlevel reflex finders. All are about the same price,

though the smaller format cameras are rarer and go for 100% more.

| R2* $15 | £8 | DM25 | FF77 |

Eho Stereo Box: (EH102); C1936, simple box camera for stereo pairs 6 x 13cm on roll film, wire frame finder and reflex finder.

| R2* $110 | £58 | DM181 | FF562 |

Altiflex: (EH103); C1936-39, TLR for 6 x 6 frames on roll film with Victar or Trinar 75mm lens in Automat, Prontor II or Compur shutter, side mounted focusing handle.

| R3* $55 | £29 | DM91 | FF281 |

Altiscope: (EH104); C1936, stereo camera for 6 x 13cm stereo pairs, or 6 x 6 single non-stereo frames, Victor f4.5/75mm lenses, simple three speed shutter, the same optical finder as used on the Altissa box camera (EH100).

| R4* $150 | £79 | DM247 | FF767 |

Altix: (EH105); C1937, 35mm VFR camera for 24 x 24mm frames on regular 35mm film, Laack f3.5/3.5cm lens, simple shutter. The first of the Altix cameras. (See **ALTISSA** listing for post-war cameras).

| R3* $45 | £24 | DM74 | FF230 |

L'Electra Plastica Industria S.A. (L.E.P.I.S.A.) Barcelona, Spain.

Fotex: (FT200); C1960, bakelite VFR camera for 6 x 9cm on roll film, simple lens and shutter, delivered with a bakelite lens/shutter cover just like the Photax (PF105) by MIOM.

| R4* $50 | £26 | DM82 | FF256 |

E. ENJALBERT, Paris, France.

L'Alpiniste: (EJ100); Aplanatic lens; guillotine shutter. Magazine held 9 x 12cm plates which were changed manually through a leather pouch. C 1886.

| R5* $1k | £525 | DM1.6k | FF5.1k |

Le Colis Postal: (EJ101); wrapped postal package-type detective camera. C 1886.

| R* NSR $7k+ | £3.7k+ | DM11.5k+ | FF35.8k+ |

ENJALBERT-ERNEMANN

Photo Revolver (de Poche): (EJ102); revolver-type detective camera; achromatized periscopic 70mm f10 lens; between the lens rotary sector shutter. 10 exp, 2 x 2cm on dry plates. C 1883. Rotation of barrel (magazine) simultaneously changed the plate and cocked the shutter. The trigger acted as the shutter release.

R5* $20k+	£10.5k+	DM33k+	FF102.2k+

Photo Revolver (de Poche)

Le Tourist d'Enjalbert: (EJ103); Steinheil lens with waterhouse stops; 8 exp on 13 x 18cm plates. C 1880.

R5* $1k	£525	DM1.6k	FF5.1k

ERAC SELLING CO., London, England.

Erac: (ES100); pistol-type detective camera; fixed focus meniscus lens; 18 x 18mm exp on 20mm roll film. Film advance coupled to trigger and shutter. Invented by H. Covill and H. Steward. C 1931.

R4* $500	£262	DM824	FF2.6k

Erac

Heinrich ERNEMANN WERKE A.G., Dresden, Germany.

Bob 0: (EW100); Ernemann Double Erid 5" f8 lens; 4¹/₄" x 3¹/₄" exp on roll film. C 1924.

R2* $35	£18	DM58	FF179

Bob I: (EW101); Ernemann Ernastigmat 5¹/₄" f 6.8* lens; Cronos shutter; 4¹/₄" x 3¹/₄" exp on roll film. C 1924.

R2* $30	£16	DM49	FF153

Bob II: (EW102); Ernemann Ernastigmat 5¹/₄" f6.8* lens; Cronos shutter; 4¹/₄" x 3¹/₄" exp on roll film. C 1924.

R2* $30	£16	DM49	FF153

Bob III: (EW103); Ernemann Ernastigmat 4¹/₈" f6.8* lens; Cronos shutter; 3¹/₄" x 2¹/₄" exp on roll film. C 1924.

R2* $35	£18	DM58	FF179

Bob IV: (EW104); Ernemann Ernastigmat 4¹/₈" f6.8* lens; Cronos shutter; 3¹/₄" x 2¹/₄" exp on roll film. C 1924.

R2* $60	£31	DM99	FF307

Bob V: (EW105); Ernemann Ernastigmat 3" f6.8* lens; Cronos shutter; 2¹/₂" x 1⁵/₈" exp on roll film. C 1910-1913.

R2* $60	£31	DM99	FF307

Bob X: (EW106); roll film stereo camera; Ernon 65mm f6.8 lenses; 45 x 107mm exp on roll film. C 1922.

R4* $400	£210	DM659	FF2k

Bob XV: (EW107); roll film stereo camera; Ernemann Doppel-Anastigmat (Ernon) 65mm f6.8 lenses; interleaf shutter 1 - 1/1900 s, optical vf, reflecting waist level vf. 45 x 107mm exp on roll film. C 1924.

R4* $400	£210	DM659	FF2k

Bobette I: (EW110); Ernoplast 50mm f4.5 lens; Automatic central shutter 1/25-1/100 s; 22 x 33cm exp on special 40mm wide roll film. C 1923-1925.

R3* $130	£68	DM214	FF664

Ermanox f2.0 (Original): (EW111); 4.5 x 6cm miniature plate camera; Ernostar 100mm f2.0 lens; CFPS 1/20 - 1/1000 s. C 1924.

R4* $1.2k	£630	DM2k	FF6.1k

Bob XV

Ermanox f2.0 (Original)

Ermanox f1.8

Ermanox (6.5 x 9cm): (EW112); 6.5 x 9cm plate camera; Ernostar 125mm f1.8 lens; CFPS 1/20-1/1000 s. C 1925.

R4* $1.2k	£630	DM2k	FF6.1k

Ermanox f1.8: (EW113); 4.5 x 6cm miniature plate camera; Ernostar 85mm f1.8 lens; CFPS 1/20-1/1000 s. C 1926.

R4* $1.2k	£630	DM2k	FF6.1k

Erni: (EW114); Achromatic f12.5 lens; $2^5/_{16}$" x $1^3/_5$" exp on plates. C 1920.

R3* $125	£66	DM206	FF639

Ernoflex: (EW115); 4.5 x 6cm SLR camera; Ernon 75mm f3.5 lens; CFPS 1/20-1/1000 s. C 1920.

R3* $800	£420	DM1.3k	FF4.1k

Ernoflex

Ernoflex, Model II with Triple Extension: (EW116); $3^1/_4$" x 4" folding SLR camera; Ernemann Ernon $7^1/_8$" f3.5 lens; CFPS to 1/1000 s. Probably the first SLR to couple the revolving back to movable masks in the vf area. C 1926.

R4* $400	£210	DM659	FF2k

ERNEMANN

Ernoflex, Model II with Triple Extension

Globus Field View Camera: (EW117); 13" x 18" view camera; Any number of brass lenses can be found mounted on this camera; FPS; double extension bellows; polished wood with brass fittings; black cloth-covered holders. Brass importer's label: Allison & Hadaway Corp., N.Y. C 1900.

R4* $400	£210	DM659	FF2k

Stereo Ernoflex: (EW118); 45 x 107mm stereo camera; Ernostar 75mm f4.5 lenses; CFPS 1/25-1/1200 s. C 1925.

R5* $1.7k	£892	DM2.8k	FF8.7k

Stereo Ernoflex

Heag I: (EW120); Ernemann Erid 3¹⁵/₁₆" f8 lens; 3¹/₂" x 2¹/₂" exp on plates. C 1924.

R2* $40	£21	DM66	FF204

Heag II: (EW121); Ernemann Ernoplast 5¹/₄" f4.5* lens; Cronos shutter; 4¹/₄" x 3¹/₄" exp on plates. C 1924.

R2* $40	£21	DM66	FF204

Heag III: (EW122); Ernemann Erid 4¹/₈" f8 lens; Cronos shutter 3¹/₂" x 2¹/₂" exp on plates. C 1924.

R2* $40	£21	DM66	FF204

Heag IV: (EW123); Ernemann Ernastigmat 5¹/₄" f6.8 lens; Cronos shutter; 4¹/₄" x 3¹/₄" exp on plates. C 1924.

R2* $40	£21	DM66	FF204

Heag V: (EW124): Zeiss Tessar 5¹/₄" f6.3* lens; Cronos shutter; 4¹/₄" x 3¹/₄" exp on plates. C 1924.

R2* $45	£24	DM74	FF230

Heag VII: (EW125); Zeiss Tessar ¹/₄" f6.3* lens; Cronos shutter; 4¹/₄" x 3¹/₄" exp on plates. C 1924.

R2* $40	£21	DM66	FF204

Heag XI: (EW126); Zeiss Tessar 7¹/₈" f6.3* lens; Cronos shutter; 6¹/₂" x 4³/₄" exp on plates. C 1924.

R2* $45	£24	DM74	FF230

Tropical Heag XI: (EW127); 9 x 12cm tropical plate camera; Tessar 13.5cm f6.3 lens; Compur 1-1/250 s. Mahogany finish, brown bellows and brass fittings. 9 x 12cm

Tropical Heag XI:

ERNEMANN

exp on plates. C 1920.

R4* $1.4k	£735	DM2.3k	FF7.2k

Heag XII: (EW130); 10 x 15cm camera; Ernon 150mm f6.8 lens; Ernemann central shutter. C 1911.

R3* $60	£31	DM99	FF307

Heag XII: (EW131); model 3; 9 x 14cm stereo camera; Ernemann Double Anastigmat 15cm lens; shutter 1-1/300 s. C 1907.

R4* $325	£171	DM536	FF1.7k

Heag XI: (EW132); 45 x 107mm folding stereo camera; Ernemann Aplanat 65mm f6.8 lens; between lens shutter to 1/300 s. C 1914.

R4* $250	£131	DM412	FF1.3k

Kino I: (EW133); amateur movie camera; Ernemann Kinostigmat lens; 17.5mm central perforation film. C 1902.

R4* $800	£420	DM1.3k	FF4.1k

Kino I

Kino II: (EW134); amateur movie camera; Kinostigmat lens; variable sector shutter; 17.5mm film in film magazine (15 or 50m); clockwork mechanism rewound film in the magazine. C 1904.

R4* $800	£420	DM1.3k	FF4.1k

Normal Kino (Model A): (EW135); teak wood construction, specially sectioned to cancel out dimensional shifts due to changes in humidity and temperature. Internal wooden magazine held 200' of 35mm film. Hand cranked with a fly-wheel assembly to smooth out film flow. C 1914.

R5* $750	£394	DM1.2k	FF3.8k

Klapp Stereo: (EW136); Tessar 55mm f4.5 lenses; FPS; changing mechanism for 12 plates. C 1911.

R4* $900	£472	DM1.5k	FF4.6k

Tropical Klapp: (EW137); 10 x 15cm plate camera; Tessar 165cm f4.5 lens; CFPS. Teak construction with brown leather bellows and brass fittings. C 1914.

R4* $1k	£525	DM1.6k	FF5.1k

Miniature Klapp: (EW140); 4.5 x 6cm folding camera; Anastigmat 75mm f4.5 lens; FPS to 1/1000 s. 4.5 x 6cm exp on plates. C 1914-1925.

R4* $650	£341	DM1.1k	FF3.3k

Miniature Klapp

Liliput

ERNEMANN-EXPO

Liliput: (EW141); Achromatic f12.5 lens; 2 5/16" x 1 3/4" exp on plates. C 1913.

| R3* $75 | £39 | DM124 | FF383 |

Stereo Liliput: (EW142); Achromatic f12.5 lenses; 45 x 107mm exp; black enamelled metal body. C 1915.

| R4* $300 | £157 | DM495 | FF1.5k |

Simplex: (EW143); Double Erid 5 1/2" f11 lens; 3 1/2" x 2 1/2" exp on plates. C 1924.

| R2* $95 | £50 | DM157 | FF486 |

Stereo-Simplex: (EW144); Ernemann Erid 2 3/8" f8 lenses; 45 x 107mm exp on plates. C 1924.

| R3* $150 | £79 | DM247 | FF767 |

Rolf I: (EW145); Ernemann Ernastigmat 3" f6.8* lens; Cronos shutter to 1/100 s; 2 1/2" x 1 5/8" 8 exp on roll film. C 1924.

| R2* $40 | £21 | DM66 | FF204 |

Unette: (EW146); C 1924, leather covered wooden bodied box camera for 22 x 33mm exp on special 40mm roll film, meniscus lens; guillotine shutter.

| R4* $150 | £79 | DM247 | FF767 |

EUMIG,
Vienna, Austria.

Camera Eumig: (EU100); 9.5mm movie camera; interchangeable Meyer Goerlitz Anastigmat 20mm f2.8 lens; special cassettes for 9.5mm movie film. C 1935.

| R2* $50 | £26 | DM82 | FF256 |

Camera Eumig (with photo electric cell): (EU101); 9.5mm movie camera; Meyer Goerlitz Anastigmat 20mm f2.8 lens, interchangeable mount; special cassettes for 9.5mm movie film. First movie camera to have Selenium photocell coupled to lens diaphragm. C 1935.

| R3* $90 | £47 | DM148 | FF460 |

Eumig C39: (EU102); 9.5mm movie camera; f2.7 lens; 3 speeds; coupled photo-cell, with manual override. C 1939.

| R3* $75 | £39 | DM124 | FF383 |

Eumig C4: (EU103); 8mm movie camera; f2.5 lens. First 8mm camera powered by electric motor.

| R3* $75 | £39 | DM124 | FF383 |

Eumig C 16-R: (EU104); 16mm movie camera; Eumigor 25mm f1.9 lens. Spring-wound motor drive: 16 to 64 frames per s. C 1957.

| R2* $60 | £31 | DM99 | FF307 |

Eumig Nautica: (EU105); 8mm underwater movie camera; macro-zoom 9 to 30mm f1.9 lens, automatic "Servo-focus"; waterproof to depth of 30m.

| R3* $125 | £66 | DM206 | FF639 |

EXPO CAMERA CO.,
New York, New York.

Expo: (EX100); watch-style detective camera; meniscus achromatic 25mm f16 lens; rotating shutter T, I. 25 exp, 16 x 22mm on roll film in daylight loading special cassette. C 1905-1939.

| R3* $250 | £131 | DM412 | FF1.3k |

Expo Police Camera: (EX101); miniature detective camera; achromatic meniscus f16 lens, adjustable diaphragm; CFPS; 12 exp, 12 x 26mm on roll film in special cassette. C 1911.

| R4* $350 | £184 | DM577 | FF1.8k |

Expo

FAP, Fabrique d'Appareils Photographique, Suresnes, France

Norca "A": (FB100); C.1938, Bakelite 35mm VFR camera, with leather covering, 50mm/f3.5 Saphir or Flor lens in spring loaded collapsible tube, Gitzo btl shutter, speeds 1/25-1/300s, very like the Argus "A" camera (AI102).

R3* $190	£100	DM313	FF971

Norca "B": (FB101); C.1946, Bakelite bodied 35mm VFR camera, 50mm/f3.5 Saphir or Flor lens in collapsible tube, *not* spring loaded as the Norca "A" (FB100), "Rapid-Synchro" copy of Compur Rapid shutter or simpler Norca shutter, speeds 1/25-1/300s. The story goes that the director of FAB was held in a German prisoner of war camp for 5 long years. Upon his release, he quickly picked up where he left off back in 1939. As a result, the Norca "B" was one of the first French cameras on the market in quantity after WWII.

R3* $75	£39	DM124	FF383

Norca "Cmt": (FB103); Metal bodied 35mm VFR camera, keeping the same design as the Norca "A" and "B" cameras, black leather covering, top mounted accessory shoe, 50mm/f3.5 FAP Anistigmat lens in Rapid-Synchro Shutter, speeds 1-1/500s. Some dark brown cameras were made (worth 50% more).

R3* $85	£45	DM140	FF434

Le Rower: (FB104); Black bakelite VFR camera for 3 x 4cm format on special Gevaert film. Very like the Univex model A camera (UC114).

R3* $35	£18	DM58	FF179

Norca Pin Up: (FB105); based on the bakelite bodied Rower camera, 24 x 36mm format on 35mm film in special cassettes, 50mm/f3.5 FAP Anistigmat lens in Atos shutter, 1/10-1/300s, Optical VFR. Announced as the Norca PM (for petite modéle) then Norca Atomic, the name Pin up was finally chosen. Only a few hundred made.

R4* $125	£66	DM206	FF639

FAIRCHILD CAMERA & INSTRUMENT CORP., Comack, New Jersey.

Fairchild Cinephonic Eight Camera: (FA100); 8mm sound movie camera; earphones monitor omni-directional microphone. C 1960. First amateur 8mm sound-on-film system; used magnetic sound track.

R2* $100	£52	DM165	FF511

Fairchild Cinephonic Eight F Sound Zoom: (FA101); Fairchild 10 to 30mm f1.8 Zoom lens; vf with Sekonic photo-electric cell. Electric motor drive; rechargeable batteries, with charger as an extra. C 1964.

R2* $120	£63	DM198	FF613

Gilles FALLER, Paris, France.

Chapeau Photographique: (GF100); hat-type detective camera; aplanatic lens covered by button at top of hat; 9 x 12cm plates loaded in double frame. C 1884. Tripod folds into cane; camera could also be mounted in a hat provided by the buyer. Original price was 90 francs.

R5* $7.5k	£3.9k	DM12.4k	FF38.3k

Gilfa (7 x 9cm): (GF101); Anastigmat 105mm f4.5 Virlot lens; Gitzo central shutter. Mahogany finish. C 1920.

R4* $200	£105	DM330	FF1k

J. FALLOWFIELD Ltd, London, England.

Fallowfield Facile: (FL100); box-type detective camera; 12 exp, 3¼" x 4¼" on plates, Miall's patent. C 1890.

R4* $1k	£525	DM1.6k	FF5.1k

FALLOWFIELD-FED

Fallowfield Hand Camera: (FL101); valise-type detective camera; similar to Hand Camera—a small valise covered in Moroccan crocodile skin. C 1892.

R4* $500	£262	DM824	FF2.6k

Miall Hand Camera: (FL102); valise-type detective camera; 8 x 10cm exp on plates (daylight loading). Size: 15 x 18 x 25cm; weight 2.3kg. Invented by F. 0. C 1891.

R4* $3k+	£1.6k+	DM5k+	FF15.3k+

FAUVEL, Paris, France.

Fauvel: (FV100); 8 x 16cm stereo camera; rising front. C 1899.

R4* $400	£210	DM659	FF2k

Fauvel: (FV101); 45 x 107mm stereo camera; Rapid Rectilinear lens; iris diaphragm; FPS. C 1912.

R3* $500	£262	DM824	FF2.6k

Fauvel Post Card: (FV102); 9 x 14cm stereo camera; cpfs; covered with Moroccan leather. C 1899.

R4* $500	£262	DM824	FF2.6k

F.E. DSERSCHINSKI MACHINE WORKS, Charkow, USSR.

FED: (FE100); 1934-55. Cfps, 1/20 - 1/500 s, no slow speeds, no synch, CRF. Interchangeable Leica-type screw mount lens. The original FED camera was a copy of the Leica II camera. The history of the factory is quite interesting. About 700,000

Early FED and fake Leica

FED cameras were made with no technical changes. At least six different engraving styles are known to exist. A table showing serial number information is located in the ID section, and will help you in establishing the year of manufacture of a FED camera. Early cameras, *serial numbered 31-4000* bring **$350,** *numbers 4000-20,000,* **$200.** Numbers above 10,000 are quite common.

R2* $140	£73	DM231	FF716

FED-2 (First version): (FE101); 1955-57. Cfps, 1/20 to 1/500 s, no slow speeds, no synch, CRF. Interchangeable Leica-type screw mount lens. Not a true Leica copy, the first version FED-2 uses a combined rangefinder/viewfinder window, removeable back, and long base rangefinder. It kept, however the collapsible FED f3.5/50mm lens of its predecessor. US prices 50% higher.

R2* $120	£63	DM198	FF613

FED-2 (First version)

FED-2 (Second version): (FE102); 1957-64. Like the first version FED-2, except with flash synch and self timer. Cfps, 1/20 to 1/500 s, no slow speeds, no synch, CRF. Interchangeable Leica-type screw mount lens. Rigid FED/Industar 26M f2.8/52mm lens. Like the first version FED-2, except with flash synch and self timer. US prices 50% higher. (Red Blue and Green covered versions have been found, but they seem to have been recovered *outside* the factory, probably in Poland.)

R2* $100	£52	DM165	FF511

FED-2L: (FE103); 1964-70's. Cfps, 1/20 to 1/500 s, no slow speeds, synch, CRF. Interchangeable Leica-type screw mount lens, Like the second version FED-2, but now with an improved f2.8, 52mm Industar-61 lens, made with rare earth glass containing Lanthanum, and self timer. US prices 50% higher.

R2* $110	£58	DM181	FF562

FED-3 (First version): (FE104); 1962-64. Cfps, 1 to 1/500 s, slow speeds, synch, CRF. Interchangeable Leica-type screw mount lens, self timer and f2.8/52mm Industar lens. Slow speeds,different diopter adjustment system, and a changed top plate came with this model. Very few were made before the introduction of the improved second version, though prices for each are the same. US prices 50% higher.

R3* $60	£31	DM99	FF307

FED-3 (Second version): (FE105); 1964-80's. Cfps, 1 to 1/500 s, slow speeds, synch, CRF. Interchangeable Leica-type screw mount lens, self timer. Using the f2.8, 52mm Industar-61 lens, and having a single-leveltop plate, the second version FED-3 also incorporated a rapid advance lever instead of the round knob used on all earlier FED cameras. Also sold as the Revue-3, this camera was made in quite large quantities. The "Olympic" model adds about 30% to the value of the camera. US prices 50% higher.

R2* $60	£31	DM99	FF307

FED-4: (FE106); C1964. Cfps, 1 to 1/500 s, slow speeds, synch, CRF. Interchangeable Leica-type screw mount lens,self timer. Like the FED-3, with Industar-61 f2.8, 52mm lens, but with the addition of a built-in light meter. Also sold as the Revue-4. More common in Europe. US prices 50% higher.

R2* $70	£37	DM115	FF358

FED-4

FED-5A: (FE107); after 1978. Cfps, 1 to 1/500 s, slow speeds, synch, CRF. Interchangeable Leica-type screw mount lens, self timer. An improved version of the FED-

4, with the same features. US prices about 50% higher.

R2* $70	£37	DM115	FF358

FED-5B: (FE109); after 1978. Cfps, 1 to 1/500 s, slow speeds, synch, CRF. Interchangeable Leica-type screw mount lens, self timer. The same as the FED-5A, but without the built-in light meter. Not made for the export market. "Olympic" model adds 30% to the price. US prices about 50% higher.

R2* $70	£37	DM115	FF358

FED-5C: (FE110); after 1978. Cfps, 1 to 1/500 s, slow speeds, synch, CRF. Interchangeable Leica-type screw mount lens, self timer. The same as the FED-5A with the addition of a bright line viewfinder frame. US prices about 50% higher.

R2* $70	£37	DM115	FF358

FED-5C

Zarya

Zarya: (FE111); 1958-59. Cfps, 1/20 to 1/500 s, no slow speeds, synch. Interchangeable Leica-type screw mount lens. f3.5/52mm rigis mount Industar lens. Not a true Leica copy, and the only Russian Leica-type camera without a rangefinder. Very few were made, and since its original price

FED-FEX

was not much lower than the FED-2, it was not very successful on the market place. The current price does not reflect its rarity.

R3* $120	£63	DM198	FF613

FED V (B) : (FE112); 1938. The same camera as other early FED's (FE100), but with the addition of slow speeds and 1/1000 s. It is said only 40 cameras were made.

R5* NSR est $1.5k+	£787+	DM2.5k+

FED S(C) : (FE113); 1938. The same as other early FED's (FE100), except with the addition of 1/1000 s.

R4* $250	£131	DM412	FF1.3k

Counterfeit Leica: (FE114); Some early FED cameras were supplied with top plates engraved with Leitz markings. These cameras show very poor quality plating, and generally inferior workmanship when compared to the Leicas which they were attempting to mimic. On many cameras the top plate remains un-drilled where the accessory shoe would normally be placed.

R3* $350	£184	DM577	FF1.8k

FED Stereo: (FE114); C1989, 35mm stereo camera with Industar-81 f2.8.38mm lenses, simple shutter 1/30 - 1/650s, automatic exposure control. In 1990 one complete set, including FED stereo projector *did not* make its minimum reserve bid of $1250 at auction. (Though a new product, this camera has become an "instant" collectable.)

R3* $600	£315	DM989	FF3.1k

FED Stereo

FEINWERKTECHNIK GmbH, Lahr, Germany

MEC 16: (FI100); C1956, subminiature camera, f2.8/20mm lens, shutter 1/25 - 1/1000 s. 24 exp, 10 x 14mm on 16mm film, in brown, black or gold. (complete presenta-tion case adds 200%).

R2* $60	£31	DM99	FF307

MEC 16SB: (FI101); C1957, as (FI100) but for coupled TTL light meter and Heligon f2/ 22mm lens, shutter 1/30 - 1/1000s. "SB" stands for *Si*multan-*Be*lichtungsmesser. This was the first non-SLR to offer TTL metering. (complete presentation case adds 200%).

R2* $100	£52	DM165	FF511

Joseph FETTER

Photo Eclair: (JF100); concealed vest detective camera; rectilinear 40mm f8 lens; rotary sector shutter; 5 exp on 4 x 4cm plates. C 1886. Plate changed by rotating camera back. Shutter differentiates this from the Gray and Stirn models. Later model had lens at base of camera, to allow addition of a 45 degree angle vf.

R5* $3k+	£1.6k+	DM5k+	FF15.3k+

FEX, Lyon, France

Compa Fex: (FX100); Simple black wooden box camera with slide out frame finder, made during the German occupation of France. Very few have survived. C. 1942

R5* NSR est $200+	£105	DM330	FF1k

Fex: (FX101); Simple black bakelite camera for 6 x 4.5 format on roll film. Made in 1944, and replaced by the Super-Fex in 1945. Fexar lens and single speed shutter.

R4* $45	£24	DM74	FF230

Super-Fex: (FX102); Simple black bakelite camera for 6 x 4.5 format on roll film. Metal wind knob. Made in large quantities.

R2* $10	£5	DM16	FF51

Ultra-Fex: (FX103); Simple black bakelite camera for 6 x 9 format on roll film. Made in many, many versions, among which are the Sport-Fex, the Uni-Fex, and the Delta, all having the lens in a rectangular collapsible mount. One of the most commonly found French cameras.

R1* $5	£3	DM8	FF26

Super-Fex

Elite: (FX104); One of the Ultra-Fex (FX103) versions, but with built-in extinction meter, and through the use of a metal mask both 6 x 9cm and 6 x 6cm formats were possible. Often found with Colour-Fexar lens in Atos shutter.

R2* $15	£8	DM25	FF77

FINETTA WERK, P. SARABER, Goslar, Germany.

Finette: (FW102); C1947, 35mm VFR camera, Fenar f6.3/43mm lens, simple shutter.

R3* $30	£16	DM49	FF153

Finetta: (FW100); C 1950, 35mm VFR camera, Finetar f2.8/45mm lens, interchangeable mount, FPS 1/25-1/1000 s.

R2* $40	£21	DM66	FF204

Finetta Super: (FW103); C1951, 35mm VFR camera, interchangeable Finetar f2.8/45mm lens, simple shutter, 1/25 - 1/100s, flat top plate.

R2* $40	£21	DM66	FF204

Finetta 99

Finetta 88: (FW104); C1954, as (FW103) but with 1/25 - 1/200s shutter.

R2* $40	£21	DM66	FF204

Finetta 99: (FW101); 35mm VFR camera, Finetar f2.8/45mm lens, interchangeable mount; FPS 1-1/1000 s, with built-in spring motor drive.

R3* $225	£118	DM371	FF1.2k

Accessory lenses for Finetta cameras

Finettare f4.5/35mm wide angle lens: (FW001); **$25**
Finettare f4.5/70mm telephoto lens: (FW002); **$25**
Finettare f6.3/105mm telephoto lens: (FW003); **$30**

Dr. FOL, Geneva, Switzerland.

Dr. Fol's Photographic Rifle: (DF100); rifle-type detective camera; Steinheil Antiplanet lens; Thury & Amey shutter. 11 plates, 9 x 10cm in magazine. C 1884.

R5* $10k+	£5.2k+	DM16.5k+	FF51.1k+

FOSTER Instruments Pty. Ltd., Sydney, Australia.

Swiftshot: (FT100); C1951, metal box camera for 6 x 9 frames on 120 or 620 roll film, simple lens and shutter, built-in yellow filter, marked either "Model A" or "made in Australia" on the camera front, in red, black, blue, beige, grey, green or...(no joking) crocodile!

R2* $25	£13	DM41	FF128

Swiftshot

FOTH & CO.,
Berlin, Germany.
(also see Gallus)

Foth Derby I: (FO100); 127 roll film folding camera; Foth Anastigmat 50mm f3.5 lens; CFPS 1/25-1/500 s; The first model made 1" x 1¹/₂" negatives; later 16 exp, 1¹/₄" x 1¹/₄" on 127 roll film.

R2* $40	£21	DM66	FF204

Foth Derby II: (FO101); 127 roll film folding camera; Foth Anastigmat 50mm f3.5 lens; CFPS 1/25-1/500 s, CRF. 16 exp, 1¹/₄" x 1¹/₂" on 127 roll film.

R2* $70	£37	DM115	FF358

Foth-Flex: (FO102); 2¹/₄" x 2¹/₄" TLR; Foth Anastigmat 75mm f3.5 lens; CFPS 1-1/500 s; 12 exp, 2¹/₄" x 2¹/₄" on 120 roll film. C 1935.

R3* $120	£63	DM198	FF613

Foth-Flex

Foth Folding Camera: (FO103); 120 roll film folding camera; Foth Doppel Anastigmat 105mm f4.5 lens; Compound 1/25-1/100 s. Some covered in alligator skin valued 50% higher. C1930.

R4* $150	£79	DM247	FF767

Foth Derby II

FOTOBRAS S.A. Ind. & Com.,
Curtiba-Parana, Brazil

Brasilmatic Camera: (BQ100); C1950, metal box camera for 6 x 9cm frames on roll film, simple lens and shutter.

R3* $30	£16	DM49	FF153

FOTO-FEX KAMERAWERK, Fritz
Kraftanski, Berlin, Germany

Mini-Fex: (KX100); C1930, subminiature VFR camera for 13mm x 18mm frames on 16mm perforated film, various lens and shutters offered including Astrar f2.7 or "ultra fast" Pan-Tachar f1.8/25mm lens, Compur or Pronto shutter.

R4* $600	£315	DM989	FF3.1k

Mini-Fex MG: (KX101); C1939, sub-miniature VFR camera for 13mm x 18mm frames on 16mm perforated film, Trioplan f3.5 or "ultra fast" Pan-Tachar f1.8/25mm lens, Pronto shutter. The "MG" in the name refers to the German "*Maschinen Gewahr*", meaning machine gun. one sliding movement of a button located on the camera side armed the shutter, released the shutter, and transported the film.

R4* NSR est $900	£472	DM1.5k	FF4.6k

Schoolboy-Box: (KX102); C1929, metal box camera for 4cm x 6cm plates, meniscus lens, two speed shutter.

R3* $20	£10	DM33	FF102

FRAMA-FRANKA

FRAMA, Franz Matthias, Dresden, Germany.

This photo retailer sold cameras under its house brand names, which were actually made by companies like Balda and Agfa.

Framax: (FF100); C1930, metal folding camera for 6 x 9cm frames on roll film, f4.5 or 6.3 lens, Prontor shutter among others.

R2* $15	£8	DM25	FF77

Framafix: (FF101); C1930, metal folding camera for 6 x 9cm *or* 6 x 4.5 on roll film, Xenar f4.5/105mm lens among others.

R2* $15	£8	DM25	FF77

Knipsy: (FF102: C1930, metal folding camera for 6 x 9cm frames on roll film, front lens focusing Trioplan f6.3 or f4.5/105mm lens, Vario or other shutter.

R2* $15	£8	DM25	FF77

Plana: (FF103); C1930, folding bed camera for 6 x 9cm plates or film packs, Xenar f4.5/105mm lens among others, Vario, Prontor or Compur shutter, wire frame finder.

R3* $40	£21	DM66	FF204

Rolly: (FF104); C1930, metal folding camera for 6 x 9cm on roll film, Anastigmat f4.5/105mm lens among others, Vario or Pronto shutter, wire frame finder.

R2* $20	£10	DM33	FF102

FRANKA Camera Werke Bayreuth, Germany

Bubi: (FG100); C1915, strut folding camera for 6 x 4.5 plates or film packs, simple shutter and lens, wire frame finder.

R3* $80	£42	DM132	FF409

Bubi Velo: (FG101); C1915, strut folding camera for 6 x 4,5cm plates of film packs, Velonar f6.8/75mm lens, Compound shutter, wire frame finder.

R3* $125	£66	DM206	FF639

Bubi 3 x 4: (FG102); C1930, metal folding camera for 3 x 4cm frames on 127 film, *not*

like either (FG100) or (FG101), Victar f4.5/75mm lens among others, Prontor shutter.

R2* $20	£10	DM33	FF102

Vest Pocket Model 50: (FG103); C1921, strut folding camera for 6 x 4.5 plates or filmpacks, like (FG101) but now with waist level finder and dialset Compur.

R3* $125	£66	DM206	FF639

Bonafix: (FG104); C1930-1955, metal folding camera for 6 x 9cm or 6 x 4.5 frames on roll film, f6.3/105mm lens, Vario shutter, *most* cameras after 1950 have chrome top plate, and allow 6 x 6cm instead of the 6 x 4.5cm format.

R2* $15	£8	DM25	FF77

Idafix: (FG105); C1930, metal folding camera for 6.5 x 11 frames on 130 roll film, Velostigmat f6.3/135mm lens, Pronto shutter.

R3* $15	£8	DM25	FF77

Rolfix: (FG106); C1936-56, metal folding camera for 6 x 9cm or 6 x 6cm on 120 roll film, Trioplan f4.5/105mm lens among others, Compur shutter, several different variations.

R2* $15	£8	DM25	FF77

Solida: (FG107); C1934-56, metal folding camera for 6 x 4.5 frames on roll film, optical VFR, Victar f2.9/70mm lens among others, Compur shutter, several different variations.

R2* $30	£16	DM49	FF153

Solida I: FG108); C1955, folding camera for 6 x 6cm or 4 x 4cm frames on 120 roll film, f4.5/75mm lens among others, Vario shutter.

R2* $25	£13	DM41	FF128

Solida II: (FG109); C1955, folding camera for 6 x 6cm or 4 x 4cm frames on 120 roll film, duel VFR for 4 x 4 and 4 x 6, Ennagon f4.5/75mm lens among others, Pronto or Prontor shutter, variations made with lever advance and automatic frame counting.

R3* $40	£21	DM66	FF204

Solida IIL: (FG110); C1955, like (FG108) but with built-in uncoupled EV light meter, 6 x 6cm only.

R3* $25	£13	DM41	FF128

F

Solida III: (FG111); C1955, like (FG108) but with faster Radionar f2.9/80mm lens, 6 x 6cm only.

R2* $25	£13	DM41	FF128

Solida IIIL: (FG112); C1955, like (FG111) but now with uncoupled rangefinder.

R3* $45	£24	DM74	FF230

Solida Record B: (FG113); C1960, new cheaper version of (FG108) available with or without lever advance or automatic frame counting. F8/80mm lens, simple shutter.

R2* $15	£8	DM25	FF77

Solida Record T: (FG114); C1963, all metal VFR camera for 6 x 6cm or 4 x 4cm on 120 roll film, f8/70mm lens with front lens focusing, simple shutter, available with lever advance and automatic frame counting for 6 x 6cm frames only.

R2* $15	£8	DM25	FF77

Franka: (FG115); C1950, 35mm VFR camera, Radionar f2.9/50mm lens, Compur shutter, lever wind, exposure table on top plate.

R3* $45	£24	DM74	FF230

Frankanette: (FG116); C1958, 35mm VFR camera, Isconar f2.8/45mm lens among others, Pronto shutter.

R2* $15	£8	DM25	FF77

Frankanette L: (FG117); C1958, 35mm VFR, Ennagon f2.8/45mm lens among others, Pronto shutter, built-in meter.

R2* $15	£8	DM25	FF77

Super Frankanette: (FG118); C1958, 35mm VFR camera, Xenar f2.8/45mm lens among others, Prontor-SVS shutter.

Super Frankanette L: (FG119): C1958, 35mm VFR camera with built-in light meter, Westanar f2.8/45mm lens among others, Prontor shutter, lever wind.

R2* $20	£10	DM33	FF102

Super Frankanette E: (FG120), C1958, 35mm RFR camera, Xenar f2.8/45mm lens, Printor-SVS shutter, CRF.

R2* $30	£16	DM49	FF153

Super Frankanette EL: (FG121): C1958, 35mm VFR with built-in meter and CRF,

Xenar f2.8/45mm I Prontor -SVS shutter.

R2* $40	£21	DM66	FF204

Super Frankanette SLK: (FG122): C1958, 35mm VFR camera with built-in *coupled* light meter, Xenar f2.8/45mm lens, Prontor-SLK shutter.

R2* $20	£10	DM33	FF102

Francolour: (FG123); C1960, 35mm VFR camera with Frankar f2.8/45mm lens, Pronto or Vario shutter, lever wind.

R2* $15	£8	DM25	FF77

FRANCAIS,
Paris, France.

Le Cosmopolite: (FR100); 2 Francais Rectilinear lenses (bayonet mounts) with waterhouse stops; behind the lens shutter. 9 x 12cm exp on plates. C 1887.

R4* $400	£210	DM659	FF2k

G. FRANK & PEARSALL,
Brooklyn, New York.

The Compact Camera: (GP100); 6$\frac{1}{2}$" x 8$\frac{1}{2}$" view camera; 6$\frac{1}{2}$" x 8$\frac{1}{2}$" exp on dry plates. C 1883.

R5* $1.5k+	£787+	DM2.5k+	FF7.7k+

FRANKE & HEIDECKE,
Braunschweig, Germany.

Heidoscop: (FH100); 45 x 107mm reflex stereo camera; Zeiss Tessar 55mm f4.5 lens; Compound 1-1/300 s; 45 x 107mm exp on plates. C 1921.

R3* $400	£210	DM659	FF2k

Heidoscop: (FH101); 6 x 13cm plate and cut-film reflex stereo camera; Zeiss Tessar 75mm f4.5 lenses; Compound shutter 1-1/300 s; 6 x 13cm exp on plates or cut-film.

R3* $350	£184	DM577	FF1.8k

Rolleidoscop: (FH102); 45 x 107mm reflex stereo camera; Zeiss Tessar 75mm f4.5 lenses; Compur 1-1/300 s; 45 x 107mm exp on roll film.

R3* $1.2k	£630	DM2k	FF6.1k

Rolleidoscop: (FH103); 6 x 13cm reflex stereo camera; Zeiss Tessar 75mm f4.5 lenses; Compur 1-1/300 s; 6 x 13cm exp on roll film. C 1926.

| R3* $800 | £420 | DM1.3k | FF4.1k |

16S: (FH104); subminiature camera; Tessar 25mm f2.8 lens; 12 x 17mm exp on 16mm film. The first with only one lens.

| R3* Black: $100 | £52 | DM165 |
| Red/green: $150 | £79 | DM247 |

35: (FH105); 35mm camera; Tessar 40mm f3.5 coated lens; shutter 1/2-1/500 s. Black German model add 75%C 1970.

| R2* $150 | £79 | DM247 | FF767 |

35: (gold-plated model): (FH106); 35mm camera; Carl Zeiss Tessar 40mm f3.5 coated lens; shutter 1/2-1/500 s. C 1970.

| R4* $800 | £420 | DM1.3k | FF4.1k |

Heidoscop

Rollei 35 Gold-plated model

Rolleicord I: (FH107); Zeiss Triotar 75mm f4.5 lens; Compur shutter 1-1/300 s. C 1933-1935. Original camera body, nickel plated art-deco design. Later version (after 1934) was covered with leather, **$150**. Difficult to find in excellent condition.

| R3* $180 | £94 | DM297 | FF920 |

Rolleicord IA: (FH110); Zeiss Triotar 75mm f4.5 or f3.8 lens; Compur shutter 1-1/300 s. C 1935-1941.

| R3* $80 | £42 | DM132 | FF409 |

Rolleicord II: (FH111); Zeiss Triotar 75mm f3.5 lens—equipped with factory coated 75mm f3.5 Triotar or Xenar lens after 1950.

Rolleicord I

Compur shutter 1-1/300 s (1938-1945); Compur-Rapid shutter 1-1/500 s (1945-1951) - flash synch (1950-1951). Snr 612,000-1,135,999.

| R3* $75 | £39 | DM124 | FF383 |

Rolleicord III: (FH112); Zeiss Triotar or Xenar 75mm f3.5 lens; Compur-Rapid shutter 1-1/500 s. Snr 1,137,000-1,344,050. C 1950-1953.

| R3* $75 | £39 | DM124 | FF383 |

Rolleicord IV: (FH113); Xenar 75mm f3.5 lens; Synchro-Compur shutter 1-1/500 s. Snr 1,344,051-1,390,999. C 1953-1955.

| R3* $100 | £52 | DM165 | FF511 |

Rolleicord V: (FH114); Xenar 75mm f3.5 lens; Synchro-Compur shutter IVS 1-1/500 s. Snr 1,500,000-(?). C 1955-1957.

| R3* $90 | £47 | DM148 | FF460 |

Rolleicord Va: (FH115); Xenar 75mm f3.5 lens; Synchro-Compur MXV shutter 1-1/500 s. Snr 1,584,000-1,940,999. C 1957-1960.

| R3* $100 | £52 | DM165 | FF511 |

Rolleiflex (Original): (FH116); Zeiss Tessar 75mm f4.5 lens until 1929; Zeiss Tessar 75mm f3.8 lens after 1929; Compur shutter 1-1/300 s. Snr up to 200,000. C 1929-1932.

| R4* $200 | £105 | DM330 | FF1k |

Rolleiflex Standard 1932: (FH117); Zeiss Tessar 75mm f4.5, f3.8 or f3.5 lens; Compur shutter 1-1/300 s. Snr 200,000-567,550. C 1932-1937.

| R4* $125 | £66 | DM206 | FF639 |

Rolleiflex 1937: (FH120); Zeiss Tessar 75mm f3.5 lens until 1945; Zeiss Tessar or Xenar 75mm f3.5 after 1945. Snr 280,000-1,000,000. C 1937-1949.

| R3* $100 | £52 | DM165 | FF511 |

Rolleiflex New Standard 1939: (FH121); Zeiss Tessar 75mm f3.5 lens; Synchro-Compur shutter 1-1/500 s. Snr 805,000-928,999. C 1939-1941.

| R3* $100 | £52 | DM165 | FF511 |

Rolleiflex 1950: (FH122); Zeiss Tessar 75mm f3.5 (coated lenses marked "T") or Schneider Xenar 75mm f3.5 (coated lenses marked with red triangle) lens; Compur shutter 1-1/500 s. Snr 1,100,000-1,168,000. C 1949-1951.

| R2* $125 | £66 | DM206 | FF639 |

Rolleiflex "MX": (FH123); Zeiss Tessar or Xenar 75mm f3.5 lens; Synchro-Compur

shutter 1-1/500 s. Snr 11,000-1,427,999. C 1951-1954.

| R2* $125 | £66 | DM206 | FF639 |

Rolleiflex 2.8A: (FH124); Zeiss Tessar 80mm f2.8 lens; (a few cameras were mfd with Biometar 80mm f2.8 lens, and are much sought after, worth 150% or more); Compur-Rapid shutter 1-1/500 s. Snr 1,101,000-(?). C 1950-1953.

| R2* $125 | £66 | DM206 | FF639 |

Rolleiflex 2.8C: (FH125); Xenotar 80mm f2.8 lens; Synchro-Compur shutter 1-1/500 s. Snr 1,260,250-1,475,278. C 1953-1956.

| R3* $225 | £118 | DM371 | FF1.2k |

Rolleiflex "MX" (EVS): (FH126); Zeiss Tessar or Xenar 75mm f3.5 lens; Synchro-Compur shutter LVS 1-1/500s. Snr 1,428,000-1,729,999. C 1954-1956.

| R2* $125 | £66 | DM206 | FF639 |

Rolleiflex 2.8D: (FH127); Zeiss Tessar or Xenotar 80mm f2.8 lens; Synchro-Compur EVS shutter 1-1/500 s. Snr 1,600,000-1,620,999. C 1955-1956.

| R3* $250 | £131 | DM412 | FF1.3k |

Rolleiflex (Original)

Rolleiflex 2.8E: (FH130); Zeiss Planar or Xenotar 80mm f2.8 lens; Synchro-Compur MXV shutter 1-1/500 s. Snr 1,621,000-1,665,999. C 1958-1959. **$650**. Rolleiflex 2.8E-2; Snr 2,350,000-2,357,999. C 1959-1962. **$700**. Rolleiflex 2.8E-3; Snr 2,360,000-(?). C 1962-1965.

| R3* $750 | £394 | DM1.2k | FF3.8k |

Rolleiflex 3.5E: (FH131); Zeiss Planar or Xenotar 75mm f3.5 lens; Synchro-Compur LVS shutter 1-1/500 s. Snr 1,740,000-1,869,000. C 1957-1959. **$400**. Rolleiflex 3.5E-2; Snr 2,480,000-2,482,099. C 1960-1962. **$450**. Rolleiflex 35.E-3; Snr 2,380,000-(?). C 1962-1965.

| R3* $450 | £236 | DM742 | FF2.3k |

Rolleiflex 2.8F

Rolleiflex 3.5E

Rolleiflex 3.5F: (FH132); Zeiss Planar 75mm f3.5 coated lens; Synchro-Compur LVS shutter 1-1/500 s.

| R3* $400 | £210 | DM659 | FF2k |

Rolleiflex 2.8F: (FH133); Zeiss Planar 75mm f2.8 coated lens; Synchro-Compur LVS shutter 1-1/500 s.

| R4* $800 | £420 | DM1.3k | FF4.1k |

Rolleiflex 4 x 4cm (1931): (FH134); Zeiss Tessar 60mm f3.5 or f2.8 lens; Compur shutter 1-1/300 s; Compur-Rapid shutter 1-1/500 s, after 1935. Snr 200,000-600,000. C 1931-1939.

| R3* $175 | £92 | DM288 | FF894 |

Rolleiflex 4 x 4cm (1938): (FH135); Zeiss Tessar 60mm f2.8 lens; Compur-Rapid shutter 1-1/500 s. Snr 622,000-733,000. C 1938-1941.

| R3* $225 | £118 | DM371 | FF1.2k |

Rolleiflex 4 x 4cm (1957): (FH136); Zeiss Tessar 60mm f2.8 lens; Synchro-Compur shutter 1-1/500 s. C 1957.

| R2* $225 | £118 | DM371 | FF1.2k |

Rollei-Magic: (FH137); 2¹/₄" x 2¹/₄" TLR; Schneider Xenar 75mm f3.5 coated lens; Prontormat-S shutter 1/30-1/300 s; 12 exp, 2¹/₄" x 2¹/₄" on 120 roll film. Snr 2,800,000-2,534,999. Selenium photo-electric exp meter. C 1954-1957. Check care-

Rolleiflex 4 x 4cm

Wide-Angle Rolleiflex

fully, this model seldom operates properly.

| R3* $125 | £66 | DM206 | FF639 |

SL26: (FH138); SLR Instamatic camera; Tessar 40mm f2.8 lens, interchangeable front element; behind-the-lens shutter 1/2-1/500 s. Instamatic film cartridge. C 1970.

| R3* $125 | £66 | DM206 | FF639 |

Tele-Rolleiflex: (FH140); 2¹/₄" x 2¹/₄" TLR; Sonnar 135mm f4 coated lens; Synchro-Compur shutter 1-1/500 s; 12 exp, 2¹/₄" x 2¹/₄" on 120 roll film. C 1974.

| R4* $1k | £525 | DM1.6k | FF5.1k |

Wide-Angle Rolleiflex: (FH141); 2¹/₄" x 2¹/₄" TLR; Distagon 55mm f4 coated lens; Synchro-Compur shutter 1-1/500 s; 12 exp, 2¹/₄" x 2¹/₄" on 120 roll film. C 1974.

| R4* $1.8k | £945 | DM3k | FF9.2k |

FRANKLIN PHOTOGRAPHIC INDUSTRIES INC., Chicago, Illinois.

Franklin Magazine 8: (FP100); 8mm movie camera; mfd under Kodak license; Cine Raptar Wollensak 2" f2.5 lens. C 1942.

| R2* $25 | £13 | DM41 | FF128 |

French Detective Camera: (BB156); H. Duplovich 120mm f6.8 lens; 6 x 9cm exp; plates changed by chain mechanism. Mfd in France. C 1895.

| R5* $2k+ | £1.1k+ | DM3.3k+ | FF10.2k+ |

French Dry Plate Camera: (BB157); 7 x 9cm format rigid wooden camera; insertable disc stops. Mfd in France. C 1880.

| R3* $375 | £197 | DM618 | FF1.9k |

French Sliding Box daguerreotype Camera: (BB162);
Photographe a verres combines, 190mm f6 lens; pivoting plate shutter. Interchangeable front lens elements for various focal lengths; 6.5 x 7.5cm image. Mfd in France. C 1845.

| R5* $10k+ | £5.2k+ | DM16.5k+ | FF51.1k+ |

French Espionage Camera: (BB160); pre-war subminiature detective camera; mfps 1/20-1/250 s; 45 exp. Mfd in France. C 1940. Invariably found without lens.

R5* $800+	£420+	DM1.3k+	FF4.1k+

French Espionage Camera

French Tailboard Camera: (BB163); 13" x 18" tailboard camera; wide angle lens; removable ground glass back; shifting front lens standard (stereo); brass handle; red bellows. Mfd in France. C 1890's.

R3* $375	£197	DM618	FF1.9k

FT Russian Panoramic Camera: (BB165); rotating Industar 50mm f5 lens; shutter 1/100, 1/200, 1/400 s; 12 exp, 24 x 110mm on 35mm film. Mfd in Russia. C 1955.

R4* $400	£210	DM659	FF2k

French Stereo Viewer (floor model): (BB161); glass and paper stereo viewer. Chinese-style carved ivory design; ornate brass handles. Illumination by candle. Mfd in France. C 1880.

R5* NSR $3k+		
£1.6k+ DM5k+		
FF15.3k+		

French Stereo Viewer (floor model)

FT Russian Panoramic Camera

G

GALILEO OPTICAL, Milan, Italy.

Condor I: (GO100); 35mm RFR camera; Galileo Eliog 560mm f3.5 lens; Galileo Iscus Rapid shutter 1-1/500 s, CRF. C 1954.

R3* $100	£52	DM165	FF511

Gami 16: (GO101); subminiature camera; Esanitar 25mm f1.9 lens; shutter 1/2-1/1000 s; 12 x 17mm exp on 17mm film in special cassettes; CRF. C 1955.

R4* $375	£197	DM618	FF1.9k

GAMMA PRECISION MACHINE, Rome, Italy.

Gamma-I: (GV100); 1947. Cpfs, 1/20-1000 s, CRF, special bayonette mount Koristka Victor f3.5/55mm lens. Internal film cutter allowed exposed 35mm roll film in special cassettes to be removed from the camera for processing in mid roll. Odd shaped camera body. Quite rare.

R4* $450	£236	DM742	FF2.3k

Gamma (Special): (GV101); 1948. The same body style as the Gamma-I, but without RFR or VFR.Cpfs, 1/20-1000 s, special bayonette mount Koristka Victor f3.5/55mm lens. Internal film cutter allowed exposed 35mm roll film in special casettes removed from the camera for processing in mid roll. Odd shaped camera body. extremely rare.

R5* $1.5k	£787	DM2.5k	FF7.7k

Gamma-III: (GV102); 1950-51. The same body style as the Gamma-I, but with slow speeds.Cpfs, 1-1000 s, interchangeable Leica-type screw mount Koristka Victor f3.5/55mm lens or Beta f3.5/50mm lens.Internal film cutter allowed exposed 35mm roll film in special casettes to be removed from the camera for processing in mid roll. Shares the same odd shaped camera body as the other Gamma cameras, but has a different frame counter than Gamma-II.

R4* $550	£289	DM907	FF2.8k

Gamma-II: (GV103); 1950. The same body style as the Gamma-I, but with slow speeds.Cpfs, 1-1000 s, interchangeable Leica-type screw mount Koristka Victor f3.5/55mm lens or Beta f3.5/50mm lens.Internal film cutter allowed exposed 35mm roll film in special casettes removed from the camera for processing in mid roll. Quite rare. Even rarer Airforce version with f2.0/50mm Epitamitar lens valued at about 300% higher.

R4* $500	£262	DM824	FF2.6k

Gamma-II

GAMMA WORKS, Budapest, Hungary.

Duflex: (GW100); C1947, 35mm SLR, historically important for having an instant return mirror, 24 x 32mm frame on 35mm

R5* $1.5k	£787	DM2.5k	FF7.7k

Duflex

GANDOLFI LTD.,
Hampshire, England.

*Louis Gandolfi, later Louis Gandolfi
& Sons, was founded in 1885. The
company is still in production with
elder son Frederick as consultant.
The earliest Gandolfi cameras were
named The Compactum, The Collapsible, and The Special, all dating
from 1895. The Compactum was
made in sizes from half plate to 12"
x10" which were priced from £4 to
£8. The Premier and the Simplex
followed and all were predecessors
of the Imperial which became the
mainstay of the tapered bellows field
camera designs from Gandolfi.
These cameras are rare and no price
indications are available.*

Precision

Universal

Prison

Universal square bellows camera: 1899.
This was the first regular production model
made in six sizes: half plate; whole plate; 8"
x 10"; 12" x 10"; 15" x 12"; 18" x 16" at prices
ranging from £5 to £21. Later 5" x 4" and 5"
x 7" models were added. Made from selected Cuban or Honduras mahogany with
solid brass fittings, this was a tailboard
camera with fixed front and rear focusing. It
had double swing reversible back, rise and
cross front parallel bellows. Approximately
1,000 of these cameras were produced,
many of which have survived and are in
every day use. Prices range from £250 to
£1,000 depending on size and condition.

Imperial camera: By 1908 Gandolfi had
extended his range with a tapered bellows
camera having focusing front and rear standards and swing and tilt movements which

make it the clear predecessor of the present
day precision camera. Imperial was made in
half-plate, whole plate, 10" x 8" and 12" x 10"
sizes, costing in 1908 from £5 to £10. This
camera continued with minor changes until
World War 2. Briton Camera selling for little
more than half the price of the Imperial,
which it superficially resembled, attempted
to widen the market but was short lived.

**Universal folding hand and stand cam-
era:** This was a de luxe Spanish mahogany
camera covered with Morocco leather and
bearing some similarities to the well known
Sanderson design. It was first introduced
about 1907 in 1/4 plate and 5" x 4" sizes but
by 1910 was supplied additionally in postcard, half-plate and 7" x 5" at prices ranging
from £8 to £15. At different times from 1902
Gandolfi offered magazine box type cam-

GANDOLFI-ANTONIO GATTO

eras and a range of tripods, stands, shutters and lenses. Some of these bear signs of French origin and others may be the result of exchanging catalogue items with other manufacturers such as Thornton Pickard. Mostly they were sold over relatively short periods but the hand and stand cameras remained until the late thirties.

Precision tapered bellows camera: Introduced in 1945 and continued in manufacture at the present time, this is truly a universal camera with a wide range of movements. Convenient in the studio, in its element on location where weight and bulk are important, this camera is usually constructed in Honduras or, later Brazilian mahogany but Burmese teak and Indian rosewood examples are occasionally found. The rigidity and hard wearing qualities of Gandolfi cameras make them equally likely to be found in use as in collections. The woodwork is deeply French polished and the solid heavy gauge brass fittings are hard lacquered. Black polished wood and satin chrome plated examples are occasionally found. Early models have hinged focusing screens and use double book form plateholders in wood and brass to match the camera. Since the early 1960s, international standard spring backs have been available, taking the familiar standard cut film holder from any reputable maker. Excellent facilities, flexible movements and extraordinary durability have ensured the survival of this design to the present day. Cameras individually made to such high standards of craftsmanship are necessarily expensive but whether old or new they constitute a sound investment as well as a universal camera. New prices range from about £950 for 4" x 5" to £1,500 for 8" x 10" models. Older used models may be found from £300 to £1,200 depending on size and condition.

Prison camera: Gandolfi produced a number of specialised cameras for Government departments. The prison service used Gandolfi equipment for identification records, and Gandolfi is famed for the special camera made to photograph the interior of Queen Mary's Doll's House in 1924.

Wide angle cameras: Especially worthy of mention are the box type wide angle cameras fitted with the famous Goerz Hypergon lens. With extreme angles of view, the 75mm lens covering 8" x 10", and small apertures, no focusing was required and no bellows provided. These cameras are much sought after and complete with lens in good condition trade at £600 to £800 depending on size.

ANTONIO GATTO, Pordenone, Italy.

Sonne-IV: (GJ100); 1948. Cfps, 1/20 to 1/1000 sec, CRF, interchangeable Leica-type screw mount Adlenar f3.5/50mm lens. On the earliest versions, a rising sun is engraved next to the rangefinder window. No models I, II, or III seem to have been made. quite rare, some sales near the $1000 mark, but the true worth seems to be about half that.

R4* $475	£249	DM783	FF2.4k

Sonne-V: (GJ101); 1950. Cfps, 1 -1/1000 sec, flash synch, interchangeable Leica-type screw mount Schneider Xenar f3.5/50mm lens, or f2.8/50mm lens. Also found with "T" Elionar f3.5/50mm lens. Quite rare.

R4* $475	£249	DM783	FF2.4k

Sonne-V (above) and Sonne-C (below)

Sonne-C: (GJ102); 1951. Cfps, 1 -1/1000 sec, flash synch, interchangeable Leica-type screw mount Schneider Xenar f3.5/50mm lens, or f2.8/50mm lens. Also found with "T" Elionar f3.5/50mm lens. Similar to the Sonne-V, but with changed top cover.

R4* $500	£262	DM824	FF2.6k

Sonne-C4: (GJ103); 1953. Cfps, 1 - 1/1000 sec, flash synch, interchangeable Leica-type screw mount Schneider Xenar f3.5/50mm lens, or f2.8/50mm lens. Also found with "T" Elionar f3.5/50mm lens. Seperate slow speed control, and combines RFR/VFR window. Also known as the Sonne-Colour camera. Quite rare. It is difficult to find any Sonne cameras in condition "C" or better.

R4* $600	£315	DM989	FF3.1k

Sonne-C4

L. GAUMONT & CIE, Paris, France.

Block-Notes: (GI100); 4.5 x 6cm vest pocket camera; Tessar f6.8 lens. C 1903. 4.5 x 6cm model, $90-$175. 6 x 9cm model.

R3* $200	£105
DM330	FF1k

Block-Notes Stereo: (GI101); 45 x 107mm stereo camera; Tessar f6.3 lenses. C 1903.

R3* $350	£184	DM577	FF1.8k

"Reporter" Tropical Camera: (GI102); 135mm f4.5 lens; FPS; 9 x 12cm exp on cut

"Reporter" Tropical Camera

film. C 1924.

R5* $1k	£525	DM1.6k	FF5.1k

Spido: (GI103); 9 x 12cm; Zeiss Krauss Protar 136mm f8 lens; Decaux pneumatic shutter; 12 plates. C 1899.

R3* $225	£118	DM371	FF1.2k

Spido Stereo: (GI104); 6 x 13cm stereo camera; Hermagis Anastigmatic 85mm f6.3 lenses; variable speed guillotine shutter. C 1922.

R3* $200	£105	DM330	FF1k

Spido Stereo (9 x 18cm model): (GI105); black leather covered jumelle style camera; Goerz Dagor 110mm f6.8 lenses; Decaux 6 speed shutter. Changing mechanism for 12 plates, 9 x 18cm. Panoramic setting; rising and sliding lens panel. C 1900.

R3* $350	£184	DM577	FF1.8k

G. B. Multiplying Camera: (BB166); F. L. Chevalier lens; 12 exp, 25 x 25mm on 6 x 13cm plates by sliding and turning the plate holder. Mfd in France. C 1900.

R4* $475	£249	DM783	FF2.4k

GENIE CAMERA CO., Philadelphia, Pennsylvania.

Genie: (GC100); box-type detective camera; push-pull movement changes plates and advances exp counter on brass magazine. 3¹/₄" x 4¹/₄" exp on plates in magazine. C 1890.

R4* $500	£262	DM824	FF2.6k

G. GENNERT,
New York, New York.

Long Focus Montauk: (GC100); brass shutter; red bellows; polished wood interior. Front and rear bellows extension for long focus (close-up photography). C 1890.

| R4* $150 | £79 | DM247 | FF767 |

Montauk: (GC101); 4" x 5" box-type detective camera. C 1890.

| R4* $150 | £79 | DM247 | FF767 |

Montauk Multiplying Camera: (GC102); shifting lens standard; sliding back. 32 exp on 5" x 7" plate. C 1890.

| R4* $500 | £262 | DM824 | FF2.6k |

Montauk Stereo: (GC103); hand/stand-type stereo camera; Beck Symmetrical Rapid Rectilinear 5" lens or Bausch & Lomb; Bausch & Lomb iris diaphragm-type between lens shutter; short baseboard; rising front; reflecting finder. 3 sizes: $4^3/4$" x $6^1/2$", 5" x 7", 5" x 8". C 1899.

| R4* $375 | £197 | DM618 | FF1.9k |

Kamerawerk Adolf GERLACH,
Wuppertal, Germany

Ideal: (ID100); C1952-56, metal camera for 6 x 6 frames on roll film, simple f7.7 lens mounted in a collapsible tube, simple one speed shutter, cheap construction.

| R3* $15 | £8 | DM25 | FF77 |

Trixette:(ID101); C1954, metal camera for 6 x 6 frames on roll film, coated f5.6/75mm Supra-Anastigmat lens in "Spezial" shutter, 1/25 - 1/200s.

| R3* $50 | £26 | DM82 | FF256 |

Trixette I:(ID102); C1956, metal camera for 6 x 6 frames on roll film, coated f5.6/ 75mm Supra-Anastigmat lens in "Spezial" shutter, 1/25 - 1/200s, basically the same camera as (ID101) but with improved spring system for folding the lens, still interesting.

| R3* $50 | £26 | DM82 | FF256 |

Ideal Box: (ID103); C1955, metal box camera for 6 x 9 frames on roll film, simple lens and shutter.

| R2* $15 | £8 | DM25 | FF77 |

Luckyflex (G.G.S., Milan)

Ideal Colour 35: (ID104); 35mm VFR camera with coated Nixon or Nixonar f3.5/4.5cm lens "Spezial" shutter 1/25 - 1/200s. collected more for the "Nixon" name on the lens than for any other reason!

| R3* $25 | £13 | DM41 | FF128 |

GEYER MASCHINEN,
Berlin, Germany.

Geyer Camera: (GY100); 16mm movie camera; Carl Zeiss Triotar 25mm f2.9 lens. Hand crank or spring motor drive. C 1929.

| R4* $100 | £52 | DM165 | FF511 |

GEYMET AND ALKER,
Paris, France.

Jumelle Photographique (Jumelle de Nicour): (GK100); binocular-type detec-

G.G.S.-GOERZ

tive camera; 50 exp, 4 x 4cm in removable magazine. Patented by Octave Nicour. C 1866. The first camera to use this disguise.

`R5* $10k+  £5.2k+  DM16.5k+  FF51.1k+`

G.G.S.,
Milan, Italy

Luckyflex: (GG200); C1948, metal TLR for 35mm film, focusing Solar f3.2/50mm lens, GGS shutter, 1/20 - 1/300s, very small production, maybe 2000 units.

`R3* $900  £472  DM1.5k  FF4.6k`

Alph. GIROUX AND CO.,
Paris, France.

> *The Giroux was the world's first commercially made camera. It was designed by Daguerre, inventor of the process that bears his name. In 1839, Daguerre gave Alphonse Giroux the exclusive rights to distribute his camera. This example was imported into the U.S. by Francois Gouraud, Daguerre's first agent in the country. In April 1840, the camera was sold by Gouraud to Dr. Bemis, a Boston physician. A limited number of the cameras distributed by Daguerre & Giroux have a seal affixed to the side of the camera bearing the signatures of both these men. The slow achromatic landscape lens with an aperture of f15 and the low sensitivity of early Daguerreotype plates mandated long exposures of up to 45 minutes in full sunlight.*

Giroux Daguerreotype Camera: (GE100); daguerreotype camera; Achromatic landscape 15" f15 lens by Chevalier; metal plate on front of lens tube controlled exp time; ground glass for viewing and focusing. Single exp, 16.5 x 21.5cm on daguerreotype plates. Invented by Louis Jacques Mande Daguerre. C 1839. First commercially produced camera.

`R5*  NSR`

Giroux Daguerreotype Camera

Gitza: (BB167); 120 roll film folding camera; Anastigmat Pontiac Special f4.5 lens; shutter 1/25-1/150 s; molded plastic construction, similar to Ebner (see Ebner). Mfd in France.

`R2* $90  £47  DM148  FF460`

A. & B. GLOCK.

Glock: (GL100); field-type stereo camera; single lens on sliding panel for sequential exp; rising front; 18 x 24cm. C 1890.

`R4* $600  £315  DM989  FF3.1k`

C. P. GOERZ,
Berlin, Germany.

Anschutz Camera: (GZ100); Clement & Gilmer Wide Angle 25cm f15 lens, but usually found with original Goerz lens; eye level finder; CFPS. Introduced by Ottomar

Anschutz Camera

GOERZ

Anschutz, Prussia. C 1890.

| R4* $1.5k+ | £787+ | DM2.5k+ | FF7.7k+ |

Anschutz: (GZ101); 9 x 12cm folding camera; Goerz Double Anastigmatic Series III No. 0, 120mm ;lens, CFPS. C 1895.

| R3* $150 | £79 | DM247 | FF767 |

Anschutz: (GZ102); 9 x 12cm folding camera; Dagor 135mm f6.8 lens; CFPS C 1912.

| R3* $200 | £105 | DM330 | FF1k |

Anschutz De Luxe: (GZ103); 9 x 12cm folding camera; Goerz Doppel Anastigmat 180mm f6.8 lens; covered in dark green leather; CFPS; C 1910.

| R3* $250 | £131 | DM412 | FF1.3k |

Anschutz Stereo: (GZ104); 9 x 18 stereo camera; Goerz Doppel-Anastigmat 130mm lenses; Anschutz CFPS; 9 x 18cm exp on plates. CFPS; C 1912.

| R4* $300 | £157 | DM495 | FF1.5k |

Folding Reflex: (GZ105); 4" x 5" SLR camera; Goerz Doppel-Anastigmat f4.8 lens; Goerz Anschutz CFPS. 4" x 5" exp on plates. C 1912.

| R4* $275 | £144 | DM453 | FF1.4k |

Hypergon-Doppel-Anastigmat Wide Angle lens: (GZ106); Series X, 75mm f22 lens. Rotating fan blade in centre to permit uniform exp. Covers to 11'"x 14" plates.

| R5* $1k | £525 | DM1.6k | FF5.1k |

Hypergon Wide Angle lens

C.P. GOERZ, Austria.

Minicord: (GZ107); 16mm subminiature TLR camera; Helgor 25mm f2.0 lens; mfps

Minicord

1/10-1/400 s; 10 x 10mm exp on 16mm film in special cassettes; eye level viewing through roof prism. C 1951.

| R4* $350 | £184 | DM577 | FF1.8k |

Reporter: (GZ110); book-type detective camera; Goerz Aplanat 60 degree angle coverage lens; gravity shutter; 4 x 5.5cm exp on roll film. C 1889.

| R5* $5k | £2.6k | DM8.2k | FF25.6k |

Stereo Ango: (GZ111); Goerz Dagor 120mm f6.8 lens; FPS 1/10-1/1000 s. Paired exp on 9 x 18cm dry plates; film pack adapter; rising and sliding lens panel. C 1906.

| R4* $300 | £157 | DM495 | FF1.5k |

Stereo Photo Binocle: (GZ112); binocular-type detective camera; Dagor 75mm f6.8 lens; guillotine shutter; 45 x 107mm exp on plates. Could function as a mono or a stereo camera. C 1899.

| R5* $1.5k | £787 | DM2.5k | FF7.7k |

Stereo Vest Pocket Tenax: (GZ113); 45 x 107mm stereo plate camera; Dopp-Anastigmat Celor 60mm f4.5 lens; shutter

Stereo Vest Pocket Tenax

1/2-1/250 s. C 1920.

R3* $300	£157	DM495	FF1.5k

Tenax: (GZ114); 6 x 9cm roll film and plate camera; Goerz Anastigmat 12.5mm f6.3 lens; Goerz dial-set shutter 1-1/200 s. 6 x 9cm exp on roll film and cut film. C 1922.

R2* $50	£26	DM82	FF256

Vest Pocket Tenax: (GZ115); 4.5 x 6cm camera; Dogmar 75mm f4.5 lens; shutter 1-1/250 s. C 1909.

R3* $125	£66	DM206	FF639

Goldeck 16: (BB170); subminiature camera; Colour Enit 20mm f2.8 lens; shutter 1/25-1/200 s; 30 exp, 10 x 14mm on 16mm film.

R3* $200	£105	DM330	FF1k

GOLDSCHMID, Switzerland.

Binocle: (GD100); binocular-type detective camera; Steinheil 15cm f6.3 lens; guillotine shutter; frame loaded plates, 5 x 6cm. One eye-piece was attached to the lens; the other to the plate loader. C 1890.

R5* $3.5k+	£1.8k+	DM5.8k+	FF17.9k+

GOLTZ & BREUTMANN, Dresden, Germany.

Mentor-Compur-Reflex: (GB100); 6 x 9cm SLR; Tessar 105mm f4.5 lens; Compur 1-1/250 s; 6 x 9cm exp on plates. C 1928.

R3* $200	£105	DM330	FF1k

Mentor-Compur-Reflex

Mentor Folding Reflex: (GB101); 3¹/₄" x 4¹/₄" folding reflex camera; Tessar 150mm f4.5 lens; CFPS 1/20 - 1/1000 s. C 1914.

R3* $200	£105	DM330	FF1k

Mentor Sport Reflex Camera: (GB102); 3¹/₄" x 4¹/₄" reflex camera; Tessar 150mm f4.5 lens; FPS 1/8-1/300 s. C 1927.

R3* $200	£105	DM330	FF1k

Mentor Stereo Reflex: (GB103); 45 x 107mm stereo SLR camera; Zeiss Tessar 105mm f4.5 lenses; CFPS 1/15-1/1000 s. 45 x 107mm exp on plates. C 1914.

R4* $750	£394	DM1.2k	FF3.8k

Mentorette: (GB104); 6 x 6cm TLR; Mentor 75mm f3.5 lens; CFPS 1/15-1/600 s; 12 exp, 2¹/₄" x 2¹/₄" on 120 roll film. C 1936.

R4* $150	£79	DM247	FF767

Le Gousset: (BB171); achromatic lens; one speed shutter; 4.5 x 6cm film pack. Mfd in Paris, France. C 1910.

R4* $175	£92	DM288	FF894

Graph-Check Sequential Camera: (BB172); 8 lens camera takes eight sequential photos on one sheet of 4" x 5" Polaroid film; each image is delayed incrementally from 1/10 - 4 s. For analyzing physical and mechanical motion. Still in frequent use.

R*3 $450	£236	DM742	FF2.3k

GOMZ-GOLDAMMER

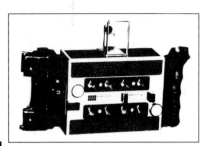

Graph-Check Sequential Camera

GOMZ, (STATE OPTICAL/ MECHANICAL WORKS), USSR.

Leningrad: (In Cyrillic or Roman letters): (GG100); 1953-59. Cfps, 1 - 1/1000 s, adjustable flash synch, combined RFR/VFR, with frame lines for 35mm, 50mm, 85mm, and 135mm fields of view. Built-in spring drive for film transport. 10 exposures at 2-3 per second are possible when the spring is fully wound. Jupitor-8 f2.0/50mm lens. This camera was not made especially for the secret police as is sometimes mentioned. At 900 Rubels, it was the most expensive domestic 35mm camera offered in the USSR. Prices are 25-50% higher for this camera in Japan.

R3* $300	£157	DM495	FF1.5k

Sport *(Cnopm)*: (GG101); 1936(?), CFPS, 50mm/f3.5 lens, the first Russian single lens reflex camera. Uses special cassettes for 35mm for 24mm X 36mm negative size.

R4* $900	£472	DM1.5k	FF4.6k

Sport (Cnopm)

Sputnik: (GG102); C1957, Bakelite stereo camera, for 6 x 13cm frames on 120 roll film f4.5/75mm lenses, ground glass focusing on reflex waistlevel VFR, between-the-lens shutter 1/10 - 1/100 s, later cameras have 1/15s - 1-150s. (complete outfit with viewer adds 40%).

R3* $275	£144	DM453	FF1.4k

Sputnik

Smena: (GG103); C1953, Bakelite 35mm VFR camera, f4.5/40mm lens, shutter 1/10 - 1/100s.

R3* $25	£13	DM41	FF128

Smena 2: (GG104); C1956, Bakelite 35mm VFR camera, f4.5/40mm lens, shutter 1/10 - 1/200s, accessory shoe. This camera was copied by the Chinese in their "Yangtze River" and "Hua Mountain" cameras.

R3* $25	£13	DM41	FF128

Lubitel: (GG110); C1954, bakelite TLR for 6 x 6cm on roll film, focusing f4.5/75mm lens, shutter 1/10 - 1/200s, copy of Voigtländer Brilliant.

R2* $15	£8	DM25	FF7.7

Lubitel II: (GG111); C1956, as (GG110) but for flash synch.

R2* $15	£8	DM25	FF77

Gerhard GOLDAMMER, Frankfurt, Germany

Goldeck 16: (GA200); C1960, subminiature camera for 10 x 14mm frames on 16mm movie film, *interchangeable* Colour-Ennit f2.8/20mm lens, shutter 1/25 - 1/200s, lever advance.

| R3* $80 | £42 | DM132 | FF409 |

Tele-Ennit f2.8/50mm lens for (GA200): (GA001); **$35**

Golda: (GA201); C1950, 35mm RFR camera, uncoupled RFR, Trinar f3.5/45mm lens and Prontor shutter in collapsible tube mount.

| R3* $50 | £26 | DM82 | FF256 |

Gugo-Knips: (GA202); C1950, VFR camera for 6 x 6cm frames on 120 roll film, f8, f4.5, f3.5, or f2.9 lens and Vario or Pronto shutter in collapsible tube mount.

| R2* $20 | £10 | DM33 | FF102 |

Goldix: (GA203); C1960, VFR camera for 4 x 4cm frames on 127 film, Goldeck f7.7/60mm lens, simple shutter.

| R2* $15 | £8 | DM25 | FF77 |

(GRAFLEX) THE FOLMER & SCHWING MFG. CO., New York.

Deceptive Angle Graphic: (GX100); detective camera; rapid rectilinear 12.5cm f11 lens, also available with Goerz Double Anastigmat or Zeiss Collinear. 8 x 10.5cm plates. Right-angle detective-type finder. False lens on front of camera; taking lens on side of camera. C 1901-1904.

| R5* $3.5k+ | £1.8k+ | DM5.8k+ | FF17.9k+ |

The Folding Pocket Graphic: (GX101); Graphic R.R. lens; Automatic shutter; 3¹/₄" x 4¹/₄" exp. C 1904.

| R3* $175 | £92 | DM288 | FF894 |

The Graflex Camera: (GX102); Zeiss Series VIIA f6.3* lens; CFPS 1/10-1/1200 s. 4 models: 4" x 5", 5" x 5", **$500.** 6¹/₂" x 8¹/₄" 8" x 10", C1904.

| R4* $1k+ | £525+ | DM1.6k+ | FF5.1k+ |

The Graphic Camera: (GX103); Goerz Series III* lens; sector shutter; leather covered mahogany. C 1904. 3 models: 4" x 5", **$200.** 5" x 7", 8" x 10", **$700.**

| R4* |

The Graphic Sr: (GX105); Bausch & Lomb Zeiss Convertible Series VIIa* lens; Diaphragm shutter. 2 models: 4" x 5", 5" x 7". C 1904.

| R4* $200 | £105 | DM330 | FF1k |

The Graphic Twin Lens Special: (GX106); Zeiss Convertible No. 7 Series VIIa* lens; diaphragm shutter; 4" x 5" exp. C 1904.

| R5* $1.7k | £892 | DM2.8k | FF8.7k |

The Graphic Twin Lens Special

GRAFLEX

Reversible Back Cycle Graphic Special: (GX107); Goerz Series III* lens; sector shutter; optional CFPS. 4 models: 4" x 5", 5" x 7", 6½" x 8½", 8" x 10". C 1904.

R3* $200	£105	DM330	FF1k

The Reversible Back Graflex Camera: (GX110); Zeiss Series VIIA f6.3* lens; CFPS 1/10-1/1200 s. 2 models: 4" x 5", 5" x 7". C 1904.

R3* $450	£236	DM742	FF2.3k

Reversible Back Graphic: (GX111); Bausch & Lomb Zeiss Convertible Series VIIA* lens; diaphragm shutter. 4 models were sold: 4" x 5", 5" x 7", 6½" x 8½", 8" x 10". C 1904.

R3* $225	£118	DM371	FF1.2k

Reversible Back Graphic Special: (GX112); plastigmat* lens; diaphragm shutter. 3 models: 4" x 5", 5" x 7", 6½" x 8½", C 1904.

R3* $225	£118	DM371	FF1.2k

The Sky Scraper Camera - Reversible Back - Double Swing: (GX113); Century Rapid Convertible lens; Wollensak shutter; maroon leather bellows, brass fittings. Walnut construction; rising front panel; extreme tilting back. 3 models: 8" x 10", 11" x 14", 14" x 17". C 1904.

R4* $350	£184	DM577	FF1.8k

The Sky Scraper Camera

The Sky Scraper Special Camera: (GX114); Hypergon-Doppel-Anastigmat 75mm f22 lens; special recessed lens board permits use of extremely short focus lenses.

2 models: 8" x 10", 11" x 14". C 1904.

R4* $800	£420	DM1.3k	FF4.1k

Stereoscopic Graphic: (GX115); Graphic R.R. lens; CFPS 1/10-1/1200 s, 5" x 7" exp. C 1904.

R4* $1.2k	£630	DM2k	FF6.1k

The Telescopic Graphic Camera: (GX116); Graphic R.R.* lens; Automatic* shutter; 5" x 7" exp. C 1904.

R4* $750	£394	DM1.2k	FF3.8k

The Telescopic Stereo Graphic: (GX117); matched Graphic R.R. lenses; CFPS 1/10-1/1200 s. C 1904.

R5* $2k+	£1.1k+	DM3.3k+	FF10.2k+

The Tourist Graflex: (GX120); Cooke Series III f6.5* lens; CFPS. 2 models: 4" x 5", 5" x 7". C 1904.

R3* $400	£210	DM659	FF2k

The Triple Lens Stereo Graphic: (GX121); matched pair of No. 7 Series VIIa Bausch & Lomb Zeiss Convertible lenses; CFPS 1/10-1/1200 s. 5" x 7" exp. C 1904.

R5* $2k+	£1.1k+	DM3.3k+	FF10.2k+

(GRAFLEX) FOLMER & SCHWING DIV., Eastman Kodak Co., Rochester, New York.

The Auto Graflex: (GX122); Bausch & Lomb Zeiss Tessar Series IIb f6.3* lens; CFPS 1/10-1/1000 s. 3 models: 3¼" x 4¼", 4" x 5", 5" x 7". C 1907-1923.

R3* $125	£66	DM206	FF639

Banquet Panoramic View Camera: (GX123); 7 x 17; tilting front; front and rear rack and pinion focusing. Mahogany finish, brass fittings. C 1920.

R4* $950	£499	DM1.6k	FF4.9k

Cirkut Camera: (GX124); Turner-Reich Convertible Anastigmat Series II* lens; Century No. 4 shutter. No. 5 Cirkut Camera (GX125), $1500 No. 6 Cirkut Camera (GX126), $2000 Still used by enthusiasts.

R4* $1.2k+	£630+	DM2k+	FF6.1k+

No. 10 Cirkut Camera: (GX127), early model fan operated, $1200; later model, governor operated.

R4* $2.25k+ £1.2k+ DM3.7k+ FF11.5k+

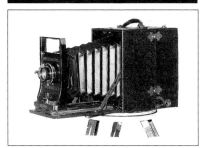

No. 10 Cirkut Camera

No. 16 Cirkut Camera (GX130).

R4* $3k+ £1.6k+ DM5k+ FF15.3k+

The Cirkut Outfit: (GX131); panoramic camera; consists of R.B. Cycle Graphic with Cirkut Panorama attachment. Prices include a complete set of gears. C 1908. No. 6 Cirkut Outfit, **$2300.** No. 8 Cirkut Outfit.

R4* $2.75k £1.4k DM4.5k FF14.1k

Graphic No. 0: (GX132); Zeiss Kodak Anastigmat f6.3 lens; CFPS 1/4-1/500 s; 6 or 12 exp, 4.5 x 6cm on roll film. C 1909-1912.

R3* $250 £131 DM412 FF1.3k

Graphic No. 0

The Naturalist's Graflex: (GX133); Bausch & Lomb Zeiss Protar lens, Series VIIa, No.

19 f6.3* lens; CFPS 1/10-1/1000 s; 4" x 5" exp. C 1907-1921.

R5* $3k+ £1.6k+ DM5k+ FF15.3k+

The 1A Graflex: (GX134); Kodak Anastigmat f4.5* lens; CFPS 1/10-1/1000 s; 2¹/₂" x 5¹/₄" exp on 116 roll film. C 1909-1925.

R3* $200 £105 DM330 FF1k

1A Graflex

Press Graflex

The Press Graflex: (GX135); Bausch & Lomb Zeiss Tessar Series Ic No. 16 f4.5*

lens; CFPS 1/5-1/1500 s; 5" x 7" exp. C 1908.

| R4* $400 | £210 | DM659 | FF2k |

R.B. Tele Graflex: (GX137); CFPS 1/10-1/1000 s. 3¹/₄" x 4¹/₄", C 1915-1923, **$125.** 4" x 5", C 1912-1923, **$200.**

| R4* |

The Revolving Back Auto Graflex: (GX140); Bausch & Lomb Zeiss Tessar Series IIb No. 6 f6.3* lens; CFPS 1/10-1/1000 s. 2 models: 3¹/₄" x 4¹/₄", 4" x 5". C 1909-1940.

| R3* $125 | £66 | DM206 | FF639 |

The Revolving Back Cycle Graphic: (GX141); Bausch & Lomb Plastigmat* lens; Volute shutter. (Graflex Focal Plane Shutter available as an accessory). 4 models: 4" x 5", 5" x 7", 6¹/₂" x 8¹/₂", 8" x 10". C 1908.

| R3* $175 | £92 | DM288 | FF894 |

Speed Graphic (Original): (GX142); Kodak Anastigmat f4.5* lens; cpfs 1/10-1/1000 s. 3¹/₄" x 4¹/₄", C 1913, 4" x 5", C 1912-1927, 3¹/₄" x 5¹/₂", C 1912, 5" x 7", C 1913-1940.

| R3* $125 | £66 | DM206 | FF639 |

The Stereo Auto Graflex: (GX146); Bausch & Lomb Zeiss Tessar f6.3* lenses; CFPS 1/10-1/1000 s; 5" x 7" exp. C 1908.

| R4* $1.2k | £630 | DM2k | FF6.1k |

Stereo Graflex: (GX147); Zeiss Series VIIa No. 7* lens; CFPS 1/10-1/1000 s; 5" x 7" exp. C 1908.

| R4* $1.2k | £630 | DM2k | FF6.1k |

The Stereoscopic Graphic: (GX150); Bausch & Lomb Protar VIIa No. 7 f6.3*

Stereoscopic Graphic

lenses; CFPS 1/10-1/1000 s; 5" x 7" exp. C 1908.

| R5* $1.5k+ | £787+ | DM2.5k+ | FF7.7k+ |

The 3A Graflex: (GX151); Bausch & Lomb Zeiss Tessar Series IIb No. 5A f6.3* lens; CFPS 1/10-1/1000 s; 3¹/₄" x 5¹/₂" exp on 122 roll film. C 1907-1926.

| R3* $100 | £52 | DM165 | FF511 |

(GRAFLEX) FOLMER GRAFLEX CORP., Rochester, New York.

Anniversary Speed Graphic: (GX152); Kodak Anastigmat 5¹/₂" f4.5 lens; Compur 1-1/250 s; CFPS 1/10-1/1000 s. 3¹/₄" x 4¹/₄", C 1940-1947, **$95.** 4" x 5", (GX153), C 1940-1947.

| R2* $175 | £92 | DM288 | FF894 |

Graflex Fingerprint Camera: (GX155); pre-focused lens for making 1:1 photos of fingerprints or small objects; built-in illumination. C 1930.

| R3* $100 | £52 | DM165 | FF511 |

National Graflex—Series I: (GX156); Bausch & Lomb Tessar 75mm f3.5 lens, non-interchangeable mount; CFPS 1/30 - 1/500 s. Ten exp, 2¹/₄" x 3¹/₄" on 120 roll film. C 1933-1935.

| R3* $175 | £92 | DM288 | FF894 |

National Graflex—Series II: (GX157); Bausch & Lomb Tessar 75mm f3.5 lens, interchangeable mount; CFPS 1/30-1/500 s. 10 exposures, 2¹/₄" x 3¹/₄" on 120 roll film. C 1934-41.

| R3* $250 | £131 | DM412 | FF1.3k |

Bausch & Lomb 140mm f6.3 Telephoto lens: (GX001); for (GX157).

| R3* $150 | £79 | DM247 | FF767 |

GRAFLEX

Graflex Fingerprint Camera

R.B. Graflex, Series B: (GX160); Kodak Anastigmat f4.5 lens, screw thread interchangeable mount; CFPS 1/10-1/1000 s. 2¹/4" x 3¹/4", C 1925-1951, 3¹/4" x 4¹/4", (GX161), C 1925 -1942, 4" x 5", (GX162), C 1925-1942.

| R2* | $125 | £66 | DM206 | FF639 |

R.B. Graflex, Series C: (GX163); Cooke 6¹/2" f2.5 lens; CFPS 1/10-1/1000 s; 3¹/4" x

R.B. Super D Graflex

4¹/4" exp. C 1926-1935.

| R2* | $150 | £79 | DM247 | FF767 |

R.B. Graflex, Series D: (GX164); CFPS 1/10-1/1000 s; 3¹/4" x 4¹/4", C 1928-1941,**$85**. 4" x 5", C 1928-1945.

| R2* | $150 | £79 | DM247 | FF767 |

R.B. Home Portrait Graflex: (GX166); Zeiss Tessar 10"* lens; CFPS 1-1/500 s; 5" x 7" exp. C 1912-1942.

| R4* | $300 | £157 | DM495 | FF1.5k |

G

R.B. Super D Graflex: (GX167); Kodak Ektar 152mm f4.5* lens with semi-auto diaphragm; CFPS 1/5-1/1000 s. 3¹/4" x 4¹/4", C 1941-1963, **$225**. 4" x 5" (GX170), C 1948-1958.

| R3* | $400 | £210 | DM659 | FF2k |

Speed Graphic: - 4" x 5": (GX171); Zeiss Tessar f4.5* lens; Dial-set Compur 1-1/300 s; CFPS 1/10-1/1000 s; 4" x 5" exp. C 1928-1939.

| R3* | $175 | £92 | DM288 | FF894 |

GRAFLEX INC., Rochester, New York.

Combat Graphic (70mm): (GX172); 70mm roll film combat camera; Kodak Ektar 100mm f2.8 coated lens; CFPS 1-1/500 s; 2¹/4" x ¹/4" on 70mm film. Spring-wind motor drive, CRF. C 1942.Complete set 3 lenses, case doubles the price.

| R4* | $700 | £367 | DM1.2k | FF3.6k |

Combat Graphic (70mm)

Combat Graphic: (GX173); 4" x 5" sheet film combat camera; Kodak Anastigmat Special 127mm f4.7 lens; Graphic shutter 1-1/400 s, CFPS 1/30 - 1/1000 s; 4" x 5" exp

GRAFLEX

on cut film and film pack. Water and dust resistant wooden construction with olive drab paint. C 1942. Standard camera used by the U.S. Armed Forces in WWII.

R3* $300	£157	DM495	FF1.5k

Combat Graphic 4" x 5"

Graphic Jet: (GX174); 35mm motor drive camera; Graflex Optar 50mm f2 coated lens; Copal SVK, 1-1/500 s, CRF. "Jet-O-Matic" motor consists of CO2 charger - drive motor automatically advances film and cocks shutter after each exp. Each CO2 charger cycles 6 to 8 rolls of 20 exp 35mm film, at a maximum rate of 2 exp per s. Rapid wind film advance and shutter cocking may also be operated manually. Push button focusing moves film plane while lens remains stationary. Selenium photo-electric exp meter coupled to shutter. Mfd. in Japan, for

Graphic Jet

Graflex Inc., Rochester, N.Y. C 1961.

R4* $250	£131	DM412	FF1.3k

Graphic 35: (GX175); 35mm rf camera; Graflex 50mm f3.5 coated lens; Prontor 1-1/300 s. C 1956.

R2* $50	£26	DM82	FF256

Graphic 35

Stereo Graphic: (GX184); 35mm stereo camera, optical VFR, fixed focus Graflar 35mm/f4 lenses, single shutter speed, 1/50s, each lens was set for a slightly different point of focus, thereby ensuring at least one of the stereo pair to have the major subject in sharp focus. This was known as the "Depthmaster" system. The same camera was sold as the "Wray Stereo Camera" in England.

R2* $90	£47	DM148	FF460

Graphic View Camera: (GX176); 4" x 5" metal view camera. C 1941-1950.

R3* $200	£105	DM330	FF1k

Miniature Speed Graphic: (GX177); Kodak Anastigmat Ektar 107mm f3.7 lens; Compur shutter 1 - 1/250 s, CFPS 1/10-1/1000 s; 2¼" x 3¼" exp. C 1938-1947.

R3* $250	£131	DM412	FF1.3k

Pacemaker Crown Graphic: (GX180); Kodak Ektar 101mm f4.5* coated lens; Kodak Flash Supermatic shutter 1-1/400 s. No FPS. 2¼" x 3¼", **$200**; 3¼" x 4¼", **$125**; 4" x 5", **$300**. Still used by enthusiasts.

R3*

Pacemaker Speed Graphic: (GX181); Kodak Ektar 101mm f4.5* coated lens; Kodak Flash Supermatic shutter 1-1/400 s,

Pacemaker Crown Graphic

Pacemaker Speed Graphic

CFPS 1/30-1/1000 s. The Pacemaker is the only Graphic model with a single body release for both front and FPS. 2¹/₄" x 3¹/₄", C 1947-1958, **$250**. 3¹/₄" x 4¹/₄", (GX182), C 1947-1962, **$125**. 4" x 5", (GX183), C 1947-1970.

R3* $300	£157	DM495	FF1.5k

Super Speed Graphic: (GX185); 4" x 5" press camera; Graflex Optar 135mm f4.7 coated lens; special high speed between the lens Graflex shutter 1-1/1000s, without FPS , CRF.

R2* $160	£84	DM264	FF818

Super Speed Graphic

GREAT WALL CAMERA FACTORY, Beijing, China.

Great Wall DF-2: (GQ100); 1970's. 120 roll film Slr, metal behind the lens shutter, 1/30 - 1/200 s, ruby windows for frame counting, removable metal mask for 6X4.5 size negatives. Waist level VFR, coated 90mm screw mount lens. Later models incorporated self timer, and flash synch. This copy of the 1930's "Super Pilot" is no longer in production.

R3* $90	£47	DM148	FF460

G

Great Wall SZ-1: (GQ101); 1970's. Between the lens leaf shutter, 1 - 1/300 s, combined RFR/VFR, fixed f2.8/45mm lens, built-in spring motor film advance. A copy of a Ricoh camera, early cameras sometimes had the political slogan "Serve the People" in Mao's handwriting on the top plate, and are quite rare, even in China. This adds 200% to the value.

R3* $100	£52	DM165	FF511

Great Wall SZ-1

Great Wall SZ-2: (GQ102); 1970's. Between the lens leaf shutter, 1 - 1/300 s, combined RFR/VFR, fixed f2.8/45mm lens, built-in spring motor film advance. As the Great Wall SZ-1, but with internal changes.

R3* $100	£52	DM165	FF511

J. J. GRIFFIN AND SON, London, England.

Cyko No. 1: (GS100); 6.5 x 9cm all aluminium camera; Aplanatic 12cm lens; guillotine shutter. C 1902.

R4* $600	£315	DM989	FF3.1k

GRIFFITHS-GUNDLACH

Pocket Cyko: (GS101); all aluminium folding camera; 6.5 x 9cm exp. C 1902.

R4* $600	£315	DM989	FF3.1k

W. GRIFFITHS & CO.,
Birmingham, England.

The Guinea Detective or Hand Camera: (WG100); valise type detective camera; single achromatic f9 lens; T and I settings. C 1891. Original cost was one guinea.

R5* $350	£184	DM577	FF1.8k

Grundmann, Leipzig Detective camera: (BB174); wooden box detective camera; focusing lens tube; string set shutter; 9 x 12cm plates.

R4* $850	£446	DM1.4k	FF4.3k

GUANGDONG Camera
Factory, Guangdong, China.

Pearl River: (GP100); 2¼" x ¼" TLR; Pearl River 75mm f3.5 coated lens; Pearl River shutter 1/25-1/250 s. 12 exp, 2¼" x 2¼" on 20 roll film. Mfd in China. C 1965.

R3* $75	£39	DM124	FF383

Ets. E. GUERIN & CO.,
Paris, France.

Le Furet (The Ferret): (GU100); 35mm camera; Hermagis Anastigmatic 40mm f4.5 lens; 3 speed rotary shutter; 25 exp on 35mm film. Designed in 1913; marketed C 1923-1929. Smallest pre-Leica 35mm

Le Furet

---

camera. Invented by M. Maroniez.

R4* $1.5k	£787	DM2.5k	FF7.7k

The Guilford: (BB175); view camera; Ross Extra Rapid brass lens; leather lens cap. Walnut finish, brass fittings and black bellows. Mfd in England.

R3* $150	£79	DM247	FF767

GUILLEMINOT ROUX & CIE,
Paris, France.

Guilleminot Detective Camera: (GR100); detective camera; Aplanat 150mm f9 lens; rotary sector shutter with 8 speeds. Ground glass viewing. Walnut finish, brass fittings. C 1900.

R4* $800	£420	DM1.3k	FF4.1k

Le Sphinx: (GR101); Aplanat lens; rotary sector shutter; plate changing mechanism - 9 x 12cm dry plates. C 1891.

R5* $1.1k	£577	DM1.8k	FF5.6k

GUNDLACH-MANHATTAN
OPTICAL CO., New York.

Bo Peep Camera: (GN100); 4" x 5" folding plate camera; reversible finder; red bellows; solid wood front; wood interior. C 1898.

R3* $150	£79	DM247	FF767

Bo Peep Camera

Korona I: (GN101); 4" x 5" folding camera; Gundlach Optical Triple Convertible lens and shutter; long focus bed; side, rear, top and front open for red double extension bellows. C 1900's.

R4* $200	£105	DM330	FF1k

Korona IV: (GN102); 4" x 5" folding camera; Rapid Convertible lens; Gundlach Manhattan shutter 1-1/100 s; 4" x 5" exp on dry plates.

| R3* $125 | £66 | DM206 | FF639 |

Korona Panoramic View: (GN103); 4" x 12" panoramic view camera; Triple Convertible Turner Reich lens. 4 sizes: 5" x 12", 7" x 17", 8" x 20", 12" x 20".

| R4* $1k | £525 | DM1.6k | FF5.1k |

Korona I

Korona IV

Korona Panoramic View

Korona Royal Stereo

Korona Royal Stereo: (GN104); 5" x 7" stereo camera; rear tilts; front shift. Polished wood interior with nickel plated fittings. C 1920's.

| R4* $600 | £315 | DM989 | FF3.1k |

Night-Hawk Detective Camera: (GN105); box type detective camera; string set shutter; 4" x 5" exp on plates. Leather and wood finished versions.

| R4* $350 | £184 | DM577 | FF1.8k |

Night-Hawk Detective Camera

Wizard Duplex No. 1: (GN106); folding 3¹/₄" x 4¹/4" combination plate and roll film camera; roll holder for No. 3 Folding Pocket Kodak Film made by Eastman Kodak is removable for plate use. C 1904.

| R4* $375 | £197 | DM618 | FF1.9k |

Wizard Duplex No. 2: (GN107); combination roll film and plate folding camera. Hinged back is removable to permit accurate ground glass focusing. C 1904.

| R4* $375 | £197 | DM618 | FF1.9k |

GUTHE & THORSCH

GUTHE & THORSCH,
Dresden, Germany.

> Later Kamera Wertstätten and in 1959 VEB Kamera und Kinowerke Dresden, finally becoming part of the giant VEB Pentacon. For simplicity cameras are grouped by name with no regard as to which named company produced them

G

KW Patent Etui 6.5 x 9: (GT100); C1930, 6.5x 9cm folding plate camera, Tessar 120mm f4.5 lens among others, (earliest cameras have dial set, later ones have rim set) Compur shutter 1-1/250 s among others, double or single extension bellows, known for its ultra slim design.

R3* $75	£39	DM124	FF383

KW Patent Etui

KW Patent Etui 9 x 12: (GT105); C1930, 9 x 12cm folding plate camera, Trioplan f3.8/135mm lens among others, (earliest cameras have dial set, later ones have rim set)Compur shutter 1 - 1/250s among others, known for its ultra slim design.

R3* $60	£31	DM99	FF307

KW Patent Etui Deluxe: (GT101); C1932, 6.5 x 9cm *or* 9 x 12cm folding plate camera,Tessar lens among others, Compur shutter 1 - 1/250 s. Brown or blue or red leather covering with matching bellows.

R4* $300	£157	DM495	FF1.5k

Pilot Twin Lens Reflex: (GT102);C1931, 127 roll film TLR camera, Schneider Xenar

Pilot Twin Lens Reflex

5cm f3.5 lens among others, Compur, shutter 1-1/300 s; 3 x 4cm exp on 127 roll film, early cameras have the "Pilot" name in script, after 1935 "Pilot" is in all upper case printing.

R4* $400	£210	DM659	FF2k

Pilot 6: (GT103); C1934, roll film SLR for 6 x 6cm frames on 120 film, KW Anastigmat f2.9, f3.5, f4.5 or f6.3/75mm lens, FPS, early models 1/25 - 1/100s, later models 1/15-1/150s.

R2* $75	£39	DM124	FF383

Pilot Super: (GT104); C1936, roll film SLR for 6 x 6cm or 6 x 4.5cm frames on roll film, screw mount Laack f2.9/75mm lens among others, FPS 1/20-1/200s, built-in extinction meter.

R3* $90	£47	DM148	FF460

KW Reflex Box: (GT106); C1936, roll film SLR for 6 x 9cm frames on 120 film, f6.3 or 4.5/105mm lens, FPS 1/25 - 1/100s.

R3* $130	£68	DM214	FF664

Praktiflex: (GT107); C1937, 35mm SLR interchangeable Xenar f3.5/50mm lens

GUTHE & THORSCH

Pilot Super

among others, CFPS 1/20 - 1/500s, top mounted shutter release, fixed waist level finder.

R3* $70	£37	DM115	FF358

Praktiflex II: (GT108); C1940, 35mm SLR interchangeable Xenar f3.5/50mm lens among others, CFPS 1/20 - 1/500s, *front* mounted shutter release, fixed waist level finder.

R3* $70	£37	DM115	FF358

Praktica: (GT109); C1948, 35mm SLR, post-war version of the Praktiflex, different in name and shutter speeds only (1 - 1/500s) only.

R2* $50	£26	DM82	FF256

Praktica FX: (GT110); C1954, as (GT109) but now with F and X synch connections on the camera front.

R2* $50	£26	DM82	FF256

Praktica FX 2: (GT111); C1956, as (GT110) but with new finder hood and PC type synch.

R2* $50	£26	DM82	FF256

Praktica FX 3: (GT112); C1958, as (GT111)

but now with automatic aperture.

R2* $50	£26	DM82	FF256

Praktina FX: (GT113); C1954, 35mm SLR with interchangeable Biotar f2/50mm lens among others, CFPS 1 - 1/1000s, built-in direct vision VFR, often found with spring motor and 250 exposure back (motor and back each add 100%).

R2* $60	£31	DM99	FF307

Praktisix: (GT114); C1955, roll film SLR for 6 x 6cm frames on 120 film, interchangeable Tessar or Biometer f2.8/80mm lens, CFPS 1 - 1/1000s, interchangeable waistlevel VFR, often found with shutter problems.

R3* $150	£79	DM247	FF767

Praktisix II: (GT115); C1969, as (GT114) but with brighter finder and the same shutter problems.

R2* $150	£79	DM247	FF767

Pentacon six: (GT116); C1970, as (GT115) but now made by VEB Pentacon, and capable of 120 (twelve exposures 6 x 6cm) or 220 (twenty four exposures 6 x 6cm) film operation.

R3* $150	£79	DM247	FF767

Pentacon six TL: (GT117); C1975-90, the last in the line of 120 SLRs from Dresden, finally the shutter is more reliable, and the film advance is redesigned. This camera is often bought by someone who wants to start on medium format with a small budget, or by a collector looking for an interesting usable piece at a bargain price.

R2* $150	£79	DM247	FF767

Lenses and accessories for Praktisix/Pentacon six

Flektagon f50mm f4 wide angle lens: (GT001); **$175.** Flektagon 65mm f2.8 wide angle lens: (GT002); **$125.** Biometer 120mm f2.8 telephoto lens: (GT003); **$125.** Sonnar 180mm f2.8 telephoto lens: (GT004); **$200.** Sonnar 300mm f4 telephoto lens: (GT005); **$175.** Orestegor 300mm f4 telephoto lens: (GT006); **$125.** Orestegor 500mm f4 telephoto lens: (GT007) **$300.** TTL prism meter: (GT008); **$50.** Magnifying finder: (GT009); **$30.** Prism finder: (GT010); **$30.**

Electra II

HAAKE ET ALBERS, Frankfurt a/M, Germany.

Badecker: (HA100); book type detective camera; Voigtlander Euryscop 80mm lens; 24 exp on 4.5 x 6cm plates. C 1892.

R5* $4k+	£2.1k+	DM6.6k+	FF20.4k+

HAGLUND, Germany.

L'Album Camera: (HB100); book type detective camera; guillotine shutter. 2 plates, 10 x 12.5cm in pivoting magazine. C 1889.

R5* $4k+	£2.1k+	DM6.6k+	FF20.4k+

Hanimar

HANIMEX (HANnes IMport and EXport), Australia.

Though not actually a manufacturer of cameras, Hanimex is a very large dealer in photographic equipment. Like so many other large photographic houses, HANIMEX contracted with camera manufacturers for "house brands".

Holiday 35

Electra II: (HX100); C1961, 35mm VFR camera, Hanimar f2.8/45mm lens, automatic aperture and shutter control by means of a built-in Selinium light meter, focusing by use of four separate shutter release buttons, actually a Dacoramatic 4D.

R2* $25	£13	DM41	FF128

Hanimar: (HX101); C1953, 35mm VFR camera with interchangeable Finetar f2.8/45mm lens, shutter 1/25 - 1/200s, actually a Finetta 88.

R* $30	£16	DM49	FF153

Holiday 35: (HX102); C1957, 35mm RFR camera, Kominar f3.5/4.5cm lens, leaf shutter 1 - 1/300s, CRF, looking like the Petrie 35.

R2* $30	£16	DM49	FF153

Eaglet: (HX103); metal box camera for 6 x 6cm or 6 x 4.5cm on 120 rollfilm, simple lens and shutter, made in Italy by Fototecnica.

R2* $25	£13	DM41	FF128

Hanimex Box: (HX104); C1955, metal box camera for 6 x 9cm frames on roll film,

Eaglet

simple lens and shutter, built-in yellow filter, actually an Alka box camera made by Vredeborch in West Germany.

R2* $20	£10	DM33	FF102

E. HANAU,
Paris, France.

L'Omnigraphe: (EH100); guillotine shutter. 12 plates, 9 x 12cm. C 1887 (1906 with Planar lens.)

R5* $2k+	£1.1k+	DM3.3k+	FF10.2k+

Le Marsouin: (EH101); 45 x 107mm stereo camera; Tessar 55mm f6.3 lenses; 3 speed guillotine shutter. 12 stereo exp on 45 x 107mm dry plates in push-pull magazine.

R4* $450	£236	DM742	FF2.3k

Le Handy: (BB180); Lemardley 135mm f7.7 lens; guillotine shutter 1/25-1/100 s. 9 x 12cm exp; helical focusing. Mfg in Paris, France. C 1900.

R4* $750	£394	DM1.2k	FF3.8k

Hapyucc [Narciss]: (BB181); Sometimes called the Narcissus SLR subminiature camera; removable pentaprism. Mfd in U.S.S.R.

Hapyucc

C 1960.

R3* $650	£341	DM1.1k	FF3.3k

George HARE,
London, England.

George Hare Stereoscopic Wet Plate: (GH100); brass bound teak? wood camera; Petzval lenses; 2 sets of waterhouse stops in leather cases; flap shutter; rack focusing from rear. C 1865-1870.

R5* $4k+	£2.1k+	DM6.6k+	FF20.4k+

Tourist Stereo Camera: (GH101); 8 x 17cm stereo camera; Dallmeyer 110mm f11 lens; sliding lens panel; 8 x 17cm exp in Berry system magazine. C 1860.

R5* $2k+	£1.1k+	DM3.3k+	FF10.2k+

Victor HASSELBLAD,
Sweden.

Hasselblad 1600F: (VH100); 120 roll film SLR; Kodak Ektar 80mm f2.8 coated lens, interchangeable bayonet mount; CFPS

Hasselblad 1600F

1- 1/1600 s. 12 exp,$2^{1}/4$" x $2^{1}/4$" on 120 roll film in special magazine. C 1948-1954.

R3* $500	£262	DM824	FF2.6k

Hasselblad 1000F: (VH101); 120 roll film SLR; Zeiss Tessar 80mm f2.8 coated lens, interchangeable bayonet mount; CFPS 1-1/1000 s. 12 exp, $2^{1}/4$" x $2^{1}/4$" in special magazine. C 1954-1960.

R3* $400	£210	DM659	FF2k

Hasselblad Super Wide Camera: (VH102); 120 roll film SLR; Carl Zeiss Biogon 38mm f4.5 coated non-removable lens with 90 degree field of view; Synchro-Compur shutter 1-1/500 s. 12 exp, $2^{1}/4$" x $2^{1}/4$" in special magazine. C 1956-1960.

R4* $1k	£525	DM1.6k	FF5.1k

Hasselblad Super Wide Camera

Dr. Hans HENSOLD -> see ISO

HERCO, HERBERT GEORGE CO.

Donald Duck Camera: (HG100); plastic camera; 127 roll film.

R2* $45	£24	DM74	FF230

Roy Rogers and Trigger 620 Snap Shot Camera: (HG101); plastic box camera. 8 exp on 620 roll film.

R2* $30	£16	DM49	FF153

J. Fleury HERMAGIS, Paris, France.

Hermagis Field Camera: (HE100); Hermagis Aplanastigmat 210mm f6.8 lens;

Thornton Pickard roller blind shutter. 5" x 7" exp on plates. Rotating maroon bellows; polished walnut with brass fittings.

R4* $200	£105	DM330	FF1k

Instantaneous Stereoscopic Camera: (HE101); Hermagis Aplanat f8 lens; 8 speed guillotine shutter. 12 stereo exp on 8 x 16cm dry plates. C 1888.

R5*		NSR	

Jumelle Hermagis: (HE102); 6.5 x 9cm camera; Aplanastigmatic lens. C 1895.

R4* $175	£92	DM288	FF894

Velocigraphe: (HE103); satchel type detective camera; Hermagis rapid rectilinear lens; central rotary shutter. $12^{1}/4$" plates or 25 exp on film. Invented by Ricard et Lacroix. C 1891.

R5* $1k	£525	DM1.6k	FF5.1k

A. HERZOG, New York.

Herzog Camera: (HZ100); periscopic 100mm f8 lens; $3^{1}/4$" x $4^{1}/4$" plates. C 1876.

R5* $2k+	£1.1k+	DM3.3k+	FF10.2k+

Dr. Adolf HESEKIEL & CO., Berlin, Germany.

Archimedes Stereoscop Camera: (HC100); 35mm stereo camera; Aplanat; Zeiss Anastigmat; Goerz Double Anastigmat lenses; B & I shutter, pneumatic release; $8^{1}/4$" x 17cm exp. C 1904.

R5* $2.5k+	£1.3k+	DM4.1k+	FF12.8k+

Dr. A. Hesekiel's Quarter-Plate: (HC101); Goerz 140mm f6.3 double anastigmat lens; FPS (no markings). Mahogany, nickel fittings. C 1895.

R5* $2k+	£1.1k+	DM3.3k+	FF10.2k+

Pompadour: (HC102); pocket book-type detective camera; Certomat 105mm f8 lens; 3 speed shutter. 6.5 x 9cm exp on plates. Consists of folding Certo in crocodile skin covered pocketbook. C 1907.

R5* $10k	£5.2k	DM16.5k	FF51.1k

HESS-IVES CORP.,
Philadelphia, Pennsylvania.

Hicro Color Camera: (HS100); Meniscus lens; Wollensak Ultro shutter; 3¹/₄" x 4¹/₄" exp on plates. C 1915.

R3* $125	£66	DM206	FF639

Ives' Kromskop Triple Camera: (HS101); single shot tri-colour camera. Mahogany finish, brass fittings. C 1899.

R5* $8k+	£4.2k+	DM13.2k+	FF40.9k+

HETHERINGTON & HIBBEN,
Indianapolis, Indiana.

Hetherington Magazine Camera: (HH100); 4" x 5" box-type detective camera. All operations such as: plate changing, aperture changing and shutter tensioning are accomplished by means of key inserted from outside the camera box. C 1890.

R4* $500	£262	DM824	FF2.6k

Hetherington Magazine Camera

Emil HOFERT, EHO KAMERA
FABRIK, Dresden, Germany.

*See Altissa for post war
camera production*

Baby Box Eho: (HF100); Duplar f11 lens; 3 x 4cm frames on 127 roll film.

R2* $30	£16	DM49	FF153

Eho: (HF101); C 1932, box camera, Duplar f11/50mm lens; single speed shutter; 3 x 4cm frames on 127 roll film.

R2* $50	£26	DM82	FF256

Stereo Box Eho: (HF102); C 1930, box camera, Duplar 80mm f11 lens; 5 stereo exp, 6 x 13cm or 10 single exp, 6 x 6cm frames on 120 film.

R3* $125	£66	DM206	FF639

Eho Box 110: (HF103); C1930, metal box camera, f11 lens, simple shutter, 6 x 9cm frames on roll film.

R2* $15	£8	DM25	FF77

Altissa Box: (HF104); C1930, box camera for 6 x 6 frames on roll film, optical VFR on early cameras is a simple squared tube affair, later cameras used a large distinctive VFR, simple f10 lens, simple shutter. This same camera was continued after 1945 with little outward change and is not so rare. It was copied by the Chinese in the 1950s and called the "Xing Fu".

R2* $15	£8	DM25	FF77

Super Altissa: (HF105); C1930, as (HF104) but with focusing f4.5 lens.

R2* $25	£13	DM41	FF128

Altiflex: (HF106); C1935, metal TLR for 6 x 6cm frames on roll film, lever focusing Victor f4.5/75mm lens among others, Automat, Prontor or Compur shutter.

R3* $45	£24	DM74	FF230

Altiscope: (HF107); C1935, stereo camera for 6 x 13 frames on roll film, Victor f4.5 lenses, simple shutter, lever focusing.

R3* $125	£66	DM206	FF639

HORNE & THORNTHWAITE,
England.

Wet Plate Camera: (HT100); Petzval lens. C 1850.

R5* $2k+	£1.1k+	DM3.3k+	FF10.2k+

E. I. HORSMAN & CO.,
New York.

No. 3 Eclipse Camera: (EI100); folding view camera; meniscus lens - 3 insertable metal circular stops; 4¹/₄" x 6¹/₂" exp on dry plates. C 1896.

R4* $250	£131	DM412	FF1.3k

HOUGHTON'S

HOUGHTON'S LTD., London, England.

Houghton's was a popular British camera maker, until Germany started making cameras after World War I. Klito and Ensign were two of their trade names, the latter being the more popular of the two. When Houghton's merged with Butcher, the two trade names were used together. Ensign Limited became the selling company; after 1930, the company rejuvenated and through mergers became Barnet Ensign, then Barnet-Ensign-Ross and finally Ross Ensign.

Commando: (HO100); Ensar 75mm f3.5 lens; Epsilon shutter 1-1/200 s, crf; 6 x 6cm exp on roll film. 12 or 16 exp on 120 film - format selected by adjusting internal baffles prior to loading film. Camera is unusual in that rf was coupled to the film plane—lens and mount were fixed. The pressure plate was spring loaded to adjust to film plane movement. C 1946.

R2* $50	£26	DM82	FF256

Cupid: (HO101); Meniscus 70mm f12 lens; guillotine shutter; 36 x 56mm exp on 120 roll film. C 1922.

R2* $60	£31	DM99	FF307

Ensign Auto Kinecam Sixteen B: (HO102); 16mm movie camera; Anastigmat Cinar 1" f2.6 lens. C 1932.

R2* $50	£26	DM82	FF256

Ensign Carbine No. 6 Tropical Model: (HO103); Zeiss Tessar 10.5cm f4.5 lens; Compur shutter 1/250 s. Brass body; tan bellows. C 1925.

R4* $225	£118	DM371	FF1.2k

Ensignette: (HO104); aluminium bodied folding roll film camera; Zeiss Tessar 75mm f6.8 lens; single speed shutter. No 1: 1½" x 2¼" exp, No. 2: 2" x 3" exp, No. 2 Junior: 2¼" x 3¼".

R2* $225	£118	DM371	FF1.2k

Ensign Popular Tropical Reflex: (HO105); 3¼" x 4¼"' tropical SLR; Ross Xpres 6" f4.5 lens; CFPS. Teak wood and brown leather bellows, brass fittings. C 1917.

R4* $1k+	£525+	DM1.6k+	FF5.1k+

Ensign Roll Film Reflex Tropical Model: (HO106); 6 x 9cm roll film SLR camera; Aldis 4¼" f7.7 lens; single speed shutter. C 1925.

R4* $750+	£394+	DM1.2k+	FF3.8k+

Folding Klito: (HO107); 6 x 9cm folding plate camera; Symmetrical "Rectimat" f11 lens; Ensign-Simplex shutter 1/25-1/100 s.

R2* $40	£21	DM66	FF204

"Holborn" Postage Stamp Camera: (HO110); 9 postage stamp size exp. C 1900.

R4* $400	£210	DM659	FF2k

Klito No. 0: (HO111); Rapid Rectilinear lens, adjustable focus with supplementary lenses; guillotine shutter. 3¼" x 4¼" dry plates; drop plate changing mechanism. C 1906.

R2* $50	£26	DM82	FF256

Klito No. 3: (HO112); Beck Symmetrical f8 lens; rack and pinion focusing; guillotine shutter 2-1/100 s; 3¼" x 4¼" dry plates, drop plate changing mechanism. C 1908.

R2* $50	£26	DM82	FF256

The Sanderson Camera: (HO113); 4" x 5" tropical camera; Homocentric f6.3 lens; Compur 1-1/200 s. 4" x 5" exp on cut film.

R4* $1.5k	£787	DM2.5k	FF7.7k

The Sanderson Camera

Sanderson View Camera: (HO114); Suter B. No. 5 Aplanat lens; 8" x 10" plates. Mahogany wood, brass fittings. C 1900.

R4* $500	£262	DM824	FF2.6k

Ticka: (HO115); pocket-watch camera (similar to Expo); Meniscus 30mm f16 lens; 25 exp, 22 x 16mm on roll film in special cassette. C 1907. The Ticka and Expo were made under licence by separate manufacturers, from the Swedish inventor Magnus Niell.

R4* $200	£105	DM330	FF1k

Ticka

Tropical Watch Pocket Carbine No. 4: (HO116); Aldis Butcher f4.5 lens; Compur 1-1/250 s. C 1925.

R3* $150	£79	DM247	FF767

Tropical Watch Pocket Carbine No. 4

HURLBUT MANUFACTURING CO., Belvidere, Illinois.

Hurlbut Velox Magazine Detective Camera: (HU100); magazine-type detective camera. C 1890. Plates are gravity fed into position; then returned to storage by inverting the camera.

R4* $650	£341	DM1.1k	FF3.3k

R. HUTTIG A.G., Dresden, Germany.

Atom: (HJ100); 90mm f8 lens; Compound shutter 1-1/250 s; 4.5 x 6cm plates. C 1908.

R4* $250	£131	DM412	FF1.3k

Cupido: (HJ101); Helios Rapid Rectilinear lens; Lloyd central shutter 1-1/100 s; 9 x 12cm exp. C 1906.

R2* $60	£31	DM99	FF307

Fichter's Excelsior Detective: (HJ102); drop plate magazine camera; rectilinear lens; rotating shutter; 12 exp, 9 x 12cm. C 1893.

R4* $800	£420	DM1.3k	FF4.1k

Aviso: (HJ103); plate box camera; 4.5 x 6cm exp, magazine load. Sold in England as the Gnome camera.

R4* $300	£157	DM495	FF1.5k

Lloyd Stereo Camera: (HJ104); Busch Aplanatic 90mm f8 lenses; Stereo Compound shutter 1-1/200 s. 9 x 18cm exp on plates or roll film. 2 sizes: 8 x 14cm, 9 x 18cm. C 1906.

R4* $225	£118	DM371	FF1.2k

Monopol: (HJ105); rectilinear lens; variable speed rotary sector shutter; 9 x 12cm dry plates in magazine. C 1895.

R4* $150	£79	DM247	FF767

Stereo Ideal: (HJ106); 6 x 13cm stereo camera; Lloyd Anastigmatic 90mm f6.8 lenses; pneumatic central shutter 1-1/100 s. C 1906.

R4* $225	£118	DM371	FF1.2k

ICA

ICA A.G., Dresden, Germany.

Artist Reflex: (IC100); C1910, Zeiss Tessar 15cm f4.5 lens; FPS 1/11-1/1000 s; 3¼" x 4¼" exp. Sliding lens panel.

R3* $160	£84	DM264	FF818

Aviso: (IC118); C1920, box camera for 4.5cm x 6cm plates or sheet film with internal changing mechanism, meniscus lens, simple shutter, which is quite visible on the front of the camera.

R3* $45	£24	DM74	FF230

Aviso Nr.4: (IC119); C1920, box camera for 4.5cm x 6cm single plates, meniscus lens, simple shutter, which is quite visible on the front of the camera.

R3* $55	£29	DM91	FF281

Atom Nr. 53: (IC101); C1913, *horizontal format,* folding VFR camera, for 4.5cm x 6cm plates, several lens and shutter combinations including Tessar f6.3 or f4.5/65mm lens Compur shutter 1-1/300 s.

R3* $350	£184	DM577	FF1.8k

Atom Nr. 51: (IC133); C1913, *vertical format* folding VFR camera, for 4.5cm x 6cm plates, several lens and shutter combinations including Maximar f5.4/9cm lens, Automat or Compur shutter, VFR mounted below the lens.

R3* $150	£79	DM247	FF767

Bébé Nr. 40: (IC131); C1920, strut folding VFR camera for 4.5cm x 6cm film packs or plates, several lens and shutter combinations, including Tessar f6.3 or f4.5/7.5cm lens, Compur shutter.

R3* $190	£100	DM313	FF971

Bébé Nr. 41: (IC132); C1920, strut folding VFR camera for 6.5 x 9cm film packs or plates, several lens and shutter combinations, including Maximar f6.8/12cm lens, Compur shutter.

R3* $100	£52	DM165	FF511

Corrida Nr. 156: (IC156); C1920s, folding camera for 9cm x 12cm plates or film packs, lever focusing, several lens and shutter combinations offered including Icar f6.3/13.5cm lens, Automat shutter.

R3* $40	£21	DM66	FF204

Cupido Nr. 75: (IC135); C1920s, self erecting folding VFR camera for 6cm x 9cm or 6.5cm x 9cm plates or film packs, several lens and shutter combinations including Tessar f4.5/12cm lens, Compur shutter.

R3* $60	£31	DM99	FF307

Cupido Nr. 77: (IC136); C1915, horizontal self erecting folding VFR camera for 7.5cm x 10.8cm or roll film, several lens and shutter combinations offered including Hekla f6.8/10.5 cm lens, Automat shutter.

R3* $60	£31	DM99	FF307

Cupido Nr. 79: (IC137); C1918, vertical self erecting folding VFR camera for 7.5cm x 10.8cm or roll film , several lens and shutter combinations offered including Tessar f6.3/13.5cm lens, Automat shutter.

R3* $40	£21	DM66	FF204

Folding Reflex: (IC102); compact folding SLR camera; Zeiss Tessar f4.5 lens; CFPS 1/15-1/1000 s. C 1925. Model A: 2¼" x 3¼" exp on film packs, $150. Model B: 9 x 12cm exp on plates or film packs.

R4* $200	£105	DM330	FF1k

Icarette A: (IC103); C1925, folding roll film camera; f6.3 lens; 12 exp, 2¼" x 2¼".

R2* $35	£18	DM58	FF179

Ideal Nr. 111: (IC104); C1925, folding plate camera for 6cm x 9cm or 6.5 x 9cm, several lens and shutter combinations available including Protar f6.3/10.5cm lens, Compur shutter.

R2* $50	£26	DM82	FF256

Ideal Nr. 205: (IC155); C1925, folding plate camera for 9cm x12cm plates, several lens and shutter combinations available including Tessar f4.5/13.5cm lens, Compur shutter.

R2* $50	£26	DM82	FF256

Ideal Nr. 246: (IC156); C1925, folding plate camera for 9cm x12cm plates, double extension bellows, several lens and shutter combinations available including Tessar f6.3/15cm lens, Compur shutter.

R2* $50	£26	DM82	FF256

Lloyd Stereo Nr. 675: (IC105); C1910, folding stereo/panoramic camera for 8 x 14cm exp on plates or roll film, several lens and shutter combinations offered including Maximar Double Anastigmatic f6.8/90mm lens, Stereo Compur shutter 1-1/100 s. Rising and sliding front, panoramic setting.

R4* $250	£131	DM412	FF1.3k

Minimum Palmos Nr. 453: (IC106); C1920s, strut type folding VFR camera for 4.5 x 6cm exp on plates, several lens and shutter combinations offered including Tessar f4.5/8cm lens, CFPS 1 - 1/1000 s.

R4* $275	£144	DM453	FF1.4k

Minimum Palmos Nr. 454: (IC151); C1920s, strut type folding VFR camera for 6 x 9cm or 6.5cm x 9cm plates, several lens and shutter combinations were available, including Tessar f6.3/12cm lens, CFPS 1 - 1/1000 s.

R3* $150	£79	DM247	FF767

Minimum Palmos Nr. 456: (IC152); C1920s, strut type folding VFR camera for 9cm x12cm plates, several lens and shutter combinations offered including Tessar f4.5/15cm lens, CFPS 1 - 1/1000 s.

R3* $150	£79	DM247	FF767

Minimum Palmos Nr. 457: (IC153); C1920s, strut type folding VFR camera for 10cm x 15cm plates, several lens and shutter combinations offered including Amatar f6.8/16.5cm lens, CFPS 1 - 1/1000 s.

R3* $150	£79	DM247	FF767

Niklas Nr. 109: (IC107);C1920s, folding bed plate camera for 6 x 9cm exp on plates, Ica Doppel Anastigmat 12cm f6.8 lens, Dialset Compur shutter.

R3* $40	£21	DM66	FF204

Polyskop Nr. 603: (IC110); C1920s, box type stereo camera for single 4.5cm x 10.7cm plates, fixed focus achromat lenses, simple single speed shutter.

R4* $100	£52	DM165	FF511

Polyscope Nr, 605: (IC140);C1920s, box type stereo camera for single 4.5cm x 10.7cm plates,several lens and shutter combinations available including Hekla f6.8/6cm lenses, shutter to 1/250s.

R3* $150	£79	DM247	FF767

Polyscope Nr, 605/1:(IC141);C1920s, box type stereo camera for 4.5cm x 10.7cm plates, delivered with magazine back for 12 plates, several lens and shutter combinations available including Maximar f6.8/6cm lenses, simple shutter.

R3* $170	£89	DM280	FF869

Polyscope Nr, 606: (IC142);C1920s, close focusing box type stereo camera for single 4.5cm x 10.7cm plates,several lens and shutter combinations available including Hekla f6.8/6cm lenses, shutter to 1/250s.

R3* $150	£79	DM247	FF767

Polyscope Nr, 606/1: (IC143);C1920s, close focusing box type stereo camera for 4.5cm x 10.7cm plates, delivered with magazine back for 12 plates, several lens and shutter combinations available including Maximar f6.8/6cm lenses, simple shutter.

R3* $170	£89	DM280	FF869

Polyscope Nr, 607: (IC144);C1920s, box type stereo camera for single 4.5cm x 10.7cm plates, focusing and close focusing capability, several lens and shutter combinations available including Tessar f6.3/6.5cm lenses, shutter to 1/250s.

R3* $190	£100	DM313	FF971

Polyscope Nr, 607/1:(IC145);C1920s, box type stereo camera for 4.5cm x 10.7cm plates, focusing and close focusing capability, delivered with magazine back for 12 plates, several lens and shutter combinations available including Tessar f4.5/6.5cm lenses, shutter to 1/250s.

R3* $200	£105	DM330	FF1k

Polyscope Nr, 608:(IC146);C1920s, close focusing folding strut stereo camera for sin-

ICA

gle 4.5cm x 10.7cm plates,several lens and shutter combinations available including Hekla f6.8/6cm lenses, shutter to 1/250s.

R3* $160	£84	DM264	FF818

Polyscope Nr, 608/1: (IC147);C1920s, folding strut type stereo camera for single 4.5cm x 10.7cm plates,several fixed focus lens and shutter combinations available including Hekla f6.8/6cm lenses, shutter to 1/250s.

R3* $150	£79	DM247	FF767

Polyscope Nr, 608/2: (IC148);C1920s, close focusing folding strut type stereo camera for 4.5cm x 10.7cm plates, delivered with magazine back for 12 plates, several lens and shutter combinations available including Novar f6.8/6cm lenses, shutter to 1/250s.

R3* $175	£92	DM288	FF894

Polyscope Nr, 608/3: (IC149);C1920s, folding strut type stereo camera for 4.5cm x 10.7cm plates, delivered with magazine back for 12 plates and shutter combinations available including Tessar f4.5/6.5cm lenses, shutter to 1/250s.

R3* $225	£118	DM371	FF1.2k

Polyscope Nr, 609: (IC150);C1920s, box type stereo/panoramic camera for single 6cm x 13cm plates, focusing lenses, several lens and shutter combinations available including Tessar f6.3/9cm lenses, Compur shutter to 1/150s.

R3* $250	£131	DM412	FF1.3k

Polyscope Nr, 609/1: (IC111);C1920s, box type stereo/panoramic camera for 6cm x 13cm plates, delivered with magazine back for 12 plates, focusing lenses, several lens and shutter combinations available including Tessar f4.5/10.5cm lenses, Compur shutter to 1/150s.

R3* $275	£144	DM453	FF1.4k

Stereofix Nr. 604: (IC152);C1920s, truncated box type stereo camera for 4.5cm x 10.5cm plates or film packs, several lens and shutter combinations available including Tessar f6.3/6.5cm lenses, Compur shutter, with close up focusing.

R4* $150	£79	DM247	FF767

Stereofix Nr. 604/1: (IC153);C1920s, truncated box type stereo camera for 4.5cm x 10.5cm plates or film packs, several lens and shutter combinations available including Tessar f6.3/6.5cm lenses, Compur shutter, without close up focusing.

R4* $150	£79	DM247	FF767

Stereo Ideal: (IC112); C1920s, 6 x 13cm stereo camera; Zeiss Tessar 9cm f6.5 lenses; Compur shutter 1-1/250 s.

R4* $300	£157	DM495	FF1.5k

Stereolette: (IC113); C1912, compact folding stereo camera for 4.5cm x 10.7cm plates, Anastigmatic 60mm f6.8 lenses; Stereo Compur shutter 1-1/250 s.

R3* $225	£118	DM371	FF1.2k

Stereo Palmos: (IC114); C 1920s, folding stereo camera for 6cm x 13cm plates, Zeiss Tessar 80mm f4.5 lenses, CFPS 1/30-1/1000s.

R4* $300	£157	DM495	FF1.5k

Trilby Nr. 5: (IC120); C1919, metal box camera for 6cm x 9cm plates with internal changing mechanism for 6 plates, meniscus lens, simple shutter, single waist level VFR.

R3* $65	£34	DM107	FF332

Trilby Nr. 11: (IC121); C1919, metal box camera for 6cm x 9cm plates with internal changing mechanism for 6 plates, achromat 12cm lens, simple shutter, double waist level VFR.

R3* $65	£34	DM107	FF332

Trilby Nr. 12: (IC122); C1919, metal box camera for 6.5cm x 9cm plates with internal changing mechanism for 6 plates, achromat 12cm lens, simple shutter, double waist level VFR.

R3* $65	£34	DM107	FF332

Trilby Nr. 13: (IC123); C1919, metal box camera for 6cm x 9cm plates with internal changing mechanism for 12 plates, achromat 12cm lens, simple shutter, double waist level VFR.

R3* $80	£42	DM132	FF409

Trilby Nr. 14: (IC124); C1919, metal box camera for 6.5cm x 9cm plates with internal changing mechanism for 12 plates, achromat 12cm lens, simple shutter, double waist level VFR.

| R3* $80 | £42 | DM132 | FF409 |

Trilby Nr. 17: (IC125); C1919, metal box camera for 9cm x 12cm plates with internal changing mechanism for 6 plates, meniscus lens, simple shutter, waist level VFR.

| R3* $80 | £42 | DM132 | FF409 |

Trilby Nr. 18: (IC126); C1919, metal box camera for 9cm x 12cm plates with internal changing mechanism for 12 plates, achromat 14cm lens, simple shutter, double waist level VFR.

| R3* $80 | £42 | DM132 | FF409 |

Trilby Nr. 20: (IC127); C1919, metal box camera for 9cm x 12cm plates with internal changing mechanism for 12 plates or 24 sheet film holders, achromat 14cm lens, simple shutter, double waist level VFR.

| R3* $90 | £47 | DM148 | FF460 |

Trilby Nr. 29: (IC128); C1919, leather covered wooden box camera for 9cm x 12cm plates with internal changing mechanism for 12 plates or 24 sheet film holders, achromat 14cm lens and three built-in auxilliary lenses for focusing at 1, 3, and 5 meters, 1 - 1/100s shutter, double waist level VFR.

| R3* $100 | £52 | DM165 | FF511 |

Trilby Nr. 31: (IC129); C1919, leather covered wooden box camera with polished mahogany interior for 9cm x 12cm plates with internal changing mechanism for 12 plates or 24 sheet film holders, achromat 13.5cm lens and three built-in auxilliary lenses for focusing at 1, 3, and 5 meters, 1 - 1/100s shutter, double waist level VFR, opening front.

| R3* $100 | £52 | DM165 | FF511 |

Trilby Nr. 33: (IC130); C1919, leather covered wooden box camera with polished mahogany interior for 9cm x 12cm plates with internal changing mechanism for 24 plates or 24 sheet film holders, focusing Alpha f11/14.5cm or Helios f8/13cm lens, Ica Automat shutter 1 - 1/100s shutter, double waist level VFR, opening front.

| R3* $100 | £52 | DM165 | FF511 |

Trona Nr. 210: (IC158); C1920s, folding camera for 9cm x 12cm plates or film packs, double extension bellows, several lens and shutter combinations available including Novar f6.8/13.5cm lens, Automat shutter.

| R2* $40 | £21 | DM66 | FF204 |

Tropica: (IC115); C 1925, 5" x 7" tropical camera; Carl Zeiss f4.5 lens; Compur shutter 1-1/250 s; 5" x 7" exp on plates, teak construction with enamelled or nickel plated fittings.

| R4* $1.2k | £630 | DM2k | FF6.1k |

Universal Juwel: (IC116); C1925, Tessar 165mm f4.5 lens; Compur shutter 1-1/250 s; double extension, rotating back, wide-angle feature, rising and sliding panel.

| R4* $100 | £52 | DM165 | FF511 |

Victrix Nr. 48: (IC117); C1925, 4.5 x 6cm folding plate camera, several lens and shutter combination including Ica Dominar f4.5/75mm lens, Compur shutter.

| R3* $150 | £79 | DM247 | FF767 |

Volta Nr. 105: (IC134); C1920, folding VFR camera for 6cm x cm or 6.5cm x 9cm plates or film packs, Alpha f11/12cm or Novar f6.8/10.5cm lens, Automat shutter.

| R3* $40 | £21 | DM66 | FF204 |

IDEAL TOY CORP., Hollis, New York.

Kookie Kamera: (ID100); comic plastic novelty camera; plastic meniscus 80mm f11 lens; single speed shutter; 4.5 x 4.5cm exp on "in-camera" processed positive paper. C 1968.

| R3* $175 | £92 | DM288 | FF894 |

IHAGEE KAMERAWERK, A.G., Dresden, Germany.

Exakta A: (IH100); 127 roll film SLR camera; Zeiss Tessar 75mm f3.5 lens, interchangeable mount; CFPS 1/25 - 1/1000 s; 8 exp, 1⅝" x 2½" on 127 film. C 1934-39/40.

| R3* $170 | £89 | DM280 | FF869 |

Exakta B: (IH101); 127 roll film SLR camera; Zeiss Tessar 75mm f3.5 lens, interchangeable mount; CFPS 12-1/1000 s. 8 exp, 1⅝" x 2½" on 127 roll film. C 1934-39/ 40.

R3* $200	£105	DM330	FF1k

Exakta B

Night Exakta

Night Exakta: (IH102); 127 roll film SLR camera; Dallmeyer Super-Six 80mm f1.9 lens, interchangeable mount; CFPS 12-1/1000 s. Similar to Exakta B except for modified large size outer diameter focusing ring. Contrary to popular belief, ordinary Exakta lenses and Night Exacta lenses were perfectly interchangeable!

R4* $350	£184	DM577	FF1.8k

Exakta C: (IH103); Similar to Model B with addition of plate back adapter for plates and cut film, with rear ground glass focusing. When plate back is used, reflex finder cannot be utilized. C 1937-1945.

R4* $150	£79	DM247	FF767

Zeiss lenses for VP Exakta

55mm f8.0 Tessar (IH001); **$45**
120mm f6.3 Tele-Tessar (IH002); **$120**
180mm f6.3 Tele-Tessar (IH003); **$175**
250mm f5.5 Tele-Tessar (IH004); **$175**

Kine Exakta: (IH104); 35mm SLR camera; Tessar 50mm f2.8 lens, interchangeable bayonet mount; CFPS 1/10-1/1000 s. Snr up to 648,000(?). First 35mm SLR camera commercially produced. C 1936-1946. Round magnifier **$800**, Rectangular magnifier.

R3* $300	£157	DM495	FF1.5k

Kine Exakta II: (IH105); 35mm SLR camera; Biotar 50mm f2 lens, interchangeable bayonet mount; CFPS 12-1/1000 s. Snr 648,000-655,000(?). C 1949-1950.

R2* $75	£39	DM124	FF383

Exakta V: (IH106); 35mm SLR camera; Xenon 50mm f2 lens, interchangeable bayonet mount; CFPS 12-1/1000 s. Snr 665,000-695,000(?). First 35mm SLR with interchangeable finder. Known as the Varex in the USA. C 1950.

R3* $100	£52	DM165	FF511

Exakta VX: (IH107); 35mm SLR camera; Tessar 50mm f2.8 lens, interchangeable bayonet mount; CFPS 12-1/1000 s. Snr 695,000-(?). Similar to Exakta V except has preset lens. Known as the Varex VX in the USA. C1955.

R2* $100	£52	DM165	FF511

Exakta VX

Exakta VXIIa: (IH110); 35mm SLR camera; Zeiss Pancolar 50mm f2 lens, interchangeable bayonet mount; CFPS 12-1/1000 s. Similar to Exakta VX, but has quieter slow speed shutter mechanism, and a third, "F" type flash socket was added. C 1957.

R2* $100	£52	DM165	FF511

Exakta VXIIa

Zeiss Lenses for the Kine Exakta

35mm f2.8 Flektogon, (IH005); **$35**
40mm f4.5 Tessar, (IH006); **$25**
75mm f1.5 Biotar, (IH007); **$200**
80mm f2.8 Tessar, (IH008); **$100**
85mm f4.0 Triotar, (IH009); **$70**
105mm f3.5 Tessar, (IH010); **$90**
135mm f4.0 Triotar (uncoated), (IH011); **$60**
135mm f4.0 Triotar (coated), (IH012); **$80**
165mm f3.5 Tessar, (IH013); **$80**
180mm f6.3 Tele-Tessar, (IH014); **$125**
180mm f2.8 Sonnar, (IH015); **$200**
250mm f6.3 Tele-Tessar, (IH016); **$200**
300mm f4.0 Sonnar, (IH017); **$250**
Stereflex set for use on normal lenses, (IH018); **$600**

Exakta 6/6: (IH111); C1938, 6 x 6cm SLR camera; Tessar 8cm f2.8 lens; CFPS 12-1/1000 s. 12 exp on 120 roll film.

R4* $750	£394	DM1.2k	FF3.8k

Exakta 66: (IH112); C1954, 6 x 6cm SLR camera; CFPS 12-1/1000 s. Tessar 80mm f2.8 lens. 12 exp on 120 roll film. Originally announced at the 1952 Leipzig Fair, this camera finally was delivered in 1954. About 2000 were made, and it seems that all them were exported to the USA. Not at all like the Exakta 6/6 (IH111), and should not be considered as just another body style, but as a rarity in its own right!

R4* $1k	£525	DM1.6k	FF5.1k

Roll-Paff: (IH113);C1922, 6 x 6cm SLR box camera;f6,8 Trioplan lens; single speed mirror shutter; 12 exp on 120 roll film.

R4* $100	£52	DM165	FF511

Exakta 66

Roll-Paff

Patent Klapp Reflex: (IH114); C1925, compact folding SLR camera; Dogmar 125mm f4.5 lens; CFPS 1/15-1/1000 s. 6.5 x 9cm exp.

R4* $350	£184	DM577	FF1.8k

Ultrix Auto: (IH115); C1934, 4 x 6.5cm roll film folding camera for 127 film; Schneider Xenar 70mm f4.5 lens; Compur shutter 1-1/300 s.

R2* $50	£26	DM82	FF256

Exa: (IH116); C1952, 35mm SLR taking Exakta mount lenses, but with a very simple shutter, removable waist level finder, and limited range of shutter speeds.

R2* $55	£29	DM91	FF281

Exa Ia: (IH117); C1965, redesigned body now with lever advance.

R2* $35	£18	DM58	FF179

Exa VX 100:(IH118); C1968, now with external automatic aperture.

R2* $35	£18	DM58	FF179

Exa Ib: (IH119); C1975, now with internal automatic aperture.

R2* $35	£18	DM58	FF179

Exa IIb:(IH120); C1965, as (IH117) but with built-in, permanent pentaprism.

R2* $35	£18	DM58	FF179

ILFORD LTD., London, England.

Advocate: (IL100); 35mm camera; Dallmeyer 35mm f3.5 lens; shutter 1/25 - /200 s. C 1949.

R2* $100	£52	DM165	FF511

Advocate

Witness: (IL101); 35mm camera; Dallmeyer Super-Six 2" f1.9 lens; FPS 1-1/1000 s; crf. C 1951.

R4* $700	£367	DM1.2k	FF3.6k

Witness

INGERSOLL & BROS., New York.

Shur-Shot Camera: (IB100); small all-wood plate camera; meniscus lens; guillotine shutter. Single exp on 2½" square, glass plates. C 1897.

R4* $225	£118	°DM371	FF1.2k

INTERNATIONAL METAL & FERROTYPE CO., Chicago, Illinois.

The Diamond Gun Ferrotype Camera: (IM100); large nickel plated all metal ferrotype camera in shape of a cannon, constructed so as to attract attention to a street operator. Has internal masks for formats down to button tintypes. Camera is 18" in length and 8" in diameter.

R5* $1.2k	£630	DM2k	FF6.1k

INTERNATIONAL PROJECTOR CORP., New York.

Simplex Pockette: (IP100); 16mm movie camera; interchangeable Kodak Anastigmat 25mm f1.9 lens. Used 50 ft. Kodacolour cartridges. C 1933.

R2* $45	£24	DM74	FF230

I.O.R., Bucharest, Romania

Orizont: (IO100); C1960, metal 35mm VFR camera, Tricolor f3.2/50mm lens, simple shutter 1/30 - 1/125.

R4* $50	£26	DM82	FF256

Orizont

Orizont Amator: (IO101); C1970. plastic and metal 35mm VFR camera, Fotoclar f2.8/40mm lens, combined aperture/shutter f2.8@1/30s - f16@1/300s.

| R4* $15 | £8 | DM25 | FF77 |

Irwin Magazine Movie Camera Model 16: (BB182); 16mm movie camera; f4.5 or f8 lens. One of the first 15mm movie cameras to use a magazine (50 ft) load. Spring motor drive. Mfd in U.S. C 1930.

| R2* $20 | £10 | DM33 | FF102 |

ISO, INDUSTRIA SCIENTIFICA OTTICA S.R.L., Milan, Italy.

Duplex 120: (IS100); 35mm stereo camera, 25mm/f6.3 fixed focus Iperang lenses, shutter speeds 1/25-1/100s.

| R3* $250 | £131 | DM412 | FF1.3k |

Duplex Super 120: (IS101); 35mm stereo camera, 35mm f3.5 fixed focus Iriar lenses, shutter speeds 1/10-1/200 s.

| R3* $150 | £79 | DM247 | FF767 |

Iso Standard: (IS102); C1953, 35mm RFR camera, Leica copy, interchangeable Iriar f3.5 or 2.8/50mm lens, among others, CFPS shutter speeds 1/20 - 1/1000s, interchangeable eyepieces for use with different focal length lenses, no strap lugs.

| R4* $900 | £472 | DM1.5k | FF4.6k |

Iso Meter Lux: (IS103); C1947, 35mm RFR camera, Leica copy, interchangeable Trixar f3.5/50mm lens, CFPS 1 - 1/1000s, coupled vertical RFR, built-in light meter.

| R4* $1.25k | £656 | DM2.1k | FF6.4k |

Iso Bilux: (IS104); C1950, 35mm RFR camera, Leica copy, interchangeable Trixar f3.5/50mm lens, CFPS 1 - 1/1000s, bottom trigger wind.

| R4* $1.25k | £656 | DM2.1k | FF6.4k |

Iso Reporter: (IS105); C1954, as (IS104) but with improvements.

| R4* $1.25k | £656 | DM2.1k | FF6.4k |

Hensold Reporter: (IS106); C1955, as (IS105) but made for Dr. Hans Hensold of Wetzlar, and engraved with the Hensold name, Arion f1.9/5cm lens among others.

| R4* $1.25k | £656 | DM2.1k | FF6.4k |

Iso Junior: (IS107); C1953, like (IS104) but without bottom trigger wind, knob wind only, only a handful of cameras were made.

| R5* NSR est $1.25k £656 DM2.1k FF6.4k |

Hensold Reporter

Jos-Pe

Japanese Photographic Rifle: (BB184); anti-aircraft training rifle; copy of Thornton Pickard rifle. Mfd in Japan.

R4* $600	£315	DM989	FF334.1k

JAPY & CIE,
France.

Le Pascal: (JA100); meniscus lens with three stops; shutter has two speeds, B; 12 exp, 40 x 55mm. Leather covered wood and metal body, brass trim. C 1898.

R4* $600	£315	DM989	FF334.1k

JEANNERET AND CO.,
Paris, France.

Monobloc: (JE100); 6 x 13cm stereo camera; Boyer Saphir 75mm f4.5 lenses; Stereo Compur shutter 1-1/150 s. Inter-change-able (rising) lens panel. C 1925.

R3* $225	£118	DM371	FF1.2k

JOHNSON AND HARRISON
England.

Pantascopic Camera: (JO100); panoramic wet plate camera; Grubb 20cm lens. Spring motor rotates camera on platform. 19 x 31cm wet plate. C 1862.

R5* $12k+	£6.3k+	DM19.8k+	FF61.3k+

F. JONTE,
Paris, France.

F. Jonte Field Camera: (FJ100); 5" x 7" field camera; Rapid Rectilinear lens. Bellows rotate for format change. Polished mahogany finish, brass fittings. Mother-of-pearl label with mfr. name.

R4* $300	£157	DM495	FF1.5k

JOSEPH PETER,
Hamburg, Germany.

Jos-Pe: (JP100); single shot, tri-colour camera; Steinheil Munchen Anastigmat Quinar 10.5cm f2.5 lens; Compound shutter 1/2-1/100 s; 3¼" x 4¼" exp on plates. C 1925.

R5* $2k	£1.1k	DM3.3k	FF10.2k

L. JOUX,
Paris, France.

Steno Jumelle: (JX100); Goerz 130mm f8 Anastigmat lens; 5 speed guillotine shutter; 12 exp, 9 x 12cm on plates. C 1894.

R3* $350	£184	DM577	FF1.8k

JUMEAU & JANNIN,
Paris, France.

Le Cristallos: (JJ100); meniscus lens; rotary shutter. 6 x 9cm exp on film. C 1890.

R4* $250	£131	DM412	FF1.3k

Jumelle Bertoni: (BB185); stereo camera; Elio 7cm f5.5 lens; shutter 1-1/200 s; leather covered wooden body; magazine; 45 x 107mm. C 1900.

R4* $350	£184	DM577	FF1.8k

Max JURNICK.

Tom Thumb Camera: (JU100); detective camera concealed in wooden box; Rapid Rectilinear lens; spherical shutter. C1889. Camera alone, **$2000**; in box, **$3000**.

R5*

KALART CO.,
New York, New York.

Kalart: (KA100); C1948-1950, 3¹/₄" x 4¹/₂" press camera; Wollensak Raptar 127mm f4.5 coated lens; Rapax shutter 1 - 1/400 s. Dual left and right RFR windows for left-eye or right-eye operation. Has die-cast aluminium body with all built-in parts. Rising and lateral lens movements. The "Electric Brain" controls dual shutter release triggers; safety interlock requires holder to be inserted and the slide withdrawn to release the shutter. Two plug-in flash reflectors for midget lamps can be mounted on top of camera; interlocks prevent lamps from firing unless shutter has been cocked, film holder inserted and side pulled. Built-in "Focuspot".

R3* $300	£157	DM495	FF1.5k

Kalart

Kamera Werkstätten see -> Guthe & Thorsch

Alfred C. KEMPER, Chicago, Illinois.

Kombi: (KF100); miniature metal-bodied camera and graphascope; biconvex single element 1¹/₄" lens, pinhole diaphragm; non-self-capping behind-the-lens shutter. 25 exp, 1¹/₈" x 1¹/₈" round or square on special ¹/₄" x 30" roll film. C 1893.

R3* $200	£105	DM330	FF1k

KENNEDY INSTRUMENTS, London, England

KI Monobar: (KE100); 1954 35mm monorail view camera, using cut film holders, ground glass focusing, very unusual.

R3* $1.25k	£656	DM2.1k	FF6.4k

KERN, Aarau, Switzerland.

Kern Folding Camera: (KN100); Kern Anastigmat 120mm f4.5 lens; Compur shutter 1 - 1/200 s. 3¹/₄" x 4¹/₄" exp. Aluminium construction. C 1920.

R4* $400	£210	DM659	FF2k

Micro Cine: (KN101); smallest projector for 9.5mm film. Size: 2.5 x 5 x 10cm. C 1926.

R3* $125	£66	DM206	FF639

Stereo Kern: (KN102); 35mm stereo camera; Kernon 35mm f3.5 lenses; guillotine shutter 1/25-1/300 s. C 1920.

R4* $1k	£525	DM1.6k	°FF5.1k

Super Stereo: (KN103); 35mm stereo camera; Kern f3.5 lens. 20 x 20mm format. Interlens separation increased to 64mm. C 1930.

R4* $1.2k	£630	DM2k	FF6.1k

Thomas KERR, Walthamstow, England.

Abraham's Detective Camera: (TK100); wooden box-type detective camera; plate changing by lever. C 1888.

R4* $700	£367	DM1.2k	FF3.6k

KEYS STEREO PRODUCTS, U.S.A.

Trivision Camera: (KS100); C1946, fixed focus f8 lenses; single speed shutter 1/50 s. 6 stereo or 12 single exp on 828 film.

R3* $75	£39	DM124	FF383

KEYSTONE MFG. CO., Boston, Massachusetts.

Keystone Capri K-30: (KY100); 8mm movie camera; Keystone Elgeet 1/2" f1.9 lens. C 1950.

R1* $15	£8	DM25	FF77

Keystone K774L Electric Eye Zoom: (KY101); 8mm movie camera; Elgeet zoom 9 to 27mm f1.8 lens. Manual or auto exp.

R2* $35	£18	DM58	FF179

Keystone Model K8: (KY102); 8mm movie camera; Wollensak Cine Velostigmat 13mm f2.5 lens, interchangeable mount. 8, 16 or 48 frames per s. C 1935.

R1* $10	£5	DM16	FF51

Keystone Movie Camera Model C: (KY103); 16mm movie camera; 100 ft. capacity; black oval shape. C 1932.

R1* $25	£13	DM41	FF128

KGB, USSR

F21: (KP100); C1980, metal VFR camera for 18 x 24mm frames using special cassettes, built-in spring motor, f2/28mm fixed focus lens. These cameras started out bringing very high prices, upwards of $3500. Now the market has calmed a bit, and recently one changed hands for $700. It is rumoured that a large stock of cameras exists. It will be interesting to see what happens to the price.

R3* $1k	£525	DM1.6k	FF5.1k

F21: (KP101); C1980, as (KP100) but with focusing lens.

R3* $1.3k	£682	DM2.1k	FF6.6k

F21: (KP102); C1980, as (KP100) but with f2.8 fixed focus lens.

R3* $1k	£525	DM1.6k	FF5.1k

F21

F21: (KP103); C1980, as (KP100) but with f2.9 lens in a fixed mount, automatic exposure control by an electric "eye" located inside the lens.

R4* $1.2k	£630	DM2k	FF6.1k

Benjamin KILBURN.

Kilburn Photographic Gun: (KL100); gun-type detective camera. 10.5 x 12.5cm exp on plates; trigger released shutter. C 1884.

R5*		NRS	

KIN-DAR CORPORATION

Kindar Stereo Camera: (KD100); 35mm stereo camera; Steinheil Cassar f3.5 coated lenses; shutter 1/10-1/200 s. Designed by Seton Rochwhite. C 1953.

R3* $125	£66	DM206	FF639

Kindar Stereo Camera

K.K.W. Lighter Camera: (BB191); cigarette lighter and compass. Pressing shutter

K.K.W. Lighter Camera

release on this toy trips a lighter. Mfd in Japan. C 1975.

| R2* $25 | £13 | DM41 | FF128 |

KMZ Krasnogorsk, U.S.S.R.

Zenit Photosniper: (KM100); 35mm camera; Tair 300mm f4.5 coated lens, interchangeable screw mount; cfps 1/30-1/500 s. Zenit camera mounted on gunstock with telephoto lens. C 1960. Outfit including normal lens, filters for 300mm lens, screwdrivers, and empty film cassettes.

| R2* $125 | £66 | DM206 | FF639 |

Zenit Photosniper 12: (KM101); C1970-today (written "Photosnaiper on the shoulder stock but referred in English translation Soviet literature without the "a".) The same outfit as (KM100), with the introduction of a modified Zenit 12 black camera body, which includes a built-in light meter, and integral connections to the gunstock and 300mm lens. The modified body is designated "12S". At least one european sale for $300 in 1990, but many others at less than half that price!

| R2* $125 | £66 | DM206 | FF639 |

Zenit Photosniper: (KM102); Latest version of (KM100) now sporting a Zenit Automat 35mm SLR with aperture priority, a Telezenitar-K f4.5/300mm lens in "K" type bayonet mount, and a redesigned shoulder stock. Available *new*, but not found yet in great numbers in the "West".

| R3* $175 | £92 | DM288 | FF894 |

Zenit: (KM105); C1953, 35mm SLR, interchangeable (39mm screw mount) 50mm normal lens, CFPS 1/30 - 1/500s, non-instant return mirror.

| R2* $65 | £34 | DM107 | FF332 |

Zenit S (C): (KM106); C1956, as (KM105) but with flash synch.

| R2* $55 | £29 | DM91 | FF281 |

Franz KOCHMANN, Korellewerk Dresden, Germany.

After 1945 this factory was "nationalized" and became part of the Werkestätte für Feinmechanik und Optik (WEFO), VEB, Dresden, East Germany. Post-war cameras made by this firm are treated as a continuation of the pre-war line, and are found at the end of this listing.

Korelle: (FK100); C1932, 4 x 6.5cm roll film camera, various lens and shutter combinations including Radionar 75mm f3.5 lens, Compur shutter 1-1/250 s.

| R2* $50 | £26 | DM82 | FF256 |

Korelle P: (FK101); 4.5 x 6cm folding plate camera, various lens and shutter combinations including Xenar f2.9 lens, Compur shutter 1-1/250 s.

| R3* $450 | £236 | DM742 | FF2.3k |

Reflex-Korelle: (FK102); C1932, SLR camera for 6 x 6cm frames on 120 roll film, Ludwig-Dresden Victar f2.9 or f3.5/75mm lens, interchangeable screw mount,CFPS, 1/25-1/500s, black painted name plate, external selftimer, double stroke lever advance.

| R3* $125 | £66 | DM206 | FF639 |

Reflex-Korelle II: (FK103); C1934, SLR camera for 6 x 6cm frames on 120 roll film, Ludwig-Dresden Victar f2.9 or f3.5/75mm lens, interchangeable screw mount,CFPS, 2 - 1/500s, *chrome name plate*, external selftimer, double stroke lever advance.

| R3* $150 | £79 | DM247 | FF767 |

Reflex-Korelle

K

Reflex-Korelle Chrome III: (FK104); C1936, SLR camera for 6 x 6cm frames on 120 roll film, Radionar or Xenar f3.5 or Radionar f2.9/75mm lens, interchangeable bayonet mount,CFPS, 2 - 1/1000s, chrome name plate, VFR hood, and front plate, internal selftimer, single stroke lever advance.

R3* $175	£92	DM288	FF894

Sport Korelle 66: (FK105); C1939, folding VFR camera for 6 x 6cm frames on 120 roll film , Tessar f2.8/8cm lens, interchangeable mount, CFPS to 1/1000s.

R4* $175	£92	DM288	FF894

Korelle K: (FK106); C1933, Bakelite 35mm half frame VFR camera 18mm x 24mm frames on standard 35mm film, various lens were available including Tessar f3.5 or f2.8/35mm lens, Compur shutter (dark brown body brings 100% more, as does Leitz Elmar f3.5/3.5cm lens.)

R3* $375	£197˙	DM618	FF1.9k

Korelle 6x6: (FK107); C1932, folding VFR camera for 6 x 6cm frames on 120 roll film , various lens and shutter combinations available including Radionar f2.9 or f3.5/75mm lens, Prontor or Compur shutter.

R3* $45	£24	DM74	FF230

Korelle 6x9: (FK108); C1932, folding VFR camera for 6 x 9cm frames on 120 roll film,

various lens and shutter combinations available including Radionar f4.5/105mm lens, Prontor or Compur shutter. R*

R3* $45	£24	DM74	FF230

Enolde A, I, Ia, II, III, IV, V, VI: (FK109); C1918, folding plate or sheet film cameras in 6.5cm x 9 cm, 9cm x 12cm, and 10cm x 15cm sizes, leather covered wooden or metal bodies, rising and shifting fronts, more expensive models have double extension bellows, many lens and shutter combinations including Meyer, Steinheil, Rodenstock, and Schneider lenses and Vario, Ibsor and Compur shutters, models include I, Ia, A, II, III, IV, V and VI, all of which differ only slightly. (+30% for 6.5cm x 9cm size and double extension bellows).

R3* $40	£21	DM66	FF204

Enolde: (FK110); C1930, folding camera for 6cm x 9cm frames on roll film, unusual focusing tube/viewfinder swings away from the camera body and attaches to the lens standard when the camera is opened in the working position, moving the lens thereby focuses the image in the VFR, Zeiss Tessar f4.5/105mm lens, Compur shutter.

R4* $300	£157	DM495	FF1.5k

Meister-Korelle: (FK111); C1950, SLR for 6cm x 6cm frames on roll film, interchangeable Tessar f3.5/9cm Primotar f3.5/85mm lens, CFPS 1 - 1/1000s.

R3* $175	£92	DM288	FF894

EASTMAN KODAK CO., Rochester, New York.

On January 1, 1881 George Eastman became partners with Henry Strong, (a family friend and buggy-whip manufacturer) to become the Eastman Dry Plate Company, with Strong as president and Eastman as treasurer. Dry plates were their prime source of income, being distributed at that time by the E. & H. T. Anthony Co. In 1884 when the switch was being made to flexible film to use in the Eastman-Walker roll holder, the company was incorporated as the Eastman Dry Plate and

The Kodak (Original Kodak)

Film Co., with fourteen sharehold-
ers. In 1889 a new corporation was
formed and called the Eastman Co.
at 343 State Street, Rochester, New
York. A wooden box made by
Rochester cabinet maker Frank
Browner, with metal parts by
Yawman and Erbe and lens by
Bausch & Lomb became the original string cocking Kodak for roll
flexible film ("you push the button
and we do the rest"). The name was
then changed to Eastman Kodak
Co. of New York; in 1901 it became
the Eastman Kodak Co. of New Jersey.

The Kodak (Original Kodak): (EK100);
Rapid Rectilinear lens; barrel shutter; 100
exp, 2¹/₂" diameter. C 1888-1889.

| R5* $2.75k | £1.4k | DM4.5k | FF14.1k |

No. 1 Kodak: (EK101); Rapid Rectilinear
lens; sector shutter; 100 exp, 2" diameter. C
1889-1895.

| R4* $700 | £367 | DM1.2k | FF3.6k |

No. 2 Kodak: (EK102); Rapid Rectilinear
lens; sector shutter; 100 exp, 3¹/₂" diameter. C 1889-1897.

| R4* $400 | £210 | DM659 | FF2k |

No. 3 Kodak: (EK103); focusing box roll
film camera; Bausch & Lomb Universal lens;
sector shutter; 100 exp, 3¹/₄" x 4¹/₄". C
1890-1897.

| R4* $400 | £210 | DM659 | FF2k |

No. 3 Kodak Junior: (EK104); Bausch &
Lomb Universal lens; sector shutter; 60 exp
3¹/₄" x 4¹/₄". C 1890-1897.

| R4* $375 | £197 | DM618 | FF1.9k |

No. 4 Kodak: (EK105); Bausch & Lomb
Universal lens; sector shutter; 48 exp,
4" x 5". C 1890-1898.

| R4* $350 | £184 | DM577 | FF1.8k |

No. 4 Kodak

No. 4 Kodak Junior: (EK106); Bausch &
Lomb Universal lens; sector shutter; 48 exp,
4" x 5". C 1890-1897.

| R4* $350 | £184 | DM577 | FF1.8k |

No. 4 Folding Kodak: (EK107); Bausch &
Lomb Universal lens; special Kodak sector
shutter*; 48 exp, 4" x 5". C 1890-1892.

| R4* $500 | £262 | DM824 | FF2.6k |

Eastman Interchangeable View 5" x 8": (EK109); brass Rapid Rectilinear lens; waterhouse stops; behind-the-lens shutter. Tilting back; rising and falling front; ground glass back; side tripod holder attachment; ivory label. C 1885.

R4* $375	£197	DM618	FF1.9k

No. 4 Folding Kodak Improved: (EK110); Bausch & Lomb Universal lens; Bausch & Lomb Iris Diaphragm shutter*; 48 exp, 4" x 5". C 1893-1897.

R4* $500	£262	DM824	FF2.6k

No. 5 Folding Kodak (first model): (EK111); special Kodak sector shutter; film or plates; Eastman-Walker roll holder for 54 exp, 5" x 7" on roll film. C 1890.

R5* $500	£262	DM824	FF2.6k

No. 5 Folding Kodak

No. 5 Folding Kodak (second model): (EK112); Barker shutter; Eastman-Walker roll holder for 54 exp, 5" x 7" on roll film. C 1892.

R5* $550	£289	DM907	FF2.8k

No. 5 Folding Kodak Improved: (EK113); Bausch & Lomb Universal lens; Bausch & Lomb Iris Diaphragm shutter; double swing, sliding front. Eastman-Walker roll holder for 54 exp, 5" x 7" on roll film or plates. Provisions for stereo. C 1893-1897.

R5* $500	£262	DM824	FF2.6k

No. 6 Folding Kodak Improved: (EK114); Bausch & Lomb Universal lens; Bausch & Lomb Iris Diaphragm shutter; 48 exp, $6^{1}/_{2}$"x $8^{1}/_{2}$". C 1893-1895.

R5* $1k	£525	DM1.6k	FF5.1k

"A" Ordinary Kodak: (EK115); single lens; Special sector shutter; 24 exp, $2^{3}/_{4}$"x $3^{1}/_{4}$". C 1891-1895.

R5* $1k	£525	DM1.6k	FF5.1k

"A" Ordinary Kodak

"A" Daylight Kodak: (EK116); single lens; fixed diaphragm; Special sector shutter; 24 exp, $2^{3}/_{4}$"x $3^{1}/_{4}$". C 1891-1895.

R5* $1k	£525	DM1.6k	FF5.1k

"B" Ordinary Kodak: (EK117); single lens; revolving waterhouse diaphragm. Special sector shutter; 24 exp, $3^{1}/_{2}$" x 4". C 1891-1895.

R5* $600	£315	DM989	FF3.1k

Eastman Interchangeable View 8" x 10": (EK118); 8" x 10" view camera; Prosh triple model shutter and lens. Separate front extension; ivory label. C 1888.

R3* $450	£236	DM742	FF2.3k

"B" Daylight Kodak: (EK120); Double lens; revolving waterhouse diaphragm. Special sector shutter; 24 exp, $3^{1}/_{2}$" x 4". C 1891-1895.

R4* $450	£236	DM742	FF2.3k

"C" Ordinary Kodak: (EK121); Single lens; revolving waterhouse diaphragm. Special sector shutter; 24 exp, 4" x 5". C 1891-1895.

R4* $750	£394	DM1.2k	FF3.8k

"C" Daylight Kodak: (EK122); Double lens; revolving waterhouse diaphragm. Special sector shutter; 24 exp, 4" x 5". C 1891-1895.

R4* $400	£210	DM659	FF2k

No. 4 Kodak: (EK123); leather covered box camera; Achromatic lens*; rotating

waterhouse stops; Kodet (built-in) shutter. 4" x 5" plate or roll holder. C 1894-1897.

R4* $425	£223	DM701	FF2.2k

No. 4 Folding Kodet: (EK124); 4" x 5" folding camera; 6¹/8" lens; finder for horizontal or vertical photos on 4" x 5" plates or film; leather covered mahogany construction. C 1894.

R4* $425	£223	DM701	FF2.2k

No. 4 Folding Kodet Special: (EK125); Achromatic lens*; Kodet (built-in) shutter*. 4" x 5" plate or roll holder. C 1895-1897.

R4* $400	£210	DM659	FF2k

No. 4 Folding Kodet Special

No. 4 Folding Kodet Junior: (EK126); Achromatic lens; Kodet (built-in) shutter. 4" x 5" plate or roll holder. C 1894-1897.

R4* $400	£210	DM659	FF2k

No. 5 Folding Kodet: (EK127); Achromatic lens*; Kodak (built-in) shutter*. 5" x 7" plate or roll holder. C 1895-1897.

R5* $500	£262	DM824	FF2.6k

No. 5 Folding Kodak Special: (EK130); Rapid Rectilinear lens; Kodet (built-in) shutter*. 5" x 7" plate or roll holder. C 1895-1897.

R4* $500	£262	DM824	FF2.6k

Pocket Kodak: (EK131); Single lens; rotary shutter; 1¹/2"x 2" exp on 102 roll film. First model had round vf. C 1895-1896, $80-$115. Second model has rectangular vf. C 1896-1900.

R3* $125	£66	DM206	FF639

No. 3 Folding Pocket Kodak De Luxe: (EK132). C 1907.

R4* $350	£184	DM577	FF1.8k

No. 4 Folding Pocket Kodak: (EK133); Suter Anastigmatic 150mm f6.3 lens; Ibsor shutter 1-1/100 s; 4" x 5" exp. C 1899.

R2* $45	£24	DM74	FF230

No. 1A Folding Hawk Eye: (EK134); Bausch & Lomb Rapid Rectilinear lens; ball-bearing shutter; 6.5 x 11cm exp. C 1905.

R2* $40	£21	DM66	FF204

No. 2 Bullet: (EK135); Achromatic lens; rotary shutter; 3¹/2" x 3¹/2" exp on 101 roll film. C 1895-1896.

R2* $60	£31	DM99	FF307

No. 2 Bullet Improved: (EK136); Achromatic lens; rotary shutter 3¹/2" x 3¹/2" exp on 101 roll film or single plate holder. C 1896-1900.

R2* $75	£39	DM124	FF383

No. 2 Bullet Special Kodak: (EK137); covered box camera; Rapid Rectilinear lens; Triple-Action shutter; for plates or roll film; 3¹/2" x 3¹/2" exp. C 1899.

R3* $75	£39	DM124	FF383

K

No. 2 Bulls-Eye: (EK140); fixed focus achromatic lens; rotary shutter; 12 exp, 2¹/2" x 3¹/2" on 101 roll film. C 1896-1913.

R2* $45	£24	DM74	FF230

No. 2 Bulls-Eye

No. 2 Bulls-Eye Improved: (EK141); Achromatic lens; Rotary shutter; 3¹/2" x 3¹/2" exp on 101 roll film. C 1896-1913.

R2* $30	£16	DM49	FF153

No. 2 Bulls-Eye Special: (EK142); Rapid Rectilinear lens; Eastman Triple Action

KODAK

shutter; 3^1/$_2$" x 3^1/$_2$" exp on 101 roll film. C 1898-1904.

| R2* $45 | £24 | DM74 | FF230 |

No. 4 Bullet: (EK143); box camera for film or plates. C 1896.

| R3* $90 | £47 | DM148 | FF460 |

No. 4 Bulls-Eye: (EK144); roll film camera; rotary shutter; focused by external sliding lever. C 1896.

| R3* $85 | £45 | DM140 | FF434 |

No. 4 Bulls-Eye Improved: (EK145); Achromatic lens; Rotary shutter; 4" x 5" exp on 103 roll film. C 1896-1904.

| R2* $35 | £18 | DM58 | FF179 |

No. 4 Bulls-Eye Special: (EK146); Rapid Rectilinear lens; Eastman Triple Action shutter; 4" x 5" exp on 103 roll film. C 1898-1904.

| R2* $70 | £37 | DM115 | FF358 |

No. 2 Folding Bulls-Eye: (EK147); Achromatic lens; Rotary shutter; 3^1/$_2$" x 3^1/$_2$" exp on 101 roll film. C 1899-1901.

| R2* $60 | £31 | DM99 | FF307 |

No. 2 Falcon: (EK150); box camera; 4^1/$_2$" Achromatic lens; rotary 3 stop shutter; 12 exp, 3^1/$_2$" x 3^1/$_2$" on 101 roll film. C 1897-1899.

| R3* $70 | £37 | DM115 | FF358 |

No. 2 Falcon

No. 2 Eureka: (EK151); leather covered box camera; Achromatic lens; Rotary shutter; 3^1/$_2$" x 3^1/$_2$" exp on 106 roll film. C 1898-1899.

| R3* $100 | £52 | DM165 | FF511 |

No. 2 Eureka , Model B: (EK152); leather covered box camera; rotary shutter; 3^1/$_2$" x

No. 2 Eureka

3^1/$_2$" exp on plates or roll film.

| R3* $100 | £52 | DM165 | FF511 |

No. 2 Eureka Junior: (EK153); leatherette covered box camera; 3^1/$_2$" x 3^1/$_2$" plates. C 1899.

| R3* $90 | £47 | DM148 | FF460 |

No. 4 Eureka: (EK154); Achromatic lens; Rotary shutter 4" x 5" exp on 109 roll film. C 1899.

| R3* $80 | £42 | DM132 | FF409 |

No. 1 Panoram Kodak: (EK155); Rapid Rectilinear lens; swinging lens and focal plane slit; 2^1/$_4$" x 7" exp on 105 roll film. C 1900-1901.

| R3* $225 | £118 | DM371 | FF1.2k |

No. 1 Panoram Kodak , Model B: (EK156); Meniscus lens*; swinging lens and focal plane slit; 2^1/$_4$" x 7" exp on 105 roll film. C 1901-1903.

| R3* $175 | £92 | DM288 | FF894 |

No. 1 Panoram Kodak , Model C: (EK157); Meniscus lens; swinging lens and focal plane slit; 2^1/$_4$" x 7" exp on 105 roll film. C 1903-1907.

| R3* $175 | £92 | DM288 | FF894 |

No. 1 Panoram Kodak , Model D: (EK160); Meniscus lens; swinging lens and focal plane slit; 2^1/$_4$" x 7" exp on 105 roll film. C 1907-1926.

| R3* $175 | £92 | DM288 | FF894 |

No. 3A Panoram Kodak: (EK161); Meniscus lens; swinging lens and focal plane slit; 3^1/$_4$" x 10^3/$_8$" exp on 122 roll film. C 1926-1928.

| R3* $350 | £184 | DM577 | FF1.8k |

No. 4 Panoram Kodak: (EK162); Rapid Rectilinear lens; swinging lens and focal plane slit; 3¹/₂" x 12" exp on 103 roll film. C 1899-1900.

| R3* $170 | £89 | DM280 | FF869 |

No. 4 Panoram Kodak, Model D: (EK163); Meniscus lens; swinging lens and focal plane slit; 3¹/₂" x 12" on 103 roll film. C 1907-1924.

| R3* $175 | £92 | DM288 | FF894 |

No. 2 Flexo Kodak: (EK164); Achromatic lens; Rotary shutter; 3¹/₂" x 3¹/₂" exp on 101 roll film. C 1899-1913.

| R3* $75 | £39 | DM124 | FF383 |

No. 3 Cartridge Kodak: (EK165); Rapid Rectilinear lens*; Eastman Triple Action* shutter; 4¹/₄" x 3¹/₄" exp on 119 roll film. C 1900-1907.

| R3* $120 | £63 | DM198 | FF613 |

No. 4 Cartridge Kodak: (EK166); Rapid Rectilinear* lens; Eastman Triple Action* shutter; 4" x 5" exp on 104 roll film. C 1897-1907.

| R3* $90 | £47 | DM148 | FF460 |

No. 5 Cartridge Kodak: (EK167); Rapid Rectilinear* lens; Eastman Triple Action shutter; 5" x 7" exp on 115 roll film or plates. C 1898-1901.

| R3* $100 | £52 | DM165 | FF511 |

No. 5 Cartridge Kodak

No. 0 Folding Pocket Kodak: (EK170); Meniscus lens; Automatic shutter; 2¹/₂" x 1⁵/₈" exp on 121 roll film. C 1902-1906.

| R3* $90 | £47 | DM148 | FF460 |

No. 0 Brownie: (EK171); Meniscus lens; Rotary shutter; 4 x 6cm on roll film. C 1914.

| R2* $25 | £13 | DM41 | FF128 |

No. 1 Brownie , Model B: (EK172); Meniscus lens; Rotary shutter; 2¹/₄" x 2¹/₄" exp. C 1900-1915.

| R2* $25 | £13 | DM41 | FF128 |

No. 2 Brownie: (EK174); cardboard box camera; six exp, 2¹/₄" x 3¹/₄" on roll film. Original cost, $1.00; accessory vf, $.25; film cost $.10. C 1901-1924. $175; in box, $85.

| R2* $175 | £92 | DM288 | FF894 |

No. 2 Folding Brownie , Model A: (EK175); Achromatic meniscus lens; Pocket Automatic shutter; 6 x 9cm exp. C 1904.

| R?* | $? |

No. 2 Stereo Brownie: (EK176); folding roll film stereo camera; paired exp, 3¹/₄" x 2¹/₂" each; shutter adjustable for I, B & T; four lens openings. C 1905.

| R4* $400 | £210 | DM659 | FF2k |

No. 2 Brownie , Model C: (EK177); box roll film camera; 2¹/₄" x 3¹/₄ exp. C 1905.

| R2* $15 | £8 | DM25 | FF77 |

No. 2A Folding Autographic Brownie: (EK180); Achromatic lens; ball-bearing shutter; 2¹/₂ x 4¹/₄ exp. C 1915.

| R2* $20 | £10 | DM33 | FF102 |

No. 3 Brownie: (EK181); Meniscus lens; Rotary shutter; Took 3¹/₄ x 4¹/₄ size exp. C 1908.

| R2* $15 | £8 | DM25 | FF77 |

No. 00 Cartridge Kodak Premo: (EK182); 35mm roll film box camera; meniscus lens; 1¹/₄ x 1³/₄ exp on roll film. First Kodak to use 35mm film; smallest box camera produced by Kodak. C February 1916.

| R3* $50 | £26 | DM82 | FF256 |

No. 1 Folding Pocket Kodak: (EK183); Achromatic lens; Rotary shutter*; 2¹/₄ x 3¹/₄ exp on 105 roll film. C 1898-1915.

| R3* $125 | £66 | DM206 | FF639 |

KODAK

No. 00 Cartridge Kodak Premo

No. 1A Folding Pocket Kodak: (EK184); Achromatic lens; Pocket Automatic* shutter; 2¹/₂" x 4¹/₂" exp on 116 roll film. C 1899-1915. Version no. 1 - 2 vfs, **$75**. Version no. 2 - 1 vf.

R3* $45	£24	DM74	FF230

K

No. 1A Folding Pocket Kodak (left) with second version (right)

No. 1A Folding Pocket Kodak Special: (EK185); Rapid Rectilinear* lens; F.P.K. Automatic shutter; 2¹/₂" x 4¹/₄" exp on 116 roll film. C 1908-1912.

R3* $50	£26	DM82	FF256

No. 1A Folding Pocket "RR" Kodak: (EK186); similar to No. 1A Folding Pocket Kodak Special . Kodak Ball Bearing shutter. C 1912-1915.

R2* $50	£26	DM82	FF256

No. 2 Folding Pocket Kodak: (EK187); Achromatic* lens; Eastman Automatic shutter; 3¹/₂" x 3¹/₂" exp on 101 roll film. C 1899-1903.

R2* $20	£10	DM33	FF102

No. 3 Folding Pocket Kodak: (EK190); Rapid Rectilinear* lens; Unicum* shutter; 3¹/₄" x 4¹/₄" exp on 118 roll film. C 1900-1915.

R2* $25	£13	DM41	FF128

No. 3A Folding Pocket Kodak: (EK191); Rapid Rectilinear lens; F.P.K. Automatic shutter; 3¹/₄" x 5¹/₂" exp on 122 roll film. C 1903-1915.

R2* $25	£13	DM41	FF128

No. 1A Special Kodak: (EK192); Zeiss Kodak Anastigmat f6.3 lens; Bausch & Lomb Compound* shutter; 2¹/₂" x 4¹/₄" exp on 116 roll film. C 1912-1914.

R3* $40	£21	DM66	FF204

No. 3 Special Kodak: (EK193); Zeiss Kodak Anastigmat f6.3 lens; Bausch & Lomb Compound shutter; 3¹/₄" x 4¹/₄" exp on 118 roll film. C 1911-1914.

R3* $60	£31	DM99	FF307

No. 3A Special Kodak: (EK194); Zeiss Kodak Anastigmat f6.3 lens; Bausch & Lomb Compound shutter*; 3¹/₄" x 5¹/₂" exp on 122 roll film. C 1910-1914.

R3* $75	£39	DM124	FF383

No. 4 Folding Kodak: (EK195); Rapid Rectilinear lens; F.P.K. Automatic shutter; 4" x 5" exp on 123 roll film. C 1907-1912.

R3* $70	£37	DM115	FF358

No. 4A Folding Kodak: (EK196); Rapid Rectilinear lens; Bausch & Lomb Automatic shutter; 4¹/₄" x 6¹/₂" exp on 126 roll film. C 1906-1912.

R2* $80	£42	DM132	FF409

No. 4 Screen Focus Kodak: (EK197); Rapid Rectilinear lens; Kodak Automatic shutter; 4" x 5" exp on 123 roll film. C 1904-1909.

R4* $300	£157	DM495	FF1.5k

3B Quick Focus Kodak: (EK200); Meniscus Achromatic lens, Rotary shutter; 3¹/₄" x 5¹/₂" exp on 125 roll film. C 1906-1911.

R4* $250	£131	DM412	FF1.3k

Stereo Kodak Model 1: (EK201); Kodak Anastigmat f7.7 lenses; Stereo Automatic shutter; pair of 3¹/₈" x 3³/₁₆" exp on 101 roll film. C 1917-1925.

R4* $350	£184	DM577	FF1.8k

No. 2 Stereo Kodak: (EK202); box-type stereoscopic camera; periscopic 5" f14 lenses; wl finder; oscillating sector between-the-lens shutter. 2, 3 or 5 paired exp, 3³/₈" x 3³/₈" on roll film. C 1901-1905. The only box-type stereo camera for roll film produced in America.

R4* $550	£289	DM907	FF2.8k

No. 2 Stereo Kodak

No. 4A Speed Kodak: (EK203); Bausch & Lomb Zeiss Tessar f6.3 lens; Kodak fps; 4¹/₄" x 6¹/₂" exp on 126 roll film. C1908-13.

R4* $400	£210	DM659	FF2k	°

No. 1A Speed Kodak: (EK204); Zeiss Kodak Anastigmat f6.3 lens; Graflex fps; 2¹/₂" x 4¹/₄" exp on 116 roll film. C1909-13.

R4* $225	£118	DM371	FF1.2k

Kodak Enlarging Outfit: (EK205); for 4" x 5" or smaller; ground glass back; accessory for lantern slide camera; monorail; polished oak finish. With original box. C 1920.

R3* $125	£66	DM206	FF639

No. 1 Autographic Kodak Junior: (EK206); Achromatic lens; Kodak Ball Bearing shutter; 2¹/₄" x 3¹/₄" exp on 120 roll film. C 1914-1926.

R1* $15	£8	DM25	FF77

No. 1 Autographic Kodak Special: (EK207); Zeiss Kodak Anastigmat f6.3 lens; Optimo shutter; 2¹/₄" x 3¹/₄" exp on A120 roll film. C 1915-1920. $45 New model: Kodak Anastigmat f6.3* lens; Kodamatic shutter. C 1921. $40.

R3* $45	£24	DM74	FF230

No. 1 Autographic Kodak Special, Model B: (EK210); Kodak Anastigmat f6.3 lens; Kodamatic shutter 2¹/₄" x 3¹/₄" exp on A120 film. C 1922-1926.

R2* $50	£26	DM82	FF256

No. 1A Autographic Kodak: (EK211); Rapid Rectilinear lens; Kodak Ball Bearing shutter; 2¹/₂" x 4¹/₄" exp on 116 roll film. $15 New model: Kodak Anastigmat f7.7 lens; Kodak Ball Bearing shutter. C 1917-1924.

R1* $15	£8	DM25	FF77

No. 1A Autographic Kodak Junior: (EK212); Achromatic* lens; Kodak Ball Bearing shutter; 2¹/₂" x 4¹/₄" exp on A116 roll film. C 1914-1926.

R1* $10	£5	DM16	FF51

No. 1A Autographic Kodak Special: (EK213); Zeiss Kodak f6.3 lens; Bausch & Lomb Compound* shutter; 2¹/₂" x 4¹/₄" exp on A116 roll film. C 1914-1916.

R2* $25	£13	DM41	FF128

No. 1A Autographic Kodak Special with coupled rangefinder: (EK214); Kodak Anastigmat f6.3 lens; Optimo shutter; 2¹/₂" x 4¹/₄" exp on A116 roll film. C 1917-1923. $85 New model: Kodak Anastigmat f6.3 lens; Kodamatic shutter. C 1923-1926.

R3* $100	£52	DM165	FF511

No. 2C Autographic Kodak Junior: (EK215); Achromatic lens; Kodak Ball Bearing shutter; 2⁷/₈" x 4⁷/₈" exp on A130 roll film. C 1916-1927.

R1* $10	£5	DM16	FF51

No. 2C Autographic Kodak Special: (EK216); Kodak Anastigmat lens; Kodamatic shutter; 2⁷/₈" x 4⁷/₈" exp on A130 roll film. C 1923-1928.

R2* $25	£13	DM41	FF128

No. 3 Autographic Kodak: (EK217); Rapid Rectilinear lens; Kodak Ball Bearing* shutter; 3¹/₄" x 4¹/₄" exp on A118 roll film. C 1914-1926.

R1* $15	£8	DM25	FF77

No. 3 Autographic Kodak Special: (EK220); Zeiss Kodak Anastigmat f6.3 lens; Bausch & Lomb Compound shutter; 3¹/₄" x 4¹/₄" exp on A118 roll film. C 1914-1924.

R2* $40	£21	DM66	FF204

No. 3A Autographic Kodak: (EK221);

Rapid Rectilinear lens; Kodak Ball Bearing shutter; 3^1/4" x 5^1/2" exp on A122 roll film. C 1918-1927.

R3* $15	£8	DM25	FF77

No. 3A Autographic Kodak Junior: (EK222); Achromatic lens; Kodak Ball Bearing shutter; 3^1/4" x 5^1/2" exp on A122 roll film. C 1918-1927.

R1* $15	£8	DM25	FF77

No. 3A Autographic Kodak Special: (EK223); Zeiss Kodak Anastigmat f6.3lens; Bausch & Lomb Compound shutter; 3^1/4" x 5^1/2" exp on A122 roll film.

R3* $60	£31	DM99	FF307

No. 3A Autographic Kodak Special with coupled range-finder: (EK224); Zeiss Kodak Anastigmat f6.3 lens; Optimo shutter; 3^1/4" x 5^1/2" exp on A122 roll film. C 1916-1924. First mfd camera with CRF.

R3* $100	£52	DM165	FF511

Vest Pocket Kodak Special: (EK226); Zeiss Kodak Anastigmat f6.3lens; Kodak Ball Bearing shutter; 1^5/8" x ^{1}/2" exp on 127 roll film. C 1912-1914.

R2* $25	£13	DM41	FF128

Vest Pocket Autographic Kodak Special: (EK227); Zeiss Kodak Anastigmat f6.9* lens; Kodak Ball Bearing shutter. C 1915-1926.

R2* $45	£24	DM74	FF230

Vest Pocket Kodak Model B: (EK230); Meniscus lens; Rotary shutter; 1^5/8" x 2^1/2" exp on 127 roll film. C 1925-1934.

R2* $40	£21	DM66	FF204

Vest Pocket Kodak Series III: (EK231); Kodak Anastigmat f6.3 lens; Diomatic shutter; 1^5/8" x 2^1/2" exp on 127 film. C1926-34.

R2* $40	£21	DM66	FF204

No. 1A Gift Kodak: (EK232); 116 roll film folding camera; Achromatic lens; Kodex

Vest Pocket Kodak Series III

shutter; 2^1/4" x 4^1/4" on 116 roll film. C 1930. Art Deco design. (add 300% for complete set with box.)

R4* $250	£131	DM412	FF1.3k

No. 1A Gift Kodak

Beau Brownie: (EK233); box camera; Doublet lens; 116 roll film. C 1930-1932.

R3* $100	£52	DM165	FF511

Boy Scout Kodak: (EK234); Meniscus lens; Rotary shutter; 1^5/8" x 2^1/2" exp on 127 roll film. C 1930-1934.

R3* $200	£105	DM330	FF1k

Girl Scout Kodak: (EK235); Meniscus lens; Rotary shutter 1^5/8" x 2^1/2" exp on roll film. C 1929-1934. Engraved with the official Girl Scout emblem.

R3* $200	£105	DM330	FF1k

Camp Fire Girls' Kodak: (EK236); Meniscus lens; Rotary shutter. C 1931-1934.

R4* $300	£157	DM495	FF1.5k

Kodak Ensemble: (EK237); (Kodak Petite in suede leather case with mirror, compact and lipstick). C 1929-1933.

R4* $750	£394	DM1.2k	FF3.8k

Kodak Petite: (EK240); Vest Pocket Kodak

No. 2C Pocket Kodak Series III cameras

shutter; 2⁷/₈" x 4⁷/₈" exp on 130 roll film. C 1924-1931.

R2* $15		£8	
	DM25		FF77

No. 3 Pocket Kodak Series III: (EK247); Kodak f7.9 lens; Kodex shutter; 3¹/₄" x 4¹/₄" exp on 118 roll film. C 1926-1933.

R2* $25	£13	DM41	FF128

Kodak Bullet: (EK250); 127 roll film camera; meniscus lens; sector shutter. C 1935.

R2* $15	£8	DM25	FF77

Kodak 50th Anniversary Box: (EK251); brown with silver seal. C 1938.

R2* $60	£31	DM99	FF307

Model B Camera, in blue, brown, gray, green or red. Black bellows are not original, and sell for 50% less. Meniscus lens; Rotary shutter; 1⁵/₈" x 2¹/₂" exp on 127 roll film. C 1929-1933.

R3* $175	£92	DM288	FF894

Vanity Kodak: (EK241); Similar to Vest Pocket Kodak Series III Camera in blue, brown, gray, green or red. (see above) C 1928-1933. Vanity Kodak Ensemble: Art-deco case includes lipstick, compact with face powder, mirror and change pocket, with Vest Pocket Kodak Series III, Model B. C 1928-1931.

R4* $425	£223	DM701	FF2.2k

Kodak Coquette: (EK242); (Kodak Petite with matching lipstick holder and compact.) C 1930-1931.

R4* $750	£394	DM1.2k	FF3.8k

No. 1 Pocket Kodak Special: (EK243); Kodak Anastigmat f6.3 lens; Kodamatic shutter; 2¹/₄" x 3¹/₄" exp on 120 roll film. C 1926-1929.

R2* $25	£13	DM41	FF128

No. 1A Pocket Kodak Series II: (EK244); Achromatic lens; Kodex shutter 2¹/₂" x 4¹/₄" exp on 116 roll film. In blue, brown, gray, green or red. C 1928-1931.

R2* $35	£18	DM58	FF179

No. 1A Pocket Kodak: (EK245); Achromatic lens; Kodex shutter; 2¹/₂" x 4¹/₄" exp on 116 roll film. C 1926-1931.

R2* $15	£8	DM25	FF77

No. 2C Pocket Kodak Series III: (EK246); Kodak Anastigmat f7.7* lens; Diomatic

Kodak 50th Anniversary Box

Kodak Baby Brownie Special: (EK252); 127 roll film camera; meniscus lens; sector

Kodak Baby Brownie Special

KODAK

shutter; 8 exp on 127 roll film. C 1939.

R1* $10	£5	DM16	FF51

Kodak Regent: (EK253); Tessar 105mm f4.5 lens; Compur Rapid shutter 1-1/250 s; compact RFR; 6 x 9cm on 620 roll film. C 1935.

R3* $150	£79	DM247	FF767

Kodak Regent II: (EK254); Schneider Xenar 105mm f3.5 lens; Compur Rapid shutter 1-1/400 s, CRF; 6 x 9cm exp. C 1939.

R4* $550	£289	DM907	FF2.8k

Suprema: (EK255); Schneider Xenar 80mm f3.5 lens; Compur Rapid shutter 1-1/400 s; 6 x 6cm exp on 620 roll film. C 1939.

R4* $375	£197	DM618	FF1.9k

Kodak Six-16: (EK256); Meniscus Achromatic lens; Kodak shutter; 2¹/₂" x 4¹/₄" exp on 616 roll film. C 1932-1936.

R1* $15	£8	DM25	FF77

Kodak Six-20: (EK257); 620 roll film camera; Kodak Anastigmat 100mm f4.5 coated lens; No. 1 Diodak shutter   1/10 - 1/100 s; 2¹/₄" x 3¹/₄" exp on 620 roll film. C 1932-1937.

R2* $15	£8	DM25	FF77

Kodak Six-20 (left) and Six-20 with Compur shutter (right)

Kodak Six-20: (EK260); 620 roll film camera; Kodak Anastigmat 105mm f4.5 lens; Compur shutter 1-1/250 s; 2¹/₄" x 3¹/₄" exp on 620 roll film. C 1932-1937.

R2* $50	£26	DM82	FF256

Kodak Senior Six-20: (EK261); Kodak Anastigmat f6.3 lens; Kodex shutter; 2¹/₄" x 3¹/₄" exp on 620 roll film. C 1937-1939.

R2* $15	£8	DM25	FF77

Jiffy Kodak Six-20: (EK262); Twindar lens; Sector shutter; 2¹/₄" x 3¹/₄" exp on 620 film. C 1933-1937.

R1* $10	£5	DM16	FF51

Kodak Vigilant 616 Special: (EK263); 616 roll film folding camera; Kodak Anastigmat 12mm f4.5 lens; No. 2 Supermatic shutter 1-1/400 s; 8 exp on 616 roll film. C 1940.

R1* $15	£8	DM25	FF77

Kodak Vigilant Six-20: (EK264); Kodak Anastigmat f6.3 lens; Diomatic shutter; 2¹/₄" x 3¹/₄" exp on 620 roll film. C 1939-1948.

R1* $15	£8	DM25	FF77

Kodak Monitor Six-20: (EK265); Kodak Anastigmat Special f4.5 lens; Supermatic shutter; 2¹/₄" x 3¹/₄" exp on 620 roll film. C 1939-1948.

R1* $15	°£8	DM25	FF77

Kodak Monitor Six-16: (EK266); Kodak Anastigmat Special f4.5 lens; Supermatic shutter; 2¹/₂" x 4¹/₄" exp on 616 roll film. C 1939-1946.

R1* $15	£8 °	DM25	FF77

Super Kodak Six-20: (EK267); Kodak Anastigmat Special f3.5 lens; Kodak shutter controlled by Selenium photo-electric exp meter, CRF. 2¹/₄" x 3¹/₄" exp on 620 roll film. C 1938-1945. First camera with built-in photo-electric exp control.

R4* $1k	£525	DM1.6k	FF5.1k

Kodak Duex: (EK270); 620 roll film camera; 16 exp on 620 roll film. C 1940-1946.

R3* $20	£10	DM33	FF102

Kodak Bantam: (EK271); 828 roll film camera; Kodak Anastigmat 53mm f6.3 lens; shutter, T, I.

R1* $15	£8	DM25	FF77

Kodak Bantam Special: (EK272); Kodak Anastigmat Ektar f2 lens; Compur Rapid

Kodak Duex

shutter 1-1/500 s, CRF. 28 x 40mm exp on 828 roll film. C 1936-1940.

R3* $300	£157	DM495	FF1.5k

Kodak Bantam Special

Kodak Bantam f5.6: (EK273); Kodak Anastigmat Special lens; Kodak shutter. C 1938-1941.

R2* $15	£8	DM25	FF77

Kodak Bantam f8: (EK274); Kodalinear f8 lens; sector shutter; 28 x 40mm exp on 828 roll film. C 1938-1946.

R1* $15	£8	DM25	FF77

Kodak Bantam f4.5: (EK275); Kodak Anastigmat Special f4.5 lens; Kodak shutter. C 1938-1948.

R1* $15	£8	DM25	FF77

Kodak Flash Bantam: (EK276); Kodak Anastigmat Special f4.5 lens; Kodak Flash Synch shutter. C 1947-1953.

R1* $15	£8	DM25	FF77

Kodak Retina - Stuttgart type no. 117: (EK277); 35mm vf camera; Schneider-Kreuznach Xenar Anastigmat 5cm f3.5 lens; Compur 00 1-1/300 s. Large nickel plated knobs for film wind and rewind; rewind clutch lever positioned in film wind knob. Single

Kodak Flash Bantam

film sprocket on top of camera with short shaft. Black lacquer with nickel trim. C July 1934-July 1935.

R3* $110	£58	DM181	FF562

Kodak Retina - Stuttgart type no. 118: (EK280); 35mm vf camera. Similar to Stuttgart type no. 117 except: the rewind clutch lever was moved from film wind knob to the back of top cover, the film sprocket shaft extends across camera body. Black lacquer, nickel trim. C July 1935-April 1936.

R2* $100	£52	DM165	FF511

Kodak Retina - Stuttgart type no. 119: (EK281); 35mm RFR camera; Schneider Xenar 5cm f3.5 or Kodak Anastigmat Ektar 5cm f3.5 lens; Compur 00 1-1/300 s. Wind and rewind knobs reduced in diameter; exp counter moved to raised housing on right side of camera. Black lacquer, nickel trim. C April 1936-January 1938.

R2* $100	£52	DM165	FF511

Kodak Retina - Stuttgart type no. 126: (EK282); 35mm vf camera; Kodak Ektar 5cm f3.5 lens (also Tessar, Alcor, Angenieux and Ysar lenses); Compur-Rapid shutter 1-1/500 s. Chrome or black lacquer with

Kodak Retina - Stuttgart type

KODAK

Retina I

Retina I (Compur-Rapid shutter)

polished aluminium trim. Some cameras provided with accessory shoe. C March 1936-October 1937.

| R2* $60 | £31 | DM99 | FF307 |

Kodak Retina I - Stuttgart type no. 141: (EK283); 35mm vf camera; Kodak Ektar 5cm f3.5 lens (also Xenar); Compur or Compur-Rapid 1-1/500 s. Body shutter release in front edge of enlarged exp counter. Wind and rewind knobs taller than previous model. C October 1937-March 1939.

| R2* $80 | £42 | DM132 | FF409 |

Kodak Retina I - Stuttgart type no. 143: (EK284); 35mm vf camera; Schneider Xenar 5cm f3.5 lens; Compur shutter 1-1/300 s. Similar to Stuttgart type no. 141 except: black lacquer finish, chrome wind and rewind knobs. C January 1938-March 1939.

| R2* $90 | £47 | DM148 | FF460 |

Kodak Retina I - Stuttgart type no. 148: (EK285); 35mm vf camera; Kodak Ektar 5cm f3.5 lens; Compur-Rapid shutter 1 - 1/500 s. Exp counter reduced in size and moved closer to vf. First Retina to have film transport coupled to shutter to prevent double exp. C March 1939-December 1940. Chrome finish.

| R2* $85 | £45 | DM140 | FF434 |

Kodak Retina I - Stuttgart type no. 149: (EK286); 35mm vf camera; Schneider Xenar 5cm f3.5 lens; Compur-Rapid shutter 1-1/300 s. Similar to Stuttgart type no. 148 except, black lacquer finish and trim. C March 1939-December 1940.

| R2* $70 | £37 | DM115 | FF358 |

Kodak Retina I - Stuttgart type no. 010: (EK287); 35mm vf camera; Retina Xenar

50mm f3.5 coated lens (also Ektar, Xenar, Zenar, Rodenstock lenses); Compur-Rapid shutter 1-1/500 s. Mfd from combination of prewar and postwar parts. Same body and interlock as Stuttgart type no. 011, otherwise similar to Stuttgart type no. 148. Chrome finish. C May 1946-April 1949.

| R2* $70 | £37 | DM115 | FF358 |

Kodak Retina I - Stuttgart type no. 013: (EK290); 35mm vf camera; Retina Xenar 5cm f3.5 or f2.8 coated lens; Compur-Rapid shutter 1-1/500 s (X synch was added to some cameras in 1949; after 1950 it was added to all production cameras.) One piece chrome top cover with integral vf. C April 1949-January 1951. Chrome.

| R2* $80 | £42 | DM132 | FF409 |

Kodak Retina Ia - Stuttgart type no. 015: (EK291); 35mm vf camera; Retina Xenar 50mm f3.5 or f2.8 coated lens (also Rodenstock, Heligon, Ektar lenses); Compur-Rapid shutter 1-1/500 s, X flash synch. First Retina with top mounted rapid-wind film-advance coupled to shutter cocking. C January 1951-July 1951.

| R2* $90 | £47 | DM148 | FF460 |

Kodak Retina Ia - Stuttgart type no. 15: (EK292); 35mm vf camera; Retina-Xenar 50mm f3.5 or f2.8 coated lens (also Kodak Ektar lens); Synchro-Compur shutter 1-1/500 s, X-M flash synch. Similar to Stuttgart type no. 015 except for X-M flash indicator dial on top of rewind knob instead of under camera. C July 1951-April 1954.

| R2* $90 | £47 | DM148 | FF460 |

Kodak Retina Ib - Stuttgart type no. 018: (EK293); 35mm vf camera; Xenar 50mm

Retina I (black lacquer finish)

Retina Ia

f2.8 coated lens, interchangeable front component; Synchro-Compur LVS 1-1/500 s, VXM flash synch. New body design with rounded contours, concealed bellows, first bright frame vf in Retina camera. C 1954-1958.

| R2* $95 | £50 | DM157 | FF486 |

Kodak Retina IB - Stuttgart type no. 019: (EK294); 35mm vf camera; Xenar 50mm f2.8 coated lens, interchangeable front component; Synchro-Compur LVS 1-1/500 s, VXM flash synch. Similar to Stuttgart type no. 018 except, top cover enlarged vertically to accept built-in, non-coupled selenium single-range exp meter. Enlarged vf with second window added in 1958 to permit projected frame line. C 1957-1960.

| R2* $100 | £52 | DM165 | FF511 |

Kodak Retina II - Stuttgart type no. 122: (EK295); 35mm RFR camera; Schneider-Kreuznach Anastigmat Ektar 5cm f3.5 lens (also 5cm f2 Xenon lens); Compur-Rapid shutter 1-1/500 s. First Retina with separate optical vf and CRF. Retractable body release, rewind knob brake lever. C October 1936-June 1937.

| R2* $110 | £58 | DM181 | FF562 |

Kodak Retina II - Stuttgart type no. 142: (EK296); 35mm RFR camera; Schneider-Kreuznach Xenon 5cm f2.8 lens (also other lenses); Compur-Rapid shutter 1-1/500 s, CRF. Similar to Stuttgart type no. 122, except film wind knob instead of slow wind lever; top cover redesigned. C June 1937-May 1939.

| R2* $110 | £58 | DM181 | FF562 |

Kodak Retina IIa - Stuttgart type no. 150: (EK297); 35mm RFR camera; Schneider Kreuznach Xenon 5cm f2.8 lens; Compur-Rapid shutter 1-1/500 s. Redesigned top cover. First Retina with combined vf and CRF. Smaller (extensible) rewind knob. C May 1939-December 1940.

| R2* $120 | £63 | DM198 | FF613 |

Kodak Retina II - Stuttgart type no. 011: (EK300); 35mm RFR camera; Retina-Xenon 50mm f2.0 coated lens (also Heligon and 47mm Kodak Ektar lenses); Compur-Rapid shutter 1-1/500 s, CRF. First RFR Retina with coated lenses (although variations exist with uncoated lenses). Serial no. inside back; Rochester imports prefixed with letters "EK". C Summer 1946-Spring 1949.

| R2* $100 | £52 | DM165 | FF511 |

Retina Ib

Retina II

Kodak Retina II - Stuttgart type no. 014:
(EK301); 35mm RFR camera; Retina-Xenon 50mm f2 or Retina-Heligon f2 coated lenses; Compur- Rapid shutter 1-1/500 s, X synch, CRF. Similar to Stuttgart type no. 011 except has redesigned sloping front plate on front of shutter, also X flash synch. C Summer 1949-January 1951.

R2* $100	£52	DM165	FF511

Kodak Retina IIa - Stuttgart type no. 016:
(EK302); 35mm RFR camera; Retina-Xenon 50mm f2 coated lens; Compur-Rapid shutter 1-1/500 s, X flash synch, CRF. Similar to Stuttgart type no. 014 except rapid-wind film-advance lever coupled to shutter cocking mechanism. C January 1951-July 1951. Synchro-Compur with XM flash synch installed between July 1951-August 1954.

R2* $100	£52	DM165	FF511

Kodak Retina IIc - Stuttgart type no. 020:
(EK303); 35mm RFR camera; Xenon-C 50mm f2.8 coated lens, interchangeable front component (also Heligon-C lens); Synchro-Compur LVS 1-1/500 s, VXM flash sunch, CRF. Redesigned body with rounded contours and concealed bellows. Accepts either 80mm f4 telephoto or 35mm f5.6 wide-angle lens components. C 1954-1958.

R2* $100	£52	DM165	FF511

Kodak Retina IIC - Stuttgart type no. 029:
(EK304); 35mm RFR camera; Xenon-C 50mm f2.8 coated lens, interchangeable front component (also Heligon-C lens); Synchro-Compur LVS 1-1/500 s, VXM flash synch, CRF. This camera is similar to Stuttgart type no. 020 except enlarged vf has bright frame lines for 50mm, 35, and 80mm lenses. C 1958.

R2* $140	£73	DM231	FF716

Kodak Retina IIIc - Stuttgart type no. 021:
(EK305); 35mm RFR camera; Xenon-C 50mm f2 coated lens, interchangeable front component; Synchro- Compur LVS 1-1/500 s, VXM flash synch, CRF. Similar to Stuttgart type no. 020 except, non-coupled selenium photo-electric exp meter with hinged cover, built into top cover. C 1954.

R2* $125	£66	DM206	FF639

Kodak Retina IIIC - Stuttgart type no. 028: (EK306); 35mm RFR camera; Xenon-

Kodak Retina IIIC

C 50mm f2 coated lens, interchangeable lens component (also Heligon-C lens); Synchro-Compur LVS 1-1/500 s, VXM flash, synch, CRF. Similar to Stuttgart type no. 021 except selenium meter redesigned. Has plastic honeycomb - no hinged cover; enlarged vf has bright frame lines for 50mm, 35mm and 80mm lenses. C 1958-1961.

R3* $225	£118	DM371	FF1.2k

Retina lenses and accessories

Kodak Retina IIc, IIIc and IIIC cameras with Retina-Xenon C lens are matched for use with the Retina-Longar-Xenon C 80mm f4 and Retina Curtar-Xenon C 35mm f5.6 lenses; Kodak Retina cameras with Retina-Heligon lenses are matched for use with the Retina-Heligon C 80mm f4 and the Retina-Heligon C 35mm f4.5 lenses. Cameras with Xenon lenses were originally distributed in the US market, while cameras with Heligon lenses were distributed in the overseas market, both lenses are optically equivalent.

35-80 Multi finder: (EK004); **$25**
Xenon or Heligon f5.6/35mm lens: (EK005); **$35**
Xenon or Heligon f4/80mm lens: (EK006); **$45**

Kodak Retina IIIs: (EK307); Retina-Xenon 50mm f1.9 lens; Synchro-Compur shutter 1-1/500 s. C 1959-1961.

R2* $75	£39	DM124	FF383

Kodak Instamatic Reflex: (EK308); 35mm SLR, interchangeable Xenon 50mm f1.9 lens or Xenar 50mm f2.8 lens.

R2* $110	£58	DM181	FF562

Kodak Retina Reflex

Kodak Retina Reflex: (EK310); C 1958-1959, 35mm SLR, interchangeable Retina-Xenon 50mm f2 lens; Synchro-Compur shutter 1 - 1/500 s.

R2* $125	£66	DM206	FF639

Kodak Retina Reflex S: (EK500); C1959-60, 35mm SLR, interchangeable Xenar f2.8/50mm lens, Synchro Compur shutter, coupled light meter.

R2* $125	£66	DM206	FF639

Kodak Retina Reflex III: (EK311); C 1961-1964, 35mm SLR, interchangeable Xenon f1.9/50mm lens; Synchro-Compur shutter 1-1/500 s.

R2* $125	£66	DM206	FF639

Kodak Retina Reflex IV: (EK501); C1964-67, 35mm SLR, interchangeable Xenar or Ysarex f2.8/50mm lens, or Xenon or Heligon f1.9/50mm lens, Synchro Compur, shutter speed and lens opening visible in the VFR.

R2* $125	£66	DM206	FF639

Kodak Retinette: (EK312); C 1952-1954. Recomar f4.5/45mm lens; Pronto SV shutter 1 -1/300 s.

R2* $40	£21	DM66	FF204

Kodak Retinette

Match-Box (-X): (EK313); match-box detective camera; 25mm f5, f11 lens; 1/50 s shutter; 10 x 10mm exp on 16mm film. C 1945. Made for the American O.S.S. to be used as a spy camera.

R5* $2.5k	£1.3k	DM4.1k	FF12.8k

Kodak Pony 828: (EK314); Kodak Anaston f4.5 lens; Kodak Flash 200 shutter; 28 x 40mm exp on 828 roll film. C 1949-1959.

R1* $10	£5	DM16	FF51

Kodak Pony 828

Kodak Pony 135: (EK315); Kodak Anaston f4.5 lens; Kodak Flash 200 shutter; 36 exp on 35mm film. C 1950-1954.

R1* $10	£5	DM16	FF51

Kodak 35: (EK316); C 1938-1948, 35mm VFR camera, Kodak Anastigmat lens, Kodex shutter among others.

R2* $35	£18	DM58	FF179

Kodak 35 (Military): (EK317); C1938-1951, 35mm VFR camera, Kodak Anastigmat f4.5 lens/51mm Kodak No. 1 Diomatic shutter 1/25-1/150 s, B. T. C .

R3* $150	£79	DM247	FF767

Kodak 35 (Military)

KODAK

Kodak 35 (Early version)

Kodak 35 (Later version)

Kodak 35 (Lastversion)

Kodak 35 Rangefinder: (EK320); C 1940-1951, Kodak Anastigmat Special f3.5 lens, Flash Kodamatic shutter, CRF.

R2* $30	£16	DM49	FF153

Kodak Ektra: (EK321); Kodak Ektar 50mm f1.9* lens; cfps 1-1/1000 s; 36 exp on 35mm roll film. Features interchangeable magazine back, rapid film advance, CRF.

Kodak 35 Rangefinder

Kodak Ektra

C 1941-1948.

R4* $600	£315	DM989	FF3.1k

Interchangeable lenses for Ektra camera

Ektar 50mm f3.5 lens, **$150**
Ektar 50mm f1.9 lens, (EK001); **$100**
Ektar 35mm f3.3 lens, (EK002); **$125**
Ektar 90mm f3.5 lens, (EK003); **$125**
Ektar 135mm f3.8 lens, (EK004); **$125**
Ektar 153mm f4.5 lens, (EK005); **$800**

Kodak Signet 35: (EK322); Kodak Ektar 50mm f3.5 lens; Kodak Synchro 300 shutter. C 1951-1958.

R2* $20	£10	DM33	FF102

Kodak Signet 40: (EK323); Kodak Ektanon 50mm f3.5 lens; Kodak Synchro 400 shutter. C 1956-1959.

R2* $20	£10	DM33	FF102

Kodak Signet 30: (EK324); Kodak Ektanar 50mm f2.8 lens; Kodak Synchro 250 shutter. C 1957-1959.

R2* $20	£10	DM33	FF102

Kodak Signet - "Signal Corps, U.S. Army Camera, Still picture KE-7(1)": (EK325); 35mm RFR camera; Kodak Ektar 44mm f3.5 lens; Kodak Synchro 300 shutter. Black finish.

R3* $125	£66	DM206	FF639

Kodak Signet - Signal Corps

Kodak Signet 50: (EK326); Kodak Ektanar 50mm f2.8 lens; Kodak Synchro 250 shutter. C 1957-1960.

R2* $40	£21	DM66	FF204

Kodak Signet 80: (EK327); C 1958-1962, interchangeable Kodak Ektanar f2.8/50mm lens; behind the lens shutter, built-in light meter.

R3* $60	£31	DM99	FF307

Kodak Signet 80

Signet Multi Frame Finder: (EK001); **$20**
Signet Wide Angle lens f3.5/35mm: (EK002); **$30**
Signet Telephoto lens f4/90mm: (EK003); **$30**

Kodak Automatic 35: (EK330); Kodak Ektanar 50mm f2.8 lens; Kodak Synchro 80 shutter. Auto exp control. C 1959.

R2* $45	£24	DM74	FF230

Kodak Automatic 35

Kodak Motormatic 35F: (EK331); Kodak Ektanar 50mm f2.8 lens; Kodak Automatic Flash shutter. Spring-wound motor drive. C 1962.

R3* $55	£29	DM91	FF281

Kodak Pupille: (EK332); Schneider Xenon 50mm f2 lens; Compur shutter $1^3/_{16}$" x $1^9/_{16}$" exp on 127 roll film. C 1932.

R4* $300	£157	DM495	FF1.5k

Kodak Pupille

Kodak Ranca: (EK333); Nagel Anastigmat f4.5 lens; Pronto shutter; $1^3/_{16}$" x $1^9/_{16}$" exp on 127 roll film. C 1932-1934.

R4* $300	£157	DM495	FF1.5k

Kodak Vollenda: (EK334); Radionar Anastigmat 50mm f3.5* lens; Compur shutter; $1^3/_{16}$" x $1^9/_{16}$" exp on 127 roll film. C 1932-1937. $75. With Leitz Elmar 50mm f3.5 lens, $300.

R3*

Kodak Vollenda (6 x 9cm model): (EK335); folding camera; Elmar 10.5cm f4.5 lens; Compur shutter 1 - 1/250 s; 8 exp, 6 x 9cm on 120 roll film. C 1939.

R3* $275	£144	DM453	FF1.4k

K

KODAK

Kodak Duo Six-20: (EK336); Kodak Anastigmat 75mm f3.5 lens; Compur* shutter; $1^5/8$" x $2^1/4$" exp on 620 roll film. C 1934-1937.

R3* $40	£21	DM66	FF204

Kodak Duo Six-20 (rangefinder model): (EK337); Schneider Kreuznach Xenar 75mm f3.5 lens; Compur Rapid shutter 1-1/500 s, CRF; $1^5/8$" x $2^1/4$" exp on 620 roll film. C 1937

R3* $300	£157	DM495	FF1.5k

Kodak Recomar 18: (EK338); Kodak Anastigmat f4.5 lens; Compur shutter; $2^1/4$" x $3^1/4$" exp on film pack. C 1932-1940.

R3* $40	£21	DM66	FF204

Kodak Recomar 33: (EK340); Kodak Anastigmat f4.5 lens; Compur shutter; $3^1/4$" x $4^1/4$" exp on film pack. C 1932-1940.

R3* $50	£26	DM82	FF256

Kodak Medalist I: (EK341); Kodak Ektar 100mm f3.5 lens; Supermatic shutter 1 - 1/400 s, CRF; 8 exp, $2^1/4$" x $3^1/4$" on 620 roll film. C 1941-1946.

R3* $125	£66	DM206	FF639

Kodak Medalist II

Kodak Medalist II: (EK342); Kodak Ektar 100mm f3.5 lens; Flash Supermatic 1 - 1/400 s, CRF; 8 exp, $2^1/4$" x $3^1/4$" on 620 roll film. C 1946-1952.

R3* $200	£105	DM330	FF1k

Kodak Reflex: (EK343); TLR; Kodak Anastigmat 75mm f3.5 lens; Flash Kodamatic shutter; 12 exp, $2^1/4$" x $2^1/4$" on 620 roll film. C 1946.

R2* $30	£16	DM49	FF153

Kodak Tourist: (EK344); Kodak Anaston f4.5 lens; Flash Kodamatic shutter; 8 exp, $2^1/4$" x $3^1/4$" on 620 roll film. C 1948-1951.

R1* $15	£8	DM25	FF77

Kodak Stereo: (EK345); 35mm stereo camera; Kodak Anastigmat 35mm f3.5 lenses; Kodak Flash 200 shutter 1/25-1/200 s. 29 stereo pairs, 23 x 24mm on 35mm film. C 1954-1959.

R2* $110	£58	DM181	FF562

Kodak Chevron: (EK346); Kodak Ektar 78mm f3.5 lens; Synchro-Rapid shutter 1-1/800 s; 12 exp, $2^1/4$" x $2^1/4$" on 620 roll film. C 1953-1956.

R3* $150	£79	DM247	FF767

Kodak Chevron

Cine Kodak (first model): (EK347); 16mm hand-cranked camera; die-cast aluminium body; 25mm f3.5 anastigmat lens. Originally furnished with eye-level finder only. Waist level finder, motor drive, interchangeable lens, single-frame and slow-motion devices added later. First offered as complete outfit only, consisting of camera, projector, tripod and screen at cost of $325. Designated Model A after July 1925. C June 1923.

R4* $250	£131	DM412	FF1.3k

Cine Kodak Model B: (EK350); 16mm spring motor driven movie camera; first introduced in July 1925, with f6.5 20mm fixed focus lens and waist level finder only, priced at $70. Subsequent models offered close-up attachment, f3.5 and f1.9 focusing lens,

Kodak Stereo

Cine Kodak (first model)

and eye-level finders. In November 1928, it was offered in gray and brown, with interchangeable 78mm f4.5 telephoto lens. (add 100% for coloured models) C 1925-1931.

R2* $30	£16	DM49	FF153

Cine Kodak Model BB: (EK351); smaller sized 16mm movie camera; 50 ft film capacity; interchangeable lens; half-speed button (8 frames per s) for satisfactory exp under poor light conditions. With f1.9 lens, was available in brown, black, gray and blue; with f3.5, black only. C April 1929. (add 100% for coloured models).

R2* $30	₲£16	DM49	FF153

Cine Kodak 16 Model K: (EK352); 16mm movie camera; interchangeable lens; half-

speed button; available in black, brown, blue or gray. C 1930. (add 100% for coloured models).

R2* $30	£16	DM49	FF153

Cine Kodak Eight Model 20: (EK353); first 8mm amateur movie camera; Anastigmat 13mm f3.5 lens; parallax correcting vf located in handle; spring motor. 25 ft. spool of 16mm panchromatic film, double perforated. Half the film width was exposed; the spool reversed and the other half then exposed. After processing the film was split lengthwise and spliced giving 50 ft of 8mm width film, with projection time of 4 minutes and 10 seconds. C July 1932.

R2* $15	£8	DM25	FF77

Kodascope Eight Model 20: (EK354); 8mm movie projector for 60 cycle A.C.; first 8mm projector; used 32 candlepower, 6V auto headlight bulb. C July 1932.

R2* $15	£8	DM25	FF77

Cine Kodak Eight Model 60: (EK355); 8mm movie camera; Anastigmat f1.9 lens; interchangeable with f4.5 1½" telephoto lens available at extra cost; vf in handle. One of the handsomest movie cameras designed by Kodak, all exterior parts were bright chromed; interior was machined and polished. C October 1932.

R2* $20	£10	DM33	FF102

Kodascope Eight Model 60: (EK356); 8mm movie projector for 60 cycle A.C. C July 1932.

R2* $15	£8	DM25	FF77

K

Cine Kodak Special I

Cine Kodak Special I: (EK357); 16mm movie camera; came with all desirable refinements; two-lens holder; variable shutter; speeds from 8 to 64 frames per s, or single exp; removable magazine for 100 or 200 ft of film; hand crank and backwind; reflex and eye-level finders; footage meters on camera, film chamber and frame counter. C April 1933.

R3* $275	£144	DM453	FF1.4k

Cine Kodak Eight Model 25: (EK360); 8mm movie camera; anastigmat f2.7 lens; vf in handle; similar to Model 20, except for faster lens. C July 1933.

R1* $10	£5	DM16	FF51

Magazine Cine Kodak: (EK361); 16mm movie camera; Kodak Anastigmat 25mm f1.9 lens; spring wound motor for 8, 16 or 24 frames per s. C 1936.

R1* $15	£8	DM25	FF77

Cine Kodak Model E: (EK362); 16mm movie camera; Kodak Anastigmat 25mm f1.9 lens; spring motor drive, 3 speeds; C 1937 with f3.5 lens; 1940 with f1.9.

R2* $50	£26	DM82	FF256

Cine Kodak Magazine 8: (EK363); 8mm movie camera; Anastigmat focusing 13mm f1.9 lens, interchangeable; 4 speeds; rapid load film cassettes; vf adjustable for 7 different lenses. C 1940.

R1* $15	£8	DM25	FF77

Cine Kodak Royal: (EK364); 16mm movie camera; Kodak Cine Ektar 25mm f1.9 lens; magazine load; spring motor drive; 16, 24 or 64 frames per s. C 1950.

R2* $20	£10	DM33	FF102

KODAK

Brownie Movie Camera: (EK365); 8mm movie; Ektanon 13mm f2.3 lens. C 1951.

| R1* $10 | £5 | DM16 | FF51 |

Brownie Projector: (EK366); 8mm movie projector. C 1952.

| R1* $10 | £5 | DM16 | FF51 |

Brownie Automatic Movie Camera: (EK367); 8mm movie camera; Ektanon 13mm f2.3 lens; photo-electric cell coupled to diaphragm. C 1959.

| R1* $10 | £5 | DM16 | FF51 |

Kodak Cine Scopemeter Camera: (EK370); 8mm movie camera; 3 lens turret for 6.5, 13 and 24mm f1.9 lenses; photo-cell coupled to diaphragm; built-in skylight filter and type A conversion filter. C 1959.

| R2* $15 | £8 | DM25 | FF77 |

Kodak Zoom 8 Automatic Camera: (EK371); 8mm movie camera; zoom 9 to 24mm f1.9 lens; auto exp; telescopic vf with parallax correction. C November 1959.

| R2* $20 | £10 | DM33 | FF102 |

Kodak Escort 8 Movie Camera: (EK372); 8mm movie camera; zoom 10 to 25mm lens by spring movement. C 1964.

| R1* $15 | £8 | DM25 | FF77 |

Kodak Instamatic M4 Movie Camera: (EK373); 8mm movie camera; Kodak Ektanar 13mm f1.8 lens; Super 8 Kodachrome II in special cassettes; CdS cell controls exp; PX13 battery. The M2, M4 and M6 cameras, as well as a series of Instamatic projectors were all introduced with Kodak's announcement of the new Super-8 film. M2: manual diaph-ragm adjustment, 13mm f1.8 lens; M6: automatic zoom 12 to 36mm f1.8 lens. C May 1965.

| R1* $20 | £10 | DM33 | FF102 |

Super 8: (EK374); 8mm movie camera, Instamatic movie camera, taking only Super 8 film (Kodachrome II in special cassettes) which was introduced simultaneously to the market. C May 1965.

| R1* $15 | £8 | DM25 | FF77 |

Kodak Ektasound 140: (EK375); 8mm sound movie camera; zoom Ektar 9 to 21mm f1.2 lens; battery powered; first Super 8

sound camera permitting movies in available light, without movie lights. C 1973.

| R2* |

In 1963, Eastman Kodak brought out the #126 film designation for the second time. This use of a simple to load film cassette did much to increase the sale of Kodak film.

In order to provide the same packaging for their films, other manufacturers had to pay a fee to Kodak. In typical Kodak fashion, just when the competition was tooling up to make 126 cameras, the 110 Pocket Instamatic came on the market, helping to make obsolete 126 size film and cameras. 126 size Instamatics have since become collectible cameras, and offer the beginner as well as the advanced collector a source of inexpensive and interesting cameras.

Instamatic 44: (EK376); 1969-73, Knob wind, uses flash cubes.

| R2* $10 | £5 | DM16 | FF51 |

Instamatic 100: (EK377); 1963-66, Lever wind, uses AG1 flashbulbs, first Instamatic, the most collectable.

| R1* $15 | £8 | DM25 | FF77 |

Instamatic 104: (EK378); 1965-68, Lever wind, uses flash cubes.

| R1* $5 | £3 | DM8 | FF26 |

Instamatic 124: (EK379); 1968-71, Lever wind, uses flash cubes.

| R1* $5 | £3 | DM8 | FF26 |

Instamatic 134: (EK380); 1968-71, Spring motor drive, with light meter, uses Flash cubes.

| R3* $25 | £13 | DM41 | FF128 |

Instamatic 150: (EK381); 1964-66, Spring motor drive, uses AG1 bulbs.

| R2* $20 | £10 | DM33 | FF102 |

Instamatic 154: (EK382); 1965-69, Spring motor drive, uses Flash cubes

| R2* $20 | £10 | DM33 | FF102 |

KODAK

Instamatic 174: (EK383); 1968-71, Spring motor drive, uses Flash cubes.

R2* $20	£10	DM33	FF102

Instamatic 250: (EK384); 1965-67, Lever wind, uses AG1 bulbs, coated f2.8 lens focusing from 2.5' to infinity, shutter speeds 1/30-1/250s, made in Germany.

R2* $35	£18	DM58	FF179

Instamatic 300: (EK385); 1963-66, Lever wind, light meter, uses AG1 bulbs.

R2* $15	£8	DM25	FF77

Instamatic 300: (EK386); 1965-69, Lever wind, light meter, uses AG1 bulbs.

R2* $10	£5	DM16	FF51

Instamatic 304: (EK387); 1965-69, Lever wind, light meter, uses Flash cubes.

R2* $10	£5	DM16	FF51

Instamatic 314: (EK388); 1968-71, Lever wind, light meter, uses Flash cubes.

R2* $10	£5	DM16	FF51

Instamatic 324: (EK389); 1966-68, Lever wind, light meter, uses Flash cubes, made in Germany.

R2* $10	£5	DM16	FF51

Instamatic 400: (EK390); 1963-66, Spring motor drive, light meter, uses AG1 bulbs.

R2* $30	£16	DM49	FF153

Instamatic 404:(EK391); 1965-69, Spring motor drive, light meter, uses Flash cubes.

R2* $30	£16	DM49	FF153

Instamatic 414:(EK392); 1968-71, Spring motor drive, light meter, uses Flash cubes.

R2* $30	£16	DM49	FF153

Instamatic 500: (EK393); 1963-66, Lever wind, PC connection and hot shoe, light meter, f2.8 lens, speeds 1/30-1/500s, made in Germany.

R3* $50	£26	DM82	FF256

Instamatic 700: (EK394); 1963-66, Spring motor drive, uses AG1 bulbs, light meter, f2.8 lens, shutterspeeds 1/60-1/250s.

R3* $50	£26	DM82	FF256

Instamatic 704: (EK395); 1965-69, Spring motor drive, uses Flash cubes, light meter, f2.8 lens, shutterspeeds 1/60-1/250s.

R2* $50	£26	DM82	FF256

Instamatic 714: (EK396); 1968-70, Spring motor drive, uses Flash cubes, light meter, f2.8 lens, shutterspeeds 1/60-1/250s.

R2* $50	£26	DM82	FF256

Instamatic 800: (EK397); 1964-66, Spring motor drive, AG1 bulbs, rangefinder, light meter, f2.8 lens, shutterspeeds 1/60-1/250s.

R2* $75	£39	DM124	FF383

Instamatic 804: (EK398); 1965-70, Spring motor drive, uses Flash cubes, built-in range-finder, light meter, f2.8 lens, shutterspeeds 1/60-1/250s.

R1* $75	£39	DM124	FF383

Instamatic 814: (EK399); 1968-70, Spring motor drive, uses Flash cubes, built-in range-finder, light meter, f2.8 lens, shutterspeeds 1/60-1/250s.

R2* $75	£39	DM124	FF383

Instamatic X-15: (EK400); 1970-76, Lever wind, uses "X" cubes which require no battery to be fired.

R1* $5	£3	DM8	FF26

Instamatic X-15F: (EK401); 1976-1986, Lever wind, uses Flip flash.

R1* $5	£3	DM8	FF26

Instamatic X25: (EK402); 1970-74, Spring motor drive, uses "X" cubes.

R2* $15	£8	DM25	FF77

Instamatic X30: (EK403); 1970-74, Lever wind, light meter, uses "X" cubes.

R2* $15	£8	DM25	FF77

Instamatic X35: (EK404); 1970-76, Lever wind, light meter, uses "X" cubes.

R2* $15	£8	DM25	FF77

Instamatic X35F: (EK405); 1976-86, Lever wind, light meter, uses "Flip flash".

R2* $15	£8	DM25	FF77

Instamatic X45: (EK406); 1970-74, Spring motor drive, light meter, uses "X" cubes.

R2* $15	£8	DM25	FF77

Instamatic X90: (EK407); 1970-73, Spring motor drive, light meter, uses "X" cubes, f2.8 lens, coupled rangefinder, shutterspeeds 1/60-1/250s.

R2* $60	£31	DM99	FF307

Instamatic S-10: (EK408); 1967-70, Knob wind on the end of the camera body, pop out lens, uses Flash cubes.

R2* $5	£3	DM8	FF26

Instamatic S-20: (EK409); 1967-71, Knob wind on the end of the camera body, pop out lens, light meter, uses Flash cubes.

R2* $10	£5	DM16	FF51

Hawkeye II: (EK410); Knob wind, uses flash cubes, grey and black, used as a give-away premium.

R2* $5	£3	DM8	FF26

Hawkeye: (EK411); Lever wind, uses seperate flash gun, Chrome and olive.

R1* $5	£3	DM8	FF26

Instamatic 50: (EK412); Lever wind, made in Rochester for the export market.

R2* $10	£5	DM16	FF51

Hawkeye-F: (EK413); Lever wind, uses Flip flash.

R2* $5	£3	DM8	FF26

Hawkeye-R4: (EK414); Lever wind, uses Flash cubes.

R2* $5	£3	DM8	FF26

Hawkeye-A1: (EK415); Spring motor drive, with light meter, uses Flash cubes.

R2* $40	£21	DM66	FF204

Hawkeye-X: (EK416); Lever wind, uses "X" cubes, much like the Instamatic X15.

R2* $5	£3	DM8	FF26

Note: Individual Kodak camera models were supplied with a variety of lens and shutter combinations during their production spans.

KOLAR,
Prague, Czechoslovakia

Kola: (KQ100); C1936, VFR camera for 4 x 4cm or 3 x 4cm on 127 film or 24 x 36mm on 35mm film, Zeiss Tessar f2.8/60mm lens, Compur Rapid shutter, early cameras have a folding VFR, later versions use a tubular finder. One "home made" gold plated model seen for sale for more than $1000!

R4* $300	£157	DM495	FF1.5k

Kola

KOGAKU SEIKI:
Japan.

Nippon: (KO100); 1942 cfps, 1/20- 1/500 sec, no RFR, vfr only, screw mount K.O.L. Xebec F2.0/5cm lens. This camera was also known as the "Nippon Standard".

R5*	NSR

Nippon: (KO101); 1943 cfps, 1- 1/500 sec, seperate RFR/vfr windows, screw mount Sun Xebec F2.0/5cm lens. A copy of the Leica III, without diopter adjustment, this camera was also known as the "Nippon III".

R5* $2.5k	£1.3k	DM4.1k	FF12.8k

E. B. KOOPMAN, New York.

The Presto Camera: (KB100); C 1899 meniscus lens with rotating stops; single speed shutter; 4 exp, 18 x 18cm on special roll film. Invented by H. Casler.

R4* $800	£420	DM1.3k	FF4.1k

K

KONISHIROKU,
Japan.

Sakura Pocket Camera: (KH100); 1907. Folding plate camera for 8.2cm X 10.8cm glass plates. Rapid Rectiliniar F8 lens T,I,B shutter. Quite rare.

R4* $500	£262	DM824	FF2.6k

Idea: (KH101); 1909 Folding 4 x 5 camera for glass plates or sheet film, front shifts and revolving back. Tessar F6.3/165mm lens, Compur shutter, both imported from Germany. Quite rare.

R4* $450	£236	DM742	FF2.3k

Idea "A": (KH102); 1909-24 Folding 8cm X 10cm camera for glass plates. Many versions were made during its production, early cameras used imported lenses and shutters, either from the USA or Germany. All are quite rare.

R3* $125	£66	DM206	FF639

Idea Hand Camera: (KH103); 1930-35 Folding, 8cm X 10.5cm or 6.5cm X 9cm camera for glass plates. Many versions were made during its production, most cameras used imported lenses and shutters, either from the USA or Germany. Less rare than the Idea "A" camera. An exception is the Idea Hand Camera of 1935, with one of the first Nikkor lenses, which is about 20 times more valuable.

R3* $75	£39	DM124	FF383

The Pearl II: (KH104); 1909 Folding roll film camera, 8cm X 10.5cm on 118 roll film. The first Japanese roll film camera. Models III, and IV could also use glass plates. All are rare.

R3* $125	£66	DM206	FF639

Special Pearl: (KH105); 1913 Folding roll film camera, 8cm X 10.5cm on glass plates, or 8cm X 13.7cm on 101 roll film. Quite rare.

R3* $150	£79	DM247	FF767

Pearl No. 2: (KH106); 1923-31 Folding roll film camera, 6cm X 9cm or 6cm X 4.5cm on 120 roll film. Several versions with various shuttersWooden body This is the first Japanese camera to use 120 roll film.

R3* $75	£39	DM124	FF383

The Lily Camera: (KH107); 1909-38 Folding plate cameras of various sizes, most with German lenses and shutters. Early cameras are quite rare. A tropical Lily was said to have been made in the 1930's, and was the only tropical camera to come from Japan. Either the tropical model, or a camera equipped with an Anytar lens, made by Nippon Kogaku (Nikon), are valued at about 20 times the value of any other Lily camera.

R3* $70	£37	DM115	FF358

Pearlette: (KH108); 1928-40 Folding roll film camera using lazy tong struts, and 127 film. Simple fixed focus lenses or various types. Some cameras had provision for 4cm X 6.5cm and 3cm X 4cm negative sizes on 127 film. Similar in looks to the Vest Pocket Kodak. The earliest camera lacked the unusual close-up lens attached to the wire frame finder. The line was started again after the Second World War, and the Pearl name found its way to quite a number of roll film cameras, both 127 and120.

R3* $75	£39	DM124	FF383

Semi-Pearl: (KH109); Folding rollfilm camera for 16 exposures on 120 film Hexar 7.5cm/f4.5 lens, Durex shutter, 1-1/100s, C. 1938.

R3* $45	£24	DM74	FF230

Pearl I: (KH110); 1949 Folding roll film camera, uncoupled RFR, leaf shutter,1 - 1/500 sec, Hexar F4.5/75mm lens. 6cm X 4.5cm on 120 film. The Pearl RS used a Konirapid shutter.

R2* $65	£34	DM107	FF332

Konica 35: (KH111); 35mm camera with CRF btl shutter, speeds 1-1/500s, Hexar 50mm/f3.5 lens. marked "Made in Occupied Japan".

R3* $95	£50	DM157	FF486

KORSTEN,
Paris, France.

La Litote: (KT100); 45 x 107mm stereo; Aplanatic lenses; 3 speed guillotine shutter. Leather covered box camera. C 1902.

R4* $150	£79	DM247	FF767

Komaflex-S

KOWA CO., LTD.,
Nagoya, Japan.

Komaflex-S: (KW100); 127 roll film SLR camera; Prominar 65mm f2.8 coated lens; Seikosha-SLV shutter 1 -1/500 s, MX synch.

R3* $100	£52	DM165	FF511

Ramera: (KW101); combination portable AM radio and detective camera; Prominar 65mm f2.8 coated lens; 3 speed synch

Konica 35

shutter; 20 exp, 10 x 14mm on 16mm film (Minolta 16 cassettes). C 1959.

R3* $125	£66	DM206	FF639

Kowa 35 N: 1960: Leaf shutter, 1/25 - 1/300 sec, vfr only, fixed Prominar F.C. F3.5/45mm lens. interesting trigger wind mechanism.

R2* $55	£29	DM91	FF281

Kowa SW: 1964: Leaf shutter, 1 - 1/500, vfr only, using a strange system, available in Black or chrome. Fixed wide angle F3.2/28mm lens. Perhaps more valuable as a user camera than a collectors item.

R2* $200	£105	DM330	FF1k

Kowaflex: 1960-64: Leaf shutter, 1 - 1/500 sec, fixed Kowa F2.0/50mm, or F1.9/50mm lens. Inexpensive 35mm Slr, with wide angle and telephoto conversion lenses available. Several models, some with built-in light meters including SE, SER, SET, SETR. Only the Kowa UW 190, sporting a fixed F4/19mm lens seems to be highly prized, bringing about 8 times the price of an ordinary Kowaflex.

R2* $50	£26	DM82	FF256

KOZY CAMERA COMPANY,
Boston, Massachusetts.

Pocket Kozy Camera: (KZ100); meniscus lens; single speed shutter; 9 x 9cm exp on roll film. C 1892.

R4* $200	£105	DM330	FF1k

KRASNOGORSK MECHANICAL WORKS,
Krasnogorsk, USSR.

Zorki-1: (ZR100); 1948-56, Cfps, 1/20 - 1/500 s, no slow speeds, no synch, CRF. Interchangeable Leica-type screw mount, f3.5/50mm Industar-22 lens in collapsible mount, though some rigid mount lenses were made. Lens serial numbers usually indicate year of production as the first two digits. The null series camera with both FED and Zorki markings and FED f3.5/50mm lens is worth $500. Prices are 20% higher in the United States for ordinary Zorki-1 cameras. Australian and Japanese collectors are starting to buy at higher prices too.

R2* $100	£52	DM165	FF511

Zorki-2: (ZR101); 1955, Cfps, 1/20 to 1/500 s, no slow speeds, no synch, CRF. Interchangeable Leica-type screw mount, f3.5/50mm Industar-22 lens in collapsible mount, though some rigid mount lenses were made. Lens serial numbers usually indicate year of production as the first two digits. This camera differs from the Zorki-1 by the addition of a self timer. Though very few Zorki-2 cameras were made, their current price does not reflect their rarity.

R4* $200	£105	DM330	FF1k

Zorki-S (C): (ZR102); 1956-58, Cfps, 1/20 to 1/500 s, no slow speeds, synch, CRF. Interchangeable Leica-type screw mount, f3.5/50mm Industar-22 lens in collapsible mount, or rigid mount f3.5/50mm Industar 50 lens. Camera serial numbers indicate year of production as the first two digits. Though not an exact copy of the Leica II(D); this camera keeps many of the features of the previous Zorki cameras. The rigid mount lens adds 15% to the value of the camera. Models in green and grey were made and add 100% or more to the price.

R2* $80	£42	DM132	FF409

Zorki-2S (C): (ZR103); 1956-58 Cfps, 1/20 to 1/500 s, no slow speeds, synch, CRF. Interchangeable Leica-type screw mount, rigid mount f3.5/50mm Industar-50 lens or F2.0/52mm Jupitor-8. Camera serial numbers indicate year of production as the first two digits. This camera differs from the Zorki-C by the addition of a self timer.

R2* $80	£42	DM132	FF409

Zorki-3: (ZR104); 1954-55 Cfps, 1 to 1/1000 s, slow speeds, no synch, CRF. Interchangeable Leica-type screw mount, rigid mount F2.0/50mm Jupitor-8 lens. Camera serial numbers indicate year of production as the first two digits. Very few Zorki-3 cameras were made, but the collectors market price does not reflect this.

R3* $110	£58	DM181	FF562

Zorki-2

Zorki-3

K

Zorki-3M: (ZR105); 1955 Same as the Zorki-3, slow speeds moved to the top dial.Cfps, 1 to 1/1000 s, slow speeds, no synch, CRF. Interchangeable Leica-type screw mount, rigid mount F2.0 Jupitor-8. Camera serial numbers indicate year of production as the first two digits. More common than the Zorki-3, but almost the same market value.

R2* $90	£47	DM148	FF460

Zorki-3S *(C):* (ZR106); 1956. This camera adds flash synch and a redesigned top cover to the features of the Zorki-3M. Cfps, 1 to 1/1000 s, slow speeds, synch, CRF. Interchangeable Leica-type screw mount, rigid mount F2.0 /50mm Jupitor-8 lens. Camera serial numbers indicate year of production as the first two digits.

R2* $100	£52	DM165	FF511

Zorki-4: (ZR107); 1956-73 Cfps, 1 to 1/1000 s, slow speeds, synch, CRF. Interchangeable Leica-type screw mount, rigid mount f3.5/50mm Industar-50 lens or F2.0/52mm Jupitor-8 lens. Camera serial num-

bers indicate year of production as the first two digits. This camera differs from the Zorki-C by the addition of a self timer. Some cameras were marked celebrating the 50th anniversary of the communist party in Russia. These models more than double the price of the camera.

R2* $60	£31	DM99	FF307

Zorki-4K: (ZR108); 1973-77 Cfps, 1 to 1/1000 s, slow speeds, synch, CRF. Interchangeable Leica-type screw mount, rigid mount F2.0 52mm Jupitor-8. Camera serial numbers indicate year of production as the first two digits. This camera is the same as the Zorki-4, with the addition of a rapid wind lever, and a fixed take-up spool. The Zorki-4K was made in large numbers, and was widely exported. Quite popular in Europe where it is commonly found, this camera fetches about 30% more in the United States.

R2* $60	£31	DM99	FF307

Zorki-5: (ZR109); 1958-59 Cfps, 1 to 1/1000 s, slow speeds, synch, CRF. Interchangeable Leica-type screw mount, rigid mount f3.5/50mm Industar-50 lens or F2.0/

52mm Jupitor-8 lens. Camera serial numbers indicate year of production as the first two digits. Incorporates a longer base rangefinder (67mm) than previous Zorki cameras, uses a combined RFR/vfr window.

R2* $90	£47	DM148	FF460

Below: Russian pre-war lenses

Botton: Russian post-war lenses and the 2cm viefinder

Zorki-6: (ZR110); 1960-66 Cfps, 1 to 1/1000 s, slow speeds, synch, CRF. Interchangeable Leica-type screw mount, rigid mount f3.5/50mm Industar-50 lens or F2.0/52mm Jupitor-8 lens. Camera serial numbers indicate year of production as the first two digits. This camera is the same as the Zorki-5, with the addition of a hinged back and a self timer. Less common in the US than in Europe.

R2* $90	£47	DM148	FF460

Zorki-10: (ZR111); Not a Leica copy, but based on Ricoh cameras of the 1960's. Fixed lens, automatic shutter, CRF.

R3* $50	£26	DM82	FF256

Zorki-11: (ZR113); Fixed lens, automatic shutter, the same as the Zorki-10, but without a coupled rangefinder.

R3* $50	£26	DM82	FF256

Zorki-12: (ZR114); Fixed lens, automatic shutter, 1/2 frame format.

R4* NSR est $275	£144	DM453	FF1.4k

Russian accessory lenses after 1945

20mm, f5.6, MP-2, (ZR001); - **$200** w/o finder (w/finder **$500**)
28mm, f4.5, FED, (ZR002); - **$100**
28mm, f6.0, Orion-15, (ZR003); - **$100**
35mm, f2.8, Jupiter-12, (ZR004); - **$90**
50mm, f3.5, FED Macro (ZR005); -**$100**
85mm, f2.0, Jupiter-9, (ZR006);- **$90**
100mm, f6.3, FED, (ZR007); - **$110**
135mm, f4.0, Jupiter-11, (ZR008); - **$85**

Russian accessory finders

2cm optical finder: (ZR014); **$300**
Universal finder for 28, 35, 50, 80, and 135mm views: (ZR015); **$40**

Russian accessory lenses before 1945

FED F2.0/50mm, (ZR010); - **$130**
FED F3.5/50mm, close focusing, (ZR011); - **$300**
FED F6.3/100mm, (ZR012); - **$100**
FED f4.5/28mm, (ZR013); - **$100**

E. KRAUSS, Paris, France.

Eka: (KR100); Krauss Tessar 50mm f3.5 lens; Compur shutter 1-1/300 s; 100 exp, 30 x 42mm on non-perforated 35mm film. C 1924.

R4* $900	£472	DM1.5k	FF4.6k

Photo Revolver: (KR101); revolver-type detective camera; Krauss Tessar 40mm f4.5 lens; shutter in helical mount 1/25, 1/50 and 1/100 s. 48 exp on 2.2 x 3.6cm plates or roll film holder for 25, 50 or 100 exp, 20 x 30mm. C 1921.

R5* $2.5k+	£1.3k+	DM4.1k+	FF12.8k+

Photo Revolver

Takyr: (KR102); Zeiss Krauss 136mm f6.3 lens; Sigriste fps. 3¹/₄" x 4¹/₄" exp on plates. C 1906.

R4* $400	£210	DM659	FF2k

G. A. KRAUSS, Stuttgart, Germany.

Krauss Peggy I: (GA100); 35mm camera; often found with Zeiss Tessar 50mm f3.5

lens, though many lens options were available; Compur shutter 1-1/300 s. C 1935.

R3* $450	£236	DM742	FF2.3k

Krauss Peggy I:

Krauss Peggy II: (GA101); 35mm RFR camera; often found with Schneider Xenon 45mm f2 lens, though many lens options were available; Compur shutter 1-1/300 s, CRF. C 1935.

R3* $600	£315	DM989	FF3.1k

Dr. Rudolph KRUGENER, Bockheim, Germany.

Delta Camera: (KG100); C1895, folding plate camera; meniscus lens; 3 speed rotary shutter; 9 x 12cm exp on plates.

R4* $175	£92	DM288	FF894

Delta Klapp: (KG101); C1904, Rapid Aplanatic lens; pneumatic shutter 1/15-1/100 s; 3$^{1}/_{4}$" x 4$^{1}/_{4}$" exp on plates. Double ext bellows.

R4* $150	£79	DM247	FF767

Delta Magazine Camera: (KG102); C1892, Aplanat 145mm f13 lens; string cocked guillotine shutter; 12 exp, 9 x 12cm on dry plates.

R4* $700	£367	DM1.2k	FF3.6k

Delta Patronen Flach Kamera: (KG103); C1903, Rapid Rectilinear lens; central shutter 1-1/100 s; 3$^{1}/_{4}$" x 4$^{1}/_{4}$" exp on plates or roll film.

R4* $125	£66	DM206	FF639

Delta Periskop: (KG104); C1903, Periskop 150mm f12 lens; central shutter 1/25-1/100 s; 3$^{1}/_{4}$" x 4$^{1}/_{4}$" exp on plates.

R4* $100	£52	DM165	FF511

Dr. Krugener's Book Camera: (KG105); C 1889, book-type detective camera; Rectilinear 60mm f12 lens; guillotine shutter; 24 exp on 40 x 40mm plate.

R5* $4.5k+	£2.4k+	DM7.4k+	FF23k+

Dr. Krugener's Million Camera: (KG106); C 1903, 9 x 18cm stereo camera; Rapid Periskop lenses; guillotine shutter. 9 x 18cm exp on roll film.

R4* $175	£92	DM288	FF894

Mini Detective: (KG107); C1900, miniature box detective camera. Leather changing bag for 12 plates; polished mahogany wood; size: 4" x 3$^{1}/_{4}$" x 7".

R4* $700	£367	DM1.2k	FF3.6k

Normal Simplex: (KG110); C1900, 9 x 12cm reflex camera; three diaphragm stops on sliding brass bar. Vf fitted to concealed bellows; mahogany finish.

R4* $1.5k	£787	DM2.5k	FF7.7k

Simplex Magazine Camera: (KG111); C1889, TLR detective camera; Achromatized Periscopic 100mm f10 lens; sector self-capping shutter; 24 exp, 6 x 8cm on dry plates.

R4* $1.3k	£682	DM2.1k	FF6.6k

Simplex Magazine Camera

Delta Stereo: (KG112); C1900-1909, folding stereo camera for 9cm x 18cm plates, Aplanat lenses and simple two speed shutter, some models allowed the use of roll film.

R4* $300	£157	DM495	FF1.5k

Vestpocket Kronos: (KG113); C1920, strut folding VFR camera for 4.5cm x 6cm plates, Anticomar f4.2/75mm lens, Compur shutter.

R3* $175	£92	DM288	FF894

Stereo Kronos: (KG116); C1920, strut folding stereo camera for 4.5cm x 10.7cm plates, Anticomar f3.5/75mm lenses, Compur Stereo shutter.

R4* $350	£184	DM577	FF1.8k

Quer Kronos: (KG118); C1920, metal bodied horizontal folding camera for 9cm x 12cm glass plates, Anticomar f6.3/10.5cm lens, Compur shutter.

R3* $60	£31	DM99	FF307

Nestor: (KG114); C1920, horizontal folding VFR camera for 6cm x 6cm frames on roll film, Anticomar f5.4/75mm lens, Compur shutter.

R3* $35	£18	DM58	FF179

Pastoscope: (KG115); C1900, strut folding stereo camera 4.5cm x 10.7cm plates, Simplex f7.7/60mm lenses, simple four speed shutter.

R4* $275	£144	DM453	FF1.4k

KUNICK, WALTER KG,
Frankfurt, Germany.

Lighter Petie: (KU100); cigarette lighter-type detective camera; built along lines of Petie Compact, camera separable; meniscus 24mm f11 lens; single speed shutter; 16 exp, 16 x 16mm on 16mm roll film. C 1957. Red, green, blue, deco or leather and chrome finish.

R3* $300	£157	DM495	FF1.5k

Petie: (KU101); subminiature camera; meniscus 25mm f9 lens; single speed shutter; 16 exp, 14 x 14mm on 16mm. C 1958.

R3* $50	£26	DM82	FF256

Petie Vanity-Case: (KU102); ladies compact-type subminiature detective camera; 35mm f9 lens; single speed shutter. 16 exp, 14 x 14mm on 16mm roll film. Red, green,

blue, deco or leather with chrome/gold finished case contains lipstick, compact and camera. C 1958.

R4* $450	£236	DM742	FF2.3k

KÜRBI & NIGGELOH, BILORA
Radevormwald, Germany.

Radix 56: (KK100); C1950, metal 35mm VFR camera for 24 x 24mm frames on 35mm film, Biloxar f5.6/40mm lens, simple shutter, lever advance.

R2* $25	£13	DM41	FF128

Radix 35B (KK101); C1950, as (KK100) but for Biloxar f3.5 lens.

R2* $25	£13	DM41	FF128

Radix 35S: (KK102); C1950, as (KK100) but for Schneider Radionar f3.5/38mm lens.

R2* $25	£13	DM41	FF128

Radix 35BH: (KK103); C1951, as (KK101) but for improved shutter, 1/2 - 1/200s.

R3* $30	£16	DM49	FF153

Radix 35SH: (KK104); C1951, as (KK102) but for improved shutter, 1/2 - 1/200s.

R3* $30	£16	DM49	FF153

Boy: (KK105); C1950, bakelite box camera for 6 x 4.5 frames on 127 film, simple lens and shutter.

R2* $20	£10	DM33	FF102

Luxus Boy: (KK106); C1954, *red* bakelite box camera for 6 x 4.5cm frames on 127 film, f11 lens, simple shutter.

R2* $45	£24	DM74	FF230

Bilora Stahl-Box: (KK107); C1950, metal box camera for 6 x 9cm frames on roll film, reflex VFRs, simple lens and shutter.

R2* $10	£5	DM16	FF51

Bilora Blitz Box: (KK108); V1950, as (KK107) but with synchro contacts.

R2* $10	£5	DM16	FF51

Bilora Blitz Box D: (KK109); metal box camera for 6 x 9cm frames on roll film, simple lens and shutter, *optical* VFR allowing for better positioning of the flash.

R2* $10	£5	DM16	FF51

KÜRBI

Bilora Standard Box: (KK110); C1950, metal box camera for 6 x 9cm frames on roll film, f11 lens and simple shutter.

R2* $10	£5	DM16	FF51

Bilora Special Box: (KK111); C1950, as (KK110) but with built-in close-up lens.

R2* $10	£5	DM16	FF51

Bilora Mikro Box: (KK112); C1953, special purpose metal box camera, *no VFR*. (one offered for $75 in April, 1991).

R3* NSR est $50	£26	DM82	FF256

Bilora Bonita 66: (KK113); C1953, TLR type box camera for 6 x 6cm frames on roll film, simple lens and shutter.

R2* $20	£10	DM33	FF102

Bilora Bella: (KK114); C1950, metal VFR camera for 6 x 4.5cm frames on 127 film, all black with chrome trim, simple f9 lens and shutter.

R3* $15	£8	DM25	FF77

Bilora Bella

Bilora Bella 55: (KK115) C1955, as (KK114) but with chrome top plate and simple *f8 lens*.

R3* $15	£8	DM25	FF77

Bilora Bella D: (KK116); C1957, as (KK115) but now in "Swiss-Air Blue" and "Fashion-Grey".

R2* $20	£10	DM33	FF102

Bilora Bella 44: (KK117); metal VFR camera for 4 x 4cm frames on 127 film, simple f8 lens and shutter.

R2* $10	£5	DM16	FF51

Bilora Bella 44

Bilora DC 4: (KK118); as (KK117) but with Trinar f5.6/55mm lens in vario shutter, or Trinar f3.5/55mm lens in Prontor shutter.

R2* $10	£5	DM16	FF51

Bilora Bella 46: (KK119); C1957, metal VFR camera for 4 x 6cm frames on 120 roll film, simple lens and shutter, available in "Swiss-Air Blue" and "Fashion-Grey".

R2* $20	£10	DM33	FF102

Bilora Bella 66: (KK120); C1957, metal VFR camera for 6 x 6cm frames on 120 roll film, simple lens and shutter, available in "Swiss-Air Blue" and "Fashion-Grey".

R2* $20	£10	DM33	FF102

LAMPERTI & GARBAGNATI, Italy.

Lamperti: (LG100); 9 x 18cm stereo detective camera; 13cm lens; 3 speed guillotine shutter. Leather covered wooden body; rack focusing; 9 x 18cm exp on plates. C 1890.

R4* $450	£236	DM742	FF2.3k

LANCART, Paris, France.

XYZ: (LA100); subminiature camera; nickel plated finish. C 1935.

R4* $800	£420	DM1.3k	FF4.1k

J. LANCASTER & SON, Birmingham, England.

Camrex Deluxe: (LN100); 3¹/₄" x 4¹/₄" folding hand camera; RR lens; pneumatic shutter. Red leather bellows. Mahogany finish with brass fittings. C 1900.

R3* $200	£105	DM330	FF1k

Gem Apparatus: (LN101); 12 lens tin-type camera; 12 Petzval-type 2" f4.5 lenses. Shutter: horizontally sliding panel on front of camera is operated manually. 12 exp, 1¹/₁₆" x ¹³/₁₆" on ¹/₄" x 4¹/₄" ferrotype plates. C 1880.

R5* $4k+	£2.1k+	DM6.6k+	FF20.4k+

The 1888 Patent Instantograph: (LN102); 4" x 5" view camera; Lancaster & Son brass lens with adjustable diaphragm. Reversible back; red Russian leather bellows. Lancaster & Son made several models of this camera. C 1888.

R4* $350	£184	DM577	FF1.8k

Gem Apparatus

Ladies' Camera: (LN103); pocketbook-type detective camera; achromatic lens, iris diaphragm; Lancaster See-Saw single speed shutter. Quarter, half or whole plate pictures. C 1897.

R5* $2k+	£1.1k+	DM3.3k+	FF10.2k+

Lancaster's Patent Watch Camera: (LN104); collapsible watch-type detective camera; Grubb-type achromatic 45mm f22 lens; variable speed rotary shutter. Single exp, 1" x ¹/₂" on dry plates. C 1886. NSR.

R5* $15k+	£7.9k+	DM24.7k+	FF76.7k+

Lancaster's Patent Watch Camera

LANCASTER-LECOULTRE

Le Merveilleux: (LN105); 3¼" x 4¼" view camera; Aplanatic lens. 3¼" x 4¼" exp on plates. C 1888.

R4* $200	£105	DM330	FF1k

Omnigraph Detective Camera: (LN106); box-type detective camera. C 1892.

R4* $150	£79	DM247	FF767

The Rover Detective Camera: (LN107); 3¼" x 4¼" box-type detective camera; magazine load; mahogany finish. C 1892.

R4* $500	£262	DM824	FF2.6k

E. Ludwig LAUSA, Dresden, Germany

Karma Flex: (LU 100): Vidar 60mm f4.5 lens; guillotine shutter 1/25-1/100 s. 4 x 4 exp on roll film.

R3* $300	£157	DM495	FF1.5k

Leader: (BB193); 35mm stereo camera; Leader Anastigmat 45mm f4.5 lenses; shutter TMBK 1/25-1/100 s. Mfd in Japan. C 1950.

R3* $75	£39	DM124	FF383

R. LECHNER, Vienna, Austria.

Juwel: (RL100); folding stereo camera; achromat lens; shutter, T and I. Central finder; side-flaps covered retracted lens panel; leather covered metal body; 45 x 107mm exp on plates. C 1909.

R4* $350	£184	DM577	FF1.8k

Lechner's Schutzen-Camera (Marksman's Camera): (RL101); rifle-type detective camera; 30 exp, 3cm diameter on roll film. A camera that attached beneath the barrel of any gun. C 1892.

R5*	NSR

Nanna IA: (RL102); folding bellows stereo camera; Nanna Aplanat 80mm f8 lens with sliding stops; guillotine shutter. Central frame finder; 6 x 13cm exp on plates. Size: 2.5 x 19 x 10.5cm. C 1909.

R4* $375	£197	DM618	FF1.9k

LECOULTRE & CIE, LE SENTIER, Switzerland.

Compass: (LC100); 24 x 36mm miniature RFR camera; Kern CCL 3B Anastigmat 35mm f3.5 lens with variable stops to f16; rotary sector shutter - 22 speeds from 4½" to 1/500 s. Pivoting mirror for right-angle viewing, CRF. Machined Duralumin body, stereoscopic head, panoramic head, built-in yellow, orange and green filters, ground glass back with focusing magnifier, collapsible lens shade, spirit level on top of camera, built-in extinction meter visible through VFR window, hinged lens cap with depth of field scale, collapsible lens mount. Single exp on 24 x 6mm dry plates (sold ready loaded in small heavy paper "Compass envelopes" complete with dark slide). A wide range of accessories was available for the Compass: a roll film back held six exp on special 1½" film, a pocket tripod the size of a fountain pen, and an enlarger-projector that fit into a 4" x 4" x 16" box and could be powered by a 12 volt car battery. Mfg. by

Compass

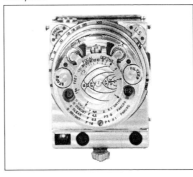

LE DOCTE-LEIDOLF

LeCoultre & Cie, Le Sentier, Switzerland for Compass Cameras, Ltd, London, England. C 1938.

R3* $900	£472	DM1.5k	FF4.6k

Armand Le DOCTE, Brussels.

Photo Detective: (LD100); Rectilinear 18cm f8 lens; flap shutter. Reflex viewer for either vertical or horizontal format. Changing mechanism for 18 plates, 8.3 x 10.8 cm. C 1889.

R5* $1.1k	£577	DM1.8k	FF5.6k

Plastron: (LD101); concealed vest-type detective camera; rectilinear 45mm lens. Size: 2cm from front to rear; 14.9cm diameter. Similar to Gray, Stirn and Photo Eclair. C 1886.

R5*		NSR	

A. LEHMANN, Berlin, Germany.

Ben Akiba: (LH100); cane-type detective camera; front meniscus 35mm f9 lens; oscillating sector, self-cocking shutter. 20 exp, 16 x 20mm on special daylight loading roll film. Handle contained extra rolls of film. Invented by Emil Kronke. C 1903.

R5* $8k	£4.2k	DM13.2k	FF40.9k

Ben Akiba

LEIDOLF Kamerawerkes, Wetzlar, Germany.

Leidox: (LY100); C1950, metal VFR camera for 4 x 4cm frames on 127 roll film, Triplon f3.8/50mm lens, Vario shutter.

R3* $20	£10	DM33	FF102

Leidox IIS: (LY101); C1952, metal VFR camera for 4 x 4cm frames on 127 film, Triplon f2.8/50mm lens, Prontor-S shutter.

R3* $20	£10	DM33	FF102

Lordox: (LY102); C1952, 35mm VFR camera, Lordon f2.8/50mm lens, Prontor-SV shutter, body release, knob wind.

R3* $35	£18	DM58	FF179

Lordomat: (LY103); C1955, 35mm RFR camera, interchangeable Lordon f1.9 or Lordonar f2.8/50mm lens, Prontor-SV or SVS shutter, double stroke lever advance operating from front to back, CRF, marked "Lordomat" on top.

R2* $60	£31	DM99	FF307

Lordomat C35: (LY104); C1956, 35mm RFR camera with built-in light meter, Lordon f1.9 or Lordonar f2.8/50mm lens, Prontor-SVS shutter, CRF, VFR with fields of view for 35mm, 90mm, and 135mm.

R3* $90	£47	DM148	FF460

Lordomat SE: (LY105); C1960, 35mm RFR camera, Lordon f1.9 or Lordonar f2.8/50mm lens, Prontor SVS shutter, new body and RFR style, CRF, less solidly built than (LY103), but still using the same interchangeable lens mounting system, marked Lordomat on the front.

R3* $50	£26	DM82	FF256

Lordox II: (LY106); C1955, 35mm VFR camera, fixed Triplon f2.8/50mm lens, Prontor-SV shutter, same body style and double stroke lever advance as (LY103).

R3* $35	£18	DM58	FF179

Lordox Junior: (LY107); C1960, 35mm VFR camera, fixed Triplon f2.8/50mm lens, Prontor-SVS shutter, same body style as (LY105).

R2* $15	£8	DM25	FF77

Lordox Junior B: (LY108); C1950, 35mm VFR camera as (LY107), but for built-in light meter.

R2* $15	£8	DM25	FF77

Lordox Blitz: (LY109); C1960, 35mm VFR camera as (LY107), but for built-in AG1

LEIDOLF-LEITZ

flash lamp holder.

R2* $15	£8	DM25	FF77

Lordomatic: (LY110); C1960, 35mm VFR camera, fixed Lordonar f2.8/50mm lens, Prontor-SLK shutter, coupled light meter.

R2* $20	£10	DM33	FF102

Accessory lenses for Lordomat cameras

Lordonar f3.5/35mm lens: (LY001); **$30**
Travenar f3.5/35mm lens: (LY002); **$30**
Telordon f5.6/90mm lens: (LY003); **$40**
Travenar f4/90mm lens: (LY004); **$40**
Travenar f4/135mm lens: (LY005); **$50**

Ernst LEITZ G.M.B.H., Wetzlar, Germany.

N.B. Leica prices are for items in original condition, one grade higher than other makes.

UR Leica

UR Leica Replica: (EL101); non-operational display replica.

R4* $1.5k	£800	DM1.6k	FF7.5

O-Series Leica: (EL102); Leitz Anastigmat 1:3.5 F-50mm lens; non-self- capping CFPS 1/20-1/500 s. C 1923.

R5* $125k	£15k?	DM70k?	FF140k?

O-Series Leica

Leica I (A) Anastigmat: (EL103); Leitz Anastigmat 1:3.5 F=50mm lens; CFPS 1/25-1/500 s. Snr 126-300. Qty 175. C 1925. The original Anastigmat design used five elements. A four element lens would indicate a later Leitz conversion or a counterfeit camera. When considering buying such a camera, it is suggested that a complete examination of the camera and lens be undertaken by an expert with the specialized tools and knowledge to determine the camera's authenticity. Any attempt by an inexperienced person to take apart Leitz Anastigmat lens to find out the number of elements used could drastically lower the cameras worth!

R5* $25k	£10k	DM35k	FF95k

Leica I (A)

Leica I (A) Elmax: (EL104); Leitz Elmax 1:3.5 F=50mm lens; CFPS 1/20-1/500 s. Snr 300-1,300. Qty 1000. C 1925-1926. The original Elmax design used five elements. A four element lens would indicate either a later Leitz conversion or a counterfeit camera.

R5* $8.5k	£5k	DM14k	FF48k

Leica I (A) Elmar: (EL105); Leitz Elmar 1:3.5 F=50mm lens; CFPS 1/20-1/500 s. Snr 1,300-71,250. Qty 53,000(?). C 1926-1930.
Four digit serial numbered Leica I (A):

R5* $1.5k	£600	DM2k	5.8K

Five digit serial numbered Leica I (A):

R5* $750	£400	DM1.3k	FF4k

Close focus (18") model Leica I (A):

R5* $750	£600	DM2k	FF5.8k

Leica I (A) Luxus: (EL106); Leitz Elmar 1:3.5 F=50mm lens; CFPS 1/20 - 1/500 s. Snr 28,692-48,441. Qty 95. Gold plated Leica I (A) with red, blue, green or brown

Leica I (A) Luxus

lizard skin. C 1928-1931.

R5* $25k?	£10k?	DM36K	FF900k?

Leica I (A) Luxus Replica: (EL107); collectors and others have remanufactured replica Luxus cameras from Leica I (A) cameras.

R4* $1.8k	£1k	DM4k	FF9.5

Leica Mifilmca: (EL108); C 1927, for use on microscope with fixed focus MIKAS attachment - using microscope optics. (one sold at auction in April, 1991 for more than $7000).

R4* $4k	£2.5	DM9.5	FF24

Leica I (A) Hektor: (EL109); Hektor 1:2.5 F=50mm lens; CFPS 1/20-1/500 s. Snr 38,662-71,230. Qty 1330. C 1930. Counterfeit Hektor cameras have been offered on the market for $4000. To verify a Hektor camera: check the serial number against the factory list; inspect the rear lens bezel for alterations.

R4* $5k	£2.5k	DM5k	FF25k

Leica I (B) Compur, Dial-set: (EL110); Leitz Elmar 1:3.5 F=50mm lens; Compur shutter

Leica I (B) Compur, Dial-set

1-1/300 s. Snr 5,700-13,200(?). Qty 638. C 1926-1929.

R4* $8.5k	£5k	DM14k	FF45k

Leica I (B) Compur, Rim-set: (EK111); Leitz Elmar 1:3.5 F=50mm lens; Compur shutter 1-1/300 s. Snr 13150-50710. Qty 969. C 1929-1930.

R4* $7.5k	£4k	DM11k	FF38k

Leica I (B) Compur, Rim-set

Leica I (C) with non-standardized lens mount: (EL112); Leitz Elmar 1:3.5 F=50mm lens; CFPS 1/20-1/500

s. Snr 37,280. C 1930-1931. When the swing-in vf mask is intact and matched 135mm and 35mm lenses are included, add $1000-$1500. First Leica with interchangeable lens mount (shown above). It is difficult to find this model in historically accurate condition (the lens flange must not have a 0 engraved at the 12 o'clock position. The rear lens bezel must be marked with the last three digits of the body serial no.) because in most cases they were standardized by E. Leitz when returned for service. **With Hektor add 20%.**

R3* $2k	£600	DM1.8k	FF5.8k

Leica I (C) with standardized lens mount: (EL113); Leitz Elmar 1:3.5 F=50mm lens;

Leica I (C)

CFPS 1/20-1/50 s. Snr 55404-99755. Qty 7231. First Leica to permit interchangeability of standardized lenses with any standardized camera body. The lens flange has a 0 engraved at the 12 o'clock position. C 1931.

R3* $600	£250	DM1k	FF2.4k

Leica I (C) with standardized lens mount

Leica II (D): (EL114); Leitz Elmar 1:3.5 F=50mm lens; CFPS 1/20-1/500 s. Snr 71,200-358,650. Qty 52509. C 1932-1948.

R3* Chrome:$300	£130	DM550	FF1.3k
Black: $450	£140	DM500	FF1.4k

Leica E (Standard): (EL115); Leitz Elmar 1:3.5 F=50mm lens; CFPS 1/20-1/500 s. Snr 101,101-355,670. Qty 27,255. C 1932-1946.

R3* 350$	250£	DM700	FF2.4k

Postwar 1946 model with Wollensak Velostigmat 50mm f3.5 lens. Snr 355,001-355,650. Qty 650.

R4* $2.5k	£850	DM2.5k	FF8k

Leica E (Standard)

Leica III (F): (EL116); Leitz Elmar 1:3.5 F=50mm lens; CFPS 1-1/500 s. Snr 107,601-343,100. Qty 69,300. C 1933-1939.

R3* Chrome: $200	£90	DM380	FF850
Black: $450	£200	DM600	FF2k

Leica 250 (FF) Reporter: (EL117); Leitz Summar 1:2 F=5cm lens; CFPS 1-1/500 s.

Leica III (F)

Leica 250 (FF) Reporter

Intro 1933. Snr 114,051-150,124. Qty 126(?).

R4* $8.5k	£6k	DM12k	FF57k

Leica 250 (GG) Reporter: (EK118); Leitz Summar 1:2 F=5cm lens; CFPS 1-1/1000 s. Snr 150,125-353,800. Qty 824(?). Disc 1942. (a reconditioned one sold at auction in April, 1991 for more than $7000!)

R4* $7.5k	£3.5k	DM11k	FF33k

Leica IIIa (G): (EL119); Leitz Elmar 1:3.5 F=50mm lens; CFPS 1-1/1000 s. Snr 156,201-357,200. Qty 92,687(?). C 1935-1950. Black body appears on factory list, but no genuine example has been verified.

R2* Chrome: $175	£75	DM380	FF700

Leica IIIb (G) - 1938: (EL120); Leitz Summitar 1:2 F=5cm lens; CFPS 1-1/1000 s. Snr 240,001-368,563. Qty 32, 105. C 1935-1950.

R2* $375	£170	DM700	FF1.6k

Leica IIIc (1939-1945): (EL121); Leitz Summitar 1:2.0/5cm, CFPS, 1 - 1/100 s, Snr 360,175-367,600, Qty, 33,750. After 1945, Snr 4,000,01-525,000; Qty 100,876.
Civilian cameras:
In chrome below Nr.400,000:

	$350	£350	DM450	FF3.3k

Above Nr. 400,000:

$150	£100	DM350	FF900

In blue-grey, with blue/grey body covering:

$2k	£600	DM2.5k	FF5.8k

With "K" after the body SNR, standing for Kugellager, meaning ballbearing. This special shutter was designed to operate in extremes of climatic conditions. In chrome, Qty 400:

$1.8k	£450	DM1.8k	FF4.3k

in blue/grey:

$2k	£550	DM2.5k	FF5.3k

Military cameras:
With "Luftwaffen Eigentum" and "FL No.38079", blue-grey body only:

$2.5k	£850	DM3k	FF8k

(one went for more than $3000 at auction in April of 1991!) complete with Summitar 1:2.0/5cm lens, also engraved "Luftwaffen Eigentum" and "FL No.38079" and "K" for Kugellager, in chrome and blue/grey:

$2.8k	£900	DM3.5k	FF9k

Marked "HEER" (meaning "Army") with f3.5/5cm Elmar also marked "HEER":

$2.5k	£1.2k	DM4.5k	FF23k

(at auction these cameras can bring higher prices. It seems they get some collectors' blood boiling and the bidding goes sky high! One auction in Fall of 1990 saw almost $4000 for this camera and lens combination, and again in April of 1991 the same price!)

Leica IIId

Leica IIId: (EL122); Leitz Summitar F=5cm lens; CFPS 1-1/1000 s. Snr 360,002-360,134; 367,000-367,325. Qty 427. C 1940-1942. Similar to the Leica IIIc (1940-1946) with self-timer. An internal inspection is necessary, however, to confirm a genuine Leica IIId camera.

R4* $7.5k	£2.3k?	DM10k	FF20k

Leica IIc: (EL124); Leitz Elmar F=5cm 1:3.5 lens; CFPS 1/30-1/500 s. Snr 440,000-451,000. Qty 11,000. C 1948-1951.

R3* $300	£110	DM700	FF1k

Leica Ic: (EL125); Leitz Elmar F=5cm 1:3.5 lens; CFPS 1/30-1/500 s. Snr 455,001-563,100. Qty 12,000. C 1949-1952.

R3* $450	£145	DM800	FF1.4k

Leica IIIa- Monte en Sarre: (EL126); mfd in France on a Leica IIIa body. Late models had IIIf flash synch. Snr 359,xxx. C 1950.

R4* $4k	£1.3k	DM5k	FF11.5k

Leica IIIf

Leica IIIf. (EL127); Leitz Elmar F=5cm 1:3.5 lens; CFPS 1-1/1000 s. Black dial version: Snr 525,001-611,000. Qty 71,000. C 1950-1952.

R3* $225	£150	DM500	FF1.4k

Red dial version: Snr 615,000-685,000. Qty 54,000. C 1952-1954.

R3* $275	£165	DM600	FF1.6k

IIIf Canada version.

R3* $2.5k	£1k	DM3k	FF9k

IIIf black version with black Elmar 50mm f3.5 lens.

R3* $7.5k	£1.5k?	DM9k	FF14k

Leica IIf: (EL128); Leitz Elmar F=5cm 1:3.5 lens; Black dial version: CFPS 1/30-1/500 s. Snr 451,000-574,000. Qty 8400(?). C 1951-1952.

R4* $250	£250	DM700	FF2.4k

Red dial version: CFPS 1/25-1/1000 s. Snr 574,000-851,000. Qty 15,240. C 1952-1957.

R4* $275	£150	DM600	FF1.6k

Leica If: (EL129); Leitz Elmar F=5cm 1:3.5 lens; Black dial version: CFPS 1/30-1/500 s. Snr 562,293-564,200. C 1952.

R4* $1.2k	£650	DM1.7k	FF6k

Red dial version: CFPS 1/25-1/500 s. Snr 564,201-851,000. C 1956.

R4* $525	£250	DM850	FF2.5k

Leica 72: (EL130); Leitz Elmar F=5cm 1:3.5 lens; CFPS 1-1/1000 s. Snr 357,301-357,500. Midland, Ontario version: qty 149.

R5* $12k	£3.5k	DM19k	FF33k

Wetzlar, Germany version: Qty 33.

R5* $15k	£4.4k	DM24k	FF41k

The Leica 72 was the only single-frame 35mm camera marketed by Ernst Leitz. C 1954.

Leica 72

Leica IIIg: (EL131); Leitz Elmar F=5cm 1:2.8 lens; CFPS 1-1/1000 s. Snr 825,001-988,280. Qty, chrome version 41,589 . C 1957-1960.

R3* $850	£500	DM1.4k	FF4.5k

Leica IIIg with Elmar lens

Leica IIIg Swedish military version: black body with chrome Elmar 50mm f2.9 lens- both marked with Swedish three crown emblem. Qty 125.

R5* $8.5k	£2.5k	DM10k	FF24k

Leica Ig: (EL133); Leitz Elmar F=5cm 1:2.8 lens; CFPS 1-1/1000 s. Qty 5,986. Snr 887,001-987,600. C 1958-1960.

R4* $850	£600	DM1.8k	FF5.8k

Leica M3: (EL134); Leitz Summicron F=5cm 1:2 lens; CFPS 1-1/1000 s. Null series Snr 00xx, **$5,350** Snr 700,000-1,164,865. First 500:

$925	£700	DM1k	FF6.7k

Double stroke:

$450	£280	DM700	FF2.6k

Serial numbers over 1,000,000:

$750	£350	DM900	FF3.3k

Black:

$2.5k	£800	DM2.5k	FF7.6k

Olive supplied to German army. C1954-1966.

$3.5k	£2.3k	DM8k	FF21k

Leica MP: (EL135); Leica Summicron F=5cm 1:2 lens; CFPS 1-1/1000 s. With Leicavit black enamel version: Snr 12-150. Qty 139:

R4* $10k	£4.5k	DM13k	FF42k

Chrome version: Snr 1-11, and 151-450, qty 310, C 1956-1957.

R4* $8.5k	£4k	DM14k	FF38k

Leica MP

Leica MP Counterfeit: (EL136); Leitz Summicron F=5cm 1:2 lens; CFPS 1-1/1000 s. 5 counterfeit MP cameras were sold in the USA for $500-$1000 each (1972);

Leica MP Counterfeit

one was resold for $2000 in Japan (it was later returned).

R4* $1.5k	£787	DM2.5k	FF7.7k

Leica M2: (EL137); Leitz Summicron F=5cm 1:2 lens; CFPS 1-1/1000 s. Snr 926,001-970,261. C 1957-1967. Button rewind release (early version). Chrome, qty 24,800.

R3* $650	£250	DM1.4k	FF2.4k

Lever rewind release (late version) with self-timer. Snr 970,261-1,165,000. Chrome, qty 59,000(?).

R3* $700	£350	DM1.1k	FF3.3k

Black enamel, qty 1350(?).

R3* $2.5k	£1k	DM2.9k	FF900

Cut-away display model, qty ?**$1000.**

Leica M2 cut-away display model

Leica M2-M: (EL138); CFPS 1-1/1000 s. Snr 1,163,771-1,164,046. Qty 275. C 1956. Complete with motor:

R4* $3.5k	£3.5k	DM8.5k	FF32k

Leica M1: (EL139); Leitz Elmar 1:2.8 50mm lens; CFPS 1-1/1000 s. Button rewind release (early version), Snr 950,001-966,729. Chrome, qty 1515(?):

Leica M1

R3* $750	£450	DM1.4k	FF4.3k

Lever rewind release (late version), Snr 966,730-1,102,900. Chrome, qty 7925(?):

R3* $750	£450	DM1.4k	FF4.3k

Olive enamel, qty 325. C 1959-1964.

R3* $3k	£1.8k	DM10k	FF16.5k

Leica MD: (EL140); CFPS 1-1/1000 s. Snr 1,102,501-1,160,820. Qty 3200 plus. C 1964-1966.

R3* $750	£500	DM1.4k	FF4.5k

Leica M4 (1967): (EL141); Leitz Summicron 1:2 50mm lens; CFPS 1-1/1000 s. Snr 1,175,001-1,286,700. Qty chrome 47,260 plus.

R3* $950	£550	DM1.6k	FF5.2k

Black enamel 4,590 plus.

R3* $2.3k	£820	DM3.8k	FF7.8k

Military olive, qty 30 plus. C 1967-1972.

R3* $4k	£2.3k	DM12k	FF20k

Leica M4-M (motordrive): (EL142); Snr 1,206,xxx-(?). Complete with motor:

R4* $4.5k	£3.3k	DM7.5k	FF30.5k

Leica M4

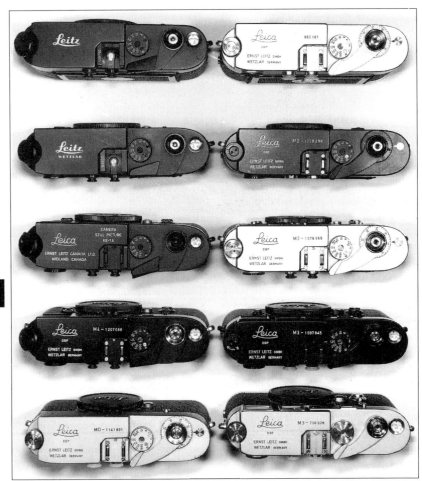

Ten different Leica 'M' cameras viewed from above. Left, top to bottom: MD-2, M4-2 (red dot), KE-7, M4 enamel, MD. Right, top to bottom: M1, M2, M2 chrome, M3, M3 chrome.

Leica M4 (1974): (EL143); Leitz Summicron 1:2 50mm lens; CFPS 1-1/1000 s. Snr 1,380,000-(?). Qty black chrome, 5000 plus. C 1974-1975.

R3* $1.8k	£650	DM3k	FF6k

Fiftieth Anniversary Leica M4, Wetzlar, Germany. C 1975. Qty black chrome 1400.

R3* $2.5k	£1.2k	DM4k	FF11.5k

Fiftieth Anniversary Leica M4, Midland, Canada. C 1975. Qty black chrome, 350.

R3* $3k	£1.8k	DM4.2k	FF15k

Leica M4-2: (EL144); Leitz Summicron 1:2 50mm lens; CFPS 1-1/1000 s. "Red-dot" version: **$2250**. Midland, Canada version and Wetzlar, Germany version. C 1978.

R3* $800	£365	DM1.4k	FF3.5k

Leica MDa: (EL145); CFPS 1-1/1000 s. Snr 1,159,001-(?). C 1966-1975.

R3* $850	£450	DM1.4k	FF4.3k

Leica M4-2

Leica MD-2: (EL146); Carl Zeiss Hologon 15mm f8 coated lens; CFPS 1-1/1000 s. C 1980. Body:

| R4* $850 | £500 | DM1.5k | FF4.3k |

Hologon lens, finder, and filter:

| R4* $2.6k |

Leica M2-R: (EL147); Leitz Dual-Range Summicron 1:2 50mm lens; CFPS 1-1/1000 s. Snr 1,248,201-1,250,200. Qty 2000. C 1969-1970.

| R3* $1.2k | £600 | DM2.8k | FF5.5k |

Leica M5: (EL148); Leitz Summicron 1:2 50mm lens; CFPS 1/2-1/1000 s. Snr 1,287,001-(?). C 1971-1975.

| R3* $900 | £700 | DM1.8k | FF6.5k |

Fiftieth Anniversary Leica M5: C 1975. Qty 1750. Black chrome version:

| R3* $2.5k | £1.5k | DM4k | FF14k |

Chrome version:

| R3* $3.5k | £1.4k | DM4.4k | FF1.6k |

Leica KE-7A, U.S. Army, Camera-Still Picture: (EL149); Leitz Elcan f2 50mm lens; CFPS 1-1/1000 s. Snr 1,294,xxx-(?). Qty released for the civilian market, 50(?) bodies; 70(?) Elcan lenses. C 1972. Civil-

ian version, with lens:

| R4* $7.5k | £2.3k | DM9k | FF21.5k |

military version, with lens:

| R4* $7.5k | £2.8k | DM9.5k | FF26k |

The U.S. Army published a Technical Manual to accompany the KE-7A. In addition to information relative to the repair, maintenance, and operation of the KE-7A, a section is provided called: DEMOLITION TO PREVENT ENEMY USE: Methods of Destruction: Use any of the following methods: (1) Smash the controls, optics, lens flange and back of camera. Smash the optics and focusing mount of the lens. Use sledges, axes, handaxes, pickaxes, hammers or crowbars; (2) Cut the cable release. Cut the leather carrying cases. Use axes, handaxes, machetes or knife; (3) Burn the carrying case. Burn the technical manuals. Use gasoline, kerosene, oil, flame throwers, or incendiary grenades; (4) Explode. If explosives are necessary, use firearms, grenades, or TNT; (5) Dispose. Bury or scatter the destroyed parts in slit trenches, fox holes, or throw them into stream. WARNING: Be extremely careful with the use of explosives and incendiary devices. Use these items only when the need is urgent.

Leica CL: (EL150); Leitz Summicron 1:2 40mm lens; CFPS 1/2-1/1000 s. Snr 1,300,001-(?). C 1973-1975.

| R3* $450 | £300 | DM850 | FF2.8k |

Leica KE-7A

Leica CL

Fiftieth Anniversary Leica CL: qty black chrome, 1750. C 1975.

| R3* $1.5k | £500 | DM1.3k | FF4.8k |

Leicaflex Standard: (EL151); Leitz Summicron 1:2 50mm lens, interchangeable bayonet mount; CFPS 1-1/2000 s. Snr 1,173,001-1,174,700.
C 1964-1968. First SLR by Leitz. Chrome version:

| R3* $300 | £180 | DM680 | FF1.7k |

black enamel version:

| R3* $1.3k | £900? | DM2k | FF7k |

Leicaflex SL: (EL152); Leitz Summilux 1:1.4 50mm lens; CFPS 1-1/12000 s. Snr 1,173,001-(?). C 1968-1974. Chrome:

| R3* $400 | £240 | DM800 | FF2.3k |

Black:

| R3* $600 | £400 | DM1.3k | FF3.8k |

Leicaflex SL2: (EL153); Leitz Summicron 1:2 50mm lens; CFPS 1-1/2000 s. Black:

| R3* $1k | £650 | DM2.2k | FF6k |

Chrome:

| R3* $1.2k | £700 | DM2.4k | FF6.7k |

Fiftieth Anniversary Leicaflex SL2. Qty black chrome, 1750. C 1975. $1300.

Leica R3 Electronic: (EL154); mfps 4-1/1000 s. C 1977. Body:

| R3* $350 | £250 | DM700 | FF2.4k |

Leicaflex SL

Leica R3 Electronic

HOVE FOTO BOOKS

For the benefit of Leica collectors and users, Hove publishes a comprehensive selection of books on the Leica.
See next page for full list.

HOVE FOTO BOOKS

HOVE BOOKS FOR LEICA COLLECTORS

Leica Collector's Guide and Compendium
by Dennis Laney
ISBN 0 - 906447 - 99 - 2
NEW – for publication Autumn 1992

Leica – The First 60 Years
by Gianni Rogliatti
ISBN 0 - 906447 - 32 - 1

Leica and Leicaflex Lenses
by Gianni Rogliatti
ISBN 0 - 906447 - 07 - 0

My Life with the Leica
by Walther Benser
ISBN 0 - 906447 - 58 - 5

The following pocket-sized books form a useful set:

Leica Pocket Book, 5th Edition
ISBN 0 - 906447 - 88 - 7

Leica Accessory Guide
ISBN 0 - 906447 - 28 - 3

Leica International Price Guide, 5th Edition
ISBN 0 - 906447 - 89 - 5

Leica catalogue reprints:

Leica General Catalogue for 1931
ISBN 0 - 906447 - 13 - 5

Leica General Catalogue for 1933
ISBN 0 - 906447 - 14 - 3

Leica General Catalogue for 1936
ISBN 0 - 906447 - 15 - 1

Leica General Catalogue for 1955/58
ISBN 0 - 906447 - 16 - X

Leica General Catalogue for 1961
ISBN 0 - 906447 - 08 - 9

Leica General Catalogue for 1975 – 50th Leica Anniversary
ISBN 0 - 906447 - 27 - 5

L

For further details on HOVE camera collectors books, as well as books for users of Leica and other cameras see our advertisement pages at the back of the book.

HOVE
FOTO
BOOKS

LEITZ

LEICA SCREW MOUNT LENSES

21mm f4 Super Angulon lens: (EL001); Qty 1400(?). C 1958-1963. **$1500**

28mm f6.3 Hektor lens: (EL002); Qty 10,000(?). C 1935-1953. **$400**

28mm f5.6 Summaron lens: (EL003); Qty 6200(?). C 1955-1963. **$500**

33mm f3.5 Stemar lens: (EL004); C 1954-1957. Complete outfit, **$4000**

35mm f3.5 Elmar lens: (EL005); Qty 42,500(?). C 1930-1950. **$175**

35mm f3.5 Summaron lens: (EL006); Qty 80,000(?). C 1949-1958. **$200**

35mm f2.8 Summaron lens: (EL007); Qty 52,000(?). C 1958. **$500**

35mm f2 Summicron lens: (EL008); Qty 500(?). C 1958. **$1500**

50mm f3.5 Elmar lens: (EL009); Qty 360,000(?). C 1926-1959. **$125**. Red scale, **$250**.

50mm f2.5 Hektor lens: (EL010); Qty 10,300(?). C 1930-1939. **$350**

50mm f2 Summar lens: (EL011); Qty 123,000(?). C 1933-1939. **$50**

50mm f2 Rigid Summar lens: (EL012); C 1933-1939. Nickel: **$1250**; chrome, **$1400**.

50mm f1.5 Xenon lens: (EL013); Qty 6000(?). C 1936-1949. **$300**

50mm f2 Summitar lens: (EL014); Qty 170,000(?). C 1939-1953. **$125**

50mm f1.5 Summarit lens: (EL015); Qty 39,000(?). C 1949-1960. **$175**

50mm f3.5 Wollensak Velostigmat lens: (EL016); C 1947-1949. **$400**

50mm f2 Collapsible Summicron lens: (EL017); Qty 61,000(?). C 1953-1961. **$300**

50mm f2 Rigid Summicron lens: (EL018); Qty 100(?). C 1958-1962. **$1250**

50mm f2 Compur Summicron lens and shutter with lever: (EL019). **$4500**

50mm f2.8 Elmar lens: (EL020); C 1957-1962. **$125**

50mm f1.4 Summilux lens: (EL021); Qty 550(?). C 1960-1963. **$2500**

65mm f3.5 Elmar lens: (EL022); C 1960-1969. Black **$810**; chrome, **$650**

73mm f1.9 Hektor lens: (EL023); Qty 7000(?). C 1932-1940. **$500**

85mm f1.5 Summarex lens: (EL024); Qty 4000(?). C 1949-1962. Black **$2500**; chrome complete with lens hood and caps, **$1000**.

90mm f2 Summicron lens: (EL025); Qty 600(?). C 1957-1962. First version with removable shade, **$1500**. Second version with built-in lens shade, **$1200**. (Original screw mount doesn't have red dot at the base of the lens mount.)

90mm f4.5 Wollensak Velostigmat lens; made in USA: (EL026); C 1945-1950. **$200**.

90mm f4 Elmar lens: (EL027); Qty 114,000(?). C 1931-1964 - from **$100**

90mm f2.8 Elmarit lens: (EL028); Qty 2000(?). C 1959-1962. **$1000**.

90mm f2.2 Thambar lens: (EL029); Qty 3000(?). Disk shade and caps. C 1935-1939. **$3500** - without filter - **$1800**.

105mm f6.3 Mountain Elmar lens: (EL030); Qty 4000(?). With shade and caps. C 1932-1937. **$1000**.

125mm f2.5 Hektor lens: (EL031); Qty 3300(?). C 1954-1963. With shade and caps **$750**

127mm f4.5 Wollensak Velostigmat lens; made in USA (EL032); C 1944-1951. **$200**

135mm f4.5 Elmar lens: (EL033); Qty 5200(?). C 1930-1936. **$125**

135mm f4.5 Hektor lens: (EL034); Qty 70,000(?). C 1933-1960. **$100**-**$150**

135mm f4 Elmar lens: (EL035); Qty 5000(?). C 1960. **$550**

180mm f2.8 Tele-Elmarit lens (bayonet mount for Visoflex II, IIa and III): (EL036); C 1965. **$950**

200mm f4.5 Telyt lens: (EL037); Qty 11,500(?). C 1935-1960. **$350**

280mm f4.8 Telyt lens: (EL038); C 1961-1970. **$450**

400mm f5 Telyt lens: (EL039); Qty 4000(?). C 1937-1967. With removable shade, **$1250**; built-in shade, **$750**.

LEICA 'M' LENSES

Hologon 15mm f8.0 lens with finder: (EL1041); **$5000**.

Super Angulon 21mm f4.0 lens: (EL1042); **$750**.

Super Angulon 21mm f3.4 lens: (EL1043); **$1000**.

Elmarit 21mm f2.8 lens: (EL1044); **$1200**.

Elmarit (old style) 28mm f2.8 lens: (EL1045); **$600**.

Elmarit (new style) 28mm f2.8 lens: (EL1046); **$800**.

RF-Summicron 35mm f2.0 lens: (EL1047); Chrome, **$650**; black laquer, **$1300**.

RF-Summaron 35mm f2.8: (EL1048); **$350**.
Summicron Chrome 35mm f2.0 lens: (EL1051); **$650**.
Summicron Black laquer 35mm f2.0 lens: (EL1052); **$1300**.
Summaron 35mm f2.8 lens: (EL1053); **$400**.
Summaron 35mm f3.5 lens: (EL1054); **$250**.
Summilux 35mm f1.4 lens: (EL1055); **$900**.
Summicron C 40mm f2.0 lens: (EL1056); **$260**.
Elmar 50mm f2.8 lens: (EL1057); **$300**.
Elmar 50mm f3.5 lens: (EL1058); **$200**.
Summarit 50mm f1.5 lens: (EL1059); **$200**.
Summicron Chrome Wetzlar 50mm f2.0 lens: (EL1060); Rigid **$300**.
Summicron Chrome Collapsible 50mm f2.0 lens: (EL1061); **$250**.
Summicron Black laquer Wetzlar 50mm f2.0 lens: (EL1062); **$1200**.
Dual Range Summicron 50mm f2.0 lens with finder: (EL1063); **$350**.
Summilux Black 50mm f1.4 lens: (EL1064); **$950**.
Summilux Chrome 50mm f1.4 lens: (EL1065); **$500**.
Noctilux 50mm f1.2 lens: (EL1066); **$1800**.
Noctilux 50mm f1.0 lens: (EL1067); **$1500**.
Summilux 75mm f1.4 lens: (EL1068); Chrome **$1500**.
Elmarit 90mm f2.8 lens: (EL1069); **$850**.
Elmar C 90mm f4.0 lens: (EL1071); **$350**.
Tele Elmarit 90mm f2.8 lens: (EL1072); **$750**.
Elmar Rigid 90mm f4.0 lens: (EL1073); **$150**.
Elmar Collapsible 90mm f4.0 lens: (EL1074); **$401**.
Summicron Black or Chrome 90mm f2.0 lens: (EL1075); **$750**.
Summicron Black (new style) 90mm f2.0 lens: (EL1077); **$900**.
Hektor 135mm f4.5 lens: (EL1078); **$100**.
Elmarit 135mm f2.8 lens: (EL1079); **$750**.
Tele Elmar 135mm f4.0 lens: (EL1080); **$650**.
Summicron 50mm f2 lens, cutaway display model, (EL1119) **$1100 (!)**

LEICA REFLEX LENSES

Leica 15mm f3.8 R lens: (EL1081); **$3000**.
Leica 16mm f2.8 R lens: (EL1082); **$1200**.
Leica 19mm f2.8 R lens: (EL1083); **$1100**.
Leica 21mm f4 R lens: (EL1084); **$1000**.
Leica 24mm f2.8 R lens: (EL1085); **$1200**.

Leica 28mm f2.8 R lens: (EL1086); **$850**.
Leica 35mm f2 R lens: (EL1087); **$750**.
Leica 35mm f2.8 R lens: (EL1088); **$350**.
Leica PA-Curtigon 35mm f4 R lens: (EL1089); **$950**.
Leica 50mm f2 R lens (Canadian): (EL1090); **$325**.
Leica 50mm f1.4 R lens: (EL1091); **$700**.
Leica 60mm f2.8 R lens: (EL1092); **$950**.
Leica 80mm f1.4 R lens: (EL1093); **$1500**.
Leica 90mm f2.8 R lens: (EL1094); **$750**.
Leica 90mm f2 R lens: (EL1095); **$750**.
Leica 100mm f4 R with mount: (EL1096); **$775**
Leica 135mm f2.8 R lens: (EL1097); **$600**.
Leica 180mm f3.4 APO lens: (EL1098); **$1300**.
Leica 250mm f4 R lens: (EL1099); **$600**.
Leica 180mm f2.8 R lens (Compact): (EL1100); **$1200**.
Leica 180mm f2.8 R lens (Original): (EL1101); **$600**.
Leica 250mm f4 R lens lightweight: (EL1102); **$1200**.
Leica 350mm f4.8 R lens: (EL1103); **$2100**.
Leica 400mm f6.8 R lens: (EL1104); **$1200**.
Leica 500mm f8 Mirror-R lens: (EL1105); **$1000**.
Leica 560mm f6.8 R lens: (EL1106); **$1500**.
Leica Angenieux P 45-90mm f2.8 lens: (EL1107); **$850**.
Leica 35-70mm f3.5 R lens: (EL1108); **$850**.
Leica 75-200mm f4.5 R lens: (EL1109); **$850**.
Leica 2X Extender R lens: (EL1110); **$650**

LEICA REFLEX ACCESSORIES

Leica R4 Motor: (EL1111); **$225**.
Leica R4 Winder: (EL1112); **$125**.
Leica R4 Data Back: (EL1113); **$125**.
Leica R4 Bellows: (EL1114); **$400**.
Leicaflex Motor: (EL1115); **$750**.
Megoflex Viewer (non-Leitz manufacture),: (EL1116); **$275**.

GENERAL ACCESSORIES

Viewfinders:

Torpedo type: VISOR, - **$300**
VISAX, VIUNA, VIZWO, VITRE, - **$275**
VIFUR, - **$250**

Other Universal Viewfinders:

VIDOM, Black,- **$100**, (early - **$125**). Chrome, **$75**
VIOOH, round body, - **$200**. Earliest, unthreaded nose piece, - **$190**, Later, pinched or sloped body, - **$85**, TUVOO, (28mm adaptor), - **$200**.

Waist level viewfinders:

AUFSU, - **$300**, without shoe, - **$350**
AYOOC, with swing lens 35mm, - **$450**
AHOOT, with swing lens 28mm, - **$500**

Right angle viewfinders:

WINKO, - **$100**
WINTU, - **$75**
(in chrome or black)

Optical viewfinders:

EARLY:
WEISU, 35mm, chrome, - **$250**, black, - **$300**
SUWOO, 50mm, - **$500**
LATER:
SBLOO, 35mm, - **$250**
SBOOI, 50mm, - **$85**
SGOOD, 85mm, - **$250**
SGVOO, 90mm, - **$150**
SHOOC, 135mm, - **$150**
SBKOO, 21mm, - **$350**
SLOOZ, 28mm, - **$300**
OIDYO, for Stereo Stemar, - **$500**

Optical sportsfinder:

FOLDING
SUOOQ, 28mm, - **$250**
SAIOO, 73mm, black or chrome, - **$300**
SEROO, 90mm, - **$250**
SYEOO, 135mm, black or chrome, - **$300**
NON-FOLDING.
SOODL, 50mm, - **$750**
SOOAW, 73mm, - **$750**
SOOUT, SEVUE, 90mm, - **$250**
SOOYV, 135mm, - **$250**

Frame finders:

FOLDING
RASUK, 50mm & 90mm, - **$75**

RASUK, 35mm & 73mm, - **$75**
RASAL, 35mm, 73mm, 90mm, &135mm, - **$150**
ROSOL, 50mm, 90mm, & 135mm, - **$75**
NON-FOLDING
SFTOO, 200mm, - **$125**
TZOON/TZFOO, tube for 200mm, - **$50**
SQTOO, 400mm, - **$150**

Rangefinders:

FODIS, FOFER, long, only in black, - **$125**
FOKOS, in black or chrome, - **$250**
HFOOK, same as FOKOS with mounting foot, - **$250**

Reflex housing, complete units:

PLOOT, - **$75**
VISOFLEX I, - **$75**
VISIFLEX II, - **$125**
VISOFLEX III, - **$375**

SMALL ACCESSORIES

Single exposure camera: OLIGO/OLEYO with IBSOR shutter, **$2000**.
Self-timer: APDOO. **$30**.
Slow-speed device: HEBOO, **$150**.
Close-up device: NOOKY, NOOKY-HESUM, **$35**.
Close-up device, 9cm: OMIFO **$250**.
Three filter turret: (EL1117); **$200**.
Panorama head, 5cm (early) FIAMA, **$100**.
Panorama head, interchangeable rings: FARUX **$100**.
De Mornay Budd Viewfinder (non-Leitz manufacture): (EL1118); **$150**.

MOTORS AND WINDERS

MOOLY motor, one-speed: **$850**.
MOOLY motor, two speed: **$1000**.
MOOLY motor IIIc: **$2500**, black or chrome; grey, **$5000**.
Rapid winder: SCNOO, chrome, **$300**.
Rapid winder: SCNOO, black/nickel, **$600**.
Rapid winder: SCNOO, IIIc, chrome, **$1000**.
Leicavit: SYOOM, **$400**.
Leicavit, M: SMYOM, **$1200**.
Leicavit, MP (black enamel): **$1500**.
Remote winder: OOFRC, **$1600**

Leitz Megoflex viewfinder

LENNOR ENGINEERING COMPANY, Chicago, Illinois, USA.

Delta Stereo: (LD200); 35mm Stereo camera with optical VFR, fixed focus La Croix 50mm/f6.3 lenses, shutter speeds of 1/25-1/100 second plus B. Shutter marked for "shade", "normal", and "very bright". Blue or black plastic body with satin finished metal cover. C.1955.

| R2* $100 | £52 | DM165 | FF511 |

Delta Stereo

LEOTAX Camera COMPANY, Japan. (see SHOWA)

Leader: (BB193); 35mm stereo camera; Leader Anastigmat 45mm f4.5 lenses; shutter TMBK 1/25-1/100 s. Mfd in Japan. C 1950.

| R3* $75 | £39 | DM124 | FF383 |

L. LEULLIER, Paris, France.

Stereochrome: (LE100); 35mm stereo camera; Boyer Saphir 40mm f3.5 fixed focus lens; guillotine shutter 1-1/300 s. C 1939.

| R3* $125 | £66 | DM206 | FF639 |

Summum: (LE101); 6 x 13cm stereo camera; Boyer Saphir 85mm f4.5 lenses; Stereo Compur shutter 1-1/150 s. Rising lens panel. C 1925.

| R3* $200 | £105 | DM330 | FF1k |

Summum-Sterechrome: (LE102); 35mm stereo camera; Berthiot Flor f3.5 lens. C 1950.

| R4* $400 | £210 | DM659 | FF2k |

S. J. LEVI, London, England.

The Pullman Detective Camera: (LV100); stereo detective camera in shape of carved leather carrying case ; roller blind shutter; bellows focusing; 5" x 7" exp on plates. C 1896.

| R4* $600 | £315 | DM989 | FF3.1k |

LEVY-ROTH, Berlin, Germany.

Minigraph: (LR100); 35mm camera; Minigraph Anastigmat 54mm f3.5 or Trioplan f3 lens; flap shutter 1/30 s and T. 50 half-frame exp, 18 x 24mm on 35mm perforated film in special cassettes. First German

35mm camera; also used as contact printer or projector. C 1915.

R4* $1.2k	£630	DM2k	FF6.1k

Minigraph

Lewis Style Daguerreotype Camera: (BB194); J. M. Harrison, N.Y. lens, 1/4-plate daguerreotypes. Mfr unknown; American construction. C 1852. One of the first American daguerreotype cameras to use a bellows.

R5* $6k+	£3.1k+	DM9.9k+	FF30.7k+

Lewis Style Daguerreotype Camera: (BB195); $1/4$ plate bellows style daguerreo-

Lewis Style Daguerreotype Camera

type camera. $1/4$ plate daguerreotypes. C 1851. One of the first American daguerreotype cameras to use a bellows.

R5* $6k+	£3.1k+	DM9.9k+	FF30.7k+

Lewis Style Daguerreotype Camera: (BB196)1/2 plate bellows style daguerreotype camera; Holmes, Booth & Hayden radial drive lens. Mfr unknown; American construction. C 1856. One of the first American daguerreotype cameras to use a bellows.

R5* $7k+	£3.7k+	DM11.5k+	FF35.8k+

W. & W. H. LEWIS, New York.

Lewis Wet Plate Camera: (LW100); wet plate studio portrait camera; exp up to 12" x 12" on wet plates. C 1862.

R5* $1k	£525	DM1.6k	FF5.1k

Lewis Wet Plate Camera

LEXA Manufacturing Co., Melbourne, Australia.

Lexa 20: (LX200); Announced October, 1948, metal box camera for 6 x 9cm frames

Lexa 20

on 120 roll film, simple lens and shutter, a number of these cameras appeared in the mid 1980's. None, however was complete with internal metal film carrier, leading to the assumption that production or other problems may have prevented the Lexa 20 from ever having been sold!

| R3* $25 | £13 | DM41 | FF128 |

L. F. O. & CO., Paris, France.

Le Franceville: (LF100); cardboard plate camera; meniscus lens; drop shutter; 4 x 4cm glass plates. C 1908.

| R3* $175 | £92 | DM288 | FF894 |

Le Franceville

V. LIEBE, Paris, France.

Monobloc: (LI100); 6 x 13cm stereo camera; Berthiot Flor 85mm f5.7 lenses; 6 speed shutter. Panoramic setting, rising front panel. C 1920.

| R3* $180 | £94 | DM297 | FF920 |

LINEX CORP., DIVISION OF LIONEL CORP., New York.

Linex: (LX100); subminiature 35mm stereo camera; f6 fixed focus lenses; shutter 1/65 s. 8 pairs of stereo exp on 16mm film in special cassette. C 1950. In the USA, prices are 50% lower. Outfit included camera, viewer and case, **$250**. Camera only:

| R3* $125 | £66 | DM206 | FF639 |

Linex

LINHOF-LONDON

LINHOF PRAZASIONS-KAMERA-WERKE G.M.B.H., Munich, Germany.

Linhof Technika IV: (LP100); 4" x 5" folding press camera; Schneider Xenar f4.5 lens; Synchro Compur shutter 1 -1/500 s, CRF. C 1953.

R3* $800	£420	DM1.3k	FF4.1k

Linhof Technika IV

Linhof Technika III: (LP101); black.

R3* $500	£262	DM824	FF2.6k

Lithoscope: (BB200); 8 x 17cm stereo camera; Aplanat lens; 4 speed shutter; 8 x 17cm exp. C 1904.

R4* $500	£262	DM824	FF2.6k

J. LIZARS,
Glasgow, Scotland.

Challenge Dayspool Tropical Camera: (LZ100); Beck Symlens lens; Bausch & Lomb shutter. Teak and brass, red leather bellows. C 1905.

R4* $750	£394	DM1.2k	FF3.8k

Challenge DeLuxe: (LZ101); 4" x 5" tropical camera; Dagor 150mm lens; 4" x 5" exp on plates. Polished mahogany, brass fittings. C 1910.

R4* $1.2k	£630	DM2k	FF6.1k

Challenge View Camera: (LZ102); compact folding 1/2 plate view camera; Lizar's Kram Triple Convertible lens and shutter; front and rear tilt and swing; built-in brass tripod base; plumb bob; double ext bellows to 17"; Spanish mahogany construction. C 1898.

R4* $300	£157	DM495	FF1.5k

Challenge Hand Camera, Model C: (LZ103); Goerz Double Anastigmat Dagor Series III 150mm f6.8 lens; Bausch & Lomb shutter, up to 1/100 s. C1902.

R4* $200	£105	DM330	FF1k

Challenge Stereo Camera, Model B: (LZ104); Aldis Anastigmat lenses; Bausch & Lomb Stereo shutter; 3¼" x 6¾" exp on plates. C 1900.

R4* $600	£315	DM989	FF3.1k

Challenge Stereo Dayspool: (LZ105); mahogany stereo camera; Aldis Anastigmat lenses; Bausch & Lomb shutter; pair of 3¼" x 3¼" exp on roll film or plates. Mahogany finish, brass hardware. C 1905.

R4* $1.5k	£787	DM2.5k	FF7.7k

LONDON STEREOSCOPIC COMPANY, London, England.

Artist Hand Camera: (LS100); Black-band 4¼" x 3¼" lens. Mahogany finish. C 1889.

R4* $2k	£1.1k	DM3.3k	FF10.2k

Carlton: (LS101); Ross Goerz Double Anastigmat 6" f7.7 lens; variable speed guillotine shutter 1-1/80 s. 4" x 5" exp on plates - changed by gravity feed. C 1895.

R4* $700	£367	DM1.2k	FF3.6k

The Dispatch Detective Camera: (LS102); wooden box-type detective camera; shutter to 1/100 s. 8 x 10.5cm or 10.5 x 12.5cm exp on plates. C 1888.

R4*	NSR

Improved Artist Reflex: (LS103); Voigtlander 15cm f4.5 Heliar lens ; CFPS. Rising front panel; tropical mahogany finish; green leather bellows. C 1910.

R5* $2k	£1.1k	DM3.3k	FF10.2k

Jumelle Capsa de Maria: (LS104); Zeiss Protar 85mm f8 lenses. C 1910.

R3* $225	£118	DM371	FF1.2k

The King's Own Tropical Camera: (LS105); Dagor lens; Volute shutter. Roll film or plates. Teak construction, brass fittings. C 1907.

R5* $1.5k	£787	DM2.5k	FF7.7k

Wet Plate Sliding Box Camera: (LS106); Petzval-type lens. 5" x 5" exp on wet plates. C 1860.

R5* $2.5k	£1.3k	DM4.1k	FF12.8k

LUMIERE & CIE, Lyons, France.

Eljy: (LM100); 35mm miniature camera, folding VFR Lumiere Lypar 40mm f3.5 lens; Lumiere shutter 1/10-1/200 s. 8 exp, 24 x 36mm on unperforated 35mm film in special cassettes; pull-out lens mount; scale focusing. C 1937.

R2* $80	£42	DM132	FF409

Eljy-Club: (LM110); 35mm miniature camera, optical VFR mounted in top housing,

Eljy

early models with built-in extinction meter, while later models sport an accessory shoe. Lumiere Lypar 40mm f3.5 lens; Lumiere shutter 1-1/00 s. 8 exp, 24 x 36mm on unperforated 35mm film in special cassettes; pull-out lens mount; scale focusing. available in Grey, yellow, red, green, white and Blue, (worth 100% more) in addition to a "Luxus" model covered in crocodile skin! (worth 200% more) C. 1951.

R3* $120	£63	DM198	FF613

Lumiclub: (LM101); Som Berthiot Flor 75mm f3.5 lens. Built-in extinction meter; telescoping lens mount; eye-level and waist-level finders; rapid wind lever. 6 x 6cm or 4.5 x 6cm format. Made from dies prepared by the Pontiac company before going bankrupt, this camera was *originally* intended to use perforated 70mm film, less than 1000 cameras are said to have been made.

R4* $225	£118	DM371	FF1.2k

Lumiére 6 x 6: (LM116); Folding camera for 6 x 6cm or 4.5 x 6cm format. on roll film 80mm f4.5 Spector lens. Built-in extinction meter; telescoping lens mount, eye-level and waist-level finders; rapid wind lever. Sharing some of the features of the more expensive Lumiclub (LM101), this camera also shared the same short life. About 1000 cameras are thought to have been made.

R4* $175	£92	DM288	FF894

Le Periphoto: (LM102); powered by spring wound motor; 55mm lens moves in an arc, while film remains stationary. Angle of view: 180 or 360 degrees. 7 x 38 cm exp on roll film. C 1901.

R5* $5k+	£2.6k+	DM8.2k+	FF25.6k+

Sterelux Lumiere: (LM103); folding stereo camera; Nacor Boyer Anastigmat 80mm f6.3 lenses; shutter 1/25-1/200 s; 6 x 13cm exp on 116 roll film. C 1920.

R3* $175	£92	DM288	FF894

Lumix: (LM104); Post WWII folding roll film camera for 8 negatives 6 x 9 on 120 film, simple lens, and one speed shutter.

R2* $15	£8	DM25	FF77

Ludax: (LM105); folding roll film camera for 8 negatives 6 x 9 on 620 film, 105mm /f6.3 Fidor lens, shutter speeds 1/10-1/200s,

L

LUMIERE

folding optical finder, body release. Made in large numbers, C.1950.

R2* $10	£5	DM16	FF51

Lumirex: (LM106); folding roll film camera for 8 negatives 6 x 9 on 620 film, 105mm / f6.3 Fidor lens, or 105mm/f4.5 Spector lens shutter speeds 1/10-1/200s, self timer folding optical finder, body release. Along with the Ludax (LM105), made in large numbers, C. 1950.

R2* $15	£8	DM25	FF77

Lumirex III: (LM107); folding roll film camera for 8 negatives 6 x 9 on 620 film, 100mm /f3.5 Angenieux type 11 lens, Prontor S shutter 1-1/300s, optical finder built-into the top housing along with an extinction meter, body release. (At the end of production, a cheaper version having 105mm/f4.5 Spector lens and Sido shutter 1/10 - 1/200s, was offered for the budget minded.)

R3* $60	£31	DM99	FF307

Lumiére 6.5 x 11: (LM111); folding camera for 6.5 x 11 negs on 616 film. folding optical finder,125mm/f4.5 Berthiot or Topaz lens, btl shutter, speeds 1-1/300s, Thought to be the last camera made for 616 film, and probably one of the few made for that film with a coated lens and flash synch.

R4* $90	£47	DM148	FF460

Optax: (LM112); 35mm black plastic camera with folding optical VFR, 50mm/f3.5 Lypar lens in collapsible mount, btl shutter, speeds 1/10-1/200s, Marking Lumiéres entry into the standard 35mm market, this first model Optax lasted only a few months in production, October 1948- Spring 1949.

R4* $175	£92	DM288	FF894

Optax 2nd model: (LM114); 35mm black plastic camera with tubular optical VFR, 40mm/f3.5 Altar lens in fixed mount, btl shutter, speeds 1/10-1/200s. A continuation of the Optax line, made in large quantities and much less rare than the original Optax (LM113).

R2* $65	£34	DM107	FF332

Starter: (LM115); 35mm black plastic camera with grey plastic top housing, 45mm/ f3.5 Lypar lens, btl shutter, speeds 1/25-1/150s, made to capture a share of the "low" end of the camera marketplace.

R2* $40	£21	DM66	FF204

Elax: (LM108); Pre WWII high quality precision folding camera for 3 x 4cm negatives on 127 film, 50mm/f3.5 Flor lens, lever wind mfps speeds 4- 1/1000s, Optical finder said to have been made by Leitz.

R4* $650	£341	DM1.1k	FF3.3k

Elax II: (LM109); Post WWII version of the Elax (LM108), thought to have been made from stocks of pre-war parts. 50../f3.5 Flor lens, lever wind mfps 4-1/1000sDiffers from (LM108) by having a satin chrome top plate. The high price of this camera on the French market killed it.

R4* $750	£394	DM1.2k	FF3.8k

Lumiflex: (LM117); Black plastic twin lens reflex camera for 6 x 6 format. The 80mm/ f4.5Spector lens is not coupled to the viewing lens, btl shutter, speeds 1-1/300s, built-in extinction meter. c.1951.

R2* $45	£24	DM74	FF230

Lumireflex: (LM118); Black plastic twin lens reflex, 80mm/f345 Spector taking lens coupled to the 80mm/f3.5 viewing lens, Atos shutter, speeds 1-1/300s, didn't sell well, and was quickly taken off the market.

R4* $90	£47	DM148	FF460

Lutac: (LM119); Simple black plastic roll film camera, very similar to the Ultra-Fex.

R2* $10	£5	DM16	FF51

H. MACKENSTEIN FABRICANT, 15 Rues de Carmes, Paris, France.

La Francie: (MF100); 45 x 107mm press-type stereo camera; Max Balbreck Aplanatic lenses; variable speed guillotine shutter. Red leather bellows. C 1906.

R3* $200	£105	DM330	FF1k

Mackenstein Tailboard Camera: (MF101); 13cm x 18cm compact view camera; Grande Angle Gibauet brass lens. Mahogany finish, brass fittings. C 1890.

R4* $600	£315	DM989	FF3.1k

Photo Livre: (MF102); book-type detective camera; rectilinear 60mm f12 lens; guillotine shutter. 24 exp, 40 x 40mm on plates. C 1890.

R5* $2.5k+	£1.3k+	DM4.1k+	FF12.8k+

Stereo Jumelle: (MF103); 6.5 x 9cm stereo camera; Goerz Dagor 110mm f6.3 lens; variable speed guillotine shutter. Magazine for 12 plates. C 1895.

R3* $200	£105	DM330	FF1k

MACRIS-BOUCHER, Paris, France.

Nil Melior Stereo: (MA100); 6 x 13cm stereo camera; Boyer Saphir or E. Krauss Tessar f4.5 lens; 7 speed spring shutter. Magazine holds 12 plates, 6 x 13cm. C 1920.

R* $175	£92	DM288	FF894

H. MADER, Isny, Germany.

The Invicibel: (HM100); Aplanat 180mm f6 lens; double action rotary shutter; 13 x 18cm plates. C 1898.

R4* $900	£472	DM1.5k	FF4.6k

MAGIC INTRODUCTION CO., New York.

Photoret Camera: (MI100); watch-type detective camera; meniscus achromatic lens; front-of-lens shutter. 6 exp, 12" diameter on 1³/4" diameter plates. C 1893. Outfit, with box and film tin, **$750**. Camera:

R4* $550	£289	DM907	FF2.8k

MAISON ERCSAM, France.

Camrex Reflex 8: (ME100); 8mm movie camera; Retrofocus Angenieux 6.5mm f1.9 lens, interchangeable mount. 4 speeds: 8, 16, 24 and 32 frames per s or single frame;

Photo Livre

Photoret Camera

M

had similar construction and features. Original model was key wound; later model had hand-crank. C 1936.

R3* $75 £39 DM124 FF383

Bolex H16: (PL104); 16mm movie camera; 3 lens turret; Kern Switar 15, 25, and 75mm lenses; speeds from 18 to 64 frames per s. Reflex viewing using a semi silvered mirror to direct a portion of the light coming through the lens to the viewfinder. A best-selling camera for more than 30 years. C 1936.

R3* $200 £105 DM330 FF1k

Bolex H9: (PL105); 9.5mm movie camera; Meyer Goerlitz 17, 25 and 75mm lenses. Similar to Bolex H16. C 1936.

R3* $90 £47 DM148 FF460

Bolex L8: (PL106); 8mm movie camera; Yvar or Kern 12.5mm f2.8 lens; 4 speeds: 12, 16, 24 and 32 frames per s; spring motor; telescopic vf with masks for 3 lenses. First compact 8mm Bolex camera. C 1942.

R2* $20 £10 DM33 FF102

Bolex C8: (PL107); 8mm movie camera; Som Berthiot Zoom Pan Cinor 12.5mm to 36mm f2.8 lens - telescopic vf attached to lens. First use of Zoom Pan Cinor lens. C 1952.

R3* $60 £31 DM99 FF307

Bolex C8SL: (PL108);

R2* $30 £16 DM49 FF153

Bolex B8: (PL110); 8mm movie camera; double lens holder for Kern Yvar 13 and 36mm lenses. C 1952.

R2* $25 £13 DM41 FF128

Bolex H16 Reflex: (PL111); 16mm movie camera; Kern Yvar 16mm, 25mm and 75mm lenses; 5 shutter speeds, 12 to 64 frames per s. Multi focal length vf for 3 lenses; reflex prism vf. C 1956.

R3* $250 £131 DM412 FF1.3k

Bolex H16-M: (PL112); 16mm movie cam-

backwind capability. 20 x 20mm vf eyepiece: the image is larger than lifesize. First 8mm movie camera with a reflex vf: a mirror was mounted on the shutter. C 1956.

R3* $90 £47 DM148 FF460

MAISON PAILLARD, Ste. Croix, Switzerland.

Bolex Auto Cine Camera (first model): (PL100); 16mm movie camera; Hermagis 25mm f3.5 lens. Reflex vf; 15m of 16mm film. C 1928.

R4* $200 £105 DM330 FF1k

Bolex Auto Cine Camera (Model B): (PL101); 16mm movie camera. Similar to first model but used 30m spools. C 1929.

R4* $100 £52 DM165 FF511

Tonkino Paillard: (PL102); first sound projector for 9.5mm or 16mm film: it was coupled to 2-speed phonograph—33 or 78 rpm. C 1932.

R4* $125 £66 DM206 FF639

Bolex H8: (PL103); 8mm movie camera. Introduced at the same time as Bolex H16;

era; Pan Cinor Zoom 17.5 to 70mm f2.4 lens. First 16mm zoom reflex movie camera. C 1958.

R3* $175	£92	DM288	FF894

Bolex D8L: (PL113); 8mm movie camera; 3 lens turret. TTL photo-electric cell measured light through-the-lens; retracted when camera was operated. C1959.

R2* $30	£16	DM49	FF153

Bolex Zoom Reflex P1: (PL114); 8mm movie camera; Som Berthiot Pan Cinor 8 to 40mm f1.9 lens; speeds from 12 to 64 frames per s. Reflex viewer; split field RFR; semi-auto exp control by CdS retractable meter. C 1961.

R2* $50	£26	DM82	FF256

Bolex Zoom Reflex Automatic K1: (PL115); 8mm movie camera; Vario-Switar 8 to 35mm lens. 3 speeds: 12, 18 and 40 frames per s; auto or manual exp. C 1962.

R2* $40	£21	DM66	FF204

Bolex H16 REX: (PL116); 16mm movie camera; multifocal vf for 7 lenses from 16mm to 150mm. Similar to Bolex H16 REX, except for multifocal length (7 fields of view) vf. Electric motor drive. C 1964.

R3* $400	£210	DM659	FF2k

Bolex 7.5 Macrozoom: (PL117); super 8 movie camera; Macrozoom 7.5 to 21mm f1.9 lens. Focusing to 13cm; auto exp; battery powered. C 1968.

R3* $70	£37	DM115	FF358

Bolex H16EL: (PL120); 16mm movie camera; Kern Vario Switar 12.5 to 100mm f1.2 lens; variable speed shutter. TTL photo-electric cell. Battery or electric power; remote control. C 1975.

R3* $120	£63	DM198	FF613

MAISON PATHE, France.

Pathe Baby (original): (MP100); Steelor and Berthiot Anastigmat f3.5 fixed focus lens. Vf attached to camera top; handcranked; 2 turns per s; special double cassette.

R2* $20	£10	DM33	FF102

Pathe Baby (original)

Pathe Baby Projector

Pathe Baby Projector: (MP101); 9.5mm projector; double perforation film; cylindrical hand crank; metal film cassettes. First model for film of 20 meters - reduced number of spool changes while viewing a long movie; in 1926 an electric motor was added. C 1924.

R2* $60	£31	DM99	FF307

Pathe Baby (with auxiliary Swiss Camo motor): (MP102); 9.5mm movie camera;

one winding of the spring-motor would run the entire roll of film through the camera. C 1927.

R2* $35	£18	DM58	FF179

Motocamera Pathe Baby Lux: (MP103); 9.5mm movie camera; anastigmat 15mm f3.5 lens; 3 speeds: 10, 15 and 21 frames per s. Film end indicator; double claw film advance; one winding of spring-motor runs entire roll of film through camera. C 1931.

R2* $40	£21	DM66	FF204

Motocamera Pathe Baby (Mondial B): (MP104); 9.5mm movie camera; Anastigmat f3.5 lens. C 1932.

R2* $25	£13	DM41	FF128

Pathe Moto Camera: (MP105); 16mm movie camera; special 16mm magazines. C 1933.

R2* $25	£13	DM41	FF128

Motocamera Pathe Baby (Royal): (MP106); 9.5mm movie camera; 2cm f2.9 lens; 2 speeds: 16 and 32 frames per s. Parallax correcting vf; exp counter and diaphragm indicator visible in vf. Size: 11.5 x 10 x 6.5cm. C 1936.

R2* $40	£21	DM66	FF204

Pathe Vox: (MP107); 9.5mm movie projector. First sound projector for 9.5mm film. C 1936.

R4* $125	£66	DM206	FF639

Motocamera Pathe Baby (National): (MP110); 9.5mm movie camera; Berthiot Cinor 20mm f3.5 lens. Double claw pull down; spring motor drive; polished metal body. C 1937.

R2* $30	£16	DM49	FF153

Pathe Webo A: (MP111); 9.5mm movie camera; Berthiot Cinor 20mm f1.9 lens. C 1946.

R2* $25	£13	DM41	FF128

Motocamera Pathe Baby: (MP112); 9.5mm movie camera; Cinor Berthiot 20mm f1.9 lens; variable speeds: 8 to 32 frames per s. C 1946.

R2* $30	£16	DM49	FF153

Motocamera Pathe Baby (National II):

(MP113); 9.5mm movie camera; Cinor 20mm f1.9 lens; variable speeds: 8 to 32 frames per s. C 1948.

R2* $30	£16	DM49	FF153

Pathe Webo A Luxe: (MP114); 9.5mm movie camera; Som Berthiot Cinor B adjustable 20mm f1.9 lens. C 1950.

R2* $25	£13	DM41	FF128

Pathe Webo M: (MP115); 9.5mm movie camera; triple lens turret for Kinoptik 20, 25 and 75mm lenses; variable speed shutter; 10 to 80 frames per s. Reflex vf. C 1950.

R3* $70	£37	DM115	FF358

MAMIYA CAMERA CO., LTD., Tokyo, Japan.

Mamiyaflex: (MC100); TLR camera; Mamiya-Sekor 105mm f3.5 coated lens, interchangeable mount; Seikosha-S 1-1/500 s. 12 exp, 2¼" x 2¼" on 120 roll film. C 1954.

R2* $175	£92	DM288	FF894

Mamiyaflex

Mamiya Pistol Camera: (MC101); pistol-type detective camera; 50mm lens; 6 square diaphragm stops; single speed shutter. 65 exp, 18 x 24mm on 35mm film. Made for Japanese police training. C 1954.

R5* $2.5k	£1.3k	DM4.1k	FF12.8k

Mamiya Six: (MC102); 2¹/₄" x 2¹/₄" RFR camera; T.S.M. Anastigmat 75mm f3.5 lens; Copal shutter 1-1/200 s. 12 exp, 2¹/₄" x 2¹/₄" on 120 roll film. Rf coupled to movable film plane; lens remains stationary. Many variations exist with slight lens/shutter combinations, all are worth about the same.

R2* $75	£39	DM124	FF383

Mamiya Six

Mamiya 16 Super (Model III): (MC103); 25mm f3.5 lens; shutter 1/2-1/200 s. 32 x 14mm exp on 16mm film in special cassettes. Slide-in yellow filter. C1953.

R2* $50	£26	DM82	FF256

MFAP, PONTIAC (Manufacture Française d'Appareils Photographique). Paris, France & Casablanca, Morocco

Pontiac: (PN100) ;1938; 6 x 9cm folding roll film camera with thermaplastic bodies offered in two models, with simple lens and single speed shutter, or front focusing 105mm/f4.5 Berthiot, in MFAP shutter with speeds of 1/25 -1/100s, plus B. Closely resembles earlier Gallus and Ebner cameras of the same design.

R3* $45	£24	DM74	FF230

Pontiac: (PN101); 1938, 6 x 9cm folding roll film camera offered in brown bakelite as a "Luxus" model.Front focusing 105mm/f4.5 Berthiot, in MFAP shutter with speeds of 1/25 - 1/100s, plus B, brown bellows.

R4* $90	£47	DM148	FF460

Pontiac: (PN116); 16 exposures on 127 roll film, polished aluminIum body, CFPS with speeds of 1/25-1/500s. SOM Berthiot Flor , 50mm, f3.5 lens in collapsible mount. At first glance the lens and mount look very much like Leica. Don't be fooled into trying to unscrew the lens. You will only end up hurting your hand, and possibly damaging the lens!

R3* $225	£118	DM371	FF1.2k

Pontiac Bloc Metal 41: (PN102); 1941, 6 x 9 folding roll film camera of cast aluminium, produced during the second World War in quite large numbers. Various 105mm/f4.5 lens and shutter combinations. The lack of quality construction material made necessary the rethinking of some design ideas, such as the use of textures body castings painted black instead of the more traditional leather covered bodies. These cameras often suffer from poor bellows, and rusting nickel plated parts. The "41" indicates the year of introduction.

M

R2* $55	£29	DM91	FF281

Bloc Metal 45: (PN103); 1946, 6 x 9cm folding roll film camera with cast aluminium body, early cameras have105mm/f4.5 Flor Berthiot or Trylor Roussel lens in Prontor II shutter, speeds of 1-1/200s, textured bodies painted black while later cameras have "leather" covering, and a Gitzo shutter labelled "Zotic-I".

R3* $50	£26	DM82	FF256

Bloc Metal 145: (PN104); 1946, 6 x 9cm folding roll film camera with cast aluminium body, 105mm/f4.5 Flor Berthiot lens in a Compur Rapid shutter marked "licence française", speeds of 1-1/400s, said to have been assembled in France from earlier Compur parts shipped from Germany.

R4* $125	£66	DM206	FF639

MFAP

Lynx-1: (PN105); 1943, 3 x 4cm on 127 film, between the lens shutter with speeds of 1/25-1/200s, front focusing 50mm/f3.5 Flor Berthiot lens, cast aluminium body, with textured finish, often painted black. Perhaps less than 100 made.

R4* $110	£58	DM181	FF562

Lynx-1

Lynx-II: (PN106); 1944, 3 x 4cm on 127 film, CFPS 1/25-1/500s, some cameras have self timer, front focusing 50mm/f2.8 or f3.5 Flor Berthiot, or f2.9 Angénieux lens in collapsible mount, cast aluminium body with textured finish, often painted black. Perhaps more than 100,000 made.

R3* $100	£52	DM165	FF511

Lynx-II

Lynx de Nuit (Night Lynx): (PN107); 1946, 3 x 4cm on 127 film, CFPS 1/25-1/500s, coated 50mm/f1.5 Flor Berthiot lens, cast aluminium body with textured finish. Very few made.

R4* $325	£171	DM536	FF1.7k

Compur Lynx: (PN108); 1946, 3 x 4cm on 127 film, fixed mount front focusing 50mm/f3.5Flor Berthiot lens, rim set Compur shutter speeds of 1-1/300s, cast aluminium body with textured finish. Very few made.

R4* $300	£157	DM495	FF1.5k

Standard Lynx: (PN109); 1948, 3 x 4cm on 127 film, CFPS 1/25-1/500s, fixed mount 40mm/f3.5 Flor Berthiot or Roussel lens, cast aluminium body with textured finish.

R4* $250	£131	DM412	FF1.3k

Super Lynx-I: (PN110); 1948, 35mm VFR camera with cast aluminium body, CFPS 1/25-1/500s coupled to film advance, 50mm/f3.5 or f2.8 Flor Berthiot lens in collapsible mount, polished or painted textured body. Unlike earlier 127 roll film Lynx's, these 35mm cameras were clearly marked on the camera body above the lens.

R4* $140	£73	DM231	FF716

Super Lynx-I

Super Lynx "Standard": (PN111); 1950, 35mm VFR camera with cast aluminium body, CFPS 1/25-1/500s coupled to film advance, 35mm/f3.5 Flor Berthiot wide angle lens in fixed mount, painted textured body.

R4* $150	£79	DM247	FF767

Super Lynx-II: (PN112); 1953, 35mm VFR camera with cast aluminium body, CFPS 1/25-1/500s coupled to film advance, self timer, 50mm/f3.5 or f2.8 Flor Berthiot lens in collapsible interchangeable bayonet mount, painted textured body. 28mm/f3.3 Angulor , 35mm/f3.5 Flor, 75mm/f2.8 Flor,

Super Lynx-II

and 90mm/f3.5 Flor accessory lenses were made for this camera. Marked "made in French Morocco" or "made in Morocco". Along with a few Super Lynx-I and Super Lynx cameras, perhaps the only camera made in Africa. A complete outfit increases the price 200%.

R4* $350	£184	DM577	FF1.8k

Super Lynx: (PN113); 1953, 35mm VFR camera with cast aluminium body, CFPS 1/25-1/500s coupled to film advance, 50mm/ f3.5 Flor Berthiot lens in fixed collapsible mount, painted textured body. Made at the same time as the Super Lynx-II, and post-dating the Super Lynx-I. This camera was a simplified version, without the self timer available on the Super Lynx-II.

R4* $225	£118	DM371	FF1.2k

Super Lynx

Baby Lynx: (PN114); 1951, 35mm VFR camera with between the lens shutter, speeds of 1- 1/300s, front focusing 50mm/

f3.5 or 2.8 Flor Berthiot lens in collapsible mount, cast aluminium body with black covering. Made in Paris and then in Morocco, early cameras were not marked with the name. Brown body covering adds 100%.

R3* $75	£39	DM124	FF383

Baby Standard: (PN115); 1953, 35mm camera with between the lens shutter, speeds of 1/25-1/200s, front focusing 50mm/ f3.9 Trylor Roussel lens in collapsible mount, cast aluminium body with black covering. Sold by Central-Photo in France, a cheaper version of the Baby Lynx with a simpler Pronto shutter.

R4* $75	£39	DM124	FF383

MIOM
(Manufacture d'Isolents et d'Objects Moulés), France.

Photax: (PF100); C1938, bakelite VFR camera for 6 x 9cm or 6 x 4.5cm on roll film, simple lens and shutter, metal focusing ring with handle, similar to the Rex camera made in Argentina.

R3* $25	£13	DM41	FF128

M

Jacky: (PF102); C1950, as PF100) but for the name.

R3* $25	£13	DM41	FF128

Photax Blindé: (PF105); C1950, bakelite VFR camera for 6 x 9cm frames on roll film, curved film plane, simple lens and shutter, redesigned body from (PF100) now without metal focusing ring, called Blindé (armoured) because of the bakelite lens/shutter cover delivered with the camera. Also made in Spain under the Fotex name (FT200).

R2* $30	£16	DM49	FF153

C. MARELLI, Rosario, Argentina

Mecabox: (MA200); C1950, "rustic" metal box camera for 6 x 9cm on roll film, simple lens and shutter.

R4* $50	£26	DM82	FF256

MARION & CO., LTD., London, England.

Marion's Metal Miniature Camera: (MJ100); Petzval-type 55mm f5.6 lens; rack and pinion focusing; guillotine drop shutter; 30 x 30mm dry plates. C 1884.

R4* $1.75k	£919	DM2.9k	FF8.9k

Marion's Radial Detective Camera: (MJ101); 1/4 plate mahogany box camera; plate changing mechanism. C 1890.

R4* $750	£394	DM1.2k	FF3.8k

No. 1 Academy Camera: (MJ102); TLR; Petzval-type 2" f5 lens; rotary shutter in front of lens; eye level finder. 12 plates in magazine. C 1885. One of the earliest TLRs.

R5* $2.5k	£1.3k	DM4.1k	FF12.8k

No. 1 Academy Camera

Soho Tropical Reflex

M

Le Parcel Detective Camera: (MJ103); wrapped package-type detective camera; fixed focus double lens; simple shutter. 8 x 10.5cm plates in simple holder. C 1885.

R5* $5k+	£2.6k+	DM8.2k+	FF25.6k+

Soho Tropical Reflex: (MJ104); 3$^{1/4}$" x 4$^{1/4}$" tropical SLR; Dallmeyer 6$^{1/2}$" f4.5 lens; CFPS 1/16-1/800 s. Teak wood, brass fittings; red leather bellows. C 1928-39.

R4* $3k	£1.6k	DM5k	FF15.3k

Soho Reflex: (MJ105) All models were made by A Kershaw and Sons of Leeds for Marion incorporating Kershaw's mirror patent of 1904.

R2* $125	£66	DM206	FF639

G. MASON & CO., Glasgow, Scotland.

G. Mason & Co. Tailboard Camera: (GM100); brass bound mahogany field camera; Ross lens; rotating disc stops; 4$^{3/4}$" x 6$^{1/2}$" tilting ground glass back; vertical and horizontal adjustment on lens board.

R3* $350	£184	DM577	FF1.8k

MAST DEVELOPMENT CO., Iowa.

Concealable Still Camera: (MD100); cigarette package type detective camera; 17.5mm f2.7 lens; shutter 1/15, 1/125, 1/500 s and B. Designed to fit inside a Lucky Strike cigarette package: three false cigarettes controlled the diaphragm, focus and shutter trip. Mfd for the U.S. Signal Corps. C 1949-1950.

R5*	NSR

MATTIOLI

La Belle Gamine: (MT100); 45 x 107mm stereo camera; Balbreck Rapid Rectilinear lenses; 3 speed guillotine shutter. 45 x 107mm exp. C 1920.

R4* $275	£144	DM453	FF1.4k

MAWSON,
Newcastle, England.

Mawson: (MM100); stereo wet plate camera; achromat lens; cylindrical diaphragm; rectangular bellows; archimedian screw focus adjustment; 3¼" x 6¾" exp on wet plates. C 1865.

R5* $4k	£2.1k	DM6.6k	FF20.4k

MAZO,
Paris, France.

Le Graphostereochrome: (MZ100); colour stereo folding camera; special slide-in filters for Autochrome and Tri-colour processes. Sliding plateholder for three plates. 10 x 15cm exp and 6 x 13cm stereo exp. Designed by Abbe Tauleigne. C 1910.

R5* $2.25k	£1.2k	DM3.7k	FF11.5k

Jumelle Mazo: (MZ101); Double Triplet 135mm f6.5 lens; 5 speed shutter; 12 quarter plates. C 1900.

R3* $125	£66	DM206	FF639

MEAGHER,
London, England.

Meagher Sliding Box Wet Plate Camera: (MG100); lens with brass barrel; rack and pinion focusing; 7" x 7" ground glass. Mahogany finish. C 1858.

R5* $2k	£1.1k	DM3.3k	FF10.2k

Meagher Stereo Camera: (MG101); collapsible box-type stereo camera; Ross landscape lens. C 1860.

R5* $4k	£2.1k	DM6.6k	FF20.4k

Meagher Wet Plate: (MG102); Dallmeyer Rectilinear lens with waterhouse stops. Ground glass focusing. Mahogany finish, maroon leather bellows. C 1860.

R5* $1k	£525	DM1.6k	FF5.1k

Magic Lantern: (BB201); child's toy; projects circular or rectangular slides. C. 1890. Complete outfit:

R3* $250	£131	DM412	FF1.3k

Magic Lantern

Laboratorias MC,
Argentina.

Joya: (MC200); C1950, Bakelite TLR box camera for 6 x 6cm frames on 120 or 620 film, simple lens and shutter.

R4* $40	£21	DM66	FF204

Joya

M

Meikai: (BB204); 35mm TLR camera; M.K. Anastigmat 50mm f3.8 lens. Mfd in Japan.

R3* $100	£52	DM165	FF511

MEGURO KOGAKU KOGYO CO, LTD., Japan.

Melcon Original: (MK101); 1955 CFPS, 1-1/500 sec, interchangeable Leica-type screw mount f3.5/50mm Hexar (Konika) lens or f2.0/50mm Nikkor-H lens. Hinged back. Less than 2000 cameras were produced, with the first two digits of the serial number giving the year of production. Quite rare.

R4* $850	£446	DM1.4k	FF4.3k

Melcon Original with non original Canon lens

Melcon-II: (MK100); 1957 CFPS, 1 - 1/500 sec, interchangeable Leica-type screw mount f2.0/50mm Nikkor-H lens. Hinged back. Very few cameras were produced. This camera looks more like a Contax or Nikon than the previous model. Extremely rare.

R5* $1.2k	£630	DM2k	FF6.1k

MEJORI OPTICAL WORKS, Japan.

Honor S1 (first version): (HR100); 1956 CFPS, 1 - 1/500 sec, seperate RFR/VFR windows, diopter adjustment. Screw mount Hexar F3.5/50mm lens. This camera is quite similar to the Ichicon 35 camera from the Dai-ichi Optical Works.

R2* $700	£367	DM1.2k	FF3.6k

Honor S1 (second version): (HR101); 1957 CFPS, 1 - 1/1000 sec, seperate RFR/VFR windows, diopter adjustment. Screw mount Honor F1.9/50mm lens. Quite rare, this camera is an improved version of the Honor S1, with the addition of 1/1000 sec to the shutter speeds.

R4* $900	£472	DM1.5k	FF4.6k

MENTOR WERKE, Dresden, Germany.

Mentor: (MW100); press-type stereo camera; Tessar 90mm f4.5 lenses with coupled diaphragms and coupled helicoid focusing. Rising front, panoramic exp. 6 x 13cm exp. C 1914-1931.

R3* $300	£157	DM495	FF1.5k

MEOPTA, Prerov, Czechoslovakia.
(now called the "Czech and Slovak Federal Republic")

Established in 1933, the Meopta Company no longer makes cameras, but does a brisk business in enlargers, opaque projectors, movie projectors, and related optical components. Several smaller camera companies were re-grouped after 1945, and absorbed by Meopta. One of these, Optikotechna, produced the first Flexaret. At its peak, Meopta was actually four factories. Prerov, where professional and amateur enlargers, and movie projectors were made, Bratislava, where slide projectors and opaque projectors were made, Hynicice, where still cameras were made (including the Stereomikroma, and Flexaret series), and Brno, where 8mm and 16mm ciné cameras were produced. A related factory in Prague produced optics for microscopes, and related devices. Meopta's lens making facilities supplied other Czech camera manufacturers, such as Druopta in Prague. Dating of Meopta cameras will be made easier and more accurate in the near future when a company prepared serial number record is expected to be made available. At the present time, however there is some internal disagreement as to production dates and figures at Meopta in Prerov. Dates used are those listed in Moepta official publications, or provided by company personnel. While some Flexaret

MEOPTA

cameras are quite common in the West, many others are not often seen. With the country's opening to the Free World, the rarity ratings on some cameras could be expected to be downgraded in the future. (Since many early Czech cameras carry little manufacturer's information on them, a few are listed here for simplicity)

Admira 8C: (EO100); 8mm movie camera; Cinor Berthiot f1.8 lens or another common lens such as the Mirar f2.8/12.5mm , interchangeable mount; 5 speeds: 10, 16, 24, 48 and 64 frames per s. C 1949.

R3* $25	£13	DM41	FF128

Mikroma: (EO105); Subminiature camera for 11mm x14mm size negatives on single perforated 16mm film. four speed shutter 1/25-1/200 s. Designed before WWII, but only produced from 1946.

R3* $125	£66	DM206	FF639

Mikroma II: (EO101); subminiature camera; Mirar 20mm f3.5 lens; shutter 1/5-1/400.s with brown or green body covering. C 1964.

R2* $125	£66	DM206	FF639

Stereo Mikroma: (EO102); subminiature stereo camera; Mirar 25mm f3.5 lenses; shutter 1/5-1/100 s. 12 to 14 stereo exp on single perforation 16mm film. Viewers are still available in Czechoslovakia, and cost about $1 !C.

R2* $190	£100	DM313	FF971

Stereo Mikromall: (EO106); subminiature stereo camera; Mirar 25mm f3.5 lenses; shutter 1/5-1/100 s. 12 to 14 stereo exp on single perforation 16mm film. As (EO102) but with improved film transport and shutter cocking systems.

R2* $170	£89	DM280	FF869

Mikronette: (EO 119); **1945** Subminiature camera for 240 exposures 11mmx14mm size on single perforated 16mm film. four speed shutter 1/25-1/200 s. Designed before WWII, and made by Optikotechna in limited numbers for the military.

R5* NSR est $1.2k	£630	DM2k	FF6.1k

Stereo 35: (EO120); 1970 cream coloured stereo camera for 35mm film, but yielding about 80 viewmaster size stereo pairs from a 36 exposure roll of film. fixed focus Mirar f3.5/25mm lenses in a simple shutter. These cameras were hard to sell, and eventually went to state owned discount shops where they were sold out for about $4 each. rare.

R3* $125	£66	DM206	FF639

Opema (II): (EO103); 1955-60 CFPS,1/25 - 1/500, CRF, combined RFR/VFR window, screw mount f3.5, f2.8, or f2.0/45mm lenses. Removable back, cassette to cassette film transport. Considered by some to be a Leica copy, the Opema uses a smaller diameter screw thread than Leica. Do not try to force your Leitz lenses, you are only asking for trouble!

R3* $225	£118	DM371	FF1.2k

Opema (I): (EO104); 1954-59 CFPS,1/25 - 1/500, as (EO103), but *without* RFR! screw mount f3.5, f2.8, or f2.0/45mm lenses. Removable back, cassette to cassette film transport.

R4* $225	£118	DM371	FF1.2k

Milona: (EO107); 1946-50, well made folding camera for 6 x 6 or 6 x 4.5 negatives on 120 roll film. Mirar f4.5/80mm lens in Prontor II or Prontor S shutter. Scale focusing from 1M Built-in slide for tilting lens to straighten converging lines when photographing buildings from a low angle. Quite rare.

R4* $90	£47	DM148	FF460

Milona

Milona II: (EO108); 1951-56, folding camera for 6 x 6 or 6 x 4.5 negatives on 120 roll film. Mirar f3.5/80mm lens in Prontor S shutter.Same lens tilting feature as (EO107) Quite rare.

R4* $100	£52	DM165	FF511

Iskra: (EO109); 1951-56, folding camera for 6 x 6 or 6 x 4.5 negatives on 120 roll film. Mirar f3.5/80mm lens in Prontor S shutter. *Without* lens tilting feature. (not to be confused with the Soviet "Iskra", which is a copy of Agfa.) Quite rare.

R4* $70	£37	DM115	FF358

Magnola: (EO110); 1947-53, ground glass focusing folding metal bodied view camera for 13 x 18cm negatives, Compound type shutter with Belar f4.5/210 lens, three built-in levels, lens tilts and shifts, according to a factory source, this camera was exported.

R4*? $600	£315	DM989	FF3.1k

Flexaret: (original) (EO111); 1945 twin lens reflex camera for 6 x 6 negatives on 120 roll film.uncoated Mirar f4.5/80mm taking lens in Prontor II shutter Optikotechna

Flexaret: (original)

Anastigmat f3/80mm viewing lens. Knob advance not coupled to shutter cocking, no provisions for double exposure prevention. Made by Opitkotechna before merging with Meopta in 1946. Quite rare.

R4* $80	£42	DM132	FF409

Flexaret II: (EO112); 1946-47 twin lens reflex camera for 6 x 6 negatives on 120 roll film. Mirar f4.5/80mm taking lens in Prontor II shutter Anastigmat f3/80mm viewing lens. Knob advance not coupled to shutter cocking, no provisions for double exposure prevention. The same camera as (EO111), but made after merger into Meopta. More common than (EO111). Transition models still have Optikotechna marked on the lenses, but not on the camera body.

R3* $50	£26	DM82	FF256

Flexaret III: (EO113); 1948-50 twin lens reflex camera for 6 x 6 negatives on 120 roll film.coated Mirar f3.5/80mm taking lens in Prontor S or Metax shutter Anastigmat f3/80mm viewing lens. crank advance coupled to shutter cocking, automatic frame counting double exposure prevention. the only crank advance model.

R3* $60	£31	DM99	FF307

Flexaret IV: (EO114); 1950-57 twin lens reflex camera for 6 x 6 negatives on 120 roll film.coated Belar f3.5/80mm taking lens in Prontor SVS or Metax shutter Anastigmat f3/80mm viewing lens. Knob advance coupled to shutter cocking, automatic frame counting double exposure prevention. First model with depth of field scale built-into the focusing handle. Easily recognised by its strange body mounted shutter release. Quite common.

R2* $35	£18	DM58	FF179

Flexaret V: (EO 115); 1958-59 twin lens reflex camera for 6 x 6 negatives on 120 roll film.coated Belar f3.5/80mm taking lens in Prontor SVS shutter Anastigmat f3/80mm viewing lens. Knob advance coupled to shutter cocking, automatic frame counting double exposure prevention. Redesigned front, focusing lever and shutter release.

R2* $50	£26	DM82	FF256

Flexaret Va: (EO 116); 1959-61 twin lens reflex camera for 6 x 6 negatives on 120 roll film coated Belar f3.5/80mm taking lens in Prontor SVS shutter Anastigmat f3/80mm viewing lens. °Knob advance coupled to shutter cocking, automatic frame counting double exposure prevention. basically (EO115) with provision for using 35mm film with the appropriate adaptor. This is the first model with this feature. (Price given is for the camera complete with 35mm adaptor set, otherwise priced as (EO115).

R2* $80	£42	DM132	FF409

Flexaret VI: (EO117); 1961-67 Grey covered body twin lens reflex camera for 6 x 6 negatives on 120 roll film.coated Belar f3.5/80mm taking lens in Prontor SVS shutter Belar f3.5/80mm viewing lens. Knob advance coupled to shutter cocking, automatic frame counting double exposure prevention , provision for using 35mm film with the appropriate adaptor. (Price given is for the camera complete with 35mm adaptor set (-30% without adaptor).

R3* $100	£52	DM165	FF511

Flexaret VII: (EO118); 1966-71 Grey covered body twin lens reflex camera for 6 x 6 negatives on 120 roll film.coated Belar f3.5/80mm taking lens in Prontor SVS shutter Belar f3.8/80mm viewing lens. Knob advance coupled to shutter cocking, automatic frame counting double exposure prevention , provision for using 35mm film with the appropriate adaptor. I he last of the Flexarets. (Price given is for the camera complete with 35mm adaptor set (-30% without adaptor).

R3* $120	£63	DM198	FF613

Optineta: (EO121); 1959 35mm VFR camera front element focusing coated f3/45mm Belar lens in Metax shutter.

R3* $30	£16	DM49	FF153

Etareta: (EO122); 1947-48 35mm VFR camera front cell focusing coated f3.5/5cm Etar II lens in collapsible mount, Etaxa shutter 1/10 - 1/200s, marked "Eta Praha" on the lens, and "made in Czechoslovakia" on the front of the camera body.

R3* $45	£24	DM74	FF230

Spektareta: (EO123); 1939 "The smallest three colour camera in the world"* Three exposures made at the same time through

Etareta

red, green, and blue filters to produce three colour seperation negatives.12 sets of negatives 24mm x 24mm per 36 exposure roll f2.9/70mm Spektar lens in Compur shutter, 1 - 1/250s crfr, parallax correcting VFR.
Made by Optikotechna, very rare (* according to the National Technical Museum in Prague!).

R5* NSR est $4k	£2.1k	DM6.6k	FF20.4k

Coloureta: (EO124); 1939 Three colour camera, much as (EO120) but without CRF. helical focusing Spektar f2.9/70mm lens in Compur shutter, 1 - 1/250s.
12 sets of negatives 24mm x 24mm per 36 exposure roll made by Optikotechna, very rare.

R*5 NSR est$3.5k	£1.8k	DM5.8k	FF17.9k

Meta: (EO125); 1956? simple 35mm VFR camera, f3.5/63mm Belar lens in focusing mount, Metax shutter, 1 - 1/400, marked "Meta" on the front of the top plate. not produced in large numbers, quite rare.

R4* $55	£29	DM91	FF281

Meta II: (EO126); 1957?, similar to (EO124), but with added coupled RFR, f3.5/63mm Belar lens, Metax shutter, 1 - 1/400s, marked "Meta" on the top plate, quite rare.

R4* $75	£39	DM124	FF383

Meta III; (EO127); 1959? 35mm camera with coupled RFR and interchangeable lenses, f3.5/35mm Meopta S.O. lens in breech mount, Metax behind the lens shutter, 1 - 1/400s, very Voightländer Prominant in appearance, this camera was never made in large scale production, and indeed may exist only in prototype form. No information is available at the moment concerning accessory lenses which might have been available.

R5* NSR est$550 £289 DM907 FF2.8k

Kamerad: (EO128); 1936 Metal TLR for 6 x 6 exposures on 120 roll film, f3.9/7.5cm Bellar from Ernst Ludwig Optical works in Dresden are used for both viewing and taking lenses Prontor II shutter, 1 - 1/175s, knob film transport with automatic frame counting. Made by the Bradác Brothers, Hovorcovice (near Prague).

R5* $125   £66   DM206   FF639

Kamerad MII: (EO129); 1936 Metal TLR for 6 x 6 exposures on 120 roll film, f2.9/7.5cm Trioplan lenses from Hugo Meyer in Görlitz are used for both viewing and taking lenses Compur shutter, 1 - 1/250s, knob film transport with automatic frame counting. Made by the Bradác Brothers, Hovorcovice (near Prague).

R5* $125   £66   DM206   FF639

Autoflex: (EO130); 1938 metal TLR for 6 x 6 negatives on 120 roll film, f2.9/7.5cm Trioplan lenses from Hugo Meyer in Görlitz are used for both viewing and taking lenses Compur shutter, 1 - 1/250s, knob film transport with automatic frame counting..made by Optikotechna. Rare.

R4* $110   £58   DM181   FF562

Optiflex: (EO131); 1938 metal TLR for 6 x 6 negatives on 120 roll film, f2.9/7.5cm Mirar lenses are used for both viewing and taking lenses Compur shutter, 1 - 1/250s, knob film transport with automatic frame counting..made by Optikotechna. Rare.

R5* $100   £52   DM165   FF511

Vega: (EO132); C1950's simple 35mm VFR camera with cassette to cassette film transport, collapsible f3.5 or 4.5 50mm lens (Druoptar or Etar) in Etaxa, Chrontax , Metax, or "no-name" shutters, with or without accessory shoe. made by Druopta, Prague.

R3* $35   £18   DM58   FF179

Druoflex I: (EO133); C 1950's bakelite TLR in the style of Lubitel, which is itself a loose copt of Voightländer Brilliant, for 6 x 6 expo-

Vega

Druoflex I

sures on 120 roll film, body by Atak nonfocusing VFR, front cell focusing taking lens, f6.3/75mm Druoptar in Chrontax shutter, 1/10 - 1/200s, made by Druopta, Prague.

R3* $35   £18   DM58   FF179

Fokaflex: (EO134); C1950's, bakelite TLR for 6 x 6 exposures on 120 roll film, boxier than the Druoflex, with unusual two piece back, fixed focus "special" lens, Fokar 2 shutter, 1/25 - 1/100s, made by Foka.

R4* $45   £24   DM74   FF230

Fokaflex

Rix

M

Rix: (EO135); C1950's bakelite TLR, smoother body than the Druoflex, grey painted metal front and focusing hood, for 6 x 6 exposures on 120 roll film, nonfocusing VFR, fixed focus fll taking lens in Fokar shutter, 1/25 - 1/75s, made Foka, rare.

R4* $45	£24	DM74	FF230

Pionyr I: (EO136); C1950s, bakelite VFR camera for 6 x 6cm or 6 x 4.5cm frames on roll film, simple lens and shutter. Made by Dufa, near Prague.

R3* $40	£21	DM66	FF204

Pionyr I

Pionyr II: (EO137); C1950s, as (EO136) but with focusing. Copied by the Chinese as the "Great Leap" camera.

R3* $40	£21	DM66	FF204

Mephisto Camera: (BB205); C1900, meniscus lens; exp controlled by lens cap. 5 exp on plates. Mfd in Germany.

R5* $900	£472	DM1.5k	FF4.6k

METROPOLITAN SUPPLY
Chicago, Illinois.

The King Camera: (MS100); miniature cardboard camera; size: 2" x 2" x 3 1/2" exp on glass plates.

Mick-A-Matic: (BB206); C1969,toy camera in shape of mouse head; meniscus lens in nose; sector shutter, flash synch using flash cubes. Shutter cannot be operated unless film is wound to stop. 12 exp on 126 roll film. Manufacturer's instructions: tag on ear says, "Treat me gently, I'm your pal".

| R3* $100 | £52 | DM165 | FF511 |

Mick-A-Matic

D. MILLARD & CO., MANUFACTURERS, Cincinnati, Ohio.

Robinson's Patent Photograph Album: (DM100); Carte-de-visite photos mounted on a fabric belt; displayed by turning knobs. C 1865.

| R4* $300 | £157 | DM495 | FF1.5k |

Robinson's Album and Photographicon

Robinson's Photographicon: (DM101); Carte-de-visite photograph viewer. Early hand-coloured stencil design. Patent April 11, 1865.

| R4* $400 | £210 | DM659 | FF2k |

T. MILLER, Manchester, England.

Adelphi Detective Camera: (TM100); box-type detective camera. C 1899.

| R3* $200 | £105 | DM330 | FF1k |

MIMOSA CAMERAS, Germany.

Mimosa I: (MQ100); 35mm box-type camera; Meyer Trioplan 50mm f2.9 lens; Compur-Rapid 1-1/500 s. C 1947.

| R4* $100 | £52 | DM165 | FF511 |

Mimosa II: (MQ101); Meritar 50mm f2.9 lens; Velax shutter 1/10-1/200 s.

| R3* $80 | £42 | DM132 | FF409 |

MINOLTA - Chiyoda Kogaku Seiko Co., Ltd., Osaka, Japan.

Konan 16 Automat: (IN100); Rokkor 25mm f3.5 lens. C 1952.

| R3* $125 | £66 | DM206 | FF639 |

Minolta Auto Press: (IN102); 6 x 9cm press camera; Promar Anastigmat Nippon 100mm f3.5 lens; Crown Rapid shutter 1-1/400 s, CRF. 6 x 9cm exp on cut film and film pack. C 1935.

| R3* $170 | £89 | DM280 | FF869 |

Minolta 35 I (Original): (IN104); 1947. Cfps, 1 - 1/500 sec, combined Rfr/Vfr window, self timer, unusual 24mm X 32mm frame size known as "Nippon" size, and also used by Nikon is found on both the "Original" and type "B" cameras. Screw mount Super Rokkor F2.8/45mm lens. 24 mm X 33mm frame size was used on the type "C" camera, and a 24mm X 34mm frame on the type "D" and "E" cameras. Types "C", "D", and "E" though rare, bring roughly 20% of the price of the original and type "B" cameras.

| R4* $500 | £262 | DM824 | FF2.6k |

Minolta Auto Press

Minolta 35 Type "E"

Minolta 35 Model II: (IN103); 1953. Cfps, 1 - 1/500 sec, combined Rfr/Vfr window, self timer, 24mm X 34mm frame size. Screw mount Super Rokkor F2.8/45mm or Super Rokkor F2.0/5cm lens. This is the most common of the Minolta Leica copies.

R2* $100	£52	DM165	FF511

Minolta 35 Model IIB: (IN105); 1958. Cfps, 1 - 1/500 sec, combined Rfr/Vfr window, self timer, 24mm X 36mm frame size. Screw mount Super Rokkor F1.8/5cm lens. This was the first Minolta to use the standard 24mm X 36mm frame size, and the last Minolta Leica copy. Though not particularly

M

rare this camera is still valuable as a Leica copy.

R2* $325	£171	DM536	FF1.7k

Minoltaflex: (IN120); 1936, TLR for 6 x 6cm on roll film, the first Japanese TLR, marked only "Minolta" on the front, Promar f3.5/75mm taking lens among others, Minolta viewing lens, shutter I - 1/300s.

R3* $125	£66	DM206	FF639

Minolta CLE: (IN110); 1980. Cfps, 1 - 1/1000 sec, electronically controlled, combined Rfr/Vfr window, "M" type bayonet mount Minolta Rokkor F2.0/40mm lens. The limited edition model available in Gold, in-

Minolta CLE

creases the price by a factor of three.

R2* $325	£171	DM536	FF1.7k

Accessory lenses for Minolta CLE

28mm/f2.8 lens: (IN001); **$375**
90mm/f4.0 lens: (IN002); **$250**

MINOX,
Geissen, West Germany.

Minox I: (MX100); subminiature detective camera; Minostigmat 15mm f3.5 fixed aperture, 3 element lens; guillotine, front-of-lens shutter 1/2 -
1/1000 s. 8 x 11mm exp on 9.5mm film in special cassettes. Snr 1-20,000. The original Minox was made from stainless steel; later models were made from aluminium. Valsts Electro-Techniska Fabrika, Riga, Latvia. C 1938.

R3* $550	£289	DM907	FF2.8k

Minox I

Minox B: (MX101); subminiature detective camera; 15mm f3.5 lens; shutter 1/2-1/1000 s. Chrome version: **$125**. Black version:

R3* $200	£105	DM330	FF1k

Minox B

Minox BL: (MX102); subminiature camera; 15mm f3.5 lens; shutter 1/2-1/1000 s. Coupled CdS exp meter.
C 1976. Chrome, **$150**. Gold:

R3* $900	£472	DM1.5k	FF4.6k

Minox C: (MX103); subminiature detective camera; 15mm f3.5 lens; electronic shutter

10 s-1/1000 s coupled to CdS exp meter for auto exp control with manual override. C 1976. Chrome version, **$120**. Black:

R3* $225	£118	DM371	FF1.2k

Minox IIIS: (MX104); subminiature camera; 15mm f3.5 lens; shutter 1/2-1/1000 s. Chrome, **$110**. Black:

R3* $350	£184	DM577	FF1.8k

Minox IIIS

MIRANDA CAMERA COMPANY,
Tokyo, Japan.

In 1946, the Orion Camera Company, predecessor of the Miranda Camera Company, Ltd., was established in Tokyo. Although the company did manufacture a limited line of photographic related products, its main function was as a service centre for professional photographic equipment.

Among the products made by Orion were a special adaptor which allowed the use of Contax or Nikon mount lenses on Leica type screw mount bodies, and the "Focabell" close-up bellows.

In 1953 after five years of research, the Phoenix SLR camera was made, but only a few hand-made examples were produced, and the camera was never marketed. In 1954, the prototype was renamed the model "T" and finally placed on the market.

In 1956, the Orion Company became "Miranda" the name with which we are so familiar.

In all, a total of 36 different basic camera models were produced before financial difficulties forced the company to close its doors in 1977.

Though much maligned in the

past as poor cousins to their more popular competitors, Miranda has seen recent growth in collector interest, to the point of the establishment of a Miranda Collectors Club. (see the "Organization" section in the front of the Blue Book for more information concerning Miranda special interest collectors organization.)

Adam Geschwind, from Sydney, Australia has been the moving force behind this section on Miranda. He has spent many hours putting together the information which appears here, along with providing the photographs for the listings. He is a fine example of the behind the scenes efforts which go into the making of each edition of the Blue Book. Adam welcomes correspondence concerning all models of Miranda cameras, and is especially interested in serial number information of both cameras and lenses for use in compiling a computer data base. He may be reached at:

Adam Geschwind, PO Box 28, Waverly Post Office, Waverly, Sydney, Australia, 2024

Mirax: (MI300); 1950 marked "Orion Camera Company" later version marked "Miranda Camera Company, mirror box with interchangeable reflex finder (after 1953), which allowed up-right TTL viewing on Nikon, Contax, Leica Canon, or similar 35mm camera bodies.

R4* $200	£105
DM330	FF1k

Orion T: (MI301); C1954, 35mm SLR with interchangeable Zunow f1.9/5cm lens in 44mm screw mount , CPFS 1 - 1/500s, removable pentaprism, knob wind, non-instant return mirror, top and front mounted shutter release.chrome body, serial number 554xxx to 556xxx. (black body adds at least 100%) *Miranda Identification hint: Many models contain the model designation before the serial number, on the back of the camera.*

R4* $800	£420	DM1.3k	FF4.1k

Orion T

Miranda T: (MI302); C1956, 35mm SLR with interchangeable Zunow f1.9/5cm, Arco f2.4/5cm, Soligar-Miranda f1.9/5cm or Miranda f1.9/5cm lens in 44mm screw mount, CPFS 1 - 1/500s, removable pentaprism, knob wind, non-instant return mirror, top and front mounted shutter release, chrome body, serial number 558xxx. (camera illustrated shows *rare* black trim on advance, rewind, shutter speed, and film counter dials.)

R3* $200	£105	DM330	FF1k

Miranda T

MIRANDA

Miranda S: (MI303); C1959, 35mm SLR with interchangeable Soligar-Miranda f2.8/ 5cm lens in 44mm screw mount, 1/30-1/ 500s, removable WL finder, pentaprism sold as accessory, knob wind, non-instant return mirror, *only front mounted shutter release,* chrome body, serial number 59xxxx.

R3* $200	£105	DM330	FF1k

Miranda ST: (MI304); C1959, 35mm SLR with interchangeable Soligar-Miranda f2.8/ 5cm lens in 44mm screw mount, 1 -1/500s, removable WL finder, pentaprism sold as accessory, knob wind, non-instant return mirror, top and front mounted shutter release, chrome body, serial number 55xxxx to 56xxxx.

R3* $200	£105	DM330	FF1k

Miranda ST

Miranda A: (MI305); C1957, 35mm SLR with interchangeable preset Soligar-Miranda f1.9/5cm lens in either 44mm screw mount or external semi-automatic (á la Exakta) bayonet mount 1 -1/1000s, removable finder, *lever wind*, non-instant return mirror, top and front mounted shutter release.

Miranda A

chrome body, serial number 57xxxx.

R2* $150	£79	DM247	FF767

Miranda AII: (MI306); C1957, same as (MI305) but for smaller frame counter dial, and red triangles marked at 20 and 36 exposures.

R3* $100	£52	DM165	FF511

Miranda B: (MI307); C1957, 35mm SLR with interchangeable black finished Prominar-Miranda f1.9/5cm external semi-automatic lens in bayonet mount , CFPS 1 -1/1000s, removable finder, lever wind, instant return mirror, top and front mounted shutter release, chrome body, serial number 58xxxx.

R2* $100	£52	DM165	FF511

Miranda C: (MI308); C1959, 35mm SLR with interchangeable black finished Prominar-Miranda f1.9/5cm external semi-automatic lens in bayonet mount , CFPS 1 -1/1000s, removable finder, lever wind, instant return mirror, self timer, top and front mounted shutter release, chrome body, serial number 60xxxx.

R2* $150	£79	DM247	FF767

Miranda D: (MI309); C1960, 35mm SLR with interchangeable preset Soligor-Miranda f2.8/5cm lens in 44mm screw mount, or bayonet mount Soligor-Miranda or Prominar-Miranda f1.9/5cm external semi-automatic lens, , CFPS 1-1/500s, lever wind, instant return mirror, new rounded body shape, *front shutter release only,* serial number 63xxxx (sequence shared by Automex III (MI3xx)

R1* $50	£26	DM82	FF256

Miranda D

Miranda DR: (MI310); C1962, 35mm SLR with interchangeable preset Soligor-Miranda f2.8/5cm lens in 44mm screw mount, or bayonet mount Soligor-Miranda f1.9/5cm external semi-automatic lens, , CFPS 1-1/500s, lever wind, instant return mirror, new rounded body shape, *front shutter release only,* split image focusing screen standard, both "Miranda" and MIRANDA" logos are found, no model designation on the camera back, red leatherette covering on the frame counter dial, serial number 65xxxx to 66xxxx.

R2* $70	£37	DM115	FF358

Miranda F: (MI311); C1963, 35mm SLR with interchangeable Auto Miranda f1.9/5cm lens, CFPS 1 - 1/1000s, (a few cameras in this series had 1/500s top speed), depth of field preview button on the camera body, no model designation on the camera back, serial number 67xxxx to 70xxxx. (Black body add 100%).

R1* $50	£26	DM82	FF256

Miranda F

Miranda FM

Miranda FM: (MI312): C1963, as model "F" (MI311), but for *non-TTL* CDS pentaprism,

any "F" body could be updated simply by adding this metered pentaprism. (Black body add 100%).

R2* $70	£37	DM115	FF358

Miranda FT: (MI313): C1967, as model "F" (MI311), but for *uncoupled TTL* CDS pentaprism, any "F" body could be updated simply by adding this metered pentaprism. (Black body add 100%).

R2* $80	£42	DM132	FF409

Miranda Fv: (MI314); C1966, as model "F" (MI311), but for no depth of field pre-view, and removable shutterspeed dial, for use when using clip on meter, model designation on the camera front, serial number 72xxxx. (Black body add 100%).

R2* $70	£37	DM115	FF358

Miranda FvM: (MI315); C1966, as model "Fv" (MI314), but for *non-TTL* CDS meter prism, model designation "Fv"on the camera front, any "Fv" camera body could be updated simply by adding this metered prism(Black body add 100%).

R2* $80	£42	DM132	FF409

Miranda FvT: (MI316); C1967, as model "Fv" (MI314), but for uncoupled *TTL* CDS meter prism, model designation "Fv"on the camera front, "T" on the prism, any "Fv" camera body could be updated simply by adding this metered prism (Black body add 100%).

R2* $80	£42	DM132	FF409

Miranda FvT

Miranda G: (MI317); C1965, 35mm SLR with interchangeable Auto Miranda f1.9/5cm lens, CFPS 1 - 1/1000s, removable

M

finder, interchangeable *focusing screens, mirror lock-up,* self timer, top and front shutter release, removable shutterspeed dial for use when using clip on meter, model designation on the camera front, (Black Body adds 100%).

R2* $90	£47	DM148	FF460

Miranda G with clip on meter

Miranda GM: (MI318); C1965-66, as (MI317) but for non-TTL CDS prism finder, any "G" camera body could be updated simply by adding this metered prism. (Black body adds 100%).

R2* $90	£47	DM148	FF460

Miranda GT: (MI319); C1967, as (MI317) but for uncoupled TTL CDS prism finder, model designation "G"on the camera front, "T" on the prism, any "G" camera body could be updated simply by adding this metered prism. (Black body adds 100%)

R2* $90	£47	DM148	FF460

Miranda GT

Miranda Sensomat: (MI320): C1969, 35mm SLR with interchangeable Auto Miranda f1.8/5cm lens, CFPS 1 - 1/1000s, coupled TTL CDS meter for stopped down metering with two button operation, all metal lever advance, serial number 81xxxx to 83xxxx.

R2* $50	£26	DM82	FF256

Miranda Sensomat

Miranda Sensomat RE: (MI321); C1970, as (MI320) but for single button meter operation, and black plastic tipped lever advance, tops of lever advance, shutter speed dial, and rewind knob are chrome, not black, serial numbers 68xxxxx.

R2* $50	£26	DM82	FF256

Miranda Sensomat RS: (MI322); C1970, as (MI321) but without meter, serial number 37xxxxx.

R2* $50	£26	DM82	FF256

Miranda Sensomat RE II: (MI323); C1975, 35mm SLR with interchangeable Auto Miranda EC f1.4 or f1.8/5cm lens, CFPS 1 - 1/1000s, single top mounted shutter release, "Q.I.S." ("Quadrascopic Image System") circular multi image rangefinder focusing system, serial number 58xxxxx to 59xxxxx. (Black body adds 100%).

R2* $50	£26	DM82	FF256

Miranda TM: (MI324); C1975, 35mm SLR with interchangeable Auto Miranda TM f1.8/5cm lens in 42mm (Praktica/Pentax size), CFPS 1 - 1/1000s, single top mounted shutter release, stopped down metering, serial number 46xxxxx (type I), slight variations seen over the production life serial number 56xxxxx (type II). (Also sold as the "Soligor TM" (MI325).

R2* $50	£26	DM82	FF256

Sologar TM: (MI325); C1975, as (MI324

Miranda TM

Sologar TM

type I) but for name, and Auto Soligor f1.8/50mm lens.

R2* $50	£26	DM82	FF256

Miranda Automex: (MI326); C1959, 35mm SLR camera with interchangeable Soligor-Miranda f1.9/5cm lens, CFPS 1 - 1/1000s, coupled Selinium light meter to 400 ASA,

Miranda Automex

provision for motor wind on some cameras though no winder has yet been found, serial number 61xxxx.

R2* $50	£26	DM82	FF256

Miranda Automex II: (MI327); C1963, as (MI326) but for redesigned flash synch and 1600 ASA sensibility, serial number 61xxxx

R2* $50	£26	DM82	FF256

Miranda Automex III: (MI328); C1964, as (MI326) but for side mounted flash synch and CDS light meter to 1600 ASA, serial number 63xxxx.

R2* $50	£26	DM82	FF256

Miranda Automex III

Miranda Sensorex: (MI329); C1967, 35mm SLR with interchangeable Auto Miranda f1.4 or f1.9/5cm lens, CFPS 1 - 1/1000s, first Miranda with open aperture metering, maximum aperture of lens in use must be set on a special dial under the front of the camera, under the rewind knob marked -1.4, 1.9, 2.8, 3.5, 4, 5.6, and 8, serial numbers 7xxxxx.

R2* $50	£26	DM82	FF256

Miranda Sensorex

Miranda Sensorex 1.8: (MI330); C1968, as (MI329) but for use with f1.8 lens instead of f1.9, serial number 9xxxxx. (Black body adds 100%).

R2* $50	£26	DM82	FF256

Miranda Sensorex II: (MI331); C1971, 35mm SLR with interchangeable Auto Miranda f1.4 or f1.8/5cm lens, CFPS 1 - 1/1000s, first Miranda with hot shoe, lens aperture selection dial moved to under rewind knob, serial number 83xxxxx. (Black body adds 100%).

R2* $80	£42	DM132	FF409

Miranda Sensorex II in chrome and black

Miranda Sensorex EE: (MI332); C1971, 35mm SLR with interchangeable Auto Miranda E f1.4 or f1.8/5cm lens, CFPS 1 - 1/1000s, shutter speed preferred automatic TTL exposure control, top shutter release only, serial number 91xxxxx. (Black body adds 50%)

R2* $80	£42	DM132	FF409

Miranda Sensorex EE-2: (MI333); C1974, 35mm SLR with interchangeable Auto

Miranda Sensorex EE. AIC in the camera body mean Allied Impex Corporation, the American owners of Miranda Company, and official importers and distributors.

Miranda EC f1.4 or f1.8/5cm lens, CFPS 1 - 1/1000s, shutter speed preferred automatic TTL exposure control, top shutter release only, shutter speeds visible in finder, Q.I.S. focusing system, serial number 93xxxxx. (Black body adds 100%).

R1* $80 ·	£42	DM132	FF409

Miranda Sensorex EE-2 in black

Miranda dx-3: (MI334); C1975, 35mm SLR with interchangeable Auto Miranda EC f1.4 or f1.8/5cm lens, electronically controlled CFPS 4 - 1/1000s, the only Miranda SLR with a fixed prism, motor drive capable, the last Model produced by MIranda, often found not working, serial number 39xxxxx. (Black body *less* 50%).

R1* $100	£52	DM165	FF511

Miranda Sensoret: (MI335); C1972, 35mm

Miranda dx-3 in black

Miranda Sensoret

RFR camera with fixed Miranda Soligor f2.8/38mm lens, Seiku ESF shutter, the only non SLR Miranda, serial number 24xxxxx.

| R3* $20 | £10 | DM33 | FF102 |

Mirax Laborec II: (MI336); C1970, 35mm SLR for laboratory use, suitable for mounting on a microscope, or telescope, CFPS 1

Mirax Laborec II

- 1/125s, two bayonet mounts and one screw mount, oversized knob advance, *cable release only top and front,* removable VF-5 vertical VFR, type A has button VFR lock, type B uses a locking ring located under the rewind knob, X synch only, serial number type A 113xxx - 115xxx, serial number type B 116xxx to 119xxx, it is not known if a Laborec I was ever made.

| R3* $250 | £131 | DM412 | FF1.3k |

Mirax Ladorec Electro-D: (MI337); C1972, 35mm SLR for laboratory use, similar to (MI336) "type A", but for black body and built-in motor winder capable of two frames/sec, 12V DC required to power the motor either from rectified/reduced AC, or from rechargeable battery unit, serial number 114xxx Mx.

| R4* $500 | £262 | DM824 | FF2.6k |

Mirax Ladorec Electro-D

Miranda Laborec: (MI338); C1975, 35mm SLR for laboratory use, as (MI336) "type B" but for name, and only Miranda bayonet and 44mm screw mount, serial number 12xxxx.

| R3* $250 | £131 | DM412 | FF1.3k |

Miranda Laborec

Miranda Laborec III: (MI339); C1975, 35mm SLR for laboratory use, as (MI338), but additional 1/250 and 1/500s shutter speeds, *the only Laborec with model designation indicated on the camera front,* serial number 21xxxxx.

R3* $250	£131	DM412	FF1.3k

Accessories and lenses for Miranda SLRs:

extension tube set, 8mm, 16mm, 32mm: (MI001); **$10**
universal helicoid: (MI002); **$5**
lens adaptors, (39mm screw, 42mm screw, Exakta, etc.): (MI003);**$5**

VF-1 WL VFR: (MI004); **$10**
VF-3 critical focusing VFR: (MI005); **$20**

VF-3 critical focusing VFR opened and closed

VF-4 critical focusing VFR: (MI006); **$20**
"M" pentaprism w/CDS meter: (MI007); **$20**
"T" pentaprism w/ TTL CDS meter: (MI008); **$30**
Focabell twin rail bellows (Miranda "T"): (MI009); **$30**
Focabell All twin rail bellows (Sensomat) : (MI010); **$30**
Focabell AIII twin rail bellows (Sensomat RE): (MI011); **$30**
Bellox JR single rail bellows (DR):(MI012); **$15**
Focabell S single rail bellows (F): (MI013); **$15**
pistol grip with release: (MI014); **$25**
microscope adaptor:(MI015); **$30**
double cable release:(MI016); **$5**
clip-on CDS light meter:(MI017); **$20**
flash bracket: (MI018); **$5**
slide copier:(MI020); **$5**
focusing screens for "G" and

Laborec:(MI021); **$5**
Miranda Panorama head:(MI022); **$30**
motor drive for Automex:(MI023); **$100**
motor drive for dx-3:(MI024); **$100**
bulk film back for dx-3:(MI025); **$100**
radio remote release for dx-3:(MI026); **$50**
scope meter for microscope use:(MI027); **$50**

Soligor Miranda lenses, preset or external automatic

28mm f2.8 automatic:(MI030); **$30**
35mmf2.8 preset:(MI031); **$20**
35mm f3.5 preset:(MI032); **$20**
35mm f2.8 automatic:(MI033); **$30**
105mm f2.8 automatic:(MI034); **$30**
135mm f2.8 preset:(MI036); **$20**
135mm f2.8 automatic:(MI037) **$35**
135mm f3.5 preset:(MI038); **$20**
135mm f3.5 automatic:(MI039); **$30**
135mm f3.5 bellows mount(MI040); **$60**
180mm f4.5 preset:(MI041); **$80**
250mm f4.5 preset:(MI042); **$100**
400mm f5.5 preset:(MI043); **$150**

Soligor Miranda lenses for Automex cameras:

28mm f2.8:(MI044); **$30**
35mm f2.8:(MI045); **$30**
105mm f2.8:(MI046); **$30**
135mm f2.8:(MI047); **$30**
135mm f3.5:(MI048); **$30**

Auto Miranda lenses for Automex cameras:

25mm f2.8:(MI049); **$50**
28mm f2.8:(MI050); **$30**
35mm f2.8:(MI051); **$30**
105mm f2.8:(MI052); **$30**
135mm f2.8:(MI053); **$30**
135mm f3.5:(MI054); **$30**
200mm f3.5:(MI055); **$100**

Auto Miranda lenses for Sensorex cameras:

25mm f2.8:(MI056); **$60**

28mm f2.8:(MI057); **$30**
35mm f2.8:(MI058); **$30**
105mm f2.8:(MI059); **$30**
135mm f2.8:(MI060); **$30**
135mm f3.5:(MI061); **$30**
180mm f3.5:(MI062); **$80**
200mm f3.5:(MI063); **$100**
52mm f3.5 **Macron**:(MI064); **$40**

Auto Miranda E lenses:

25mm f2.8:(MI065); **$60**
28mm f2.8:(MI066); **$30**
35mm f2.8:(MI067); **$30**
105mm f2.8:(MI068); **$30**
135mm f2.8:(MI069); **$30**
135mm f3.5:(MI070); **$30**
180mm f3.5:(MI071); **$100**
200mm f3.5:(MI072); **$120**
52mm f3.5 **Macron**:(MI073); **$40**

Auto Miranda EC lenses:

28mm f2.8:(MI074); **$40**
35mm f2.8:(MI075); **$40**
105mm f2.8:(MI076); **$40**
135mm f2.8:(MI077); **$40**
200mm f3.5:(MI078); **$120**
80-200mm f3.5 zoom :(MI079); **$150**
52mm f3.5 **Macron**:(MI080); **$40**

MISUZU KOGAKU KOGYO & CO., LTD., Japan.

Alta: (MI200); 1957-59 CFPS, 1-1/500 sec, seperate RFR/VFR windows, diopter adjustment. Screw mount Altanon F2.0/50mm or Altanon F3.5/50mm lens. Similar to the Leica IIIA. Maybe only 600 made.

R4* $1.7k	£892	DM2.8k	FF8.7k

Lieutenant Colonel MOESSARD, Paris, France.

Topographic Cylindrographe: (LT100); panoramic landscape camera; Rectilinear 15cm lens moves in an arc—170 degree angle of view. Built-in compass for land survey photography. C 1889.

R3*	NSR

J. D. MOLLER, Hamburg, Germany.

Cambinox-N: (JD100); C 1956 binocular with subminiature camera built-in,interchangeable Idemar 90mm f3.5 lens, bayonette mount (for 35mm, 135mm and 180mm lenses). 6 speed rotary FPS 1/30-1/800 s, 10 x 14mm exp on 16mm film, after focusing the binoculars, the distance reading is transfered to the camera lens.

R4* $1k	£525	DM1.6k	FF5.1k

Cambinox-N

Cambinox-S: (JD101); C1960, as (JD100 but in Monocular form, originally available on special order.

R4* NSR est$2k	£1.1k	DM3.3k	FF10.2k

Accessories for Cambinox
Jedmar f3.5/35mm lens: (JD001); **$250**
Jedmar f3.5/135mm lens: (JD002); **$350**
Jedmar f3.5/180mm lens: (JD003); **$400**

MOLLIER, Paris, France.

Le "Cent Vues": (ML100); C1924, metal 35mm VFR camera for 100 exp, 18 x 24mm on perforated 35mm film in special cassettes, Hermagis f3.5/40mm lens, single speed guillotine shutter or Compur shutter, also used as a projector, horizontal and vertical styles exist. Invented by Etienne N. Mollier.

R4* $1.6k	£840	DM2.6k	FF8.2k

Molteni Detective Camera: (BB207); Molteni Aplanat lens. Body unfolds to form vf; brass fittings. 9 x 12cm exp on plates. Mfg. in Paris, France. C 1885.

R5* $1.5k	£787	DM2.5k	FF7.7k

MOM,
Budapest, Hungary.

Mometta: (MM200); C1953, 35mm RFR camera, fixed mount Ymmar f3.5/50mm lens, CFPS 1/25 - 1/500s, CRF.

R3* $100	£52	DM165	FF511

Mometta

Mometta II: (MM201); C1955, as (MM200) but with interchangeable mount (42mm screw), interesting in that the lens flange to focal plane distance is the same as that

Mometta II

used on SLR cameras having a "Universal" screw mount. This would allow the SLR lens to be used on the Mometta camera.

R3* $125	£66	DM206	FF639

Mometta III: (MM202); C1958, as (MM201) but with flash synch.

R3* $125	£66	DM206	FF639

Mometta III

MONROE CAMERA CO.,
Rochester, New York.

The Monroe Camera Co. was established in 1897 at 48 Stone Street, Rochester, New York (Monroe County); the officers were Fred Sherwood as president, Albert Beir as vice president, and Charles V. Case as secretary-treasurer. In 1899 they merged with several other companies—the Rochester Optical Co., the Rochester Camera & Supply Co., the Ray Camera Co., and the Western Camera Mfg. Co.—to form the Rochester Optical & Camera Co.

Monroe No. 7 Folding Plate Camera: (MN100); 4" x 5" folding plate camera; Rapid Rectilinear lens; Unicum shutter. Double extension red bellows; reversible and shifting back; polished mahogany body, brass fittings; ivory label; leather covered case. C 1898.

R3 *$175	£92	DM288	FF894

Pocket Monroe: (MN101); folding plate camera; 3¹/2" x 3¹/2" exp on dry plates. C 1898.

R3* $180	£94	DM297	FF920

Vest Pocket Monroe: (MN102); miniature camera; collapsible bellows; single exp, 3¹/2" x 3¹/2" on dry plates. C 1898.

R3* $200	£105	DM330	FF1k

MONTANUS-Camerabau, Solingen, Germany.

Plascaflex V45: (MO200); C1950, TLR for 6 x 6cm on 120 roll film, f4.5/75mm lens, Vario shutter.

R3* $70	£37	DM115	FF358

Plascaflex PS35: (MO201); C1950, TLR for 6 x 6cm on 120 roll film, f3./75mm lens, Prontor-S shutter, as (MO200 but for lens and shutter).

R3* $70	£37	DM115	FF358

Rocca Automatic: (MO202); C1953, TLR for 6 x 6cm on 120 roll film, Trinar f2.9 or Cassar f2.8/80mm lens, Prontor-SVS shutter, interchangeable focusing hood.

R3* $100	£52	DM165	FF511

Delmonta: (MO203); C1955, TLR for 6 x 6cm frames on 120 roll film, Pluscanar f3.5/75mm lens, Vario shutter.

R3* $50	£26	DM82	FF256

Montiflex: (MO204); C1955, TLR for 6 x 6cm frames on 120 roll film, Pluscanar f3.5/75mm lens, Prontor-SVS shutter.

R3* $50	£26	DM82	FF256

Montana: (MO205); C1956, 35mm VFR camera, Deltamon f3.5/45mm lens, Vario shutter.

R2* $30	£16	DM49	FF153

Charles MONTI, Paris, France.

Lumiere Magazine Camera: (ON100); box-type magazine camera; Rapid Rectilinear 135mm f11 lens; 2 leaf scissors behind-the-lens shutter. Waist-level finder; 12 exp, 9 x 12cm on dry plates. Invented by L. Lumiere, Lyons, France. C 1892.

R4* $700	£367	DM1.2k	FF3.6k

Lumiere Magazine Camera

MOORE & CO., Liverpool, England.

Aptus Ferrotype Camera: (MO100); black leather covered wooden ferrotype camera; meniscus lens. Suction disk takes unexposed plate and swings it into position to be exposed; after exposure, the suction disk dropped the plate into the developing tank attached to the camera. Very popular among "while you wait" beach photographers. 4.5 x 6.3cm exp on plates. C 1913-1956.

R3* $225	£118	DM371	FF1.2k

M

H. MORSE, London, England.

Single Lens Stereoscopic Camera: (OR100); Ross Landscape lens. Stereo exp on 3¹/2"x 7" wet plates; camera slides laterally on rails for second exp. C 1865.

R5* $3.5k	£1.8k	DM5.8k	FF17.9k

MOVETTE INC., Rochester, New York.

Movette: (MV100); hand-cranked 17.5mm cine camera. The 17.5mm film was specially made by Eastman Kodak. C 1919.

R4* $500	£262	DM824	FF2.6k

MOY & BASTE'S.

Moy & Baste's: (MY100); 35mm professional motion picture camera; hand-crank operated; wood finish, brass fittings. C 1909.

| R4* $600 | £315 | DM989 | FF3.1k |

William MULLER, Vienna, Austria.

Delta-Stereo Flat Cartridge: (WM100); stereo folding camera; Extra Rapid Aplanat 120mm f6.5 lens (also Anastigmat 260mm f9, Triple Anastigmat 280mm f12, or Collinear III M 300). Reflecting finder; scale focusing. 9 x 18cm exp on roll or sheet film. C 1900.

| R4* $325 | £171 | DM536 | FF1.7k |

Neue Reflex Stereoskop Camera: (WM101); box-type reflex stereo camera; Suter Anastigmat 340K lens, (also Goerz Series III 120mm 510K, Voigtlander Collinear Series III 120mm 570K); FPS. 9 x 18cm exp on stereo plates. C 1901.

| R4* $500 | £262 | DM824 | FF2.6k |

Le Multicoloure: (BB210); tri-colour magazine box camera. Tri-colour filters were sequentially moved into position (behind the lens) by using external controls. Mfd in Paris, France. C 1912.

| R4* $700 | £367 | DM1.2k | FF3.6k |

Le Multi Photo: (BB211); all metal camera; two Boyer Saphir 40mm f4.5 lenses; FPS 1/70-1/500 s. 9 exp, 27 x 27mm. Also takes stereo pictures using 10 x 15cm plate holder. Mfg. in Lyon, France. C 1924.

| R4* $2k | £1.1k | DM3.3k | FF10.2k |

MULTISCOPE & FILM CO., Burlington, Wisconsin.

Al-Vista Panoramic Camera (Model 4B): (FC100); 4" x 12" exp on roll film. C 1900.

| R4* $325 | £171 | DM536 | FF1.7k |

Al-Vista Panoramic Camera (Model 5B): (FC101); 5" x 12" exp on roll film. C 1900.

| R4* $350 | £184 | DM577 | FF1.8k |

Baby Al-Vista: (FC102); panoramic camera; 2¹/₄"x 6³/₄" exp on roll film. C 1900.

| R4* $450 | £236 | DM742 | FF2.3k |

MULTI-SPEED SHUTTER CO., Morris Park, Long Island, New York; later became SIMPLEX PHOTO PRODUCTS COMPANY.

Simplex Camera: (UL100); 35mm camera; Bausch & Lomb Tessar 50mm f3.5 lens; built-in shutter 1-1/300 s. 800-35mm half-frame exp or 400-35mm full-frame exp. C 1914. The Simplex was the first commercially produced camera designed to take full-frame photographs on 35mm film.

| R5* $7k | £3.7k | DM11.5k | FF35.8k |

Simplex Camera

MURER-MUTSCHLER

Mundus Colour: (BB212); Tessar 20mm f2.7 lens; Prontor shutter 1 - 1/300 s. 8 x 14mm exp on 16mm movie film. C 1955.

R4* $400	£210	DM659	FF2k

MURER & DURONI, Milan, Italy.

Murer: (MU100); 6 x 9cm camera; Murer Anastigmat 102mm f6.3 lens with helicoidal focusing; FPS. Sliding lens cap with built-in viewer. C 1920.

R3* $100	£52	DM165	FF511

Murer Express: (MU101); mirror reflex camera; Anastigmat 9cm f7 lens; FPS 1/30-1/1000 s. Leather covered wood body. 6 x 13cm exp on plates. C 1905.

R3* $130	£68	DM214	FF664

Murer Express Stereo: (MU102); mirror reflex stereo camera; anastigmat f6.3 lens. Aluminium body. 45 x 107mm and 6 x 13cm exp on plates. C 1896-1897.

R3* $450	£236	DM742	FF2.3k

Murer Folding Express: (MU103); 45 x 107mm folding stereo camera; Anastigmatic 60mm f4.5 lens; FPS 1/15-1/1000 s. C 1920.

R4* $300	£157	DM495	FF1.5k

Murer Sprite: (MU104); 4.5 x 6cm folding camera; Rapid Aplanat 70mm f8 lens; shutter 1/25-1/100 s. C 1919. Roll film version, **$175.** Plate:

R3* $90	£47	DM148	FF460

MURRAY & HEATH, London, England.

Stereoscopic Camera: (MH100); Ross lenses, sliding box focusing. Stereo exp on 9 x 17cm wet plates. Rising front; mahogany construction. C 1865.

R5* $3.5k	£1.8k	DM5.8k	FF17.9k

MUTSCHLER, ROBERTSON & CO., Rochester, New York.

Mutschler, Robertson & Co. was founded in 1895 by Albert Mutschler and John A. Robertson. The company name was changed to the Ray Camera Co. in 1898; located at 204 Commercial Street in Rochester, New York. In 1899 they merged with several other companies - the Rochester Optical Co., the Rochester Camera & Supply Co., the Monroe Camera Co. and the Western Camera Mfg. Co. - to form the Rochester Optical & Camera Co.

Ray Folding Plate Model A: (MR100); 4" x 5" folding plate camera; Rapid Rectilinear lens; Victor shutter. Red bellows; shifting, rising and falling front; side loading. C 1898.

R3* $100	£52	DM165	FF511

Ray No. 2: (MR101); 5" x 7" folding plate camera; Rapid Rectilinear lens; Unicum shutter. Shifting, rising and falling front. Leather covered exterior; mahogany interior, brass fittings; red bellows. C 1895.

R3* $100	£52	DM165	FF511

Ray No. 4: (MR102); 4" x 5" folding plate camera; Rapid Rectilinear lens; Unicum shutter. Leather covered exterior; mahogany interior, brass fittings; red bellows. Mutschler, Robertson & Co. brass label above lens board. C 1895.

R3* $100	£52	DM165	FF511

The Ray Junior: (MR103); small box-type dry plate camera; 2½" x 2½" exp on dry plates. C 1898.

R3* $50	£26	DM82	FF256

M

Dr. August NAGEL CAMERAWERK, Stuttgart, Germany.

Pupille: (NA100); C 1930, metal VFR camera for 16 exp, 3 x 4cm on roll film, Schneider Xenon 50mm/f2.0 or Xenar f2.9 or f3.5 lens; Compur shutter 1-1/300 s. Leitz Elmar 50mm f3.5 lens doubles the price.

R4* $375	£197	DM618	FF1.9k

Ranca: (NA101); C 1931, Nagel Anastigmat 50mm f4.5 lens; Ibsor shutter 1-1/150 s.

R3* $200	£105	DM330	FF1k

Vollenda: (NA102); C 1930, Elmar 50mm f3.5 lens; Compur shutter 1-1/300s.

R4* $275	£144	DM453	FF1.4k

Vollenda

NATIONAL PHOTOCOLOR CORP., New York.

National Color Camera: (NP100); C 1938, 3 1/4" x 4 1/4" one-shot colour camera; Tessar 135mm f4.5 lens; Dial-set Compur shutter 1-1/300 s.

R4* $600	£315	DM989	FF3.1k

National Color Camera

National Photocolor One-Shot Color Camera: (NP101); C 1940, Goerz Dogmar 8 1/4" f4.5 lens; Wollensak Betax 1/2-1/50 s, CFR, built-in filters, pellicle mirrors.

R4* $650	£341	DM1.1k	FF3.3k

National Photocolor One-Shot Color Camera

J. De NECK, Belgium.

Photo Chapeau: (NE100); C 1885, hat detective camera; Steinheil landscape aplanatic lens operates through small hole in front of hat; rotary shutter, T, I. 4.5 x 5cm plates changed through black leather pouch.

R5* NSR est$10k+	£5.2k	DM16.5k	FF51.1k

NETTEL KAMERAWERK, Sontheim a/M., Germany

Argus Camera: (CN101); C 1911. monocular-type detective camera; Tessar 50mm f4.5 lens; single speed cylindrical shutter. 4.5 x 6cm exp on plates.

R4* $1k+	£525+	DM1.6k+	FF5.1k+

NEW IDEAS MFG. CO., New York, sold by Herbert & Huesgen Company, New York.

Tourist Multiple: (NI100); C 1914, 35mm camera; Bausch & Lomb Zeiss Tessar 50mm f3.5 lens; 7 speed guillotine MFPS 1/40 - 1/200 s. 750 exp, 18 x 24mm on 50' rolls of perforated 35mm cine film. Qty less than 1000. The camera originally sold for $175; the complete outfit (camera and matching projector) sold for $250. The Tourist Multiple was the first 35mm still camera produced commercially and sold in substantial quantity.

R4* $2k	£1.1k	DM3.3k	FF10.2k

Tourist Multiple

NEWMAN & GUARDIA, London, England.

Baby Sibyl: (NG100); Tessar 75mm f4.5 lens; Newman & Guardia shutter 1/2-1/200 s. C 1910. Roll film version, and plate version.

R3* $225	£118	DM371	FF1.2k

New Ideal Sibyl: (NG101); Ross Xpres f4.5 lens; Newman & Guardia shutter. 3 1/4" x 4 1/4" exp. C 1914.

R3* $200	£105	DM330	FF1k

New Special Sibyl: (NG102); 6 x 9cm; Ross Xpres 112mm f4.5 lens; special Newman & Guardia shutter. Rising and sliding front; vf adjusted for use of rise and cross facility and had two sets of adjustment marks depending on which axis the vf was turned. Two spirit levels, to check for correct horizon. 6 x 9cm exp. C 1914.

R3* $200	£105	DM330	FF1k

Newman & Guardia Pattern B Detective Camera: (NG103); 3 1/4" x 4 1/4" exp on plates. C 1895.

R3* $300	£157	DM495	FF1.5k

N

Newman & Guardia Reflex Camera: (NG104); Beck-Steinheil Unifocal f4.5 lens. C 1906.

R3* $200	£105	DM330	FF1k

Nydia: (NG105); Wray Rectilinear lens; double guillotine shutter; 12 exp, magazine changed by manipulation of plates through soft leather pouch. C 1890.

R3* $400	£210	DM659	FF2k

Special: (NG106); magazine box camera; lens board moves vertically and horizontally; pneumatic shutter. Extended bellows for closeups and copying. 3 1/4" x 4 1/4" exp, 12 plate magazine.

R3* $175	£92	DM288	FF894

Stereo Detective Camera: (NG107); Rectilinear 120mm f8 lens; guillotine shutter 1/2-1/100 s. Leather bag changing mechanism for plates. 10 x 16cm. C1895.

R4* $750	£394	DM1.2k	FF3.8k

Sibyl Excelsior Trellis: (NG108); Anastigmat f4.5 lens; Newman & Guardia shutter 2-1/150 s. C 1910.

| R3* $250 | £131 | DM412 | FF1.3k |

NICCA CAMERA WORKS, Japan.

Nicca III (Type 3): (NC100); 1949 Cfps, 1-1/500 s, seperate RFR/VFR windows, diopter adjustment, screw mount Nikkor HC f2.0/5cm lens. Now called the Nicca Camera Works Ltd. This camera is a copy of the Leica III.

| R3* $375 | £197 | DM618 | FF1.9k |

Nicca IIIA: (NC101); 1951, Cfps, 1- 1/500 s, seperate RFR/VFR windows, diopter adjustment, screw mount Nikkor HC f2.0/5cm or Nikkor SC f1.5/cm lens. The company name changed once again in November 1951 to the "Nicca Camera Company Ltd." IIIA cameras can be found with both company markings. It was also distributed by Sears Roebuck and Co. as the Tower Type-3,(NC101A) which is valued about 10% less than cameras marked "Nicca".

| R2* $275 | £144 | DM453 | FF1.4k |

Nicca IIIB: (NC102); 1951 Cfps, 1- 1/500 s, FP flash synch, seperate RFR/VFR windows, diopter adjustment, screw mount Nikkor HC f2.0/5cm or Nikkor SC f1.5/cm lens. The same as the Nicca IIIA, with flash synch added It was also distributed by Sears Roebuck and Co. as the Tower Type-3B, (NC102A) which is valued about 10% less than cameras marked "Nicca".

| R3* $275 | £144 | DM453 | FF1.4k |

Nicca IIIS: (NC103); 1952, Cfps, 1 - 1/500 s, FP and X flash synch, seperate RFR/VFR windows, diopter adjustment, screw mount

Nicca IIIS

Nikkor QC f3.5/5cm lens. It was also distributed by Sears Roebuck and Co. as the Tower Type-3S, (NC103A) which is valued about 10% less than cameras marked "Nicca".

| R2* $275 | £144 | DM453 | FF1.4k |

Nicca 4: (NC104); 1953 Cfps, 1 - 1/1000 s, FP and X flash synch, seperate RFR/VFR windows, diopter adjustment, screw mount Nikkor SC f1.5/5cm lens.

| R3* $375 | £197 | DM618 | FF1.9k |

Nicca 3S: (NC105); 1954 Cfps, 1 - 1/500 s, FP and X flash synch, seperate RFR/VFR windows, diopter adjustment, screw mount Nikkor QC f3.5/5cm lens. The same as the Nicca IIIs, with new shutter speed progression, and synch at 1/25 instead of 1/20.It was also distributed by Sears Roebuck and Co. as the Tower Camera which is valued about 10% less than cameras marked "Nicca".

| R2* $325 | £171 | DM536 | FF1.7k |

Nicca 3F: (NC106); 1956 Cfps, 1 - 1/500 s, FP and X flash synch, seperate RFR/VFR windows, diopter adjustment, screw mount Nikkor H f2.0/5cm or Nikkor S f1.4/5cm lens. One piece top plate, hinged back. It was also distributed by Sears Roebuck and Co. as the Tower Camera which is valued about 10% less than cameras marked "Nicca". A 3F version with a quick wind lever was made, and is valued at about 15% less than the wind knob version.

| R3* $450 | £236 | DM742 | FF2.3k |

Tower camera with a Culminar 8cm/f2.8 lens - similar to Nicca 3F

Nicca 5: (NC107); 1955 Cfps, 1 - 1/1000 s, FP and X flash synch, seperate RFR/VFR windows, diopter adjustment, screw mount Nikkor S f1.4/5cm or Nikkor S f2.0/5cm lens. One piece top plate, hinged back. Leica IIIF copy, with synch contact under the accessory shoe. Also sold by Sears Roebuck and Co. with the f2/50mm lens as the Tower 45, and with the f1.4/50mm lens as the Tower 46.

R2* $550	£289	DM907	FF2.8k

Nicca 33: (NC108); 1957 Cfps, 1/2 - 1/500 s, FP and X flash synch, seperate RFR/VFR windows, diopter adjustment, screw mount Nicca F2.8/50mm lens. Continued after Nicca Camera Company Ltd. was taken over by Yashica, and then known as the Yashica YE, see (YA104).

R3* $350	£184	DM577	FF1.8k

Nicca IIIL: (NC109); 1958 Cfps, 1 - 1/1000 s, FP and X flash synch, seperate RFR/VFR windows, diopter adjustment, screw mount Nikkor H f2.0/5cm lens. Completely redesigned top plate. Continued as the Yashica YF, see (YA103), after the company was taken over by Yashica.

R3* $700	£367	DM1.2k	FF3.6k

Nicnon TF Binocular Camera: (BB213); half-frame 35mm binocular camera; Nicnon 165mm f3.5 lens; Copal square MFPS 1/60, 1/125 and 1/250 s. The SLR camera uses right-hand optics of the binocular as an objective; springwound motor allows up to 20 exp per wind. C 1968.

R4* $750	£394	DM1.2k	FF3.8k

Nicnon TF Binocular Camera

NIELL AND SIMONS, Brussels.

Lopa: (NS100); meniscus 120mm f11 lens; single speed guillotine shutter. 6.5 x 9cm exp. C 1900.

R4* $600	£315	DM989	FF3.1k

NIEZOLDI AND KRAMER, Munich, Germany.

Cine Nizo 8E: (NZ100); 8mm movie camera; f2.7 lens. C 1932.

R2* $35	£18	DM58	FF179

Cine Nizo 8E

Cine Nizo 16, Model L: (NZ101); 16mm movie camera; interchangeable lens; 15m film spool; 8, 16 or 24 frames per s.

R2* $45	£24	DM74	FF230

Nizo Camera N.K.M. Model A: (NZ102); 9.5mm movie camera; Meyer Goerlitz Trioplan Anastigmat 17mm f3.5 lens. Spring motor drive. C 1926.

R2* $45	£24	DM74	FF230

Cine Nizo 16mm: (NZ103); 16mm movie camera; rotating holder for 3 lenses, from 20 to 100mm; speeds from 8 to 64 frames per s. C 1936.

R3* $75	£39	DM124	FF383

N

Nikon I

NIKON INC
Nippon Kogaku K.K.,
Tokyo, Japan.

Nikon I: (NK100); C1948-49, 35mm RFR camera; Nikkor 50mm f2 coated lens, interchangeable bayonet mount; CFPS 1 -1/500 s, CFR. 40 exp, 24 x 32mm. Qty 758. No factory installed synch; removable take-up spool. One offered in 1989 for $12,000 Worth at least $1500 if damaged, non-working, or modified in any way.

R5* Rare $9k+	£4.7k+	DM14.8k+	FF46k+

Nikon M: (NK101); C1949-52. 35mm RFR camera; Nikkor 50mm f2 coated lens, interchangeable bayonet mount; CFPS 1 -1/500 s, CFR. 36 exp, 24 x 34mm. Qty 1643. No factory installed flash synch; M prefix on serial number. With synch, (about 1700 cameras made).

R4* $1.1k	£577	DM1.8k	FF5.6k

Nikon M

without synch, (1643 cameras made).

R4* $2k+	£1.1k+	DM3.3k+	FF10.2k+

Nikon S: (NK102); C1950-54, 35mm RFR camera; Nikkor 50mm f2 coated lens, interchangeable bayonet mount; CFPS 1 -1/500 s, CFR, flash synch. 36 exp, 24 x 36mm. Qty 36,746. . Double spring synchro socket. "Made in Occupied Japan":

R4* $700	£367	DM1.2k	FF3.6k

Eight digit serial #:

R3* $500	£262	DM824	FF2.6k

Others:

R2* $350	£184	DM577	FF1.8k

Nikon S2: (NK103); C1954-55,35mm RFR camera; Nikkor 50mm f2 coated lens, interchangeable bayonet mount; CFPS 1 - 1/1000 s, CFR, flash synch. 36 exp, 24 x 36mm. Qty 56,715. Single stroke rapid wind lever, enlarged vf.

Nikon S

Black body:

R4* $3k	£1.6k	DM5k	FF15.3k

Chrome body, chrome dial:

R3* $450	£236	DM742	FF2.3k

Chrome body, black dial:

R3* $550	£289	DM907	FF2.8k

Nikon S2

Nikon S3: (NK104); C 1958, 35mm RFR camera; Nikkor 50mm f2 coated lens, interchangeable bayonet mount; CFPS 1 - 1/1000 s, CFR, flash synch. Combined range-vf for 3 lens fields. 36 exp, 24 x 36mm. Qty 14,310. Chrome body:

R3* $750	£394	DM1.2k	FF3.8k

Black body:

R4* $2.25k	£1.2k	DM3.7k	FF11.5k

Black Olympic:

R4* $3k	£1.6k	DM5k	FF15.3k

Nikon S3

Nikon S4: (NK105); C1959, 35mm RFR camera; Nikkor 50mm f2 lens, interchangeable bayonet mount; CFPS 1-1/1000 s, CFR, flash synch. 36 exp, 24 x 36mm. Qty 5698. No self-timer, manual reset frame counter. Chrome body.

R3* $1.2k	£630	DM2k	FF6.1k

Nikon SP: (NK106); C1957, 35mm RFR camera; Nikkor 50mm f2 coated lens, interchangeable bayonet mount; CFPS 1 -1/1000 s, flash synch. Combined range-vf for 6 lens fields; 1:1 viewing, parallax correction for normal and telephoto lenses, adjacent eye-level optical finder for 28mm and 35mm lenses. Self-timer. Qty 21,534. Electric motor drive available - automatically advances film and fires shutter at maximum rate of 3 exp per second. The motor is powered by 6 pen-light or 6 C size batteries. Chrome body with normal lens:

R3* $1.3k	£682	DM2.1k	FF6.6k

Black body:

R4* $2.25k	£1.2k	DM3.7k	FF11.5k

Nikon SP

Nikon SP with stereo Nikkor lenses

Nikon S3M: (NK107); C1960, half-frame 35mm RFR camera; Nikkor 35mm f2 coated lens, interchangeable bayonet mount; CFPS 1-1/1000 s, CFR, flash sync. 72 exp, 18 x 24mm, half-frame format. Qty 195. One offered in 1989 with matching S72 motor for $15,000. This same matched set today could easily command $20,000! Chrome:

R5* $10k	£5.2k	DM16.5k	FF51.1k

Black:

R5* $13k	£6.8k	DM21.4k	FF66.4k

NIKON

Nikon F: (NK114); Introduced in 1959, 35mm SLR with interchangeable lenses, backs, viewing screens, prisms etc. CFPS speeds 1-1/1000s. This camera, considered by some to be the first 35mm SLR system camera has finally reached the ranks of the collectables! With Nikon RFR equipment becoming harder and harder to find, many Nikon enthusiasts have begun the search for early Nikon SLRs, particularly Nikon F Photomics. We expect to see a greater interest in the coming years in collecting these cameras. For now at least, the early Nikon "F" Photomic cameras with serial numbers from 640000 to 641000 are actively being looked for. Because of their popularity as "working" cameras, pristine examples are particularly hard to find. Competition from users is great. (price is for low numbered camera bodies only 640000-641000, black model is about 50% more, other serial numbers are about 70% cheaper)

R4* $600	£315	DM989	FF3.1k

Nikon F cutaway model: (NK115); non working Nikon F camera sliced in half for use as a display piece, showing some of the internal workings. Includes half a lens.

R4* $650	£341	DM1.1k	FF3.3k

Nikon F made for the United States Space program: (NK116); with special markings, this camera is one of the rarest Nikon SLRs (for the moment at least!) including lens.

R5* $2k	£1.1k	DM3.3k	FF10.2k

Nikon F made for the United States Navy: (NK117); with special markings, hard to find in clean condition. Price includes motor drive and lens.

R4* $600	£315	DM989	FF3.1k

Nikkor F: (NK118); Nikon F made for the European market. Harder to find in the USA than in Germany.

R4* $450	£236	DM742	FF2.3k

Nikon F3/T: (NK119); 1983-86, full system 35mm SLR with titanium finish, fps 1-1/1000s.

R3* $950	£499	DM1.6k	FF4.9k

Nikonos I: (NK112); 35mm underwater camera; Nikkor 35mm f2.8 lens.

R3* $175	£92	DM288	FF894

Nikon Super Zoom 8: (NK113); super 8mm movie camera; Cine Nikkor Zoom 8.8m-45mm f1.8 lens; electric motor drive-12, 18 or 24 frames per s.

R3* $90	£47	DM148	FF460

NIKON ACCESSORIES

Nikon Rangefinder motor drives

Motordrive S36 for Nikon SP: (NK001); chrome, **$900**;
Motordrive S36 for Nikon SP: (NK002); black, **$950**.
Motordrive S72 for Nikon S3M: (NK003); **$4000**

Nikon Rangefinder lenses

21mm/f4 lens w/finder: (NK004); **$1500**
25mm/f4 lens chrome: (NK005); **$450**
25mm/f4 lens black: (NK006); **$550**
28mm/f3.5 lens chrome: (NK007), **$250**
28mm/f3.5 lens black: (NK008); **$300**
35mm/f3.5 lens "MIOJ": (NK009); **$300**
35mm/f3.5 lens chrome: (NK010); **$150**
35mm/f3.5 lens black: (NK011); **$200**
35mm/f2.5 lens chrome: (NK012); **$175**
35mm.f2.5 lens black: (NK013); **$250**
35mm/f2.5 lens black: type II (NK014); **$700**
35mm/f1.8 lens black: (NK015); **$1200**
35mm/f1.8 lens, type II: (NK016); **$400**
50mm/f3.5 micro lens: (NK017); **$1000+**
50mm/f3.5 collapsible lens: (NK018); **$1000**
50mm/f2 collapsible lens marked "Tokyo": (NK019); **$600**
50mm/f2 lens chrome (NK020); **$75**
50mm/f2 lens black with chrome: (NK021); **$100**
50mm/f2 lens all black: (NK022); **$400**
50mm/f1.5 lens (NK023); **$900**

NIKON

50mm/f1.4 lens "marked "Tokyo": (NK024); **$125**
50mm/f1.4 lens chrome (NK025); **$90**
50mm/f1.4 lens black and chrome: (NK026); **$100**
50mm/f1.4 lens all black: (NK027); **$500**
50mm/f1.4 lens aluminium: (NK028); **$1200+**
50mm/f1.4 lens "Olympic": (NK029); **$800**
50mm/f1.1 lens internal mount: (NK030); **$900**
50mm/f1.1 lens external mount: (NK031); **$900**
85mm/f2 lens chrome: (NK032); **$200**
85mm/f2 lens black: (NK033); **$300**
85mm/f2 lens "MIOJ": (NK034); **$500**
85mm/f1.5 lens: (NK035); **$1100**
105mm/f4 lens: (NK036); **$700**
105mm/f2.5 lens: (NK037); **$200**
135mm/f4 lens: short mount (NK038); **$300**
135mm/f4 lens: (NK039); **$600**
135mm/f3.5 lens chrome (NK040); **$100**
135mm/f3.5 lens black: (NK041); **$150**
180mm/f2.5 lens: (NK042); **$600**
250mm/f4 lens manual aperture: (NK043); **$450**
250mm/f4 lens pre-set aperture: (NK044); **$400**
350mm/f4.5 lens: (NK045); **$1200+**
500mm/f5 lens: (NK046); **$3000+**
1000mm/f6.3 lens black: (NK047); **$15;000+**
1000mm/f6.3 lens grey: (NK048); **$7000**
Stereo outfit: (NK049); **$8000**

Nikon produced innumerable accessories for their rangefinder system. They produced chrome optical finders in 35, 85, 105, and 135mm lengths. Very early 35, 85 and 135mm finders are marked Nippon Kogaku Tokyo and cover 24 x 34. Later finders are marked Nippon Kogaku Japan and cover 24 x 36. Types marked with an L on the base were designed for Leica type cameras and covered 24 x 36. Those marked with a C were made for Contaxes and have a longer foot. The 21 and 25mm finders were produced in black finish. Nikon also produced a series of brightine finders. The 35, 85, 105 and 135 brightline finders are not uncommon. The 50mm brightline is quite rare. The stereo brightline finder is extremely desirable.

21mm finder black: (NK050); **$400**
25mm finder black: (NK051); **$150**
28mm finder chrome: (NK052); **$100**
35mm finder chrome: (NK053); **$75**
35mm finder black: (NK054); **$150**
35mm "mini" finder: (NK055); **$500**
50mm finder black: (NK056); **$500**
85mm finder chrome: (NK057); **$75**
85mm finder black: (NK058); **$150**
105mm finder chrome: (NK059); **$75**
105mm finder black: (NK060); **$175**
135mm finder chrome: (NK061); **$75**
135mm finder black: (NK062); **$150**
Stereo Finder: (NK063); **$700**
Sportsfinder: (NK064); **$300**

Nikon produced a variable finder called the Variframe similar to the Leitz Vidom. The original model is finished in dull chrome and marked 24 x 32 for use with the Model I. The black screw-in 28mm adaptor for the variframe is extremely desirable. Nikon also made a very common zoom finder covering focal lengths 35 to 135mm. Some of these have markings for the Leica type lenses as well. These are quite common. The 28mm adaptor for this finder is uncommon. Two types of sportsfinder exist with yellow and silver backs.

Variframe 24x32 dull: (NK065); **$3000+**
Variframe 24x32 bright: (NK065); **$2000+**

Variframe M "MIOJ" :   (NK066); **$375**
Variframe chrome: (NK067); **$150**
Variframe black with shoe: (NK068); **$400**
Variframe black without shoe: (NK069); **$500**
28mm adaptor for variframe: (NK070); **$500+**
Varifocal Zoom "MIOJ": (NK071); **$700+**
Varifocal Zoom type I: (NK072); **$150**
Varifocal Zoom type II: (NK073); **$175**
28mm adaptor for Varifocal Zoom: (NK074); **$200**
RF Illuminator: (NK075); **$400**
Reflex housing type I: (NK076); **$3000+**
Reflex housing type II 45 degree: (NK077); **$1500+**
90 degree prism only: (NK078); **$3000+**
Bellows model I : (NK079); **$1300**
Exposure meter, grey top: (NK080); **$400**
Exposure meter, black top: (NK081); **$175**
Microflex type I: (NK082); **$1500+**
Microflex type II: (NK083); **$1500+**
"S" copy stand: (NK084); **$1000+**
"SA" copy stand: (NK085); **$700+**
"P" copy stand: (NK086); **$1200**
"PA" copy stand: (NK087); **$700**
21mm lens shade: (NK088); **$250**
25mm lens shade: (NK089); **$125**
50mm lens shade for f1.1 lens: (NK090); **$200+**
Micro Collar: (NK091); **$425**

Lenses for Nikon F:

2.1cm/f4.0 lens with finder: (NK092); **$220**
2.8cm/f3.5 lens: (NK093); **$100**
3.5cm/f2.8 lens: (NK094); **$120**
5.0cm/f2.0 lens: (NK095); **$50**
5.8cm/f1.4 lens: (NK096); **$125**
5.5cm/f3.5 preset macro lens: (NK096); **$450**
10.5cm/f2.5 lens: (NK097); **$140**
10.5cm/f4.0 lens: (NK098); **$300**
13.5cm/f3.5\ lens: (NK099); **$125**
20cm/f4.0 lens: (NK0100); **$120**
8.5 to 25cm zoom, two touch: (NK0101); **$250**

8.5 to 25cm zoom, one touch: (NK0102); **$250**
50cm mirror lens, with case and filters: (NK0103); **$450**
100cm mirror lens: (NK0104); **$3000**

Meters for Nikon F

Model 1 meter, round type: (NK0105); **$130**
Model 2 meter, long window: (NK0106); **$100**
Nikkorex type: (NK0107); **$95**
Model 3 meter, square type: (NK0108); **$100**
Booster module for the above: (NK0109); **$45**

Motors for Nikon F

Type one, number on the base plate: (NK0110); **$300**
Type two, Nippon Kogaku logo on the front: (NK0111); **$175**
Type three, marked Nikon, and numbered on the back: (NK0112); **$150**
Brown battery pack: (NK0113); **$50**
Black battery pack: (NK0114); **$40**
250 exposure back: (NK0115); **$250**

Misc. Accessories for Nikon F

Waist level finder, type one, with Nippon Kogaku logo: (NK0116): **$50**
Waist level finder type two, with Nikon F markings: (NK0117); **$30**
Copy stand for Nikon F: (NK0118); **$150**
Electronic flash, S.B. 1: (NK0119); **$100**
Flash BC 7, for flash bulbs: (NK0120); **$20**

NITTO SHASHIN YOHIN KK, Japan.

ELEGA: (NT100); C1951, 35mm VFR camera, Leica copy, Elega or Eleger f3.5/45mm lens in a fixed mount, guillotine shutter 1 - 1/200s, built-in film cutter.

| R4* $700 | £367 | DM1.2k | FF3.6k |

ODEON PHOTO,
Paris, France.

Isographe: (OD100); 6 x 13cm stereo camera, Boyer Saphir f4.5 or Berthiot Flor f5.7 lens; shutter 1-1/200 s. Two models: 6 x 13cm exp on plates, fixed focus, or 6 x 13cm exp on 620 roll film, micrometer focusing.

R4* $550	£289	DM907	FF2.8k

OFFICE GENERAL DE LA PHOTOGRAPHIE, Paris, France.

The Express Detective Nadar: (OG100); mahogany (reinforced with brass) box-type detective camera; Anastigmat Zeiss 86mm f18 wide angle lens; for 13 x 18cm plates or roll film with Eastman Walker back. Distributed by Nadar. C 1888. Nadar was the French representative of the Eastman house; he added an exposure counter.

R4* $1.5k	£787	DM2.5k	FF7.7k

Okam: (BB215); Trioplan 75mm f4.5 lens; shutter 1/5-1/1000 s. 4.5 x 6cm exp on dry plates. Mfd in Czechoslovakia. C 1935.

R3* $350	£184	DM577	FF1.8k

OKADA OPTICAL CO. LTD., Japan.

Gemmy: (OK100); pistol-type detective camera; 35mm f4.5 lens; 3 speed shutter. 11 x 18mm exp on 16mm film; film advanced by trigger action. C 1950.

R4* $2.5k	£1.3k	DM4.1k	FF12.8k

OLYMPUS OPTICAL CO., LTD, Tokyo, Japan.

Olympus Pen F: (OY102); The first 35mm half frame SLR camera made for production. Use of a porro prism does away with the familiar pentaprism hump on most other 35mm SLR cameras. FPS, to 1/500s. no metering system, but an accessory meter was available. With Zuiko 38mm/f1.8 lens This camera, along with the Pen FT (OY100) and Pen FV (OY103), is less rare in the USA, where prices for all Pen F cameras tend to be about 20% less than in Europe.

R3* $150	£79	DM247	FF767

Olympus Pen FT: (OY100); Updated version of the Pen F, using a semi-silvered mirror to permit through the lens metering, at full aperture, self timer. Black version less common, and brings 50% more. With Zuiko 38mm/f1.8 lens.

R3* $200	£105	DM330	FF1k

Olympus Pen F

Olympus Pen FV: (OY103); Simplified version of the Pen FT (OY100), using a fully silvered mirror in order to brighten the finder image. This results in the loss of through the lens metering. The last model made. With 38mm/f1.8 Zuiko lens.

R4* $200	£105	DM330	FF1k

Olympus Pen F Microscope camera: (OY104); in Chrome only.

R3* $125	£66	DM206	FF639

Olympus Pen FT Microscope camera: (OY105); in Black only.

R4* $300	£157	DM495	FF1.5k

OLYMPUS-O.P.L.

Lenses for Olympus Pen F SLR cameras

20mm/f3.5 G Zuiko Auto W lens: (OY001); **$250**
25mm/f2.8 G Zuiko Auto W lens: (OY002); **$200**
25mm/f4.0 E Zuiko Auto W lens: (OY003); **$150**
38mm/f1.8 F Zuiko Auto S lens : (OY004); **$40**
38mm/f2.8 D Zuiko Auto S lens: (OY005); Made for Europe during a six month period, without the diaphragm ring used for the Pen FT metering system, quite rare. **$120**
38mm/f2.8 Compact E Zuilo Auto S lens: (OY006); **$175**
38mm/f3.5 E Zuiko Macro lens (OY007); **$300**
40mm/f1.4 G Zuiko Auto S lens: (OY008); **$80**
42mm/f1.2 M Zuiko Auto S lens: (OY009); **$200**
60mm/f1.5 G Zuiko Auto T lens: (OY010); **$325**
70mm/f2.0 F Zuiko Auto T lens: (OY011); **$250**
100mm/f3.5 E Zuiko Auto T lens: (OY012);**$125**
150mm/f4.0 E Zuiko Auto T lens: (OY013); **$150**
250mm/f5.0 E Zuiko Auto T lens: (OY014); **$300**
400mm/f6.3 E Zuiko Auto T lens: (OY015); **$900**
800mm/f8.0 Zuiko Mirror T lens: (OY016); **$1400**
50-90mm/f3.5 Zuiko Auto Zoom lens: (OY017); **$170**
100-200mm/f5.0 Zuiko Auto Zoom lens: (OY018); **$350**
100-200mm/f5.0 Zuiko Zoom lens: (OY019); **$250**

Accessories for Pen F SLR cameras

Bellows Pen F: (OY120); **$80**
Slide copier Pen F: (OY021); **$40**
Bellows Pen F II: (OY022); **$100**
Slide copier Pen F II: (OY023); **$60**
Accessory light meter for Pen F and FV: (OY024); **$50**
Microscope adaptor Pen F: (OY025); **$50**

Olympus Ace: (OY105); 1958-60, The first Olympus 35mm RFR camera to be sold with interchangeable lenses. Four lenses including the E Zuiko 4.5cm/f2.8 normal lens were available for this camera, not three as is widely believed. with 4.5mm/f2.8 lens.

R3* $100	£52	DM165	FF511

Olympus Ace E: (OY106); 1959-61, Same as the Olympus Ace (OY105), but with the addition of match needle metering. With normal 4.5cm/f2.8 lens.

R3* $130	£68	DM214	FF664

Accessory lenses for Olympus Ace cameras

3.5cm/f2.8 E Zuiko W ACE lens: (OY026); **$75**
8cm/f4.0 E Zuiko T ACE lens: (OY027); **$100**
8cm/f5.6 E Zuiko T ACE lens: (OY028); **$50**

Olympus 35 I : (OY107); 1948-49, 24 x 32mm format on 35mm film, coated 4cm/ f3.5 Zuiko lens in Seikosha Rapid shutter.

R3* $200	£105	DM330	FF1k

Olympus 35 III : (OY108); 1949-50, 24 x 36mm format on 35mm film, the first from Olympus in this format. coated 4cm/f3.5 Zuiko lens in Seikosha Rapid shutter. Made for only three months.

R4* $200	£105	DM330	FF1k

Olympus Trip 35: (OY101); 35mm VFR camera with built-in light meter, made in very large numbers.

R1* $30	£16	DM49	FF153

Olympus Pen W: (OY109); 1964-65, Black version of the Pen S but with fixed 25mm/ f2.8 lens.

R4* $200	£105	DM330	FF1k

O.P.L. (Optique de Précision à Levallois), France.

Foca PF1 (*) one star: (OP100); 1946-53, CFPS, 1/20 - 1/500 s, viewfinder only, non-interchangeable f3.5/35mm model made only in 1946, (5300 cameras made) from 1947 to 1953 the lens was interchangeable (11,900 cameras made).Vfr shows fields of view for the 35mm lens. With minor modifi-

O.P.L.

cations, this camera became the Foca Standard (OP102) of 1953.(see ID and dating section in the front of the Blue Book for Foca serial number information).

R3* $150	£79	DM247	FF767

Foca PF1 (*) one star

Foca "Post": (OP101); 1952-?, CFPS 1/25s only, 24mm x 30mm frame size, VFR not modified, 50mm/f3.5 Oplar lens, focusing between 30 and 35cm, diaphragm blocked between f5.6 and f8. Easily recognized by four ball shaped protrusions located on the front of the camera. Used to photograph telephone registers, just as the Leica "Post" cameras.

R4* $325	£171	DM536	FF1.7k

Foca "Post"

Foca Standard: (OP102); 1953, Cfps, 1/20 - 1/500 s, Viewfinder only with field of view for 35mm lens, interchangeable screw mount f3.5/35mm or f2.8/50mm lens. Early cameras are easily distinguished from later ones by their lack of rewind lever on the front of the top plate. At least six models were made, each with slight physical variations. Not the most common of Focas, as some might think !

R3* $140	£73	DM231	FF716

Foca Standard

Foca PF2 (**) two star: (OP103);1946 Cfps, 1/20 - 1/500 s, combined RFR/VFR, 36mm interchangeable screw mount f3.5/5cm or f2.8/5cm Oplar lens. Only the 50mm lenses couple accurately with the rangefinder. Early cameras had brown body covering, worth about 75% more.

R3* $150	£79	DM247	FF767

Foca PF2 (**) two star

Foca PF2b: ((OP104); The PF2b (the "b" meaning "bis", continued in French) has

Foca PF2b

1/25 - 1/1000 s shutter and factory installed X and M synch, otherwise the same as PF2. Same price for either camera. Military examples exist and are worth about 200% more.

R3* $150	£79	DM247	FF767

Foca PF3 (***) three star: (OP105); 1952 Cfps, 1 - 1/1000 s, combined RFR/VFR, 36mm interchangeable screw mount f3.5/5cm or f2.8/5cm Oplar lens or with faster f1.9/5cm Oplarex lens. Only the 50mm lenses couple accurately with the rangefinder. With and without synch. Military examples do exist and are worth about 200% more.

R3* $225	£118	DM371	FF1.2k

Foca PF3 (***) three star

Foca PF3 L (***) three star: (OP106); 1956 Cfps, 1 - 1/1000 s, combined RFR/VFR, 36mm interchangeable screw mount f3.5/5cm or f2.8/5cm Oplar lens or with faster f1.9/5cm Oplarex lens. Only the 50mm lenses couple accurately with the rangefinder. Military examples do exist and are worth about 200% more.

R3* $225	£118	DM371	FF1.2k

Foca PF3 L (***) three star

Foca Universel: (OP107); 1946 Cfps, 1-1/1000sec, combined RFR/VFR, bayonet mount f1.9 or f2.8 50mm coated lenses coupled to the RFR. X and M synch indicated by letters.

R3* $275	£144	DM453	FF1.4k

Foca Universel "R": (OP108); 1955 Cfps, 1-1/1000sec, combined RFR/VFR , bayonet mount f1.9 or f2.8 50mm coated lenses coupled to the RFR. X and M synch. An improved version of the Universel with lever wind, and a quieter shutter. Graphic symbols indicate flash synch sockets.

R3* $300	£157	DM495	FF1.5k

Foca Universel "RC": (OP109); 1959, Cfps 1-1/1000s, combined RFR/VFR, bayonet mount f1.9, or 2.8 lens, coupled to RFR, bright line projected frame in VFR. An improved version of the Universel "R". Less than 2000 cameras are thought to have been made. Thought by some to be the best made French 35mm camera. Some outfits were made for the French Navy, and bear the markings "Marine Nationale" on the front, along with a contract number. These cameras are worth about 300% more than normal Universel "RC"s.

R3* $425	£223	DM701	FF2.2k

Foca Universel "RC"

Focaflex: (OP110); 1960 - 68 SLR, BTLleaf shutter, 1 - 1/250 s, fixed mount f2.8/5cm Neoplex lens. Since no pentaprism was used, the camera body is quite slim.

R3* $140	£73	DM231	FF716

Focaflex II: (OP111); 1962 - 68 SLR, BTL leaf shutter, 1 - 1/250 s, interchangeable bayonet mount lenses. Retroplex f4.0/3.5cm

Focaflex

Focaflex II

wide angle lens, f2.8/5cm Neoplex normal lens, f4.0/9cm Teleoplex telephoto lens and very rare f4.0./15cm Super Teleoplex lens were available.

R3* $225	£118	DM371	FF1.2k

Focaflex Automatic

Focaflex Automatic: (OP112); 1961 - 68 SLR, BTL leaf shutter, 1 - 1/250 s, fixed mount f2.8/5cm Neoplex lens. Since no pentaprism was used, the camera body is quite slim. This camera is the same as the Focaflex, with the addition of a built-in light meter.

R3* $140	£73	DM231	FF716

Foca Sport : (OP113) 1954, BTL leaf shutter, 1-1/300s, fixed f3.5/4.5cm Neoplar lens with scale focusing, knob advance and removable back.

R2* $100	£52	DM165	FF511

Foca Sport I: (OP114) 1956, BTL leaf shutter, 1-1/300s, fixed f3.5/4.5cm Neoplar lens with scale focusing, removable back, differs from Foca Sport by addition of lever advance.

R2* $100	£52	DM165	FF511

Foca Sport C: (OP115) 1957, BTL leaf shutter, 1-1/300s, fixed f3.5/4.5cm Neoplar lens with scale focusing, lever advance and removable back, differs from Foca Sport I by the addition of a built-in light meter.

R2* $100	£52	DM165	FF511

Foca Sport Ib: (OP116) 1958, BTL leaf shutter, 1-1/300s, fixed f2.8/4.5cm Oplar-Colour lens with scale focusing, lever advance and removable back, differs from Focasport I by addition of faster lens, and projected frame in the VFR.

R2* $100	£52	DM165	FF511

Foca Sport Id: (OP117) 1958, BTL leaf shutter, 1-1/300s, fixed f2.8/4.5cm Oplar-Colour lens with scale focusing, lever advance and removable back, combines the projected frame and faster lens of the Foca Sport Ib, with the light meter of the Foca Sport C.

R2* $100	£52	DM165	FF511

Foca Sport II: (OP118) 1963, BTL leaf shutter, 1-1/300s, fixed f2.8/4.5cm Oplar-Colour lens coupled to RFR, lever advance and removable back.

R2* $100	£52	DM165	FF511

Lenses and accessories for Foca and Focaflex

Screw mount
28mm f4.5 Oplex (OP001); **$80**
35mm f3.5 Oplex (OP002); **$60**
90mm f3.5 Oplex or Teleoplar (OP003); **$75**
135mm f4.5 Teleoplar (OP004); **$75**
200mm f6.3Teleoplar, for use with "Micro Foca" mirror box,(OP005); **$150**

Bayonet mount
28mm f4.5 Oplex (OP014); **$175**
35mm f3.5 Oplex (OP015); **$120**
90mm f3.5 Oplex or Teleoplar (OP016); **$150**
135mm f4.5 Teleoplar (OP017);**$160**
200mm f6.3Teleoplar, for use with "Micro Foca" mirror box,(OP018); **$250**

Accessories for rangefinder Focas
Foca Universel finder, fields of view for 28mm,35mm,50mm,90mm, and 135mm, (OP006); **$55**
35mm optical finder (OP007); **$45**
Sports finder,(OP008); **$75**

Focanox, brightline finder for 50mm lenses, (OP009); **$45**
Micro Foca mirror box, (OP010); rare, **$270**
Focascaph underwater housing, (OP011); **$225**

Lenses for Focaflex II
3.5cm f4 Retroplex (OP011); **$75**
9cm f4 Teleoplex (OP012); **$75**
15cm f4 Super-Teleoplex (OP013); rare, **$250**

Foca screwmount lenses are not the same thread size as Leica screw.

OSHIRA OPTICAL WORKS, Japan.

Emi K: (OS100); 1956 Lens shutter, 1/25 - 1/300s, VFR only, fixed Eminent Colour, or Fujiyama F2.8/50mm lens. Not often seen, but not very valuable.

R3* $45	£24	DM74	FF230

Emi 35 A: (OS101); 1956 Lens shutter, 1 - 1/300s VFR only, fixed Tri-Lausar Anistigmat

Screw mount lenses for Foca cameras. Left to right, they are the 135mm f4.5 Teleoplar, 90mm f3.5 Oplex and 28mm f4.5 Oplex

F3.5/45mm lens. Not often seen.

R3* $65	£34	DM107	FF332

OSTERREICHISHE
TELEPHON
A.G. Vienna, Austria.

Amourette: (OS100) 35mm camera; Double microscope 35mm f6.3 lens; shutter 1/25 - 1/100 s. 50 exp on 35mm film in special double cassette. C. 1925. First camera to have form of interchangeable back.

R4* $350	£184	DM577	FF1.8k

Amourette

Thomas OTTEWILL,
England.

Ottewill 8 x 10 Wet Plate Camera: (OT100); sliding box and wet plate camera; Andrew Ross lens. C.1856.

R5* $1.8k	£945	DM3k	FF9.2k

OTTICO MECCANICA ITALIANA,
OMI, Rome, Italy.

Sunshine: (OM100); C1947, three lens 35mm VFR camera for three colour seperation negatives each 9 x 12mm on standard 35mm film, f3.5/35mm lenses, simple shutter. The negatives were contact printed into positives, and then the camera was used as a projector for viewing the resulting full colour pictures! Rare and interesting, this camera has a very volatile price. (price indicated includes all parts for using as projector.)

R5* $1.8k	£945	DM3k	FF9.2k

OWLA, Japan.

Owla Stereo: (OW100); 35mm VFR stereo camera, focusing Owla Anistigmat 35mm. f3.5 lenses, shutter speeds 1/10-1/200s, top mounted accessory shoe. Two versions seem to exist with different focusing knobs. C. 1958

R3* $250	£131	DM412	FF1.3k

O

The Sunshine, a three lens camera for three colour seperation negatives, each 9 x 12mm, on standard 35mm film

PANON CAMERA CO., Tokyo, Japan.

Panon Camera: (PQ100); wide-angle panoramic VFR camera for 6 exp on 120 roll film, Panon 50mm f2.8 coated lens; 140 degree coverage angle.

R3* $1.5k	£787	DM2.5k	FF7.7k

Panon Camera

Widelux F6: (PQ101); 35mm panoramic VFR camera; revolving Schwartz 26mm f2.8 lens; revolving drum-type FPS 1/15,

1/125, 1/250 s. 21 exp, 24 x 59mm on 36mm exp 35mm film.

R3* $750	£394	DM1.2k	FF3.8k

PAPIGNY.

Jumelle Papigny: (PY100); C 1902, 8 x 16cm box-type stereo camera; Chevalier 10cm f6.5 lens; speed guillotine shutter. Bellows; rack focusing; central finder. 8 x 8cm exp on plates.

R3* $350	£184	DM577	FF1.8k

PARKER PEN COMPANY, Janesville, Wisconsin.

The Parker Camera: (PP100); subminiature camera; black & white or colour daylight loading cartridge; film exposed on inner rim of cartridge through mirror.

R4* $750	£394	DM1.2k	FF3.8k

H. V. PARSELLS ET FILS, France.

Parsell's Detective Camera: (HV100); wooden box-type detective camera; rapid rectilinear lens; pneumatic front-of-lens shutter. 6 double holders, 6.5 x 6.5cm exp. Tripod in form of cane. C 1885. With tripod.

R5* $120	£63	DM198	FF613

Pax Golden View: (BB217); 35mm RFR camera; Luminor Anastigmat 45mm f3.5 lens; 1/10-1/300 s. Mfd in Japan. C 1954.

R3* $150	£79	DM247	FF767

Pax Golden View

P

Widelux F6

Samuel PECK & CO., New Haven, Connecticut.

Peck Four-Tube Ferrotype Camera: (SP100); takes four ninth-plate tintypes. C 1868.

R5* $1.1k	£577	DM1.8k	FF5.6k

Wet Plate Camera Outfit: (SP101); C.C. Harrison lens; half-plate holder; dipping tank. Complete outfit.

R5* $1.8k	£945	DM3k	FF9.2k

VEB Pentacon see Guthe & Thorsch

PERKEN, SON & RAYMENT, London, England.

Optimus Detective Camera: (PS100); leather money-pouch type detective camera; rapid rectilinear lens; Thornton Pickard FPS. 8 x 10.5cm plates. C 1890.

R5* $600	£315	DM989	FF3.1k

Perken, Son & Rayment Detective Camera: (PS101); Thornton Pickard roller blind shutter. C 1896.

R5* $700	£367	DM1.2k	FF3.6k

Perken, Son & Co. Ltd. 4" x 5" Folding Plate Camera: (PS102); 4" x 5" folding plate camera; brass lens and shutter, rotating diaphragm stops. Removable ground glass back; reversible back. Front standard

Perken 4" x 5" Folding Plate Camera

adjustable; leather covered, brass fittings. C 1900's.

R3* $175	£92	DM288	FF894

Perken, Son & Rayment Tailboard Camera: (PS103); P.S. & R. brass barrel Rapid Euryscope lens slotted for waterhouse stops. Mahogany finish, brass fittings; maroon leather bellows and lens cap.

R3* $225	£118	DM371	FF1.2k

LE PERREUX, France.

Stereo Simda: (PX100); Roussel Microcolor 25mm f3.5 lenses; shutter 1-1/250 s, flash synch. 300 exp on 16mm movie film. C 1950.

R4* $650	£341	DM1.1k	FF3.3k

PERRY MASON & CO., Boston, Massachusetts.

The Argus: (PM100); leather handbag type detective camera. 12 exp, 8cm diameter; plate changed by turning lens mount. C 1890.

R5* $1.75k	£919	DM2.9k	FF8.9k

Harvard Camera: (PM101); tin box camera-black finish with gold striping; meniscus lens. 2¹/₂" x 4" exp on dry plates. C 1890. Given away as a premium in the 1890's.

R4* $150	£79	DM247	FF767

Harvard Camera

Le Petit Poucet: (BB222); French magazine camera; 4 x 4cm plates. Mfd in France.

R3* $80	£42	DM132	FF409

PHILLIPS-PHOTOVIT

W. PHILLIPS,
Birmingham, England.

Demon Detective Camera No. 1: (WP100); small metal detective camera; achromatic doublet 30mm f10 lens; rubber band activated flap type, front-of-lens shutter; single exp, 2¹/4" diameter on 2¹/4" square dry plates. Invented by Walter O'Reilly, mfd. for American Camera Co., London, England. C 1889.

R5* $1.2k	£630	DM2k	FF6.1k

Demon Detective Camera No. 1

Phoenix: (BB223); H. Roussel Stylor 13.5cm f4.5 lens; Compur shutter 1-1/200 s.6" x 9" exp on plates.

R3* $300	£157	DM495	FF1.5k

PHOTAVIT-WERK,
Nurnberg, Germany.

Photavit I: (PW100); C 1930, miniature camera for 14 exp, 24 x 24mm on 35mm film in special cassette. Schneider-Kreuznach Radionar f7/40mm lens among others, Photavit or Prontor II shutter.

R3* $100	£52	DM165	FF511

Photavit I Luxus: (PW101); C1930, same as (PW100) but in "Luxus" edition.

R4* $200	£105	DM330	FF1k

Photavit II: (PW102); C1935, miniature camera for 14 exp, 24 x 24mm on 35mm film

Photavit

in special cassette, Primotar f2.9/40mm lens among others, Compur shutter.

R2* $100	£52	DM165	FF511

Boltavit: (PW103); C1935, same camera as (PW102) but for name, much rarer.

R4* $150	£79	DM247	FF767

Photavit III: (PW104); C1949, miniature camera for 25 exp, 24 x 24mm on 35mm film in special cassette, Radionar f3.5/37.5mm lens, Compur shutter.

R3* $100	£52	DM165	FF511

Photavit IV: (PW105); C1950, miniature camera for 25 exp, 24 x 24mm on 35mm film in special cassette, Xenar f2.8/40mm lens, Compur shutter.

R3* $100	£52	DM165	FF511

Photavit V: (PW106); C1950, as (PW105) but with Luxar f2.9 lens.

R3* $100	£52	DM165	FF511

Photina I: (PW107); C1950, TLR for 6 x 6cm frames on 120 roll film, f4.5/75mm lens, Vario shutter.

R2* $25	£13	DM41	FF128

Photina II: (PW108); C1950, TLR for 6 x 6cm frames on 120 roll film, f3.5/75mm lens, Prontor shutter.

R2* $25	£13	DM41	FF128

Photina Reflex: (PW109); C1955, TLR for 6 x 6cm frames on 120 roll film, f3.7/75mm lens geared to viewing lens for focusing much like the Ricohflex, Prontor shutter.

R2* $30	£16	DM49	FF153

Photavit 36: (PW110); C1956, 35mm RFR camera, the first 24 x 36mm "full frame"

camera from Photavit, interchangeable Ennit f2.8/45mm lens, Prontor-SVS shutter, CRF.

| R3* $50 | £26 | DM82 | FF256 |

Photavit 36B: (PW111); C1956, as (PW110) but for built-in light meter.

| R2* $50 | £26 | DM82 | FF256 |

Photavit 36 Automatic: (PW112); C1958, 35mm RFR camera, interchangeable ennalyt f1.9/50mm lens, Prontor-SLK shutter, *coupled* built-in light meter.

| R3* $75 | £39 | DM124 | FF383 |

Photo Cycle: (BB224); Berthiot Eurigraphe 135mm f8 lens; Thornton Pickard shutter 1/15-1/90 s. 10 x 12cm exp on roll film. Mfd in France. C 1895.

| R4* $175 | £92 | DM288 | FF894 |

Photo-Etui-Jumelle: (BB225); binocular case detective camera; rapid rectilinear 120mm f12 lens; central guillotine shutter; 9 x 12cm plates. Patented by Frank-Valery. C 1892.

| R5* $1.8k | £945 | DM3k | FF9.2k |

Photolet: (BB226); meniscus 31mm f8 lens; single speed rotary shutter; 20 x 20mm exp. Mfd in France. C 1935.

| R3* $125 | £66 | DM206 | FF639 |

THE PHOTO MATERIALS CO, Rochester, New York.

The Trokonet Camera: (PH100); 4" x 5" magazine camera. 30 exp, 4" x 5" or 12

The Trokonet Camera

glass plates. C 1895.

| R4* $375 | £197 | DM618 | FF1.9k |

Photo Omnia: (BB227); 45 x 107mm stereo camera; Anastigmatic 60mm f6 lenses; variable speed shutter. Mfd in France. C 1925.

| R4* $175 | £92 | DM288 | FF894 |

Le Photoscopique: (BB230); OIP Gand Labor 45mm f3.5 lens; Ibsor shutter 1-1/150 s. 50 exp, 24 x 24mm on special cassettes. Mfd in Belgium. C 1930.

| R4* $450 | £236 | DM742 | FF2.3k |

Photo-See: (BB231); early instant picture camera with developing tank.

| R3* $35 | £18 | DM58 | FF179 |

John PIGGOTT, London, England.

English Sliding Box Wet-Plate Camera: (PT100); Petzval type lens. C 1858.

| R5* $1.5k | £787 | DM2.5k | FF7.7k |

English Sliding Box Wet-Plate Camera

PIGNONS S.A., Ballaigues, Switzerland.

Bolca I: (PG100); 35mm SLR camera; S.O.M. Berthiot 50mm f2.9 lens; interchangeable bayonet mount; CFPS 1-1/1000 s. Waist level reflex finder; split image RFR.

C 1942-1946. **$600.** Some late models were marked Bolsey Model A, rare.

R4* $700	£367	DM1.2k	FF3.6k

Bolca (Standard): (PG101); 35mm SLR camera; S.O.M. Berthiot 50mm f2.9 lens, interchangeable bayonet mount; CFPS 1-1/1000 s. Split image RFR. C 1942-1946.

R4* $600	£315	DM989	FF3.1k

Alpa (I Standard): (PG102); 35mm camera; Angenieux 50mm f2.9 lens; interchangeable bayonet mount; CFPS 1-1/1000 s, some without slow speeds, only 1/25-1/1000 s. Split image RFR. Snr begins at 11,000. C 1947-1952. Without slow speeds, prices 25% more.

R4* $600	£315	DM989	FF3.1k

Alpa (I Standard)

P

Alpa (II) Reflex: (PG103); 35mm camera; Angenieux 50mm f2.9 lens, interchangeable bayonet mount; CFPS 1-1/1000 s. Split image RFR; waist level reflex finder with flip-up magnifier. Also sold as Bolsey Reflex; called Alpax or Bolsey Reflex G with Angenieux 50mm f2.9 lens; Alitax or Bolsey Reflex H with Angenieux 50mm f1.8 lens. With f2.9 lens, or with f1.8.

R3* $350	£184	DM577	FF1.8k

Alpa (II) Reflex

Alpa (III) Prisma Reflex: (PG104); 35mm camera; Angenieux 50mm f2.9 lens, interchangeable bayonet mount; CFPS 1-1/1000 s. Split image RFR; 45 degree Kern prism finder. Called Primitax with f1.8 lens. C 1949-1952. With either lens, also with Xenon 50mm f2.0 lens.

R3* $300	£157	DM495	FF1.5k

Alpa 4: (PG105); 35mm SLR camera; Spektros Alovar f3.5 lens, interchangeable bayonet mount; CFPS 1-1/1000 s on a single dial. Enclosed (fixed housing and magnifier) 90 degree reflex vf; redesigned body configuration. C 1952- 1960.

R3* $325	£171	DM536	FF1.7k

Alpa 5: (PG106); 35mm SLR camera; Old Delft Alfinon f2.8 or Kern Switar f1.8 lens, interchangeable bayonet mount; CFPS 1-1/1000 s on single dial. 45 degree Kern eye level prism finder. C 1952-1960.

R3* $200	£105	DM330	FF1k

Alpa 6: (PG107); 35mm SLR camera; Old Delft Alfinon f2.8 or Kern Switar f1.8 lens, interchangeable bayonet mount; CFPS 1-1/1000 s on single dial. Self- timer; prism RFR on ground glass. C 1955-1959.

R3* $225	£118	DM371	FF1.2k

Alpa 7: (PG110); 35mm SLR camera; Kern Switar f1.8 lens, interchangeable bayonet mount; CFPS 1-1/1000 s on single dial. Coupled RFR (vertical base) and multi-focal (50-90-135) combined vf. C 1952-1959.

R3* $250	£131	DM412	FF1.3k

Alpa 8: (PG111); 35mm SLR camera; Kern Switar f1.8 lens, interchangeable bayonet mount; CFPS 1-1/1000 s on single dial. Added coupled RFR (vertical base) and multi-focal (50-90-135) combined vf; with prism RFR. C 1958-1959.

R3* $300	£157	DM495	FF1.5k

Alpa 7s: (PG112); half-frame 35mm SLR camera; Kern Switar f1.8 lens, interchangeable bayonet mount; CFPS 1-1/1000 s on single dial. Added coupled RFR (vertical base) and multi-focal (50-90-135) combined vf; single frame (18 x 24mm). C 1958-1959.

R4* $500	£262	DM824	FF2.6k

Alpa 4b: (PG113); 35mm SLR camera;

Spektros Alovar f3.5 lens, interchangeable bayonet mount; CFPS 1-1/1000 s on single dial. Enclosed (fixed housing and magnifier) 90 degree reflex vf; rapid return mirror; lever wind. C 1959-1965.

R3* $325	£171	DM536	FF1.7k

Alpa 5b: (PG114); 35mm SLR camera; Kern Macro Switar f1.8 lens; focus to 8", interchangeable bayonet mount; CFPS 1-1/1000 s on single dial. 45 degree Kern eye level prism finder; rapid return mirror; lever wind.
C 1959-1965.

R3* $200	£105	DM330	FF1k

Alpa 6b: (PG115); 35mm SLR camera; Macro Switar f1.8 lens, interchangeable bayonet mount; CFPS 1-1/1000 s on single dial. Self-timer, prism RFR on ground glass; rapid return mirror; lever wind. C 1959-1974.

R3* $225	£118	DM371	FF1.2k

Alpa 7b: (PG116); 35mm SLR camera; Macro Switar f1.8 lens, interchangeable bayonet mount; CFPS 1-1/1000 s on single dial. Coupled RFR (vertical base) and multifocal (50-90-135) combined vf; rapid return mirror; lever wind. C 1959-1970.

R3* $250	£131	DM412	FF1.3k

Alpa 8b: (PG117); 35mm SLR camera; Macro Switar f1.8 lens, interchangeable bayonet mount; CFPS 1-1/1000 s on single dial. Prism RFR on ground glass; rapid return mirror; lever wind. C 1956-1965.

R3* $250	£131	DM412	FF1.3k

Alpa 8b

Alpa 6c: (PG120); 35mm SLR camera; Macro Switar f1.8 lens, interchangeable bayonet mount; CFPS 1-1/1000 s on single dial. Redesigned prism-straight through viewing and uncoupled selenium exp meter; rapid return mirror; lever wind. C 1960-1969.

R3* $250	£131	DM412	FF1.3k

Alpa 9d: (PG121); 35mm SLR camera; Macro Switar f1.8 lens, interchangeable bayonet mount; CFPS 1-1/1000 s on single dial. Through-the-lens match needle Cds meter, uncoupled. C 1964-1969. Some models gold or black finish with red or green covering.

R4* $450	£236	DM742	FF2.3k

Alpa 9f: (PG122); 35mm SLR camera; Macro Switar f1.8 lens, interchangeable bayonet mount; CFPS 1-1/1000 s on single dial. C 1965-1967.

R3* $350	£184	DM577	FF1.8k

Alpa 10d: (PG123); 35mm SLR camera; reformulated Macro Switar f1.9 lens, interchangeable bayonet mount. Redesigned body configuration; through-the-lens match needle Cds meter; cross coupled zero centre meter. C 1968-1972. **$250.** Some models gold or black finish with red or green covering.

R3* $450	£236	DM742	FF2.3k

Alpa 11e: (PG124); 35mm SLR camera; reformulated Micro Switar f1.9 lens, interchangeable bayonet mount; CFPS 1-1/1000 s on single dial. Cross coupled zero centre meter with illuminated over-under exp arrows in finder. C 1970-1972. **$350.** Some models gold or black finish with red or green covering.

R3* $450	£236	DM742	FF2.3k

Alpa 10s: (PG125); half-frame 35mm SLR camera; reformulated Macro Switar f1.9 lens, interchangeable bayonet mount; CFPS 1-1/1000 s on single dial. Redesigned body configuration; cross coupled zero centre meter; single frame (18 x 24mm). C 1972.

R3* $400	£210	DM659	FF2k

Alpa 10f: (PG126); 35mm SLR camera; reformulated Micro Switar f1.9 lens, interchangeable bayonet mount; CFPS 1-1/1000 s on single dial. No meter. C 1968-1972.

R3* $325	£171	DM536	FF1.7k

Alpa 11el: (PG127); 35mm SLR camera;

reformulated Micro Switar f1.9 lens, inter-changeable bayonet mount; CFPS 1-1/1000 s on single dial. Cross coupled zero centre meter with illuminated over-under exp arrows in finder.
C 1972-1974.

R3* $375	£197	DM618	FF1.9k

Alpa 11si: (PG130); 35mm SLR camera; reformulated Micro Switar f1.9 lens, inter-changeable bayonet mount; CFPS 1-1/1000 s on single dial. Cross coupled zero centre meter (red, green, yellow L.E.D.'s). Most have black finish. C 1976-1978.

R3* $450	£236	DM742	FF2.3k

Alpa 11z: (PG131); half-frame 35mm SLR camera; reformulated Micro Switar f1.9 lens, interchangeable bayonet mount; CFPS 1/60 s. No meter; single frame (18 x 24mm). Very rare. C 1977.

R3* $500	£262	DM824	FF2.6k

Alpa 11fs: (PG132); half-frame 35mm SLR camera; reformulated Micro Switar f1.9 lens, interchangeable bayonet mount; CFPS 1-1/1000 s on single dial. Cross coupled zero centre meter; single frame (18 x 24mm). C 1977.

R3* $475	£249	DM783	FF2.4k

PINNOCK Rty. Ltd., Sydney, Australia.

Gymea Minor: (PK100); C1948, metal box camera for 6 x 6cm frames on roll film, simple lens and shutter, perhaps fifty proto-type cameras were made *for* Pinnock which itself made photographic darkroom equip-ment and sewing machines. The Gymea was never sold to the public.

R5*	NSR

Pinnock 35: (PK101); Announced Janu-ary, 1947, 35mm camera, copy of the Leica Standard, at least one prototype camera was made, and was seen by Australian lens designer and manufacturer Eric Waterhouse. No camera is known to exist today. Have you seen one?

R5*	NSR

PLAUBEL & CO., Frankfurt, Germany.

Plaubel Makina I (1924): (PU100); 6.5 x 9cm press camera; Anticomar 100mm f2.9 lens, front elements removable—can be replaced with wide-angle and telephoto com-ponents; Compur dial-set shutter 1-1/300 s. The Makina I was introduced in 1920 and discontinued in 1932. It came with non-removable 100mm f4.5 Anticomar lens until 1924; after this it came with 100mm f2.9 Anticomar lens with removable front ele-ments. 6.5 x 9cm exp on sheet film. C 1924.

R3* $225	£118	DM371	FF1.2k

Gymea Minor

Plaubel Makina I

Plaubel Makina II (1938): (PU101); 6.5 x 9cm press camera; Anticomar 100mm f2.9 lens; dial-set Compur shutter 1-1/200 s. 6.5 x 9cm exp on sheet film. C 1938.

R3* $225	£118	DM371	FF1.2k

Plaubel Makina III: (PU102); 6.5 x 9cm press camera; Anticomar 100mm f2.9 lens; Compur shutter 1-1/200 s. C 1949.

R3* $200	£105	DM330	FF1k

Plaubel Makinette: (PU103); miniature roll film camera; Supercomar 45mm f2 lens; Compur shutter 1-1/300s. 1 1/4" x 1 5/8" exp on 127 roll film. C 1935.

R4* $650	£341	DM1.1k	FF3.3k

Plaubel Rollop: (PU104); folding roll film camera; Anticomar 75mm f2.8 lens; Compur Rapid shutter 1-1/400s, CRF. 16 exp on 120 roll film. C 1935.

R3* $250	£131	DM412	FF1.3k

Plucker's Pocket Stereograph: (BB232); Darlot 21cm f8 Planigraph lens; built-in circular shutter. 13 x 18cm exp on plates. Mfg. by various opticians, including Dubroni. C 1871.

R5* $1.4k	£735	DM2.3k	FF7.2k

Hans Pock Detective Camera: (BB233); mahogany Germany camera concealed in leather satchel; guillotine shutter. Magazine with push-pull lever to change plates - sliding panel in bottom for storage.

R5* $4k+	£2.1k+	DM6.6k+	FF20.4k+

POLAROID INC., Cambridge, Massachusetts.

Polaroid 95

All Polaroids Rarity */**

Polaroid 95: (PO100); Rigid mast,

R3* $20	£10	DM33	FF102

Polaroid 95: (PO101); Spring mast,

R3* $20	£10	DM33	FF102

Polaroid 95A: (PO102);

R2* $10	£5	DM16	FF51

Polaroid 95B: (PO103);

R2* $10	£5	DM16	FF51

Polaroid 80: (PO104);

R2* $10	£5	DM16	FF51

Polaroid 80A: (PO105);

R2* $10	£5	DM16	FF51

Polaroid 80B: (PO106);

R2* $10	£5	DM16	FF51

Polaroid J33: (PO107);

R2* $10	£5	DM16	FF51

Polaroid J66: (PO110);

R2* $10	£5	DM16	FF51

Polaroid 100: (PO111);

R2* $10	£5	DM16	FF51

Polaroid 101: (PO112);

R2* $15	£8	DM25	FF77

Polaroid 110: (PO113);

R2* $20	£10	DM33	FF102

Polaroid 110A: (PO114);

R2* $60	£31	DM99	FF307

Polaroid 110B: (PO115);

R2* $60	£31	DM99	FF307

Polaroid 150: (PO116);

R2* $10	£5	DM16	FF51

P

POLAROID-PURMA

Polaroid 160: (PO117);

R2* $30	£16	DM49	FF153

Polaroid 180: (PO118);

R3* $250	£131	DM412	FF1.3k

Polaroid 195: (PO120);

R3* $250	£131	DM412	FF1.3k

Polaroid 210: (PO121);

R2* $20	£10	DM33	FF102

Polaroid 420: (PO122);

R1* $20	£10	DM33	FF102

Polaroid 450: (PO123);

R1* $25	£13	DM41	FF128

Polaroid 800: (PO124);

R1* $10	£5	DM16	FF51

Polaroid 900: (PO125);

R1* $10	£5	DM16	FF51

Polaroid SX70: (PO126);

R2* $45	£24	DM74	FF230

Polaroid SX70, Model II: (PO127);

R2* $40	£21	DM66	FF204

Polaroid SX70 Sonar: (PO130);

R2* $60	£31	DM99	FF307

POPULAR PHOTOGRAPH CO., New York.

Nodark Ferrotype Camera: (PZ100); wooden box camera; magazine loading; 26 exp, 2¹/₂" x 3¹/₂" on ferrotype plates. C 1899.

R4* $850	£446	DM1.4k	FF4.3k

Nodark Ferrotype Camera

Xavier PORTAFAX, France.

Photo Volume: (XP100); book-type detective camera; rapid rectilinear or Zeiss lens; direct vf. 9 x 12cm plates. C 1894.

R5* $1.5k	£787	DM2.5k	FF7.7k

Prince Color Camera: (BB235); 9.5mm movie camera, similar to National Pathe model; Colotar f2.7 lens. Mfd in England.

R2* $40	£21	DM66	FF204

PREMIER INSTRUMENT CORP., New York, USA.

Kardon: (PR100); 1945. Cfps, 1- 1/1000 s, diopter adjustment, screw mount F2.0/47mm Kodak Ektar. (The exact year of manufacture can be determined using the code described in the ID section of this book.) The military model has enlarged shutter winding and release controls, allowing use of the camera while wearing gloves. The military model now sells for about 20% less than the civilian model. Price given is for a civilian model with lens.

R3* $600	£315	DM989	FF3.1k

Kardon

PURMA CAMERAS

Purma Special: (PC100); Beck Anastigmat 2¹/₄" f6.3 fixed focus plastic lens; 3 speed MFPS. 16 exp, 1¹/₄" x 1¹/₄" on 127 roll film. C 1938.

R2* $50	£26	DM82	FF256

RAY-REFLEX

RAY CAMERA CO., refer to MUTSCHLER, ROBERTSON & CO.

The Record Camera: (BB237); TLR box camera; all wooden body; single exp, 3¹/4" x 4". Mfr unknown - English construction.

R5* $1.4k	£735	DM2.3k	FF7.2k

RECTAFLEX STAREA, Rome, Italy.

Rectaflex 1000:(RX102); C1949, 35mm SLR with interchangeable Xenon f2/50mm lens among others, CFPS 1 - 1/1000s, historically important along with the Contax S as being the first 35mm SLR with fixed pentaprism sold on the marketplace.

R3* $250	£131	DM412	FF1.3k

Rectaflex 1300: (RX100); C 1950, 35mm SLR camera with interchangeable Angenieux f1.8/50mm lens among others, CFPS 1-1/1300s.

R3* $350	£184	DM577	FF1.8k

Rectaflex 1300

Rectaflex Rotor with gunstock: (RX101); C1950, with special rotating mount for three different lenses, including Angenieux f1.8/90mm, f1.8/50mm and f2.8/35mm. (one offered for $2800 may or may not have been sold!)

R4* $2.25k	£1.2k	DM3.7k	FF11.5k

Rectaflex Rotor with gunstock

Rectaflex Junior:(RX103); C1950, 35mm SLR with interchangeable Xenon f2.8/50mm lens among others, CFPS 1/25 - 1/500s, the cheaper version of the Rectaflex.

R3* $180	£94	DM297	FF920

Recta: (RX104); C1953, 35mm RFR camera with interchangeable Westar f3.5/50mm lens, CFPS 1 - 1/1000s, made in only small numbers, (some say 6!) this camera never made it to the market place.

R5* NSR est$3.5k	£1.8k	DM5.8k	FF17.9k

Director 35: (RX105); C1954, 35mm VFR camera, 39mm screw mount, FPS, made only in prototype units, never delivered to the public.

R5* NSR est $3k	£1.6k	DM5k	FF15.3k

REFLEX CAMERA CO., Newark, New Jersey.

Focal Plane Postcard Camera: (RC100); postcard size camera; FPS. Ground glass focusing back; 3¹/4" x 4¹/4" exp. C 1912.

R4* $225	£118	DM371	FF1.2k

REFLEX-REVERIE

Junior Reflex Camera: (RC101); 3¹/₄" x 4¹/₄" box-type SLR; fixed focus lens; 4 speed shutter. C 1903.

R3* $130	£68	DM214	FF664

Reflex Camera: (RC102); Anastigmat 210mm f16 lens; variable speed FPS; 5" x 7" plates, space for 3 double holders. C 1898.

R3* $400	£210	DM659	FF2k

Le Reve: (BB240); 3¹/₄" x 4¹/₄" camera; Anastigmatic Roussel 135mm f6.3 or Beck 135mm f6.3 lens; Unicum or pneumatic shutter. 3¹/₄" x 4¹/₄" plates or roll film with special roll film back. Mfd in Paris, France. C 1908.

R3* $150	£79	DM247	FF767

REID & SIGRIST LTD., Leicester, England.

Reid III: (RS100); 1951-55 Cfps, 1 - 1/1000 sec, type I had no flash synch, while type II used synch contacts marked "E" for electronic flash, and "B" for bulbs. Screw mount Taylor-Hobson F2.0/2 inch lens. This camera is a high quality copy of the Leica III B. In 1958 Reid announced Models II and IA, but these cameras never made it into the market place. Type II cameras are valued 25% less than type I cameras. Price given is for type I camera with normal lens.

R3* $600	£315	DM989	FF3.1k

Reid III

Reid I: (RS101); 1958-62 Cfps, 1/20 - 1/1000 sec, no Rfr, Vfr only. Screw mount Taylor-Hobson F2.0/2 inch lens. Originally offered at £20 less than the Reid III camera, the Reid I is found mostly in the ex-military version. This military version can be easily identified by the code impressed into the leather on the back of the camera body, consisting of the letters A.P., A.P.F., or F. followed by the numbers 8810, or the marked entirely in numbers, such as 0553/8810. These markings are known, though others may exist. It is thought about 1500 of these cameras were made.

R3* $600	£315	DM989	FF3.1k

REVERE CAMERA CO., Chicago, Illinois.

Revere Stereo 33: (RV100); 35mm stereo camera; Wollensak Revere Amaton 35mm f3.5 lenses; Synchromatic or Rapax shutter 1/2-1/2000 s; MFX synch; crf. C 1952.

R3* $150	£79	DM247	FF767

Revere Stereo 33

Revere "8" Model 50: (RV101); 8mm movie camera; Anastigmat Revere 12.7mm f2.8 lens; 2 speeds: 16 and 64 frames per s.

R2* $15	£8	DM25	FF77

Revere "8" Model 60: (RV102); 8mm movie camera; 3 lens turret; telescopic vf.

R2* $15	£8	DM25	FF77

Revere "8" Model 77: (RV103); 8mm movie camera; Animar 12.7mm f2.8 lens. Variable speeds from 8 to 48 frames per s; magazine loading. C 1952.

R2* $15	£8	DM25	FF77

Revere "8" Model 80: (RV104); 8mm movie camera; Cine Nikkor 13mm f1.9 lens. 5 speeds: 12, 16, 24, 32 and 48 frames per s. C 1950.

R2* $15	£8	DM25	FF77

Revere "8" Model 99: (RV105); 8mm movie

camera; triple lens turret; 2 vf with parallax correction. 3 speeds: 8, 16 and 32 frames per s. Spring motor. C 1952.

R2* $15	£8	DM25	FF77

Revere Eyematic: (RV106); 8mm movie camera; triple lens turret for Cine Raptar 9, 13 and 32mm f1.8 lenses. Photo-electric cell coupled to diaphragm.

R2* $15	£8	DM25	FF77

Revere Magazine "16": (RV107); 16mm movie camera; Wollensak Raptar 1" f2.5 lens; telescopic vf; spring motor drive. 5 speeds: 2, 15, 24, 32 and 48 frames per s. C early 1950's.

R2* $20	£10	DM33	FF102

Revere Ranger Model 81: (RV110); 8mm movie camera; Somco Revere 12.5mm f2.5 lens. C 1947.

R2* $15	£8	DM25	FF77

REX MAGAZINE CAMERA CO., Chicago, Illinois.

Rex Magazine Camera: (RM100); meniscus lens; single speed shutter. Magazine load: 4" x 5" dry plates changed by wooden sheath. C 1899.

R3* $140	£73	DM231	FF716

Rex Photographic Outfit: (RM101); cardboard box camera, covered with black paper; 2" x 2" exp on dry plates.

R3* $55	£29	DM91	FF281

Jules RICHARD, Paris, France.

Le Glyphos Stereo Camera: (JR100); meniscus lenses; guillotine shutter. C 1905.

R2* $110	£58	DM181	FF562

Homeos: (JR101); 35mm stereo camera; Zeiss Tessar 30mm f4.5 lens; horizontal guillotine shutter 1/6-1/142 s. 2 finders: one on top for horizontal exp; one on left side for vertical exp. 27 stereo exp, 2.5 x 1.9cm or 54 single exp on 35mm film. Qty 1500(?). C 1914-1920. The Homeos was the first 35mm stereo camera.

R5* $2k+	£1.1k+	DM3.3k+	FF10.2k+

Homeos

Homeoscope: (JR102); Zeiss Krauss Anastigmat 124mm lenses; single speed guillotine shutter; 24 exp on 8 x 9cm dry plates. Leather covered; 6 x 13cm or 9 x 18cm. C 1895.

R3* $200	£105	DM330	FF1k

Verascope: (JR103); Goerz Double Anastigmatic 85mm f6.8 lens; 6 speed guillotine shutter. Plate and roll film magazine. C 1905.

R3* $90	£47	DM148	FF460

Verascope F40: (JR104); 35mm stereo camera; Optis f4.5 or Berthiot 40mm f3.5 lens; shutter 1-1/250 s. 40 stereo pairs on 35mm film, also single-frame. C 1938.

R4* $425	£223	DM701	FF2.2k

RICOH CO. LTD., Tokyo, Japan.

Golden Ricoh "16": (RI100); subminiature camera; Ricoh 25mm f3.5 lens; sector shutter 1/50-1/200 s. 20 exp on 16mm film on special cassettes. C 1956.

R2* $175	£92	DM288	FF894

Golden Ricoh "16"

Ricoh "16": (RI101); subminiature camera; Ricoh 25mm f2.8 interchangeable lens;

RICOH-ROBINSON

shutter 1/50-1/200 s. 24 exp, 10 x 14mm on 16mm film in special cassettes. C 1956.

R2* $150	£79	DM247	FF767

Ricolet: (RI102); 35mm camera; Ricoh Anastigmat 45mm f3.5 coated lens; Riken 1/25-1/50 s. C 1950.

R2* $35	£18	DM58	FF179

Ricolet

Ricoh 35: (RI103); Similar in shape to the Richolet (RI102), but with crf. Riken shutter, speeds 1-1/200s, 4.5cm/f3.5 Riken Ricomat lens.

R3* $125	£66	DM206	FF639

Ricoh 35

RIETZSCHEL GMBH OPTISCHE FABRIK, Munich, Germany.

Heli-Klack: (RZ100); folding stereo camera; 3 interchangeable lenses; Compound shutter. Rising front; rack focusing; double extension bellows. 9 x 18cm exp. C 1920.

R4* $800	£420	DM1.3k	FF4.1k

Kosmo Klack: (RZ101); 45 x 107mm stereo camera; Combinable Rietzschel 65mm f4.5 lens; Stereo Compur 1- 1/250 s. Panoramic setting; rising lens panel. C 1914-1925.

R4* $400	£210	DM659	FF2k

RILEY RESEARCH, Santa Monica, California.

Rilex: (RR100); 2¼" x 3¼" view camera; Kodak Anastigmat Spec. 127mm lens.

R4* $100	£52	DM165	FF511

John ROBERTS, Boston, Massachusetts.

John Roberts Daguerreotype Camera (1850): (RQ100); 8" x 10" daguerreotype camera; Jamin Darlot Sr. Landscape 350mm f11 lens, sliding box focusing. 8" x 10" or 6½" x 8½" plates. Largest known American daguerreotype camera. C 1850.

R5* $12k+	£6.3k+	DM19.8k+	FF61.3k+

John Roberts Daguerreotype Camera

John Roberts Daguerreotype Camera (1854): (RQ101); Holmes, Booth & Hayden, New York lens with reversing prism; 1/4 plate daguerreotypes. Boston Box style daguerreotype camera. C 1854.

R5* $8k+	£4.2k+	DM13.2k+	FF40.9k+

C. N. ROBINSON, Philadelphia, Pennsylvania.

Camera Obscura: (RY100); 32.5 x 18.5 x 19.5cm; mahogany with dovetail construction; sliding box focusing; 15 x 16cm image. C 1820-1830.

R5* $4k+	£2.1k+	DM6.6k+	FF20.4k+

J. ROBINSON & SONS, England.

Luzo Detective Camera: (RW100); first British-made box camera; Aplanat 2¹/₂" f11 lens; variable speed sector shutter. Used Eastman-type roll film, 100 exp, 6 cm diameter. C 1890.

R4* $1.5k	£787	DM2.5k	FF7.7k

Luzo Detective Camera

ROBOT-BERNING & CO., Dusseldorf, Germany.

Robot I: (RB100); C1934-1938, 35mm motor drive camera; Zeiss Tessar 32.5mm f2.8 lens, interchangeable screw mount; rotary metal shutter 1-1/500 s. 24 x 24mm exp on 35mm film in special cassettes. "Detective-type" swivelling vf. Spring motor: 24 exp on one winding.

R3* $125	£66	DM206	FF639

Robot I

Robot II: (RB101); C 1938-1950, 35mm motor drive camera; Zeiss Biotar 40mm f2 lens, interchangeable screw mount; rotary metal shutter 1-1/500 s. 24 x 24mm exp on 35mm film in special daylight loading cassettes. Spring motor: 24 exp on one winding; optional motor was available for 48 exp on one winding.

R3* $110	£58	DM181	FF562

Luftwaffe Robot: (RB102); C 1940, 35mm motor drive camera; Schneider Tele-Zenar 75mm f3.5 lens, interchangeable screw mount; rotary metal shutter 1/2-1/500 s. 24 x 24mm exp on 35mm film in special cassettes. Manufactured for the German Air Force during WWII. One variation has the double spring for 48 exp on a single wind. The finish is black enamel; internal film channel is made from black plastic material. "Luftwaffen Eigentum" always marked on rear of top cover; the Tele-Zenar 75mm f35 is marked "Luftwaffen Eigentum" on rear of lens mount or on side of barrel. Shutter speeds below 1/100 s have been ground off the shutter speed dial in some examples.

R3* $250	£131	DM412	FF1.3k

Luftwaffe Robot

R

Robot IIa: (RB103); C 1951-1953, 35mm motor drive camera; Schneider Xenon 40mm f1.9 lens, interchangeable screw mount; rotary metal shutter 1/2 - 1/500 s. 24 x 24mm exp on 35mm film in special cassettes. Spring motor for 24 exp on one winding; optional motor was available for 48 exp on one winding.

R3* $110	£58	DM181	FF562

Robot Junior: (RB104); C1951-1953, Similar to Robot IIa except does not have adjustment for right angle viewing.

R2* $100	£52	DM165	FF511

Robot Royal 24: (RB105); C1956-1959, 35mm motor drive camera; Schneider Xenar 45mm f2.8 coated lens; rotary metal shutter

ROBOT

1/2-1/500 s; crf. 24 x 24mm exp. *Has auto "burst" operation.*

| R2* $375 | £197 | DM618 | FF1.9k |

Robot Royal 24

Robot Royal 36: (RB106); C1956-1959, 35mm motor drive camera; Schneider Xenar 45mm f2.8 coated lens, interchangeable bayonet mount; rotary shutter 1/2 - 1/500 s, crf. 24 x 36mm exp. *No auto "burst" operation.*

| R3* $300 | £157 | DM495 | FF1.5k |

Robot Royal 36

Robot Star I: (RB107); C1952-1959, 35mm motor drive camera; Schneider Xenon 40mm f1.9 coated lens, interchangeable screw mount; rotary metal shutter 1/2 -1/500 s. 24 x 24mm exp on 35mm film in standard cartridge. Spring motor for 24 exp on one winding; optional motor was available for 48 exp on one winding.

| R3* $150 | £79 | DM247 | FF767 |

Robot Star II: (RB108); C1958-63, 35mm motor drive camera; Schneider Xenar f2/8/

38mm or Xenon f1.9/40mm coated lens, interchangeable screw mount; rotary metal shutter 1/2 -1/500 s. 24 x 24mm exp—on 35mm film in standard cartridge. Spring motor for 18 exp on one winding; optional motor was available for 50 exp on one winding, electromagnetic shutter release, field of view for 40mm and 75mm in VFR.

| R3* $250 | £131 | DM412 | FF1.3k |

Robot Star 25: (RB109); C1960, 35mm motor drive camera for 25 -24 x 24mm frames on standard 35mm film with one winding of the built-in spring motor, Xenar f2.8/38mm lens, burst operation up to 6 frames per second, all metal rotary shutter, 1/4 - 1/500s, electromagnetic release.

| R3* $200 | £105 | DM330 | FF1k |

Robot Star 50: (RB110); C1960, as (RB109) but with 50 shot spring motor.

| R3* $250 | £131 | DM412 | FF1.3k |

Robot 400: (RB111); C1955, Royal Robot 24 with built-in long film holder for 400 frames 24 x 24 on standard 35mm film, electric motor drive was available in addition to built-in spring motor.

| R3* $450 | £236 | DM742 | FF2.3k |

Robot Royal II: (RB112); C1955, as Royal Robot 24 (RB105) but *without RFR,* and *without burst operation.*

| R3* $200 | £105 | DM330 | FF1k |

Robot Recorder 24: (RB113); C1958, as Robot Royal 24 (RB105), but *without any finder at all, or burst operation.*

| R3* $300 | £157 | DM495 | FF1.5k |

Robot Recorder 36: (RB114); C1958, as Robot Royal 36 (RB106), but *without any finder at all.*

| R3* $275 | £144 | DM453 | FF1.4k |

Accessories for Robot cameras:

Ennalyt f4/24mm lens: (RB001); **$150**
Primotar f3.5/30mm lens: (RB003); **$45**
Xenogon f2.8/35mm lens: (RB005); **$130**
Tele-Xenar f3.8/75mm lens: (RB007); **$110**
Tele-Arton f4/90mm lens: (RB008); **$130**
Sonnar f2/90mm lens: (RB009); **$240**
Tele-Xenar f4/135mm lens: (RB010); **$150**

Tele-Xenar f4/150mm lens: (RB011); **$165**
Tele-Xenar f5.5/200mm lens: (RB012); **$250+**

universal finder 30mm-150mm: (RB0) **$70**
30mm optical finder: (RB021); **$50**
folding finder for 40mm and 75mm: (RB022); **$50**
90mm optical finder: (RB023); **$60**
135mm optical finder: (RB024); **$50**
200 optical finder: (RB025); **$90+**

accessory coupled RFR for Robot II: (RB030); **$125**
under-water housing: (RB031); **$250+**
beam-splitter microscope adaptor: (RB032); **$175**
series flash lamp holder (four lamps): (RB033); **$50+**

ROCHESTER OPTICAL AND CAMERA COMPANY, Rochester, New York.

The Rochester Optical Company was producing "Premo" cameras in 1893; it merged with several other companies in 1900 to form the Rochester Optical and Camera Company. In 1907 the firm was acquired by the Eastman Kodak Company. From 1907 to 1917 the designation was Rochester Optical Division, Eastman Kodak Company; from 1918 to 1922 - Rochester Optical Department, Eastman Kodak Company.

The Carlton Twin Lens Camera: (RO100); 4" x 5" plate TLR camera. C 1895.

R5*	NSR

Carlton View Camera: (RO101); 6¹/₂" x 8¹/₂" view camera; brass tripod base built into lens bed; reversible double swing back; polished wood body with brass fittings. 8 sizes from 4" x 5" **$200** to 11" x 14" **$400.** C 1890's.

R4*	Prices as above

The Empire State Camera: (RO102); view camera. C 1895. 5" x 7", **$100**; 8" x 10",

$300; 11" x 14", **$400**.

R3*	Prices as above

Folding Gem Poco: (RO103); 3¹/₄" x 4¹/₄" folding plate camera. Built-in shutter. Polished wood finish, red bellows. Folded size 6" x 5¹/₄" x 1¹/₂" ; weight 1 lb. C 1890's.

R3* $110	£58	DM181	FF562

The Folding Premier: (RO104); folding plate camera; Bausch & Lomb pneumatic shutter with built-in rotating waterhouse stops. C 1895.

R2* $65	£34	DM107	FF332

Carlton View Camera

The Empire State Camera

Folding Gem Poco

ROCHESTER

The Handy: (RO105); box-type camera; 4" x 5" exp on plates. C 1895.

R2* $65	£34	DM107	FF332

The Ideal Camera: (RO106); view camera. C1895. 4"x5" **$100;** 5"x7" **$125;** 8"x10", **$?**

R3*	Prices as above

The Kenwood Camera: (RO107); compact view camera; wide front for stereo lenses. C 1895. 5" x 7", **$150.** 8" x 10":

R3* $250	£131	DM412	FF1.3k

King Poco: (RO110); 6¹/₂" x 8¹/₂" folding plate camera; Rochester Symmetrical Convertible lens; Unicum shutter. Double extension red leather bellows; horizontal or vertical format swing back; mahogany. Sizes: 4" x 5" to 8" x 10". C 1890's.

R3* $175	£92	DM288	FF894

King View Camera: (RO111); 8" x 10" view camera; rising and falling front; front and rear swings; double extension red leather bellows; polished mahogany, lacquered brass fittings. Sizes: 5" x 7" to 11" x 14". Top of the line view camera, original price $36. C 1890's.

R3* $300	£157	DM495	FF1.5k

The Long Focus Premo: (RO112); 5" x 7" folding plate camera. C 1895.

R3* $175	£92	DM288	FF894

Midget Pocket Camera: (RO113); compact view camera. C 1895. 4" x 5" exp on plates. C 1895.

R2* $125	£66	DM206	FF639

The Monitor Camera: (RO114); compact view camera. C 1895. 4" x 5", **$250;** 8" x 10":

R3* $325	£171	DM536	FF1.7k

New Model Camera: (RO115); view camera. C 1895. 4" x 5", **$125;** 5" x 7", **$200;** 8" x 10":

R3* $200	£105	DM330	FF1k

New Model Improved Camera: (RO116); view camera. Polished wood finish, nickel plated fittings. C 1895. 4" x 5", **$200;** 5" x 7", **$225;** 10" x 8":

R3* $300	£157	DM495	FF1.5k

New Model Camera

New Model Stereo Camera: (RO117); stereo view camera. C 1895.

R4* $500	£262	DM824	FF2.6k

New Model Stereo Camera

The Premo: (RO120); 4" x 5" folding plate camera. C 1895.

R2* $75	£39	DM124	FF383

Poco, Series A: (RO121); 4" x 5" folding plate camera; Symmetrical brass lens. Shifting, rising and falling front; wood interior, red bellows. C 1890's.

R3* $125	£66	DM206	FF639

Poco, Series B: (RO122); 4" x 5" folding plate camera; Rapid Rectilinear Symmetrical lens; Unicum shutter. Single swing back; rising front; Poco reversible finder; red bellows. C 1890's.

R3* $110	£58	DM181	FF562

Poco, Series B

Poco, Series E: (RO123); 4" x 5" folding plate camera; built-in lens and shutter. Polished wood finish, red bellows and leather covered bed; reversible finder. Original price $8. Also in 5" x 7" size. C 1890's.

R3* $125	£66	DM206	FF639

Pony Premo No. 6: (RO124); 4" x 5" folding plate camera; Goerz Double Anastigmat 5" lens; Eastman Kodak Bausch & Lomb shutter. Reversible back with swings; shifting, rising and falling front; double extension red bellows. C 1890's.

R3* $120	£63	DM198	FF613

![Pony Premo No. 6]

Pony Premo No. 6

The Premaret: (RO125); box-type camera; 4" x 5" exp on plates. C 1895.

R3* $90	£47	DM148	FF460

The Premier: (RO126); box-type detective camera; brass lens; built-in shutter in front swing down face; 4" x 5" exp on plates. Leather exterior, cherrywood interior. C 1895.

R3* $100	£52	DM165	FF511

R

The Premo B: (RO127); folding plate camera; 4" x 5" exp on plates. C 1895.

R2* $90	£47	DM148	FF460

The Premo C: (RO130); 4" x 5" folding plate camera. C 1895.

R2* $90	£47	DM148	FF460

The Premo D: (RO131); 4" x 5" folding plate camera. C 1895.

R2* $90	£47	DM148	FF460

The Premo Sr: (RO132); 4" x 5" folding plate camera. C 1895.

R2* $100	£52	DM165	FF511

Reversible Back Premo: (RO133); folding

The Premo B

plate camera; Goerz Double Anastigmat 10³/₄" f1 lens; Bausch & Lomb 'Iris Diaphragm' shutter. Whole plate size, 6¹/₂" x 8¹/₂"

R3* $150	£79	DM247	FF767

Rochester Optical Co. 8" x 10" View Camera: (RO134); 8" x 10" view camera; rear Folmer & Schwing FPS; rising and falling front. Polished wood finish, brass fittings; red leather bellows. C 1900's.

R3* $300	£157	DM495	FF1.5k

Standard View Camera: (RO135); 8" x 10" view camera; rear focus; reversible back; mahogany finish, brass fittings. 7 sizes: 3¹/₄" x 4¹/₄" **$90** to 8" x 10" **$200** (single or double swing back). C 1890's.

R3*

The Stereoscopic Premo: (RO136); 5" x 7" folding plate camera. C 1895.

R4* $400	£210	DM659	FF2k

Telephoto Poco A: (RO137); Rapid Rectilinear lens; Bausch & Lomb shutter. 5" x 7" exp on plates. Polished wood interior, red leather bellows. C 1902.

R3* $125	£66	DM206	FF639

Telephoto Cycle B: (RO140); 5" x 7" folding; telephoto Triple Convertible lens or Zeiss, Goerz, Wide Angle or Voigtlander; double extension; reversible back; rising and falling front; back swings horizontally or

vertically; mahogany, brass fittings; covered in Moroccan leather. 4 sizes: 4" x 5" **$125** to 8" x 10" **$250**. C 1900.

R3*

Universal Camera: (RO141); compact folding 5" x 7" view camera; wide angle brass lens; rack and pinion focusing; swinging, rising and falling front; polished wood finish with brass fittings. 11 sizes from 3¹/₄" x 4¹/₄" to 17" x 20" in single and double swing models. C 1890's.

R3* $100-$300

Dr. RODEHUSER Kamera Mechanik, Heeßen, Germany.

Panta: (RF100); C1948, metal VFR camera for 6 x 4.5cm frames on 120 roll film, Ennar f4.5/74mm lens in collapsible tube mount among others, Vario or other shutter.

R2* $30	£16	DM49	FF153

Panta

ROKUWA, Tokyo, Japan.

Stereo Rocca: (RK100); stereo camera; single meniscus 42mm lens; shutter 1/30 s, B, flash. Direct vision optical finder; 24 pairs, 24 x 3mm on 120 roll film. C 1955.

R3* $170	£89	DM280	FF869

Roland: (BB241); 1⁵/₈" x 2¹/₄" RFR camera; Kleinbild Plasmat 70mm f2.7 lens; Compur Rapid shutter 1-1/400 s, crf. 16 exp, 1⁵/₈" x 2¹/₄" on 120 roll film. C 1931. Probably the first combined range-viewfinder in a commercially produced camera.

| R4* $900 | £472 | DM1.5k | FF4.6k |

Roland

Andrew ROSS,
London, England.

Andrew Ross Stereo Wet Plate: (RD100); sliding box stereo camera; dovetailed mahogany; brass lenses; rack and pinion focusing.

| R5* $2.5k | £1.3k | DM4.1k | FF12.8k |

Thomas ROSS & CO.,
London, England.

Photoscope: (RG100); binocular-type detective camera; special cassette from roll film allowing 3.5 x 4cm exp. Patented by William Sanders. C 1889.

| R5* | NSR |

Ross Divided: (RG101); 3¹/4" x 4¹/4" TLR camera; Goerz Doppel Anastigmat f7.7 lenses. C 1895.

| R4* $600 | £315 | DM989 | FF3.1k |

Ross 13" x 18" Tailboard Camera: (RG102); 13" x 18" tailboard camera; Voigtlander & Son, Brauschweig lens; shifting front for stereo; rear tilts and swings;

double extension. C 1880's.

| R3* $400 | £210 | DM659 | FF2k |

Ross Twin Lens Reflex: (RG103); Ross Homocentric 7" f6.3 lens; Bausch & Lomb pneumatic shutter 1-1/1000 s. 4" x 5" plates; rotating back. C 1891.

| R4* $800 | £420 | DM1.3k | FF4.1k |

ROUCH,
London, England.

Eureka Detective Camera: (RH100); mahogany box-form camera; 150mm f6 doublet lens; behind-the-lens roller blind shutter; flexible leather plate changing bag. C 1888.

| R4* $600 | £315 | DM989 | FF3.1k |

Rouch Excelsior Hand Camera: (RH101); two mahogany boxes joined by leather bellows; rack and pinion focusing. C 1890.

| R4* $700 | £367 | DM1.2k | FF3.6k |

ROUSSEL,
Paris, France.

Stella Jumelle: (RE100); 9 x 12cm stereo camera; Anti Spectroscopique 130mm f7.7 lens; 7 speed guillotine shutter. C 1900.

| R3* $250 | £131 | DM412 | FF1.3k |

Rubix: (BB242); subminiature camera; Hope 5mm f3.5 lens; shutter 1/25-1/100 s. 50 exp, 10 x 14mm on 16mm film. Mfg. in Japan. C 1950.

| R4* $200 | £105 | DM330 | FF1k |

R

SAKURA,
Japan.

Petal: (SA100); watch-type detective camera; 6 circular exp, on 25mm diameter disc of film. C 1950. Round style, **$300.** Hexagonal style, **$375.** Petal Outfit: film cutter, developing holder and two tins of film discs, in wooden boxes with directions.

R3* $500	£262	DM824	FF2.6k

SAMEI SANGYO,
Japan.

Samoca 35II: (SG100); 35mm camera C. Ezumar 50mm/3.5 lens shutter 1/25-1/100s. C 1957.

R2* $35	£18	DM58	FF179

Samoca 35III: (SG101); 35mm camera Ezumar Anastigmat 50mm/3.5 lens almost exactly like the Samoca II (SG100), except for the name and faster shutter! C 1958.

R2* $35	£18	DM58	FF179

Samoca Super: (SG102); 35mm camera with C Ezumar 50mm/2.8 lens, CRF and (sometimes) built-in lightmeter). btl shutter speeds 1-1/200s. Its value lies in its strange looks!

R3* $55	£29	DM91	FF281

SANDERSON CAMERA
WORKS, London, England.

Sanderson Regular Model: (SC100); 5" x 8" view camera; Rapid Rectilinear 5" x 8" brass lens; behind-lens Thornton Pickard shutter. Black leather bellows; Sanderson patent movements; British Ensign trademark. C 1900's.

R3* $300	£157	DM495	FF1.5k

Sanderson Regular Model Hand Camera: (SC101); 3¹/4" x 4¹/4" hand camera; Beck Symmetrical lens; Unicum shutter. C 1900's.

R3* $250	£131	DM412	FF1.3k

Sanderson Regular Model Hand Camera

Sanderson Tropical: (SC102); 3¹/4" x 4¹/4" tropical camera; Beck Convertible f7.7 lens; teak with brass fittings.

R4* $1.2k	£630	DM2k	FF6.1k

SANDS AND HUNTER PHOTOGRAPHIC RIFLE: (BB243); rifle-type detective camera; rapid rectilinear lens; shutter rifle barrel; 18 plates, 3.25cm in diameter. C 1885.

R5*		NSR	

SAWYERS INC.,
Portland, Oregon.

Mark IV: (AX100); 127 roll film TLR camera; Topcor 6cm f2.8 coated lens; shutter 1-1/500 s; 12 exp on 127 roll film.

R2* $60	£31	DM99	FF307

S

View-Master Personal Stereo Camera: (AX101); 35mm stereo camera; Anastigmat 25mm f3.5 coated lenses; guillotine shutter 1/10-1/1000 s, flash. Double run 5mm film produces 37 pairs on 20 exp film, or 69 pairs on 36 exp film. View master format. C 1952-1960. **$175.** Close-up attachment - 24" with case, **$125.** Close-up attachment - 36" with case, **$125.** Viewmaster film cutter, **$150.**

R3*	Prices as above

View-Master Personal Stereo Camera

View-Master Stereo Colour Camera: (AX102); German made for the European market. 35mm stereo vfr camera for viewmaster format stereo pairs. Rodenstock Trinar 20mm/f2.8 fixed focus lenses shutter coupled to lens opening using EV scale. slanting film travel allows all the frames to be made without rewinding the film, as on the Viewmaster Personal Stereo Camera (AX101). More often seen in Europe than the USA, where the price is often 25% lower.

R3* $180	£94	DM297	FF920

Scat: (BB244); subminiature camera; 8" x 11" exp on Minox cassettes. Mfd in Italy. C 1950.

R4* $200	£105	DM330	FF1k

Scat

A. SCHAEFFNER, Paris, France.

Photo Album: (FN100); book detective camera; achromat 120mm f12 lens; guillotine shutter. 9 x 12cm plate in metal double plate holders. Was also made available with rapid rectilinear lens and central guillotine shutter. Invented by Cadot. C 1890.

R5* $3k+	£1.6k+	DM5k+	FF15.3k+

SCHLESICKY & STROHLEIN OF LEIPZIG.

The Comfort: (SS100); leather covered detective camera; achromatic 80mm f7.5 lens; vertical guillotine shutter. 6 x 7.3cm exp on 8 dry plates. A turn of a spool brings the new plate into position. Invented by C. F. Schlesicky. C 1890.

R4* $500	£262	DM824	FF2.6k

Field Camera: (SS101); 24 x 30mm field camera; brass convertible lens. Blue bellows; mahogany finish, brass fittings; black striped edges. C 1880's.

R3* $250	£131	DM412	FF1.3k

German 13" x 18" Field View Camera: (SS102); compact field view camera; various lens and shutter combinations. Shifting lens board for stereo; slide locking bottom; wooden book type holder; polished wood finish, brass fittings. 2 styles made by cabinet makers in the Alsace-Lorraine area. C 1880-1920.

R3* $200	£105	DM330	FF1k

S

German 13" x 18" Field View Camera

SCHMITZ-SCOVILL

SCHMITZ & THEINEMANN, Dresden, Germany.

Uniflex: (ST100); Unar 75mm f4.5 lens; self-cocking Pronto shutter coupled to the mirror. C 1933.

R3* $110	£58	DM181	FF562

Uniflex Reflex Meteor: (ST101); Trioplan 105mm f4.5 lens; Pronto shutter; front element focusing. Box camera for 6 x 9cm exp. C 1931.

R3* $120	£63	DM198	FF613

Schnapps-O-Flex: (BB245); liquor container in shape of a camera; flash reflector uncorks from flashgun revealing clay container with one pint capacity. C 1965.

R2* $65	£34	DM107	FF332

Schnapps-O-Flex

SCOVILL MFG. CO., proprietors of American Optical Co., New York.

American Optical Revolving Back Camera: (AL100); 5" x 8" revolving back camera; front focus; revolving back (Flaming's patent); Daisy dry plate holder. Sizes: 4" x 5" to 8" x 10". C 1888.

R3* $200	£105	DM330	FF1k

American Optical View Camera: (AL101); Brass fittings and lens; lens slotted for waterhouse stops; 5 1/2" x 8 1/2" exp on plates. C 1883.

R3* $175	£92	DM288	FF894

Antique Oak Detective Camera: (AL102); wooden box-type detective camera; 4" x 5" exp on plates. C 1892.

R4* $600	£315	DM989	FF3.1k

Book Camera: (AL103); book-type detective camera; achromatized periscopic 75mm f12 lens; variable speed horizontal guillotine shutter. Single exp on 4" x 5" dry plates. C 1892.

R5* $10k+	£5.2k+	DM16.5k+	FF51.1k+

Book Camera

Centennial Stereo Outfit: (AL104); 5" x 8" stereo outfit; matched pair of stereo lenses, single achromatic Scovill lens; swing back; polished mahogany, brass fittings. Nickel plated label: American Optical Co., New York. Scovill Mfg. Co. proprietors. C 1876.

R4* $800	£420	DM1.3k	FF4.1k

Klondike: (AL105); meniscus lens; rotary shutter, T and I. 4" x 5" dry plates. C 1898.

R3* $90	£47	DM148	FF460

Knack Detective Camera: (AL106); box-type detective camera. 4" x 5" exp on plates. C 1891.

R4* $325	£171	DM536	FF1.7k

Scovill 4" x 5" Vertical View Camera: (AL107); R. Morrison N.Y. lens, rotating stops. No rising front. With holder and case. C 1881.

R3* $200	£105	DM330	FF1k

Scovill 4" x 5" Vertical View Camera

Scovill 5" x 8" View Camera: (AL110); Waterbury lens; rotating stops; original box in brass and light mahogany. C 1888.

R3* $175	£92	DM288	FF894

Scovill 5" x 8" View Camera

The Triad Camera: (AL111); leather covered box-type detective camera; 4" x 5" exp on plates or roll film - using an Eastman Walker roll holder. C 1892.

R4* $300	£157	DM495	FF1.5k

Scovill Detective Camera: (AL112); leather covered box-type detective camera; 4 x 5 Instantaneous lens; variable speed rotary shutter. 4" x 5" exp on plates. 4 sizes: 8 x 10.5cm; 10.5 x 12.5cm; 11.5 x 16.5cm;

Scovill Detective Camera

13 x 18cm. C 1886. In 1888 a pivoting vf was adapted to the camera.

R4* $1k	£525	DM1.6k	FF5.1k

Waterbury Detective Camera (Original Model): (AL113); black painted box type detective camera; string cocking shutter; 4" x 5" exp on plates. Storage for extra plate holder in recessed base of camera; "T" bar extends through base of camera for focusing. C 1888.

R4* $400	£210	DM659	FF2k

Waterbury Detective Camera (Second Model): (AL114); leather covered box-type detective camera; 4" x 5" exp on plates. "T" bar extend through base of camera for focusing. C 1890.

R4* $350	£184	DM577	FF1.8k

Improved Waterbury Detective Camera: (AL115); leather covered box-type detective camera; 4" x 5" exp on dry plates. The focusing knob has been positioned on the top front of the camera body. C 1892.

R4* $400	£210	DM659	FF2k

Waterbury 5" x 8" Field Camera: (AL116); Rubber-band shutter. Original price, $17. C 1885.

R4* $450	£236	DM742	FF2.3k

Waterbury 5" x 8" Field Camera

SEARS, ROEBUCK & CO., Chicago, Illinois.

Kewpie Kamera: (SR100); leatherette covered box roll film camera; 2¹/₄" x 3¹/₄" exp on 120 roll film. C 1921.

R1* $15	£8	DM25	FF77

Seroco 8" x 10" View Camera: (SR101); 8" x 10" view camera; Conley lens; Auto shutter. Front and rear focusing; rising and falling front; mahogany, nickel-plated. C 1920.

R3* $200	£105	DM330	FF1k

Seroco Stereo Camera: (SR102); Seroco 4" x 5" Rapid Symmetrical lenses; Wollensak shutter; 5" x 7" exp on plates. Brown leather covered wood, red bellows.

R4* $400	£210	DM659	FF2k

Tower Type 3: (SR103); C1950, 35mm RFR camera, Nikkor 50mm f2 coated lens, interchangeable screw mount; CFPS 1-1/500 s, Copy of Leica IIIa, made in Japan by Nicca Camera Company, (Nicca III or IIIA) sold by Sears, Roebuck & Co.

R3* $275	£144	DM453	FF1.4k

Tower Type 3S: (SR105); C1951, as (SR103) but for added flash synch, (Nicca IIIB).

R3* $275	£144	DM453	FF1.4k

Tower 35: (SR106); C1956, 35mm RFR camera with interchangeable Nikkor f2.8/50mm lens, CFPS 1 - 1/1000s, (Nicca 3F) with *either* lever or knob wind.

R3* $275	£144	DM453	FF1.4k

Tower 45: (SR107); C1957, 35mm RFR camera with interchangeable f2/50mm Nikkor screw mount lens, CFPS 1 - 1/1000s, flash calculator on the hinged back, (Nicca 5L).

R3* $300	£157	DM495	FF1.5k

Tower 46: (SR108); C1957, as (SR107) but delivered with Nikkor f1.4/50mm lens.

R3* $325	£171	DM536	FF1.7k

Tower Stereo: (SR104); 35mm stereo camera, vfr Isconar 35mm/f3.5 lenses; Prontor S shutter 1-1/300 s. Made by Wilhelm Witt of Hamburg, West Germany for Sears. similar to the Iloca Stereo II (WT203) C 1954.

R3* $130	£68	DM214	FF664

SECAM, Paris, France.

Stereophot: (SE100); stereo version of pen camera; consists of two Stylophot cameras mounted on a bracket, with tripod attachment. Leather carrying case. C 1955.

R4* $800	£420		
		DM1.3k	FF4.1k

Stylophot Standard: (SE101); pen-type detective camera; f6.3 coated lens; fixed shutter speed of 1/50 s. 10 x 10mm on 16mm film in a special cassette. Camera is in shape of large pen. Auto film transport advances film and cocks shutter. C 1955.

R4* $125	£66		
		DM206	FF639

Stylophot Deluxe: (SE102); pen-type detective camera; Roussel

Stylophot Standard

Anastigmat 27mm f3.5 lens; fixed shutter speed of 1/50 s. 18 exp, 10 x 10mm on 16mm film in a special cassette. C 1956.

R4* $250	£131	DM412	FF1.3k

H. Seemann Stereo Camera: (BB246); wooden stereo camera; pair of Goerz Dagor 120mm lenses, original cap; sliding front focus; ground glass screen; black ebonized wood, nickel plated fittings.

R4* $450	£236	DM742	FF2.3k

SEM, Sociéte des Etablissements Modernes, SA, Aurec, France.

Established after the second world war, by Paul Royet, the company produced cameras affordable to every household in France. From the first Sem Kim in 1946 , to the last Semflex of 1978, (Owned by Mr. Royet himself and having the serial number 500638.) these cameras left their mark with the camera enthusiasts of France. Though they didn't find their way out of France in any great numbers, they are still seen at fairs and fleamarkets in France, and sometimes hanging around the necks of provincial visitors to Paris! Merci to J-L Princelle and P-H Pont for the research they have done into the history of this very French camera, and for the detailed descriptions which can be found in the "Fotofiches" published by Fotosaga. In order to keep different models straight, I have used the designations found in the "Fotofiches" for different Semflex models. These are printed at the end of each description, in Italic type. A total of more than 350,000 Semflex cameras are estimated to have been made.

Semflex I: (SX201); 1948-49, TLR for 6cm x 6cm frames on roll film, Angénieux or Berthoit f4.5/75mm taking lens *(three elements),* f3.3 viewing lens, knob advance,

shutter 1 - 1/300s, framing counting by ruby window.*(type 1)*

R2* $60	£31	DM99	FF307

Semflex T950: (SX202); 1950-54, TLR for 6cm x 6cm frames on roll film, Angénieux or Berthoit f4.5/75mm taking lens *(three elements),* f3.3 viewing lens, knob advance, shutter 1/10 - 1/250s, grey body. *(type 2).*

R2* $60	£31	DM99	FF307

Semflex Standard 4.5: (SX203); 1955, TLR for 6cm x 6cm frames on roll film, Angénieux or Berthoit f4.5/75mm taking lens *(three elements),* f3.3 viewing lens, knob advance, shutter 1/10 - 1/250s, grey body, sports finder. *(type 3).*

R2* $60	£31	DM99	FF307

Semflex Standard 4.5: (SX204); 1956-60, as (SX202) but for cast "Semflex " logo inside a raised frame *(type 4).*

R2* $60	£31	DM99	FF307

Semflex Standard 61: (SX205); 1961-67, as (SX203) but for cast "Semflex" logo inside a raised frame with grey relief *(type 5).*

R2* $60	£31	DM99	FF307

Semflex SI: (SX206); 1950-54, TLR for 6cm x 6cm frames on roll film, Angénieux or Berthoit f3.8/75mm taking lens *(three elements),* f3.3 viewing lens, knob advance, shutter 1/10 - 1/250s, grey body, sports finder. *(type 6)* (Angénieux lens adds 25%)

R2* $70	£37	DM115	FF358

Semflex Standard 3.5: (SX207); 1953-55, TLR for 6cm x 6cm frames on roll film, Angénieux or Berthoit f3.5/75mm taking lens *(three elements),* f3.3 viewing lens, knob advance, Synchro Sem shutter 1-1/400s, grey body, sports finder, large lens bezels. *(type 7)* (Angénieux lens adds 25%).

R2* $60	£31	DM99	FF307

Semflex Standard 3.5: (SX208); 1956-63, as (SX207) but for cast "Semflex logo inside a raised frame. *(type 8).*

R2* $60	£31	DM99	FF307

Semflex II: (SX209); 1948-49, TLR for 6cm x 6cm frames on roll film, Angénieux or Berthoit f3.5/75mm taking lens *(four elements),* f3.3 viewing lens, knob advance,

S

SEM

black body. *(type 9)*. (Angénieux lens adds 25%).

| R2* $70 | £37 | DM115 | FF358 |

Semflex S II: (SX210); 1950-53, as (SX209) but for sportsfinder. *(type 10)*.

| R2* $60 | £31 | DM99 | FF307 |

Semflex Standard 3.5: (SX211); 1954, as (SX209) but for sportsfinder, , larger focusing knob which incorporates a film reminder, second ruby window for 28mm x 40mm framing. *(type 11)*.

| R2* $80 | £42 | DM132 | FF409 |

Semflex Standard 3.5 B: (SX212); 1960-64, as (SX210) but for lack of film reminder, totally grey, possibility of 24mm x 36mm or 4cm x 4cm on 120 film, cast "Semflex " logo inside raised frame with grey relief*(type 12)*

| R2* $80 | £42 | DM132 | FF409 |

Semflex Standard 3.5 B: (SX213); 1965-69, as (SX212) but for bayonet filter mount *(type 13)*.

| R2* $80 | £42 | DM132 | FF409 |

Semflex Otomatic I: (SX214); 1949, TLR for 6cm x 6cm frames on roll film, Angénieux or Berthoit f4.5/75mm taking lens *(three elements)*, f3.3 viewing lens, double throw crank advance, 1 - 1/300s. *(type 14)*.

| R2* $70 | £37 | DM115 | FF358 |

Semflex Oto SI: (SX215); 1950-52, TLR for 6cm x 6cm frames on roll film, Angénieux or Berthoit f3.8/75mm taking lens *(three elements)*, f3.3 viewing lens, double throw crank advance, 1 - 1/300s, sports finder, grey body*(type 15)*.

| R2* $80 | £42 | DM132 | FF409 |

Semflex Semi Otomatic 3.5 B: (SX216); 1956-64, TLR for 6cm x 6cm frames on roll film, Angénieux or Berthoit f3.5/75mm taking lens *(four elements)*, f2.8 viewing lens, crank advance with double exposure protection, 1 - 1/400s, sports finder, film reminder, bayonet filter mount, leather body covering.*(type 16)*.

| R2* $100 | £52 | DM165 | FF511 |

Semflex III: (SX217); 1948, *several prototypes only*, TLR for 6cm x 6cm frames on roll film, Angénieux or Berthoit f3.5/75mm taking lens *(four elements)*, f3.3 viewing lens, *folding crank advance without double exposure protection,* shutter speed and aperture visible from above. *(type 17)*.

| R5* | NSR |

Semflex Oto II: (SX218); 1949, TLR for 6cm x 6cm frames on roll film, Angénieux or Berthoit f3.5/75mm taking lens *(four elements)*, f3.3 viewing lens, crank advance, shutter 1 - 1/400s, condensing lens on VFR ground glass. *(type 18)* (Angénieux lens adds 25%).

| R2* $80 | £42 | DM132 | FF409 |

Semflex Oto S II: (SX219); 1950-53, as (SX218) but for addition of sportfinder and large magnifyer in the VFR. *(type 19)* (Angénieux lens adds 25%).

| R2* $80 | £42 | DM132 | FF409 |

Semflex Oto 154: (SX220); 1954, as (SX219) but for decorative lens bezels, film reminder, side mounted shutter release and second ruby window for 28mm x 40mm.*(type 20)* (Angénieux lens adds 25%).

| R2* $60 | £31 | DM99 | FF307 |

Semflex Oto 3.5 B: (SX221); 1955-62, as (SX220) but only Berthoit f3.5/75mm taking lens, Angénieux or Berthoit f3.3 viewing lens, shutter cocking coupled to crank film advance, black body *(type 21)*.

| R2* $60 | £31 | DM99 | FF307 |

Semflex Oto 3.5 B: (SX222); 1959-71, as (SX221) but *grey body*, possible 24mm x 36mm or 4cm x 4cm on 120 film, Compur shutter available on special order. *(type 22)* (Compur shutter lens adds 100%)

| R2* $100 | £52 | DM165 | FF511 |

Semflex 72: (SX223); 1972-74, TLR for 6cm x 6cm frames on 120 roll film, Berthiot or Tourret-Narrat f3.5/75mm lens *(four elements)*, Orec or Compur shutter, reinforced advance mechanism, film loading possible while mounted on a tripod, 36mm or 4cm x 4cm on 120 film, black body, about 1000 cameras made. (Compur shutter lens adds 100%).

| R4* $225 | £118 | DM371 | FF1.2k |

NB: Semflex Studio cameras are usually found in well used condition, as they were

THE HOVE INTERNATIONAL BLUE BOOK

the workhorse studio camera for many French portrait photographers.

Semflex Studio Oto: (SX224); 1953-54, TLR for 6cm x 6cm frames on 120 roll film, *Tele-Berthiot f5.4/150mm taking lens (four elements), f3.9 viewing lens,* shutter 1 - 1/400s, ground glass with condensing lens, sport finder, crank advance, lens panel black enamel. *(type 24).*

R3* $200	£105	DM330	FF1k

Semflex Studio Oto: (SX225); 1955-58, as (SX224) but lens panel black crinkle finish. *(type 25).*

R3* $200	£105	DM330	FF1k

Semflex Studio Standard: (SX226); 1955-59, as (SX225) but for knob advance. *(type 26).*

R3* $200	£105	DM330	FF1k

Semflex Studio Oto model 2: (SX227); 1959-71, as (SX225) but for logo cast in relief, black or grey available. *(type 27).*

R3* $200	£105	DM330	FF1k

Semflex Studio Standard 2: (SX228); 1959-71, as (SX226), but for logo cast in relief, black or grey available.*(type 28)*

R?*	$?		

Semflex Studio 72: (SX229); 1972-78, as (SX227) but for Compur shutter. *(type 29).*

R3* $200	£105	DM330	FF1k

Semflex Studio: (SX230); **"Atelier"** C1976, as (SX129) but for new film loading permitting changing rolls while attached to a tripod, a protective heavy wire frame around taking and viewing lenses served as a prudent precaution while doing this manoeuvre. *(type 30).*

R4* $325	£171	DM536	FF1.7k

Semflex "Joie de Vivre" 3.5: (SX231); 1956-64, TLR for 6cm x 6cm frames on roll film, berthiot f3.5/75mm taking lens (four elements) , f2.8 viewing lens, simple shutter 1/50s, side mounted release, (complete outfit comprising hard case, flash, eveready case, and camera adds 50%) *(type 31).*

R3* $180	£94	DM297	FF920

Semflex "Joie de Vivre" 4.5: (SX232);

1959-64, TLR for 6cm x 6cm frames on roll film, Berthiot f4.5/75mm taking lens (three elements) , f2.8 viewing lens, simple shutter 1/50s, front mounted shutter release, decorative front plate, large "S" on the VFR hood, possible 24 frames on 120 roll film.*(type 32).*

R3* $180	£94	DM297	FF920

Semflash Standard: (SX233); 1951-56, TLR for 6cm x 6cm frames on roll film, Berthiot f4.5/75mm taking lens (three elements), simple shutter 1/50s, focusing scale has seven numbers which allow distance/diaphragm flash control, *attached electronic flash,* delivered in a hard carrying case. *(type 33).*

R4* $225	£118	DM371	FF1.2k

Semflash Couple: (SX234); 1951-59, as (SX233) but with diaphragm coupled directly to the focusing mechanism., sometimes marked "Semflash Location". *(type 234).*

R4* $180	£94	DM297	FF920

Semflash Couple: (SX235); 1960, as (SX234) but with fixed "chimney" type VFR. *(type 235).*

R4* $250	£131	DM412	FF1.3k

Grenaflex

Grenaflex: (SX236); 1955-57, as (SX202) but sold under the "Grenaflex" name. *(type 36).*

R3* $80	£42	DM132	FF409

PhotoHall: (SX237); 1955-57, as (SX202) but sold under the "Photo Hall" name. *(type 37).*

R3* $80	£42	DM132	FF409

No Name Semflex: 1955-57, (SX238); as (SX202) but sold without namebrand by Manufrance. *(type 37).*

R4* $100	£52	DM165	FF511

A. SEMMENDINGER,
Fort Lee, New Jersey.

Excelsior Wet Plate Camera: (SD100); wet plate camera; 5" x 5" ground glass. C 1872.

R5* $900	£472	DM1.5k	FF4.6k

SENECA CAMERA CO.,
Rochester, New York.

Busy Bee: (AY100); 4" x 5" box-type detective camera; 4" x 5" exp on plates. C 1903.

R3* $70	£37	DM115	FF358

Chautauqua: (AY101); 3 1/2" x 4 1/2" folding plate camera.

R3* $60	£31	DM99	FF307

New Improved Seneca View Camera: (AY102); 5" x 7" view camera; Seneca Triple convertible lens and shutter. Horizontal and vertical swings; double extension reversible back; double tongued bed; plumb bob; black ebonite wood. 7 sizes from 5" x 7" **$125** to 17" x 20" **$350.** C 1900's.

R3*	Prices as above

Seneca Folding Roll Camera: (AY103); ground glass focusing on special Vidax film. C 1915.

R3* $75	£39	DM124	FF383

Seneca No. 8: (AY104); folding plate camera; Seneca Sym-Convertible lens; Seneca Auto shutter. Reversible back; black double extension bellows.

R3* $75	£39	DM124	FF383

Seneca Stereo View Camera: (AY105); Wollensak Optical Co. stereo shutter. 5" x 7" exp on plates. C 1910.

R3* $275	£144	DM453	FF1.4k

Septon Camera: (BB247); pen-type detective camera; 20mm f2.8 lens; 14 x 14mm exp on 16mm roll film. Mfd in Japan. C 1953.

R4* $750	£394	DM1.2k	FF3.8k

Sfomax: (BB250); Sfomax 30mm f3.5 lens; shutter 1/30-1/400 s, CRF; 20 exp on 16mm film in special cassettes; slide-in yellow filter. C 1950.

R4* $600	£315	DM989	FF3.1k

SHANGHAI CAMERA
FACTORY, Shanghai, China.

Shanghai 58-I:(SJ100); 1958, Cfps, 1 - 1/1000 sec, seperate Rfr/Vfr windows, diopter adjustment. Screw mount Shanghai F3.5/50mm lens. A copy of the Leica IIIB, this camera was in production for less than one year. Fewer than 2000 cameras were made, and few survived the violence of China in the 60's. Serial numbers always begin 58XXXXX. Quite rare.

R5* $3k	£1.6k	DM5k	FF15.3k

Shanghai 58-I

Shanghai 58-II: (SJ101); 1958-63, Cfps, 1 - 1/1000 sec, combined Rfr/Vfr windows, flash synch. Screw mount Shanghai F3.5/50mm lens. A continuation of the camera line started by the Shanghai 58-I. Several types exist, the earliest ones having strap lugs, five screws in the accessory shoe, and diopter adjustment, while later cameras have no strap lugs, no diopter adjustment, and only

Shanghai 58-II

three screws in the accessory shoe. Serial numbers always begin 58XXXXX.

R3* $500	£262	DM824	FF2.6k

Shanghai 203: (SJ102); 1963. Folding 120 roll film camera with between the lens leaf shutter, 1 - 1/300 s, coupled RFR, flash synch, selftimer, built-in mask for 6X6 or 6X4.5 frame size. Coated F3.5/75mm lens. This camera was produced in small numbers just before the brand name changed to "Seagull". Rare even in China.

R3* $120	£63	DM198	FF613

Seagull 203: (SJ103); 1964-1986. Folding 120 roll film camera with between the lens leaf shutter, 1 - 1/300 s, coupled RFR, flash synch, selftimer, built-in mask for 6 x 6 or 6 x 4.5 frame size. Coated F3.5/75mm lens. Somewhat Zeiss Ikon like in its styling, the Seagull 203 exists in several models, the earliest having no accessory shoe, and the latest having a black plastic top plate, and hot shoe. Common in China, though not often seen in the West.

R3* $75	£39	DM124	FF383

Shanghai TLR: (SJ104); 1958-63. TLR camera with between the lens leaf shutter, 1 - 1/300 s, flash synch, selftimer, automatic frame counting, knob advance, manual shutter cocking. Coated F3.5/75mm lens. This well made TLR survived after 1963 as the Seagull 4 TLR. Serial numbers always begin 63XXXXXX.

R3* $100	£52	DM165	FF511

Seagull 4: (SJ105); 1964. TLR camera with between the lens leaf shutter, 1 - 1/300 s, flash synch, selftimer, automatic frame counting, knob advance, manual shutter cocking. Coated F3.5/75mm lens. A continuation of the Shanghai TLR. The serial numbers always begin 4-63XXXXXX. Not to be confused with the Seagull 4A, exported in the 1970's, the Seagull 4 has Knob film advance, while the 4A uses a crank, not unlike Rollei TLRs.

R3* $80	£42	DM132	FF409

Seagull 4A: (SJ106); 1970's. TLR camera with between the lens leaf shutter, 1 - 1/300 s, flash synch, selftimer, automatic frame counting, crank advance, manual shutter cocking. Coated F3.5/75mm lens. A continuation of the Shanghai TLR. The serial numbers always begin 4A-XXXXXX. the Seagull 4A has automatic frame counting, and no provision for 6 x 4.5 framing.

R3* $60	£31	DM99	FF307

Seagull 4B: (SJ107); 1965. TLR camera with between the lens leaf shutter, 1 - 1/300 s, flash synch, selftimer, ruby window frame counting, removable metal mask for 6 x 4.5 frame size.

R3* $50	£26	DM82	FF256

Seagull 4C: (SJ108); 1968. TLR camera with manually set between the lens leaf shutter, 1 - 1/300 s, flash synch, selftimer, ruby window frame counting, removable metal mask for 6 x 4.5 frame size. Special adapter for using 35mm film, with built-in exposure counter. Not often seen in China.

R3* $125	£66	DM206	FF639

Seagull DFAB: (SJ109); 1970's. Cfps, 1 - 1/60 s, no viewing system. Sometimes equipped with F2.0/58mm lens or F1.4/50mm lens (the same as used on the Red Flag 20 camera)in 42mm screw mount for use as a CRT camera. Available without a

Seagull DFAB with f1.4/50mm lens

lens for use on microscopes. Made at the same time as the Red Flag 20 camera, and using some of the same parts. Not very popular, and quickly replaced on the marketplace by specialty Japanese cameras. Rare, even in China.

R4* $350	£184	DM577	FF1.8k

East Wind: (SJ110); 1970's. Lens shutter, 1 - 1/1000 s on the normal lens, 1 - 1/500 on all others, waist level Vrf, interchangeable magazine backs. Bayonet mount F2.8/ 80mm normal lens, with F4/50mm wide angle and F4/150mm telephoto lenses available. This Hasselblad copy was made in very small numbers at the order of Jiang Ching, the wife of Chairman Mao. Very rare even in China, usually seen in quite used condition. A complete set including filters, backs, and all three lenses adds 100% to the price. Prices are higher in Japan.

R4* $4.5k	£2.4k	DM7.4k	FF23k

Red Flag 20: (SJ111); 1971-77 Cfps, 1 - 1/1000 sec, combined Rfr/Vfr windows, field of view for 35mm, 50mm, and 90mm lens automatically selected upon mounting lens. "M" type bayonet Red Flag F1.4/50mm lens, with F1.4/35mm and F2.0/90mm lenses available. A copy of the Leica M4 camera, the Red Flag 20 was made in very small numbers, surely less than 200. The first two digits of the serial number indicate the year of manufacture. Prices have gone down from a high of $10,000 for a complete set in the early 1980's. Camera and all three

Red Flag 20

lenses adds 100% to the price. Prices are higher in Japan. Quite rare.

R4* $3.5k	£1.8k	DM5.8k	FF17.9k

SHARP & HITCHMOUGH, Liverpool, England.

Aptus Pic-Nic-Basket: (SH100); picnic basket-type detective camera; 8 x 10.5cm or 10 x 12.5cm plates. C 1889.

R5* $2k	£1.1k	DM3.3k	FF10.2k

Sherlock Holmes: (BB251); valise-type detective camera; fixed focus meniscus lens, close-up lens swings into position; single speed shutter; 6.5 x 9cm plates. C 1912.

R5* $1k	£525	DM1.6k	FF5.1k

J. F. SHEW & CO., London, England.

Aluminium Xit: (FS100); Goerz Dagor Series III f6.8 lens; mahogany and aluminium construction. C 1905.

R3* $200	£105	DM330	FF1k

Aluminium Xit

Eclipse: (FS101); Denlot rapid rectilinear lens; Rotary shutter. C 1888.

R3* $225	£118	DM371	FF1.2k

Shew Tailboard 4" x 5" Camera: (FS102); Shew lens; waterhouse stops; rubberband powered shutter. Glass plates; finder; book-type holders; original box. C 1870's.

R3* $750	£394	DM1.2k	FF3.8k

SHOWA OPTICAL WORKS, Japan.

Gemflex: (OA100); subminiature TLR camera; Gem 25mm f3.5 lens; Swallow 1/25-1/100 s; 10 exp, 14 x 14mm on 16mm roll film. C 1954.

R3* $750	£394	DM1.2k	FF3.8k

SHOWA OPTICAL CO.
Japan,
(Marked Showa Kogaku, this section also contains cameras marked Leotax Camera Co. Ltd.)

Leotax (original): (OA101) 1940. Cfps, 1/20 - 1/500, un-coupled RFR, screw mount Letana Anastigmat f3.5/50mm lens. Viewed from the front, the vfr window is to the left, of both the RFR windows, unlike most other Leica copies, and just the opposite of the later Leotax Special A and Special B cameras. Reportedly about 50 cameras made.

R5* $2k	£1.1k	DM3.3k	FF10.2k

Leotax Special A: (OA102)1942. Cfps, 1/20 -1/500, coupled RFR, seperate RFR/vfr windows,screw mount Letana Anastigmat f3.5/50mm lens. Viewed from the front, the vfr window is to the right, of both the RFR windows, unlike most other Leica copies, and just the opposite of the earlier Leotax (original).

R4* $1.5k	£787	DM2.5k	FF7.7k

Leotax Special B: (OA103) 1942. Cfps, 1 - 1/500, coupled RFR, seperate RFR/vfr windows,screw mount Letana Anastigmat f3.5/50mm lens. The same as the Leotax Special A, except with s; low speeds.

R4* $1.5k	£787	DM2.5k	FF7.7k

Leotax Special: (OA104)1946. Cfps, 1/20 - 1/500, coupled RFR, seperate RFR/vfr windows,screw mount Letana Anastigmat f3.5/50mm or State f3.5/50mm lens. The same as the Leotax Special A, but produced after the end of the Second World War.

R4* $1.3k	£682	DM2.1k	FF6.6k

Leotax Special DII: (OA105) 1947. Cfps, 1/20-1/500, coupled RFR, seperate RFR/vfr windows, screw mount C. Similar f3.5/50mm lens. This camera is the first Leotax to have the front vfr window between the two RFR windows.

R4* $600	£315	DM989	FF3.1k

Leotax Special DIII: (OA106) 1947. Cfps, 1 -1/500, coupled RFR, seperate RFR/vfr windows, screw mount C. Similar f3.5/50mm lens. The same as the Leotax Special DII, except with slow speeds. (Also produced as the NR III, and marked "made in occupied Japan". Only about 50 such examples were made.)

R4* $600	£315	DM989	FF3.1k

Leotax Special DIII NR III variation for the US Army

Leotax DIV: (OA107) 1950. Cfps, 1 - 1/500, coupled RFR, seperate RFR/VFR windows, screw mount Similar f1.5/50mm lens. Body strap lugs. Not so rare as earlier Leotax's.

R3* $325	£171	DM536	FF1.7k

Leotax DIV

Leotax S: (OA108) 1952. Cfps, 1 - 1/500, coupled RFR, F and FP synch, seperate RFR/VFR windows, screw mount Similar f1.5/50mm lens. Body strap lugs. The same as Leotax DIV, with addition of synch.

R3* $350	£184	DM577	FF1.8k

SHOWA

Leotax F: (OA109)1954. Cfps, 1-1/1000, coupled RFR, F and FP synch, seperate RFR/vfr windows, screw mount Topcor f1.5/50mm lens. Single piece top plate,body strap lugs. The first Leotax camera with 1/1000 s shutter. In 1956, the company name changed to Leotax Camera Company, and Leotax F cameras made after that time were so marked, and are considered second version F cameras.

R2* $250	£131	DM412	FF1.3k

Leotax K: (0A110)1955. Cfps, 1/25 - 1/500, coupled RFR, flash synch, seperate RFR/vfr windows, screw mount Topcor f3.5/50mm lens. Single piece top plate,body strap lugs.

R2* $225	£118	DM371	FF1.2k

Leotax T: (0A111)1955. Cfps, 1 - 1/500, coupled RFR, flash synch,seperate RFR/vfr windows, screw mount Topcor f3.5/50mm lens. Single piece top plate,body strap lugs. Similar to Leotax F, but lacking 1/1000 s shutter speed.

R2* $225	£118	DM371	FF1.2k

The following cameras are marked Leotax Camera Co. Ltd, not Showa.

Leotax TV: (LK100); 1957 CFPS, 1 - 1/500, coupled RFR, self timer, seperate RFR/VFR windows, screw mount Topcor f2.0/50mm lens. Single piece top plate, body strap lugs.

R2* $250	£131	DM412	FF1.3k

Leotax TV with Topcor f3.5/50mm lens

Leotax FV: (LK101); 1958 CFPS, 1 - 1/1000, coupled RFR, self timer, seperate RFR/VFR windows, screw mount Topcor f2.0/5cm or Leonon f2.0/50mm lens. Single piece top plate, body strap lugs.First Leotax using lever instead of knob advance.

R3* $325	£171	DM536	FF1.7k

Leotax K3: (LK102); 1958 CFPS,1/8 - 1/500, coupled RFR,, seperate RFR/VFR windows, screw mount Fujinon f2.8/5cm lens. Single piece top plate, body strap lugs.

R3* $250	£131	DM412	FF1.3k

Leotax T2: (LK103); 1958 CFPS, 1 - 1/500, coupled RFR,, seperate RFR/VFR windows, screw mount Fujinon f2.0/50mm lens. Single piece top plate, body strap lugs.

R2* $225	£118	DM371	FF1.2k

Leotax TV2 (Merit): (LK104); 1958 CFPS, 1-1/500, coupled RFR, self timer, seperate RFR/VFR windows, screw mount Topcor f2.0/5cm or Leonon f2.0/5cm lens. Single piece top plate, body strap lugs. Lever advance.

R2* $325	£171	DM536	FF1.7k

Leotax TV2 (Merit) with f2/50mm Topcor

Leotax T2L (Elite): (LK105); 1959 CFPS, 1-1/500, coupled RFR, seperate RFR/VFR windows, screw mount Topcor f2.0/5cm or Leonon f2.0/5cm lens. Single piece top plate, body strap lugs. Lever advance.

R2* $325	£171	DM536	FF1.7k

Leotax G: (LK106); 1961 CFPS, 1 - 1/1000, coupled RFR, self timer, seperate RFR/VFR windows, screw mount Topcor f1.8/5cm or Leonon f2.0/5cm lens. Single piece top plate, body strap lugs. Lever advance. More a Leica M copy in body style, the last Leotax.

R4* $1.3k	£682	DM2.1k	FF6.6k

SHOCK & Co. KG, Feinmechanik-Optik-Geratebau, Bergkamen, Germany

Panta: (SK200); C1954, metal VFR camera for 6 x 4.5cm frames on 120 roll film, Steiner f3.5/75mm lens, Vario shutter, a continuation of the Panta camera made by Dr. Rodehuser. (see (RF100).

R2* $30	£16	DM49	FF153

SIEMENS & HALSKE A.G., Berlin, Germany.

Siemens: (IE100); 16mm movie camera; spring motor driven; 2 position lens slide for rapid focal length change; 8, 16, 24 or 64 frames per s; special magazines with 15m of 16mm film. C 1933.

R3* $70	£37	DM115	FF358

Siemens Model B: (IE101); 16mm movie camera; Anastigmat Busch Glaukar 20mm f2.8 lens; spring motor driven, 6m of film at 8, 16, or 64 frames per s; special magazines with 15m of 16mm film. C 1932.

R3* $45	£24	DM74	FF230

Siemens with telescopic viewfinder: (IE102); 16mm movie camera; Schneider Xenon 25mm f1.5 lens. Telescopic vf for 25 to 100mm lens, with parallax adjustment. 4 speeds: 8, 16, 24 and 64 FPS. C 1938.

R3* $80	£42	DM132	FF409

Siemens: (IE103); 16mm movie camera; Optimat 20mm f1.5 lens with coupled meter. 4 speeds: 8, 16, 24 and 64 frames per s; special cassettes for 50 ft of 16mm film. C 1938.

R3* $60	£31	DM99	FF307

J. Guido SIGRIST, Paris, France.

Jumelle Sigrist Stereo: (JG100); Tessar 100mm f3.5 and tele-Quatryl 150mm f4.5 lenses; special FPS 1/60-1/4000 s. 6 x 13cm plates. C 1900.

R4* $10k	£5.2k	DM16.5k	FF51.1k

Sigrist: (JG101); Krauss-Zeiss Planar

110mm f3.6-f32 lens, iris diaphragm; variable speed MFPS 1/40-1/10,000 s. 18 exp, 6.5 x 9cm on dry plates. Shutter cocked automatically when plate changed. First camera with 1/10,000 s shutter speed. C 1898.

R4* $4.5k+	£2.4k+	DM7.4k+	FF23k+

SIMMON BROS., INC., New York.

Omega 120: (SB100); 2¹/₄" x 2³/₄" RFR camera; Omicron 90mm f3.5 lens; Wollensak-Rapax 1-1/400 s. 9 exp, 2¹/₄" x 2³/₄" on 120 roll film. Eye level optical vf with parallax compensation - coupled RFR. Push-pull film advance coupled to shutter cocking; large focusing heel with depth of field scale. Omega flash attachment automatically coupled to film advance permitting 6 flash bulb exp in rapid sequence. The Omega 120 was the prototype for the Koni-Omega Rapid cameras.

R3* $250	£131	DM412	FF1.3k

Omega 120

James SINCLAIR & CO., Ltd., London, England.

Sinclair Traveller Una: (SI100); Ross Combinable lens; 'NS' Perfect shutter. Duralumin construction. 2¹/₂" x 3¹/₂" exp on plates. C 1930.

R4* $3k	£1.6k	DM5k	FF15.3k

Sinclair Tropical Una: (SI101); Ross Convertible lens; Optimo shutter. Teak, brass fittings. C 1907. **$1000.** C 1929. **$1750.**

R4*	Prices as above		

Sinclair Una: (SI102); 1/2 plate camera; N & S Perfect shutter 1/2 - 1/100 s. Double extension bellows; rising front; revolving back; double spirit levels. C 1920.

R3* $175			
£92	DM288		
FF894			

Sinclair Una

Una Cameo: (SI103); 9 x 12cm folding plate; Aldis Uno Anastigmat f7.7 lens.

R3* $75	£39	DM124	FF383

Thomas SKAIFE, London, England.

Pistolgraph: (SF100); Dallmeyer Petzval-type 50mm f2.2 lens; double flap shutter. 28mm circular exp on 30 x 40mm wet collodion plates. C 1859.

R5* NSR $15k+	£8k+	DM25k+	FF77k+

Smart Stereo: (BB252); meniscus 110mm f11 lenses; guillotine shutter 1/10-1/100 s. Stereo exp on 8 x 10cm dry plates. C 1910.

R4* $300	£157	DM495	FF1.5k

SMITH, PHOTO CHEMIST, Gosport, England.

Smith Detective: (IT100); mahogany detective camera; guillotine shutter; brass vf and trim. 12 exp, 3¹/₄" x 4¹/₄" on plates - changed with leather pouch.

R4* $600	£315	DM989	FF3.1k

F. W. SMITH & CO., New York.

Monocular Duplex: (FM100); F.W. Smith & Co. Rapid Rectilinear 180mm f5.6 lens; guillotine shutter (operates in conjunction with mirror); variable speed by tension adjustment. 4" x 5" exp on plates. C 1884.

R5* $2.5k	£1.3k	DM4.1k	FF12.8k

Jas J. SMITH, Chicago, Illinois.

The Sunflower Multiplying Camera: (ST200); Portrait lens; pneumatic flap shutter. Multiple exp: 2 to 32 exp on a 4³/₄" x 6¹/₂" plate. Mahogany finish.

R4* $1k	£525	DM1.6k	FF5.1k

SANDERS & CROWHURST.

Birdland Reflex: (SN100); 1/4 plate SLR camera; Aldis Anastigmat f8 lens. Ebonized pear wood finish.

R4* $500	£262	DM824	FF2.6k

Snappy: (BB253); meniscus lens; shutter 1/25-1/1000 s; 14 x 14mm exp on 16mm roll film. Mfd in Japan. C 1950.

R3* $150	£79	DM247	FF767

Sola: (BB254); Schneider Xenar 25mm f2 lens; rotary shutter 1-1/500 s; reflex and frame vf; 13 x 18mm exp on 16mm roll film. C 1939.

R5* $1.8k	£945	DM3k	FF9.2k

SOLIGOR, Japan.

Soligor Semi-Auto: (SO100); 2¹/₄" x 2¹/₄" TLR camera; Soligor 80mm f3.5 lens; Rektor shutter 1-1/300 s. 12 exp, 2¹/₄" x 2¹/₄" on 120 roll film. C 1950.

R2* $25	£13	DM41	FF128

SPARTUS CORP., Japan.

Spartus 35: (US100); 35mm camera; brown and gray plastic.

R1* $10	£5	DM16	FF51

Soligor Semi-Auto

STAR MFG. CO., Brooklyn, New York.

Star 8" x 10" View Camera: (SM100); 8" x 10" view camera; Century Planograph Convertible lens and shutter. Roller blind lens board moves horizontally and vertically. Double ext bellows; polished wood finish, brass fittings. C 1930's.

R4* $300	£157	DM495	FF1.5k

Star Watch Camera: (BB256); watch-style detective camera; resembles Lancaster. Mfd in Japan. C 1912.

R5* NSR $10k+	£5k+	DM16.5k+	FF51k+

STEINECK KAMERAWERK, Germany.

Steineck A.B.C: (SK100); subminiature watch-style detective camera; Steinheil 12.5mm f2.5 lens; rotary MFPS 1/125 s. 8 exp, 6mm diameter on 25mm diameter film in metal cassette. C 1948.

R3* $500	£262	DM824	FF2.6k

Steineck A.B.C

G. A. STEINHEIL SONS, Munich, Germany.

Steinheil Casca I: (AG100); Culminar 50mm f2.8 lens; FPS 1/25-1/1000 s. C 1948.

R3* $200	£105	DM330	FF1k

Steinheil Detective Camera: (AG101); magazine loading box-type wooden detective camera; achromatic lens; 9 x 12cm on plates. C 1888.

R4* $800	£420	DM1.3k	FF4.1k

Steky II: (BB257); 16mm subminiature camera; Stekinar Anastigmat 25mm f3.5 coated lens; 1/25-1/100 s. 24 exp, 10 x 14mm on 16mm film in cassettes. C 1951.

R3* $100	£52	DM165	FF511

Steky II

STEREO CORPORATION, Milwaukee, Wisconsin.

Contura 35mm Stereo Camera: (SQ100); 35mm stereo camera; Volar f2.7 lens; flash. Combined range-vf window at base of camera. Double exp prevention device with override. Aluminium body finished in tan leather. Designed by Seton Rochwhite. C 1950. Only 150 mfd.

R4* $900	£472	DM1.5k	FF4.6k

STEREO CRAFTERS Inc, Milwaukee, Wisconsin, U.S.A.

Videon: (VD100); black plastic and aluminium bodied 35mm stereo vfr camera, front focusing Ilex Stereon Anistigmat 35mm/f3.5 lenses, shutter speeds 1/10-1/100s, also sold as the "Videon Challenger" C. 1953.

R3* $85	£45	DM140	FF434

Videon II: (VD101); black plastic and aluminium bodied 35mm stereo vfr camera, front focusing Ilex Stereon Anistigmat 35mm/f3.5 lenses, shutter speeds 1/10-1/100s, quite similar to the Videon (VD100), with only a few minor changes. C.1954.

R3* $90	£47	DM148	FF460

Stereograph (Stereo Marine): (BB260); binocular-type detective camera; revolving diaphragm 60mm f8 lens; guillotine shutter, T, I. 45 x 107mm exp on plates. C 1903-1923.

R5* $3.5k	£1.8k	DM5.8k	FF17.9k

Stereo Hit: (BB261); roll film stereo camera; s-Owla 4.5cm coated lenses; guillotine shutter, I, B. 8 stereo exp on 127 film (single frame capacity). Mfd in Japan.

R3* $130	£68	DM214	FF664

Stereo Jumelle de Joux: (BB262); Zeiss Krauss 110mm f8 Anastigmatic lenses; guillotine shutter. Special rotating magazine for 12 plates, 8 x 17cm. Mfd in Paris, France. C 1898.

R4* $400	£210	DM659	FF2k

Stereo Panoramique Leroy: (BB263); 1906, metal stereo camera; Krauss 82mm f9 Protar , or similar lenses 6 x 13cm exp. Stereoscopic or panoramic pictures by rotating lens in centre of camera.

R3* $400	£210	DM659	FF2k

Stereoptican Card Holder: (BB264); wood with stenciled design. Mfr unknown. C 1870.

R4* $125	£66	DM206	FF639

Stereoptican Card Holders

Stereoptican Card Holder: (BB265); paper covered box with Victorian coloured portrait. Mfr unknown. C 1880's.

R4* $125	£66	DM206	FF639

Stereoptican Viewer and Graphoscope: (BB266); table model; machined nickel and mahogany. Mfr unknown. C 1885.

R4* $300	£157	DM495	FF1.5k

J. H. STEWARD,
England.

J. H. Steward Magazine Camera: (SV100); detective drop plate magazine camera. Rising, falling and sliding front. C 1890.

R4* $200	£105	DM330	FF1k

STEWART-WARNER,
Chicago, Illinois.

Buddy 8: (SW100); 8mm movie camera; Wollensak Velostigmat f3.5 interchangeable lens. 3 speeds:

R2* $25	£13	DM41	FF128

Buddy 9 Projector: (SW101); 8mm movie projector for Buddy 8 camera. C 1934.

R2* $20	£10	DM33	FF102

Hollywood Model: (SW102); 16mm motion picture camera; f3.5 lens, waterhouse stops.

R2* $25	£13	DM41	FF128

Hollywood Model

C. P. STIRN, STIRN & LYON,
New York.

Stirn's America Detective Camera: (SL100); wooden box-type detective camera; periscopic 105mm f17 lens; 25 exp, 7.5 x 10cm on Eastman 85mm film. Probably the first camera especially made for flexible film. Invented by R. Gray, New York; mfd by Rudolph Stirn, Germany. C 1887.

R5* NSR $4k+	£2k+	DM6.6k+	FF20.4k+

Stirn's Concealed Vest Camera, No. 1: (SL101); 6" diameter detective camera; 6 circular 1³/4" exp on glass plate. C 1886. Nickel, or brass. With wooden case.

R5* $2k	£1.1k	DM3.3k	FF10.2k

Stirn's Concealed Vest Camera, No. 1:

Stirn's Concealed Vest Camera, No. 2: (SL102); 7" diameter detective camera; 4 circular 2¹/2" exp on glass plate. C 1886.

R5* $2k	£1.1k	DM3.3k	FF10.2k

Stirn's Detective Camera: (SL103); mahogany magazine camera; Aplanatic lens; variable speed rotating shutter; 2 vf. 12 exp on 6 x 8cm plates; leather changing bag back. C.1891.

R5* $1.3k	£682	DM2.1k	FF6.6k

Stirn's Stereo Detective Camera: (SL104); Aplanatic 90mm f11 lens; variable speed rotating shutter. 9 x 18cm plates - changing mechanism with leather bag. C 1893.

R5* NSR $2k+	£1.1k+	DM3.3k+	FF10k+

John STOCK & CO.,
New York.

Stereo Wet Plate Camera: (JS100); matched pair of Morrison wide-angle lenses.

S

Stereo exp on 5" x 8" wet collodion plates. C 1860.

R5*NSR $3.5k+ £1.8k+ DM5.8k+ FF18k+

SUGAYA OPTICAL CO., LTD., Japan.

Mycro III A: (SY100); Mycro 20mm f4.5 lens; shutter 1/25-1/100 s. 10 exp, 10 x 14mm on 16mm roll film. C 1950.

| R3* $60 | £31 | DM99 | FF307 |

Myracle: (SY101); subminiature camera. 10 x 14mm exp on roll film. C 1949.

| R3* $100 | £52 | DM165 | FF511 |

SUNART PHOTO CO., Rochester, New York.

Sunart Vidi No. 2: (SX100); leather covered folding plate camera; red bellows, mahogany interior. C 1898.

| R4* $100 | £52 | DM165 | FF511 |

Echo 8

E. SUTER, Basle, Switzerland.

Suter's Detective Magazine Camera: (SU100); Suter Detective lens; rotating shutter. Leather covered mahogany box camera, brass fittings. C 1890.

| R4* $400 | £210 | DM659 | FF2k |

Suter's Stereo Detective Camera: (SU101); Rectilinear lenses; rotating shutter. Changing mechanism for 9 x 18cm plates. C 1897.

| R* $800 | £420 |
| DM1.3k | FF4.1k |

SUZUKI OPTICAL CO., Japan.

Echo 8: (SZ100); cigarette lighter-type detective camera; Echor 15mm f3.5 lens; shutter 1/50 s. 8 exp, 6 x 6mm on 8mm film. C 1951.

| R4* $500 | £262 |
| DM824 | FF2.6k |

Steinheil Detective camera

TAKAHASHI KOGAKU, Japan.

Gelto D III: (TG100); 127 roll film camera; Grimmel collapsible 50mm f3.5 lens. 16 exp on 127 roll film. Gold and chrome finish. C 1930.

| R?* | $125 | £66 | DM206 | FF639 |

Romain TALBOT, Berlin, Germany.

Errtee Button Tintype Camera: (RT100); cannon shaped street camera; Laak 50mm f4.5 lens; single speed shutter. 100 exp, 1" diameter tintype plates. C 1910.

| R5* | $1.2k | £630 | DM2k | FF6.1k |

Walter TALBOT, Berlin, Germany.

Talbot Invisible Camera: (TB100); belt-type detective camera; Anastigmat f5.5 lens; shutter 1/125 s. 15 to 30 exp on 35mm film. Rapid trigger release to cock shutter and advance film. Long, thin rectangular (7 x 34cm) shape. Camera was worn on a belt under coat, with lens protruding through button hole. C 1914-1930.

| R5* | NSR |

TANAKA OPTICAL CO. LTD., Japan.

Tanack II C: (TX100); 1953-54 Cfps, 1/20-1/500, FP flash synch, hinged back seperate Rfr/Vfr windows. First produced with a screw mount Tanar F3.5/50mm lens. Later cameras used screw mount Tanar F2.8/50mm lens. Similar to the Leica IIIB, but without slow speeds.

| R4* | $400 | £210 | DM659 | FF2k |

Tanack IIIF: (TX101); 1954 Cfps, 1 - 1/500, FP flash synch, seperate Rfr/Vfr windows. First produced with a screw mount Tanar F3.5/50mm lens or Tanar F2.8/50mm lens. Same as the Tanak IIC, but with slow speeds.

| R4* | $400 | £210 | DM659 | FF2k |

Errtee Button Tintype Camera

Tanack IIIS: (TX102); 1954-55 Cfps, 1-1/500, FP and X flash synch, seperate Rfr/Vfr windows. With screw mount Tanar F3.5/50mm lens or Tanar F2.8/50mm lens. Similar to the Tanak IIIF but with additional X synch contact, and one piece top plate.

R3* $375	£197	DM618	FF1.9k

Tanack IV-S: (TX103); 1955-58 Cfps, 1-1/500, FP and X flash synch, seperate Rfr/Vfr windows. With screw mount Tanar F3.5/50mm lens ,Tanar F2.8/50mm lens or Tanar F2.0/50mm lens. Late cameras had a film type reminder dial added to the wind knob.

R3* $375	£197	DM618	FF1.9k

Tanack IV-S:

Tanack SD: (TX104); 1957 Cfps, 1-1/1000 sec, flash synch, self timer, combined Rfr/Vfr windows, bright line parallax corrected finder. Screw mount Tanar F2.0/50mm or Tanar F1.5/50mm lens. Very few of these cameras were made. More like the Contax II or Nikon S2, but using screw mount lenses.

R4* $600	£315	DM989	FF3.1k

Tanack V3: (TX105); 1958 Cfps, 1-1/500sec, flash synch on the right side next to the rewind crank, combined Rfr/Vfr window, film type reminder in the back of the camera, no self timer. Bayonet mount Tanar F2.8/50mm or Tanar F1.9/50mm or Tanar F1.5/50mm lens. Though similar to the Leica M type bayonet mount, the Tanack V3 camera used three lugs instead of four. Screw mount lenses could be used by means of a bayonet to screw mount adaptor.

R3* $475	£249	DM783	FF2.4k

Tanack VP: (TX106); 1959 Cfps, 1-1/500sec, flash synch , combined Rfr/Vfr window, film type reminder in back of camera, no self timer. Screw mount Tanar F1.8/50mm lens.Development of the V3 camera, the VP used only screw mount lenses.

R4* $450	£236	DM742	FF2.3k

Tasco Binocular Camera: (BB270); subminiature 4 x 20mm binocular camera; Tele-Tasco 112mm f5.6 coated lens; 12 exp on 110 cartridge. Mfd in Japan. C 1978.

R3* $250	£131	DM412	FF1.3k

Tasco Binocular Camera

A. & G. TAYLOR, London, England.

A & G Taylor Tailboard Camera: (TF100); 13" x 18" tailboard camera; brass Clement Gilmer lens. Mahogany finish, brass fittings; leather bellows. C 1890's.

R4* $300	£157	DM495	FF1.5k

A & G Taylor Tailboard Camera

TEK SERRA & CO., Torino, Italy.

Cinemafografici: (TE100); amateur movie

TEK-THORPE

camera; Cine Orion 50mm f3 lens. C 1925.

R3* $200	£105	DM330	FF1k

Teleca: (BB271); subminiature binocular-type detective camera; Telesigmar 35mm f4.5 coated lens; shutter 1/25, 1/50, 1/100 s; binoculars function as vf. 10 x 14mm exp on 16mm film in special cassette. Mfd in Japan. C 1950.

R4* $900	£472	DM1.5k	FF4.6k

Teleca

A. THEMSTEYR.

Photo Sport: (AT100); Laako Dyalitar 45mm f4.5 lens; Compur shutter 1 - 1/300 s. 24 x 30mm exp on 35mm film. C 1926.

R4* $400	£210	DM659	FF2k

Thomas of Pall Mall Wet Plate: (BB272); mahogany sliding box camera; Ross portrait lens, waterhouse stops. Multiplying back takes 2 exp on horizontal plate. C 1860.

R5* $2.5k	£1.3k	DM4.1k	FF12.8k

W. J. THOMPSON CO., INC., New York.

Thompson Tintype Camera: (TJ100); suitcase-type street camera.

R4*	$200
£105	DM330
FF1k	

Hythe Gun Camera

THORNTON PICKARD MFG. CO., Altrincham, England.

Hythe Gun Camera: (TP100); military rifle-type anti-aircraft camera for training British RAF machine gunners during WWI; later copied by Japanese in WWII. 300mm f8 lens; central shutter; 16 exp, 4.5 x 6cm or 11 exp, 6 x 6cm on 120 roll film. C 1915.

R4* $1k	£525	DM1.6k	FF5.1k

Ruby Duplex Tropical Reflex: (TP101); tropical SLR camera; Cooke Series IIa 6 1/2" f3.5 lens; CFPS 1-1/1000 s; 2 1/4" x 3 1/4" exp on film pack. C 1916.

R4* $3k	£1.6k	DM5k	FF15.3k

Stereo Puck: (TP102); roll film stereo box camera.

R3* $125	£66	DM206	FF639

Thornton Pickard Stereo Camera: (TP103); roll blind shutter. Mahogany finish, brass fittings.

R4* $600	£315	DM989	FF3.1k

J. THORPE, New York.

Thorpe Four-Tube Camera: (TH100); four lens camera for Carte-de-visite or wet plate. 5" x 7" exp. C 1862.

R5* $1.8k	£945	DM3k	FF9.2k

Thury & Amey Stereo Folding Camera: (BB273); Zeiss Protar 120mm f9 lenses; Thury & Amey 4-speed gu illotine shutter. Mfd in Geneva, Switzerland. C 1890.

R4* $250	£131	DM412	FF1.3k

T

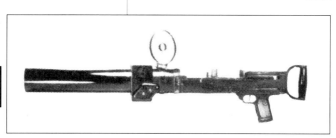

Ph. TIRANTY,
Paris, France.

Aristographe: (TI100); 35mm stereo camera; Transpar f4.5 or Tessar f4.5 lenses; Stereo Compur shutter. Iconometric direct vision finder with plumb, depth of field scale. Jacquet 12 plate 6 x 13cm magazine. C 1922.

R5*	NSR		

Simda: (TI101); 16mm camera for either single exposure or stereo pairs using either single or double perforated ciné film, fixed focus Angenieux 25mm/f3.5 of Roussel Special 25mm/f3.5 lenses, shutter speeds 1-1/250s, holds enough film for 100 shots. Available in either black or grey, also known as the "Panoramascope 3D". C.1957.

R4* $700	£367	DM1.2k	FF3.6k

A. TISCHLER HEINEMANN
& DRESSLER,
Munich, Germany.

Monachia: (TD100); meniscus lens; front of lens rotary shutter. 35 x 40mm exp. C 1889.

R4* $600	£315	DM989	FF3.1k

TISDELL & WHITTELSEY,
New York.

Tisdell & Whittelsey Detective Camera: (TW100); box-type detective camera; Achromatic meniscus lens; variable speed shutter. 3 1/4" x 4 1/4" exp on dry plates. C 1887. Leather, **$800**; wood, **$1750**.

R4*	Prices as above		

TISDELL CAMERA AND MFG.
Scranton, Pennsylvania.

Tisdell Hand Camera: (TZ100); leather covered box-type detective camera. 4" x 5" exp on dry plates. C 1893.

R4* $600	£315	DM989	FF3.1k

TKC, Japan.

Kalimar A: (TX200); 35mm camera;

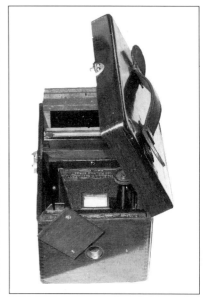

Tisdell & Whittelsey Detective Camera

Terionon 45mm f3.5 coated lens; shutter 1/25-1/200 s. C 1956.

R3* $25	£13	DM41	FF128

TOKYO CAMERA WORKS
Japan

Secrete Special: (TC100); monocular detective camera; Testar 50mm f4.5 lens. Covered in lizard skin. Japanese copy of Physio Pocket. C 1923.

R5*	NSR		

TOKYO SHASHIN,
Japan.

Mighty: (TS100); Japanese subminiature meniscus lens; single speed shutter. 13 x 13mm exp on 16mm roll film. Double vf; adjustable diaphragm.

R3* $100	£52	DM165	FF511

Tone: (BB274); subminiature camera; Tone Anastigmat 25mm f3.5 lens. Direct optical vf and waist level reflex finders. Mfd in

Tone

Japan. C 1949.

| R3* $75 | £39 | DM124 | FF383 |

TOPPER TOY DIVISION, DE LUXE READING CORPORATION, New Jersey.

Secret Sam Attache Case Camera: (TT100); toy spy attache case, pistol assembly and camera; takes 127 roll film. Includes a toy pistol, plastic bullets. C 1965.

| R4* $225 | £118 | DM371 | FF1.2k |

Secret Sam's Spy Dictionary: (TT101); plastic book-type detective camera; 16 exp on 127 film. C 1965.

| R4* $150 | £79 | DM247 | FF767 |

Secret Sam's Spy Dictionary

TRIAD CORPORATION, Encino, California.

Fotron III: (TR100); automatic camera; 10

exp, 1" x 1" on cartrdige film, 35mm wide. Built-in electronic flash with rechargeable batteries; electric film advance. C 1960.

| R3* $45 | £24 | DM74 | FF230 |

Turf folding camera: (BB183); folding camera with thermoplastic body for 16 exp 6x4.5cm on 120 film, front cell focusing Turf Extra Anistigmat 7cm/f3.8 lens, btl shutter, speeds 1/25-1/100s. made in Germany C. 1935

| R4* $300 | £157 | DM 495 | FF1.5k |

W. TYLAR, Birmingham, England.

Gnu Stereoscopic Magazine Hand Camera: (TY100); box form magazine camera; single achromat lens; rotating waterhouse stops; shutter, T, I. Single exp option; reflecting finder. 2 sets of 12 plates, $4^{3}/4$" x $3^{1}/4$". C 1904.

| R4* $600 | £315 | DM989 | FF3.1k |

Tylar Detective Camera: (TY101); guillotine shutter; 1/4 plate exp on dry plates. C 1890.

| R4* $300 | £157 | DM495 | FF1.5k |

TYNAR CORPORATION, Los Angeles, California.

Tynar: (TN100); subminiature camera; 45mm f6.3 lens; single speed guillotine shutter. 10 x 14mm exp on 16mm cassettes. C 1950.

| R3* $65 | £34 | DM107 | FF332 |

UNITED FEATURE SYNDICATE, INC.

Snoopy-Matic Camera: (UF100); meniscus lens; sector shutter. 12 exp on 126 roll film. C 1966.

R3* $100	£52	DM165	FF511

UNITEK MFG., CO., Monrova, California.

Unitek Precision Intraoral Dental Camera: (UM100); geared belt-driven moving prism with internal light source is used for oral photographs on 3¹/₄" x 4¹/₄" Polaroid film. A separate power unit charges the camera's nicad batteries and warms the optical assembly. C 1965.

R4* $250	£131	DM412	FF1.3k

Unitek Precision Intraoral Dental Camera

UNIVERSAL CAMERA CORPORATION, New York.

Buccaneer: (UC100); C1945, 35mm camera with CRF, built-in extinction meter,

Snoopy-Matic Camera

Bakelite construction collapsible Tricor 50mm f3.5 lens; Chrono-matic shutter 1/10 - 1/300 s, flash synch. (prices higher in Europe).

R2* $15	£8	DM25	FF77

Buccaneer

Corsair I

UNIVERSAL

Corsair I: (UC120); C1938, 35mm VFR camera with built-in extinction meter for special perforated film, Bakelite construction, similar to Vitar (UC116). collapsible Univex Anastigmat f4.5/50mm lens, shutter 1/25-1/200s. (prices higher in Europe)

R2* $15	£8	DM25	FF77

Corsair II: (UC121); C1946, 35mm VFR camera with built-in extinction meter, as (UC120 except uses standard 35mm film, Bakelite construction, similar to Vitar (UC116). collapsible Univex Anastigmat f4.5/50mm lens, shutter 1/25-1/200s. (prices higher in Europe).

R2* $15	£8	DM25	FF77

Cinemaster II Model G8: (UC101); 8mm movie camera; interchangeable 1/2" f2.5 lens. 3 speeds: 16, 24 and 32 frames per s.; exp meter in vf. Used either special Univex single 8 film, or standard double 8. Last movie camera made by Universal. C 1952.

R2* $20	£10	DM33	FF102

Iris: (UC102); C 1939, dark painted metal bodied VFR camera, collapsible Ilex Vitar 50mm f7.9 lens; T, B, I shutter, 8 exp on 00 roll film.

R2* $15	£8	DM25	FF77

Iris

Iris Delux: (UC126);C1939, metal bodied VFR camera, collapsible Ilex Vitar 50mm f7.9 lens; T, B, I shutter, 8 exp on 00 roll film, as (UC102, but for polished metalwork synchronised version add 50%).

R2* $15	£8	DM25	FF77

Mercury I: (UC103); C 1947, metal bodied half-frame 35mm VFR camera, interchangeable Tricor 35mm f3.5 lens, rotary sector MFPS 1/20-1/1000 s, using 35mm film in

Iris Delux, with synchro (above) and without (below)

Mercury I

special rolls.   (higher prices in Europe).

R2* $60	£31	DM99	FF307

Mercury I, model CC1500 (UC117); C 1947, metal bodied half-frame 35mm VFR, interchangeable Tricor f3.5 or f2.7/35mm lens, rotary sector MFPS 1/20-1/1500 s, using 35mm film in special rolls, as (UC103 but for 1/1500s shutter speed. (prices higher in

Europe, add 50% for f2.7 lens)

R4* $125	£66	DM206	FF639

Mercury I, with RFR accessory

Mercury II with flash

Mercury II: (UC104); C 1948, metal bodied half-frame 35mm VFR camera, interchangeable Universal Tricor 35mm f2.8 lens, rotary sector MFPS 1/20 -1/1000 s, as (UC103) but using standard 35mm film. (prices higher in Europe).

R2* $75	£39	DM124	FF383

Meteor: (UC119); C1949, metal bodied VFR camera for 6cm x 6cm frames on 620 roll film, fll lens in collapsible tube, simple shutter, built-in extinction meter. (prices higher in Europe).

R2* $10	£5	DM16	FF51

Meteor

Minicam: (UC124); C1938, brown metal bodied strut folding camera for 00 film, Ilex-Achromar 50mm lens, simple shutter.

R3* $30	£16	DM49	FF153

Minicam

Minute 16: (UC105); subminiature camera; meniscus lens; guillotine shutter. 10 x 14mm exp on 16mm film in special cartridge. C 1950.

R3* $90	£47	DM148	FF460

Norton: (UC106); black plastic camera; 6

Minute 16

exp, 1¹/₈" x 1¹/₂" on No. 00 roll film.

R2* $15	£8	DM25	FF77

Roamer I: (UC123); C1949, metal bodied folding VFR camera for 6cm x 9cm frames on either 120 or 620 film, Universal Anastigmat f6.3/100mm lens, synchromatic shutter, as (UC122) but for lens.

R2* $20	£10	DM33	FF102

Roamer II: (UC122); C1949, metal bodied folding VFR camera for 6cm x 9cm frames on either 120 or 620 film, Universal Anastigmat f4.5/100mm lens, synchromatic shutter.

R2* $20	£10	DM33	FF102

Roamer 63: (UC107); C1949, metal bodied folding VFR camera for 6cm x 9cm frames on either 120 or 620 film,Universal Anastigmat Synchromatic 100mm f6.3 lens, 6cm x 9cm frames on 120 roll film.

R2* $15	£8	DM25	FF77

Steré-all: (UC110); C 1957, 35mm stereo VFR camera, Tricor f3.5 fixed focus lens; shutter 1/50 s.

R3* $80	£42	DM132	FF409

Steré-all

Stereo Univex Model A: (UC111); paired Univex cameras attached by bracket.

R4* $250	£131	DM412	FF1.3k

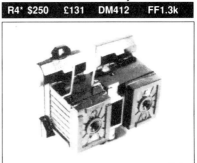

Stereo Univex Model A

Twinflex: (UC112); meniscus lens; sector shutter; reflex viewing. 6 exp on No. 00 roll film.

R3* $35	£18	DM58	FF179

Twinflex

Univex AF

U

Univex AF: (UC127); C1937, compact metal bodied strut folding camera for 00 roll film.

R2* $20	£10	DM33	FF102

Univex AF-2: (UC113); C1938, compact metal bodied strut folding camera for 00 roll film.

R2* $20	£10	DM33	FF102

Univex AF-3: (UC125); C1938, compact metal bodied strut folding camera for 00 roll film.

R2* $20	° £10	DM33	FF102

Univex Model A Camera: (UC114); C1940, VFR camera for 6 exp on Univex 00 roll film, Bakelite construction.

R2* $10	£5	DM16	FF51

Univex Model A Camera

Uniflash: (UC118); C1940, simple VFR camera for 00 film, bakelite construction, Vitar 60mm lens, sold with flash.

R2* $15	£8	DM25	FF77

Uniflash

Univex Model A8: (UC115); C 1936, 8mm movie camera, Ilex Univar f5.6 lens, frame vf. Used special patented 30 ft spools of single 8mm (pre-split) film, solely supplied by Agfa. (prices higher in Europe)

R2* $20	£10	DM33	FF102

Vitar: (UC116); 35mm VFR camera Bakelite construction, Universal Tricor Anastigmat 50mm f3.5 lens, Flash Chronomatic shutter 1/25-1/100 s, built-in extinction meter. (prices higher in Europe).

R2* $20	£10	DM33	FF102

Vitar

Univex: (UC128); C1950?: Bakelite VFR camera for 6 x 4.5 frames on roll film, simple lens and shutter, marked "Univex", but the shutter is marked "P and I" like a French camera would be. Can anyone give me any more information about this little jewel?

R4*? $55	£29	DM91	FF281

Univex:

Universal-Su-Ga: (BB275); 9.5mm movie camera; interchangeable lenses. Speeds from 8 to 64 frames per s. 15 or 30m film load on spool. Mfd in France.

| R2* $40 | £21 | DM66 | FF204 |

USINES GALLUS, Courbevoie, France.

Gallus 00: (UG100); 6 x 13cm plate magazine camera; detachable shutter unit. C 1924.

| R4* $200 | £105 | DM330 | FF1k |

Gallus 0: (UG101); 6 x 13cm plate magazine camera; for use as a stereoscope. C 1924.

| R4* $300 | £157 | DM495 | FF1.5k |

Gallus 100: (UG102); 6 x 13cm plate magazine camera; fixed focus Gallus 75mm f6.3 lens; guillotine shutter 1/5 - 1/200 s, T, B; rising front. C 1924.

| R4* $175 | £92 | DM288 | FF894 |

Gallus 110: (UG103); 6 x 13cm plate magazine camera; leather covered Gallus 100. C 1924.

| R4* $175 | £92 | DM288 | FF894 |

Gallus 120: (UG104); 6 x 13cm plate magazine camera; fixed focus Gallus 75mm f6.3 lens; Ibsor shutter 1-1/100 s; ring front; leather covered. C 1924.

| R4* $175 | £92 | DM288 | FF894 |

Gallus 130: (UG105); 6 x 13cm plate magazine camera; helicoidal focusing; Compur shutter. C 1924.

| R4* $200 | £105 | DM330 | FF1k |

Gallus 140: (UG106); 6 x 13cm plate magazine camera; helicoidal focusing; shutter 2-1/300 s. C 1924.

| R4* $200 | £105 | DM330 | FF1k |

Gallus 150: (UG107); 6 x 13cm plate magazine camera; optical finder. C 1924.

| R4* $200 | £105 | DM330 | FF1k |

Gallus: (UG108); 1938, 6 x 9cm bakelite roll film camera with various lens and shutter combinations. Looks the same as the Pontiac and Ebner cameras of that era, though not as often seen.

| R4* $75 | £39 | DM124 | FF383 |

Cady-Lux: (UG109); 1940, Metal bodied folding camera making 6 x 9cm or 6 x 6cm negatives on roll film through the use of two ruby windows, and internal masks. Fixed optical finder, and adjustable depth of field gauge on the camera top plate. Front focusing 105mm/f4.5 Berthiot Spécial lens in a Gallus shutter, speeds of 1/25-1/100s.

| R3* $50 | £26 | DM82 | FF256 |

Derby-Gallus: (UG110); 1939, 3 x 4cm on roll film, CFPS speeds of 1/25 -1/500s, optical VFR, front focusing 50mm/f3.5 Saphir lens. This camera is the continuation of the famous "Foth" Derby, originally made in Berlin, Germany. Because of the beginning of WWII, not many cameras were made.

| R3* $140 | £73 | DM231 | FF716 |

Derlux: (UG111); 1947, 3 x 4cm on roll film, CFPS speeds of 1/25-1/500s, optical VFR, front focusing 50mm/f3.5 or f2.8 Saphir lens or the more often found 50mm f3.5 Gallix lens. Early cameras use the old style "Foth" body, with a new polished aluminium lens board, later cameras were entirely polished aluminium.

| R3* $125 | £66 | DM206 | FF639 |

Lenses for Gallus 1924 models: Hermagis Aplanastigmat 75mm f6.8; Dogmar 75mm f6.3; Stylor 75mm f4.5 or f6.3; Berthiot Perigraphe 75mm f6.8; Olor 75mm f6.8 or f5.7; Tessar 75mm f6.3.

UTILITY MANUFACTURING COMPANY, Chicago, USA

NB, to make life simple, cameras made by the "Falcon Camera Company" (Chicago and New York) and the "Spartus Camera Company" are also included in this listing. Someday, it may be made clear when and how these three companies went their seperate ways, but rather than muddy the already muddied waters, here is a sample from each. Most of these cameras are much less expensive in the USA.

Spartus Full-Vue: (UT100); C1950, Bakelite TLR box camera for 6 x 6cm on roll film, simple lens and shutter.

| R2* $20 | £10 | DM33 | FF102 |

Spartus Full-Vue

Spartus Press Flash: (UT101); C1946, bakelite box camera for roll film, built-in flash reflector.

R2* $20	£10	DM33	FF102

Spartus 35: (UT102); C1950, Bakelite 35mm VFR, simple lens and shutter.

R2* $10	£5	DM16	FF51

Spartus 35F: (UT103); C1950, as (UT102) but with flash synch. (price includes flash).

R2* $15	£8	DM25	FF77

Spartus: (UT104); C1939, Bakelite strut folding camera for 3 x 4cm on 127 roll film, simple lens and shutter.

R3* $25	£13	DM41	FF128

Falcon Junior Model: (UT105); C1947, same as (UT104) but made by Falcon.

R2* $25	£13	DM41	FF128

Falcon Miniature: (UT106); C1947, Bakelite VFR camera for 3 x 4cm on 127 roll film, simple lens and shutter, several variations.

R2* $15	£8	DM25	FF77

Falcon Miniature Deluxe: (UT107); C1947, as (UT106) but in brown.

R3* $20	£10	DM33	FF102

Falcon Rocket: (UT108); C1947, stream-lined Bakelite VFR camera for 3 x 4cm on 127 roll film, simple lens and shutter.

R3* $25	£13	DM41	FF128

Falcon G: (UT115); C1937, Bakelite VFR camera for 3 x 4cm on 127 roll film, f3.5 lens in collapsible tube mount with focusing, Deltax shutter 1/25 - 1/100s.

R3* $25	£13	DM41	FF128

Falcon F: (UT116); C1937, as (UT115) but with f4.5 lens.

R3* $25	£13	DM41	FF128

Falcon Special: (UT117); as (UT116) but for built-in extinction meter.

R3* $30	£16	DM49	FF153

Falcon Press Flash: (UT120); C1939, same as (UT101).

R3* $20	£10	DM33	FF102

Falcon Miniature

Falcon G

D.F. VASCONCELLOS, Sao Paulo, Brazil

Bieka: (VL100); C1950, metal box camera for 6 x 9cm frames on roll film, simple lens and shutter.

R3* $25	£13	DM41	FF128

Bieka

Kapsa: (VL101); C1950, well made Bakelite box camera for 6 x 9cm or 6 x 4.5 cm on roll film, simple lens and shutter.

R3* $60	£31	DM99	FF307

VEGA CO., Geneva, Switzerland.

Telephote Vega: (VE100); 13 x 18cm; Achromatic 120mm f20 lens; FPS up to 1/500 s. Compact structure - long focal length achieved by refracting light beam

Kapsa

with two mirrors. C 1901.

R5* $3.5k	£1.8k	DM5.8k	FF17.9k

Vega: (VE101); book-style detective camera; Aplanatic 180mm f7.8 lens; guillotine shutter 1/2-1/100 s; closing and opening this book-style camera operates the plate changing mechanism. C 1900.

R5* $1k	£525	DM1.6k	FF5.1k

Le Verographe: (BB276); Krauss Tessar 90mm f6.3 lenses; 5 speed guillotine shutter. 2 plate magazine. Mfd in Paris, France. C 1920.

R3* $175	£92	DM288	FF894

Vestkam: (BB277); subminiature camera; TKK shutter. Mfd in Japan. C 1947.

R3* $100	£52	DM165	FF511

VICTOR ANIMATOGRAPH CO., Davenport, Iowa.

Victor Cine Camera: (VA100); 16mm movie camera; fixed focus f3.5 lens with rotary diaphragm. Hand cranked - used 16mm Cine Kodak film. Inventor and mfd: Alexander F. Victor. First 16mm movie camera to be marketed. C June 15, 1923.

R3* $175	£92	DM288	FF894

Victor Cine Camera Model 5: (VA101);

VIDMAR-VOIGTLANDER

16mm movie camera; 3 lens turret took several lenses from 15 to 150mm focal length. Critical focusing tube; optical finder with parallax correction; 5 speeds from 8 to 72 FPS. Hand cranked capability. C 1932.

R3* $75	£39	DM124	FF383

VIDMAR CAMERA CO., U.S.A.

Vidax: (VC100); 120 roll film and 2¹/₄" x 3¹/₄" sheet film press camera; Schneidser Xenotar 80mm f2.8 coated lens, interchangeable mount; Synchro-Compur 1-1/500 s, X, M flash synch. Variable crf. Interchangeable backs. 8, 12 or 16 exp on 120 roll film. C 1951.

R5* $400	£210	DM659	FF2k

Vidax

Viscawide 16: (BB280); subminiature panoramic camera; Ross 25mm f3.5 coated lens; shutter 1/60-1/300 s; 10 x 52mm exp on 16mm film in special cassette. Mfd in Japan. C 1961.

R3* $325	£171	DM536	FF1.7k

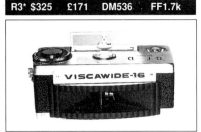

Viscawide 16

VITASCOPE CORPORATION, Providence, Rhode Island.

The Movie Maker: (VI100); inexpensive 16mm amateur movie camera. The lens opening and vf are very small. Hand-crank operated. Their motto was "Movies for the Millions". C 1931. Original price $7.50.

R2* $35	£18	DM58	FF179

VIVE CAMERA CO., Chicago, Illinois.

Vive Souvenir Camera: (VV100); premium box camera. C 1897.

R3* $125	£66	DM206	FF639

Vive No. 1: (VV101); simple lens; single speed shutter. 12 exp, 11 x 11cm on dry plates, manipulated through light tight sleeve. First American camera to use the dark sleeve to change plates. C 1898.

R3* $100	£52	DM165	FF511

Vive No. 2, Improved Model: (VV102); box magazine camera; self capping shutter. 12 exp, 4¹/₄" x 4¹/₄" on dry plates. C 1897.

R3* $90	£47	DM148	FF460

Vive No. 4: (VV103); 4" x 5" plate camera. C 1895.

R3* $80	£42	DM132	FF409

Vive Stereo Camera: (VV104); stereo box camera; 6" x 3¹/₂" exp on dry plates in magazine. C 1899.

R4* $500	£262	DM824	FF2.6k

VOIGTLANDER A.G., Braunschweig, Germany.

Voigtlander Daguerreotype Camera (Replica): (VO121); C 1956, replica of first portrait camera produced in 1841 (brass construction). Petzval

159mm f3.7 lens was 20 times faster than lens used by Daguerre in 1859. Exposure time was reduced to 1 1/2 minutes on sunny days, 80mm diameter sensitized daguerreotype plate was contained in circular brass holder. *Copies made by Voigtlander,* ; made by others, 20% less.

R4* $2.25k	£1.2k	DM3.7k	FF11.5k

Alpin: (VO100); folding plate camera; Voigtlander Collinear 120mm f6.8 lens; Kolios shutter 1-1/300 s; 9 x 12cm plates. C 1912. **$125** Stero **$600.**

R3*	Prices as above

Avus: (VO101); 9 x 12cm folding camera; Skopar 105mm f4.5 lens; Compur shutter 1-1/250 s. 9 x 12cm exp on sheet film.

R2* $40	£21	DM66	FF204

Bergheil: (VO102); folding plate camera; Heliar 12cm f4.5 lens; Compur shutter 1-1/200 s. 6.5 x 9cm exp on plates. C 1930.

R2* $60	£31	DM99	FF307

Bergheil

Bergheil De Luxe: (VO103); folding plate camera; Heliar 105mm f4.5 lens; Compur shutter 1-1/200 s. Rising and sliding front. 6.5 x 9cm exp on plates. Covered with green leather. C 1930.

R3* $175	£92	DM288	FF894

Bessa 6 x 6 (Baby Bessa): (VO104); folding roll film camera; Heliar 75mm f3.5 lens; Compur-Rapid shutter 1 -1/300 s; 6 x 6cm exp on roll film. C 1930.

R3* $40	£21	DM66	FF204

Bessa II: (VO105); roll film folding camera; Colour-Heliar 105mm f3.5 coated lens; Synchro-Compur shutter 1-1/500 s, crf, 8 exp, 6 x 9cm on 120 roll film. C 1960.

R3* $450	£236	DM742	FF2.3k

Bessa II

Brilliant: (VO106); roll film TLR camera; Voigtar 75mm f7.7 lens. Not a true TLR, effectively a box camera with a large reflecting vf, much like the Kodak Duoflex. In 1938, a focusing Brilliant appeared, bakelite body and a very different appearances. It had gears to couple the focusing mounts of the two lenses, a system used by the Kodak Reflex. Until recently, a Russian-made copy of the focusing Brilliant was sold in Britain as the Lubitel. C 1932.

R2* $25	£13	DM41	FF128

Perkeo I: (VO107); 6 x 6cm roll film camera; Colour Skopar 75mm f3.5 lens. C 1960.

R2* $35	£18	DM58	FF179

Perkeo II: (VI110); 6 x 6cm roll film camera; Colour Skopar 75mm f3.5 lens; Synchro-Compur shutter. C 1960.

R2* $45	£24	DM74	FF230

Prominent (1932): (VO111); roll film folding camera; Voigtlander Heliar 10.5cm f4.5 lens; Compur shutter 1 - 1/250 s, crf. 8 exp, 2¼" x 3¼" on 120 roll film. Built-in extinction meter, cast metal body. C 1932.

R4* $600	£315	DM989	FF3.1k

Prominent: (VO112); 35mm RFR camera; Ultron 50mm f2 coated lens, interchangeable mount; Synchro-Compur shutter 1-1/500 s, crf. Version 1, C 1953-1954, de-

Prominent rollfilm model

Prominent 35mm model

tachable accessory shoe, knob-wind film advance, $125. Version 2, integral accessory shoe, knob-wind film advance, $125. Version 3, C 1958, rapid wind film advance lever (two stroke).

R3* $175	£92	DM288	FF894

Prominent II: (VO125); C1959, as (VO112) but now with bright frame lines for 35mm, 50mm and 100mm lenses in a redesigned VFR.

R3* $225	£118	DM371	FF1.2k

Accessories for Prominent

Scoparon f3.5/35mm lens: (VO001); **$75**
Dynaron f4.5/100mm lens: (VO002); **$90**
Super-Dynaron f4.5/150mm lens: (VO003); **$200**
reflex viewer with Telomar f5.5/100mm lens: (VO004); **$260**

Stereoflektoscop: (VO113); stereo plate camera; Heliar 65mm f4.5 lenses; Compur shutter 1-1/250 s.
45 x 107mm exp on plates. C 1914.

R4* $250	£131	DM412	FF1.3k

Superb: (VO114); 6 x 6cm TLR camera; Heliar 75cm f3.5 lens; Compur shutter 1 - 1/250 s. 12 exp, 2¹/4" x 2¹/4" on 120 roll film. C 1938.

R4* $175	£92	DM288	FF894

Superb

Vag: (VO115); folding plate camera; Voigtar f6.3 or Skopar f4.5 lens; Compur shutter 1-1/200 s. C 1930.

R2* $45	£24	DM74	FF230

Virtus: (VO116); folding roll film camera; Heliar 75mm f3.5 lens; Compur shutter 1-1/250 s. 16 exp on 120 roll film. C 1935.

R4* $350	£184	DM577	FF1.8k

Vitessa: (VO117); C1956, 35mm RFR camera, fixed mount Colour Skopar f3.5 or f2.8 or Ultron f2/50mm coated lens, Synchro-Compur shutter LVS 1-1/500 s, CRF. Camera has unique rapid film advance plunger that advances the film and cocks the shutter, with and without built-in light meter.

R3* $120	£63	DM198	FF613

Vitessa

Vitessa T: (VO118); C1956, 35mm RFR camera, as (VO117) but now with rigid interchangeable mount lenses, built-in light meter.

R3* $125	£66	DM206	FF639

Accessories for Vitessa T:
Skoparet f3.4/35mm lens: (VO005); **$60**
Dynaret f4.8/100mm lens: (VO006); **$80**
Turnit VFR for 35mm, 50mm, and 100mm: (VO007); **$60**

Vito: (VO120); folding 35mm VFR camera, Skopar f3.5/5cm coated lens, Prontor II shutter. C 1950.

R2* $25	£13	DM41	FF128

Vito II: (VO131); C1951, as (VO120) but with redesigned top plate and Colour Skopar lens.

R2* $20	£10	DM33	FF102

Vito IIa: (VO132); C1953, as (VO131) but now with lever advance.

R2* $20	£10	DM33	FF102

Vito III: (VO134); C1951, folding 35mm RFR camera, Untron f2/50mm lens, Compur shutter, CRF.

R4* $125	£66	DM206	FF639

Vito B: (VO135); C1954, 35mm VFR camera, solid mount Skopar f3.5 or f2.8/50mm lens, Pronto or Prontor shutter.

R2* $25	£13	DM41	FF128

Vito BL: (VO136); C1956, as (VO135) but now with built-in light meter.

R2* $25	£13	DM41	FF128

Vito CLR: (VO123); 35mm camera with CRF Colour-Skopar 50mm/f2.8 lens Prontor 500 LK shutter, speeds 1/15 -1/500s, coupled light meter, needle visible in finder and also on the top plate. One of the last photographic products in a 120 year history of continuous camera manufacturing.

R3* $75	£39	DM124	FF383

Bessamatic: (VO126); C1959, 35mm SLR with interchangeable Skopar f2.8/50mm lens, Synchro Compur shutter, coupled built-in light meter.

R2* $90	£47	DM148	FF460

Bessamatic m: (VO127); C1962, as (VO126) but without light meter.

R3* $125	£66	DM206	FF639

Bessamatic CS: (VO128); C1965, as (VO126) but now with TTL metering.

R2* $100	£52	DM165	FF511

Ultramatic: (VO129); C1961, 35mm SLR camera with interchangeable Septon f2 or Skopar f2.8/50mm lens, Synchro Compur shutter, built-in light meter, shutter priority full automatic exposure.

R2* $100	£52	DM165	FF511

Ultramatic CS: (VO130); C1965, as (VO129) but now with TTL metering.

R3* $100	£52	DM165	FF511

VOIGTLANDER-VREDEBORCH

Accessory lenses for Vito cameras

Skoparex f3.4/35mm lens: (VO010); **$60**
Skopagon f2/40mm lens: (VO011); **$125**
Dynarex f3.4/90mm lens: (VO012); **$75**
Super-Dynarex f4/135mm lens : (VO013); **$80**
Super-Dynarex f4/200mm lens: (VO014); **$175**
Zoomar f2.8/36-82 zoom lens: (VO015); **$300**

VOKAR CORPORATION, U.S.A.

Vokar I: (VK100); 35mm RFR camera; Vokar Anastigmat 50mm f2.8 lens; leaf shutter 1/200 s. C 1946.

R2* $50	£26	DM82	FF256

VOOMP, Experimental Factory, Leningrad, USSR.

Pioneer: (VM101); C1934, 35mm RFR camera, Leica copy, screw mount VOOMP f3.5/ 50mm lens, CFPS 1/20-1/500s, no accessory shoe, 200-300 made.

R4* $1k	£525	DM1.6k	FF5.1k

VREDEBORCH G.m.b.H., Nordenham, West Germany.

Nordetta 3-D: (VR100); C1950, Strut type folding stereo camera for 127 roll film, fixed focus 8cm/f11 lenses, single speed shutter, PC flash synch, and top mounted accessory shoe.

R3* $90	£47	DM148	FF460

Pioneer

Bernard WACHTL.

Stock Apparat: (WA100); cane handle detective camera; round exp, 42mm diameter. C 1893.

R5* NSR $10k+ £5.2k+ DM17k+ FF51k+

WALKER MFG. CO., Palmyra, New York.

The TAKIV Camera: (WJ100); cardboard and leatherette multiple exp camera; rotary shutter. 4 exp, $2^{1}/_2$" x $2^{1}/_2$" on dry plates. C 1892.

R5* $900 £472 DM1.5k FF4.6k

Warzawskie Zaklady Foto-Optyczne, (WZFO) Warsaw, Poland.

Alfa-2: (WZ201); C1950, grey and white vertically styled metal 35mm VFR camera, Emitar f4.5/45mm lens.

R4* $100 £52 DM165 FF511

Druh: (WZ205); C1950s, Bakelite VFR camera for 6 x 6cm on roll film, simple lens and shutter.

R3* $20 £10 DM33 FF102

W. WATSON & SONS, London, England.

Vanneck: (WX100); Taylor and Hobson Cook lens; shutter mechanism works by means of the mirror's upward and downward action (1/25-1/100 s). Changing

Alfa-2

mechanism for 12 plates $3^{1}/_4$" x $4^{1}/_4$". C 1890.

R4* $500 £262 DM824 FF2.6k

Watson's Detective Camera: (WX101); wooden box-type detective camera; rectilinear lens; front-of-lens guillotine shutter. 8 x 11.5cm exp on plates (adapter for roll film). C 1886.

R4* $750 £394 DM1.2k FF3.8k

Watson Tailboard Camera: (WX102); rising and falling front; red Russian leather

Watson Tailboard Camera

bellows. C 1880's.

| R3* $275 | £144 | DM453 | FF1.4k |

Watson Twin Lens Reflex: (WX103); Wray Anastigmat f8 lenses. C 1890.

| R4* $400 | £210 | DM659 | FF2k |

Watson View Camera: (WX104); 13" x 18" view camera; Bush Rapid Symmetrical lens; Thornton Pickard behind-lens shutter. Reversible and tilting back; mahogany finish, brass fittings. C 1890's.

| R3* $300 | £157 | DM495 | FF1.5k |

Watson View Camera

W. BUTCHER & SONS LTD., England.

The Coronet Camera: (WY100); 1/4-plate view camera; brass lens and fittings.

| R3* $200 | £105 | DM330 | FF1k |

WELTA KAMERA WERKE, Waurich & Weber, Freital, Germany. (after 1946, VEB Welta)

Welti (pre-war): (WL100); C1936, folding 35mm VFR camera; Xenar f3.5 or f2.8, or Tessar f2.8/50mm lens; Compur shutter 1-1/300 s or Compur Rapid.shutter to 1/500s.

| R2* $45 | £24 | DM74 | FF230 |

Weltix: (WL107); C1938 folding 35mm VFR camera; Xenar f3.5 or Cassar f2.9/50mm f2.9 lens; Compur shutter 1-1/300 s.

| R2* $45 | £24 | DM74 | FF230 |

Welti (post-war): (WL120); C1946, folding

35mm VFR camera; Meritar f3.5/50mm lens, Compur shutter.

| R2* $25 | £13 | DM41 | FF128 |

Welti I: (WL121); C1954, folding 35mm VFR camera; Tessar f3.5/50mm lens,Cludor or Ovus shutter.

| R2* $25 | £13 | DM41 | FF128 |

Welti Ic: (WL122); C1955, folding 35mm VFR camera; Tessar f2.8/50mm lens, Vebur shutter, new designed top plate.

| R2* $25 | £13 | DM41 | FF128 |

Weltini: (WL106); C1935, folding 35mm camera with coupled RFR, Xenar f2.8, Xenon f2, Elmar f3.5, or Tessar f2.8/50mm lens; Compur-Rapid shutter. (add 200% or more for Elmar lens!).

| R2* $50 | £26 | DM82 | FF256 |

Weltur: (WL108); C1934, 6 x 6 or 6 x 9 folding roll film camera (6 x 4.5 possible with adapter) coupled RFR, Tessar f2.8 or 4.5, Xenar f2.8 or 3.8, or Trinar f3.8 lens, Compur or Compur Rapid shutter.

| R3* $35 | £18 | DM58 | FF179 |

Weltax (pre-war): (WL109); C1937, folding VFR camera for 6 x 9cm frames on roll film(6 x 4.5 with adapter) Trioplan f4.5, Xenar f2.8, Tessar f2.8 or Cassar f2.9//105mm lens, Prontor II, Compur or Compur Rapid shutter.

| R3* $35 | £18 | DM58 | FF179 |

Weltax (post-war): (WL123); C1946, folding VFR camera for 6 x 9cm frames on roll film(6 x 4.5 with adapter), Meritar f3.5/75mm lens, Junior shutter.

| R2* $35 | £18 | DM58 | FF179 |

Trio: (WL110); C1935, C1937, folding VFR camera for 6 x 9cm frames on roll film(6 x 4.5 with adapter) Trioplan f4.5, Tessar f4.5 or Trinar f3.8/105mm lens, Prontor II,Compur or Compur Rapid shutter.

| R2* $35 | £18 | DM58 | FF179 |

Symbol: (WL111); C1936, C1935, C1937, folding VFR camera for 6 x 9cm frames on roll film (6 x 4.5 with adapter) Weltar f6.3/105mm lens, Prontor II or Vario shutter.

| R2* $25 | £13 | DM41 | FF128 |

Solida: (WL112); C1935, folding camera

for 6 x 9 frames on roll film, coupled RFR, Xenar f3.9. Radionar f4.5 or Tessar f4.5 lens, Compur shutter.

| R3* $40 | £21 | DM66 | FF204 |

Welta: (WL113) C1930, horizontal folding plate camera in either 9 x 12cm or 10 x 15cm, FPS 1/10 - 1/1000s, Trinar, Eurynar or Xenar lenses in 135mm or 150mm were available, with or without Compur shutter.

| R3* $90 | £47 | DM148 | FF460 |

Dubla: (WL114); C1933, horizontal folding plate camera as (WL113), but only in 10 x 15cm, FPS 1/10 - 1/1000s, Trinar, Eurynar or Xenar 165mm lens, with or without Compur shutter.

| R3* $80 | £42 | DM132 | FF409 |

Welta: (WL115); C1932, folding VFR camera for 6 x 9 frames on roll film, Weltar f9/105mm lens, single shutter.

| R2* $25 | £13 | DM41 | FF128 |

Welta: (WL116); C1931, folding VFR camera for 6 x 4.5mm frames on roll film, Weltar f6.3/90mm lens, Prontor shutter.

| R2* $45 | £24 | DM74 | FF230 |

Perle: (WL117); C1936, folding VFR camera for 6 x 4.5mm frames on roll film, Weltar f4.5, Xenar f4.5, Trioplan f2.9 or Xenar f2.9/75mm lens, Prontor or Compur shutter.

| R3* $80 | £42 | DM132 | FF409 |

Perle: (WL118); C1937, folding VFR camera for 6 x 6 frames on roll film, Cassar f2.9/50mm lens, Compur shutter, parralex correcting VFR.

| R3* $60 | £31 | DM99 | FF307 |

Garant: (WL101); C1938, 6 x 9cm folding rollfilm camera; Trioplan f4.5 or Trinar f3.8/105mm lens; Compur shutter.

| R2* $30 | £16 | DM49 | FF153 |

Gucki: (WL102); C1937, strut type folding VFR roll film camera for 3 x 4cm on 127 roll film,Trinar 5cm f2.9 lens; Compur shutter.

| R3* $50 | £26 | DM82 | FF256 |

Gucki: (WL119); C1935, bed type folding VFR roll film camera for 4 x 6.5cm frames, Xenar f2.9/50mm lens; Compur shutter.

| R3* $60 | £31 | DM99 | FF307 |

Welta Perfekta: (WL103); C1934, folding TLR camera; Meyer f3.5/75mm lens; Compur shutter 1-1/300 s. 12 exp, 6 x 6cm on 120 roll film.

| R4* $200 | £105 | DM330 | FF1k |

Welta Perfekta

Reflekta (pre-war): (WL104); C1938, TLR camera; Pololyt f3.5 or f4.5/75mm lens; Blitz shutter. 6 x 6cm exp on 120 roll film.

| R3* $45 | £24 | DM74 | FF230 |

Reflekta II (post-war): (WL124); C1952, TLR camera; Pololyt f3.5/75mm lens, Prontor shutter. 6 x 6cm exp on 120 roll film, often marked "made in USSR Occupied Germany" Quite common in the USA.

| R2* $35 | £18 | DM58 | FF179 |

Weltaflex: WL125); C1954, TLR camera, Trioplan f3.5 or Rectan f3.5/75mm lens, Vebur or Prontor SVS shutter.

| R3* $60 | £31 | DM99 | FF307 |

Welta Superfekta: (WL105); 6 x 9cm TLR camera; Trioplan 10cm f3.8 lens; Compur shutter 1 - 1/250 s. Horizontal and vertical format; 6 x 9cm exp on 120 roll film. C 1934.

| R4* $350 | £184 | DM577 | FF1.8k |

W

Sica: (WL126); C1950. plastic 6 x 6 box camera, Wefo-Sicar lens.

| R3* $20 | £10 | DM33 | FF102 |

Orix: (WL126); C1958, metal half frame (18 x 24mm) VFR camera, film transport and shutter arming by rod extending from the side of the camera. Gold coloured front and back with Blue,Red,Green or Brown coloured body.Trioplan f3.5/30mm lens, three speed shutter.

R3* $75	£39	DM124	FF383

Penti: (WL127); C1959, metal half frame (18 x 24mm) VFR camera, film transport and shutter arming by rod extending from the side of the camera. Gold coloured front and back with Blue,Red,Green or Brown coloured body.Trioplan f3.5/30mm lens, three speed shutter, the same camera as (WL126) with a name change. Some people feel that this camera was made by VEB Pentacon. Probably VEB Welta assumed some manufacturing role in the grander VEB Pentacon complex, since both factories were located relatively close in Freital and nearby Dresden, respectively. Now with the two Germanys unified, in the near future a clearer picture may come to light concerning the relationships of East German camera manufacturers, and the relationship of VEB Pentacon with its "socialist" partners.

R2* $55	£29	DM91	FF281

Penti

Penti I: (WL128); C1959, metal half frame (18 x 24mm) VFR camera, film transport and shutter arming by rod extending from the side of the camera. Gold coloured front and back with Blue,Red,Green or Brown coloured body, Dimoplan f3.5/30mm lens, three speed shutter, different body style compared to (WL126) and (WL127).

R2* $55	£29	DM91	FF281

Penti II: (WL129); C1959, metal half frame

(18 x 24mm) VFR camera, film transport and shutter arming by rod extending from the side of the camera. Gold coloured body, Dimoplan f3.5/30mm lens, three speed shutter, almost the same body as (WL128).

R2* $55	£29	DM91	FF281

WEINER KAMERA WERKSTATTE, Vienna, Austria.

Wica: (WQ100);C1948-50, 35mm camera with coupled RFR, Leica copy, CFPS 1 - 1/1000s, flash synch, interchangeable Angénieux f2.9 or f1.8, Berthiot f2.8 or Heligon f2/50mm lens, *fix mounted* focusing mount *not coupled* to lenses of different focal lengths. Early model has wide seperation between the RFR/VFR eyepieces, two synch contacts and strap lugs, while later ones use close together eyepieces, one flash synch and no strap lugs. Quite rare.

R4* $1k	£525	DM1.6k	FF5.1k

Gebr. WENKE, Nurnberg, Germany.

Wenka: (WV100); C195135mm camera with CRF, 24 x 30mm frame size, interchangeable Xenar f2.8/50mm lens in 40mm screw mount; odd "FPS" located just behind the lens, 1/25 - 1/800s, CRF, early models marked "24 x 30" on the top plate. Considered by some to be a Leica copy. About 1000 camera produced C 1955.

R4* $850	£446	DM1.4k	FF4.3k

Wenka

Wenka I: (WV101); C1951-52, as (WV100)

but for top shutter speed shutter marked 1/500s.

R4*	$850	£446	DM1.4k	FF4.3k

Wenka II: C1951-52, as (WV101) but for green flash selector indicator.

R4*	$850	£446	DM1.4k	FF4.3k

WESCON Camera Company, Milwaukee, WI, USA.

Wescon: (WC200); C1955, 35mm RFR camera, collapsible f3.5/50mm Wollensak lens, Alphax shutter 1/10 - 1/200s, CRF. This camera was discovered at a camera show in Miami, Florida, in the Winter of 1991, complete with a *golden* flash and an instruction sheet. It is clearly a late Clarus camera body, but without a FPS. (The story of finding this camera is given in the introduction of this edition.)

R4*		NSR		

Wescon

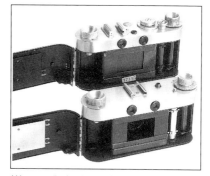

Wescon (below) and Clarus (above) from the rear, and with their backs opened

WESTERN ELECTRIC.

Plastron Gray: (WE100); shirt front detective camera; the first "button" was the lens; the second changed the plate and cocked the shutter. 6 exp, 6cm diameter on a 135mm diameter plate. C 1885. It's possible that Gray made the first cameras himself. Gray first produced his camera commercially through a company making telegraph material, Bergmann & Co., N.Y. Camera was 22mm thick with a diameter of 145mm. The 45mm f11 lens was fixed focus.

R5*	$2k+	£1.1k+	DM3.3k+	FF10.2k+

Plastron Gray

WESTERN MFG. CO., Chicago, Illinois.

Magazine Cyclone No. 2: (WF100); drop plate box camera; 12 plate magazine; after each exposure a key releases one plate to the storage chamber and a spring slides the next plate to film plane. C 1897.

R3*	$60	£31	DM99	FF307

Magazine Cyclone No. 3: (WF101);

R3*	$30	£16	DM49	FF153

Magazine Cyclone No. 4: (WF102);

R3*	$30	£16	DM49	FF153

Magazine Cyclone No. 5: (WF103);

R3*	$40	£21	DM66	FF204

Wet Plate View Camera: (BB281); Petzval type lens. 10" x 10" separate groundglass back. C 1870's.

R5*	$500	£262	DM824	FF2.6k

W

WESTERN-WHITE

Wet Plate View Camera: (BB282); 8" x 10" view camera; R.H. Moran Special portrait brass lens. Early rear focusing screw adjustment; ground glass back. C 1870's.

R5* $600	£315	DM989	FF3.1k

Sliding Box Wet Plate CAMERA: (BB283); wet plate camera; brass single achromatic lens; side dovetailing; top loading. Mfd in England. C 1850.

R5* $1.8k	£945	DM3k	FF9.2k

Sliding Box Wet Plate Camera: (BB284); mfd in England. C 1856.

R5* $1.5k	£787	DM2.5k	FF7.7k

Stereo Wet Plate Camera: (BB285); stereo wet plate camera. 3¹/₄" x 6¹/₂" exp on wet plates. Mfr unknown; English construction. C 1858.

R5* $3.5k	£1.8k	DM5.8k	FF17.9k

Stereo Wet Plate Camera

David WHITE, CO., U.S.A.

Realist 45: (WT100); 35mm stereo camera, VFR, Steinheil Munchen Cassar S 35mm/f3.5 lenses; Vero shutter 1/25 - 1/200 s. Made by Wilhelm Witt / Iloca, Hamburg, West Germany for Realist Inc. (WT204) C. 1956

R2* $225	£118
DM371	FF1.2k

Realist Macro Stereo (model 1060): (WT101); 35mm macro stereo camera; Realist Stereo Anastigmat 35mm/f3.5 coated lens, permanently set at f25; self-cocking, behind-lens shutter 1 -1/125 s. Close up focus from 3¹/₂" to 4¹/₂" . C 1971.

R4* $1.25k	£656	DM2.1k	FF6.4k

Stereo Realist (model 1041): (WT102); 35mm stereo camera; David White Co. Anastigmat 35mm/f3.5 coated lenses; shutter 1-1/150 s, CRF. Focus adjustment moves film plane. C 1951.

R2* $250	£131	DM412	FF1.3k

Stereo Realist

Stereo Realist (model 1042): (WT103); 35mm stereo camera; Kodak Ektar 35mm/ f2.8 coated lenses or David White Anastigmat 35mm f2.8 coated lenses. Shutter 1 - 1/200 s, CRF. C 1951.

R4* $550	£289	DM907	FF2.8k

Stereo Realist Custom (model 1050): (WT104); 35mm stereo camera; Realist 35mm f2.8 coated lenses, made in Germany, Shutter 1 - 1/200 s, CRF. Larger wind and rewind knobs and different frame coun-

Realist Macro Stereo (model 1060)

ter than the Realist 2.8 (WT103) C 1960.

R4* $300	£157	DM495	FF1.5k

WHITEHOUSE Products Inc., Brooklyn, USA.

Beacon: (WH200); metal and plastic VFR camera for 3 x 4cm frames on 127 film, simple lens and shutter, available in black, white, red, brown, green and blue. (European prices higher, colour other than black add %50 or more).

R2* $15	£8	DM25	FF77

Beacon 225: (WH201); metal and plastic VFR camera for 6 x 6cm frames on roll film, Doublet 70mm coated lens and simple shutter mounted in a collapsible square tube. (European prices higher).

R2* $15	£8	DM25	FF77

Beacon 225

WM. R. WHITTAKER CO., LTD., Los Angeles, California.

Micro 16: (WH100); 16mm subminiature camera; doublet lens with three waterhouse stops marked bright, dull and colour. Sector shutter with fixed speed of 1/60 s. 20 exp on 16mm film in special cassettes. C 1950.

R3* $90	£47	DM148	FF460

Pixie: (WH101); Microtar f6.3 lens; sector shutter; 16mm film in special cassettes.

R3* $60	£31	DM99	FF307

Micro 16

Pixie

THE WILLIAMSON KINEMATOGRAPH CO., LTD., London, England.

Williamson Deluxe Motion Picture Camera: (WK100); tropical cine camera; Dallmeyer Kinematograph 7.5cm lens; teak construction with flush brass bindings, designed for the tropics. C 1920.

R5* $1k	£525	DM1.6k	FF5.1k

Williamson 28mm Cine Camera: (WK101); 28mm amateur cine camera;

wooden bodied; hand crank operated. C 1920.

| R4* $700 | £367 | DM1.2k | FF3.6k |

WINDSOR CAMERA CO., U.S.A.

Windsor: (WC100); 35mm stereo camera; Windsor f3.5 lens; shutter 1/25-1/50 s. Focusing scale; direct vision optical finder. C 1957.

| R4* $150 | £79 | DM247 | FF767 |

Simon WING, Charleston, Massachusetts.

New Gem Camera: (WN100); multiple exposure camera; Darlot achromatized periscopic 120mm f6 lens; 2 blade, scissor-type shutter. 15 separate exp, 1" x 1¼" on a single 5" x 7" ferrotype plate, dry plate or sheet film. C 1901.

New Gem Camera

| R5* $1.2k | £630 | DM2k | FF6.1k |

Simon Wing/A.S. Southworth Multiplying Camera: (WN101); wet plate camera for multiple images on 4" x 5" wet collodion plates. Patent April 10, 1858.

| R5* $5k | £2.6k | DM8.2k | FF25.6k |

Simon Wing Nine Lens Multiplying View Camera: (WN102); C 1895.

| R5* $4k | £2.1k | DM6.6k | FF20.4k |

Wing 4" x 5" Multiplying View Camera: (WN103); lens standard has vertical and horizontal adjustments, to photograph multiple images on a single plate. C 1900.

| R4* $650 | £341 | DM1.1k | FF3.3k |

*Simon Wing Nine Lens
Multiplying View Camera*

WIRGIN BROTHERS, Wiesbaden, Germany.

Gewirette: (WR105); C1936, metal VFR camera for 3 x 4cm on 127 roll film with collapsible Trioplan f2.9/50mm lens, Compur shutter, tubular optical finder.

| R3* $45 | £24 | DM74 | FF230 |

Klein Edinex: (WR106); C1937, metal VFR camera for 3 x 4cm on 127 roll film, collapsible Cassar f2.8/50mm lens, Prontor shutter, accessory shoe, tubular optical finder.

| R2* $30 | £16 | DM49 | FF153 |

Edinex (24 x 36): (WR107); C1927, metal 35mm VFR camera, Radionar f3.5/50mm lens, Compur Rapid shutter, tubular optical finder, accessory shoe for "Fokas" RFR, black body indicates early cameras, chrome bodies are mostly post-war. (deduct 50% for chrome body).

| R3* $70 | £37 | DM115 | FF358 |

Edinex I (pre-war): (WR108); C1938, metal 35mm VFR camera, collapsible Cassar f2.8/50mm lens, Prontor-S shutter, accessory shoe and optical finder in one piece top plate.

| R2* $45 | £24 | DM74 | FF230 |

Edinex I (post-war): (WR109); C1949, metal 35mm VFR camera, collapsible

Radionar f2.9 or Xenon f2/50mm lens, Prontor-S or Compur Rapid shutter, accessory shoe and optical finder.in one piece top plate.

R2* $35	£18	DM58	FF179

Edinex III (pre-war): (WR110); C1939, metal 35mm camera with coupled RFR, Heligon f2/50mm lens, Compur Rapid shutter.

R4* $90	£47	DM148	FF460

Edinex III (post-war): (WR111); C1949, metal 35mm camera with coupled RFR, Radionar f2.9 or Xenon f2/50mm lens, Prontor-S or Compur Rapid shutter.

R4* $80	£42	DM132	FF409

Wirgin: (WR112); C1938, TLR for 6 x 6 on roll film, Trioplan f3.5/73mm lens, Compur shutter, identical to Welta Reflecta (LT104) but for the name plate. The same style camera was exported to the USA and sold by Peerless camera of New York as the Peerflekta.

R3* $50	£26	DM82	FF256

Edina: (WR113); C1952-54, metal 35mm camera with CRF, Cassar f3.5 or Isconar f2.8/43mm lens, Pronto or Prontor-S shutter, lever wind.

R3* $45	£24	DM74	FF230

Edixa: (WR114); C1954, metal 35mm camera with CRF, Cassar f3.5 or Isconar f2.8/43mm lens, Prontor-SVS shutter, lever wind, as (WR113) with a name change.

R2* $45	£24	DM74	FF230

Edixa I: (WR115); C1954, metal 35mm *VFR* camera Cassar f3.5 lens, Vario shutter, lever win.

R2* $25	£13	DM41	FF128

Edixa IIL: (WR116); C1955, metal 35mm camera with CRF, Cassar f3.5 or Isconar f2.8/43mm lens, Pronto or Prontor-SVS shutter, as (WR114), but for EV system on shutter.

R2* $55	£29	DM91	FF281

Edixa Reflex: (WR117); C1953, 35mm SLR, interchangeable Cassar f2.8/50mm lens (among others, some with automatic aperture), CFPS 1/25 - 1/1000s, interchange-able finder. Originally advertised as the "Komet", this camera model never made it big in the USA. Australia seems to be the one place where a collector has no problem finding a good example.

R3* $90	£47	DM148	FF460

Edixa Reflex II-B: (WR118); C1957, 35mm SLR, interchangeable Travenar f2.8/50mm lens (among others), CFPS 1 - 1/1000s, interchangeable finder, *automatic stop down, with lenses so equipped.*

R3* $90	£47	DM148	FF460

Edixa Reflex II-C: (WR119); C1957, 35mm SLR, interchangeable Travenar f2.8/50mm lens (among others), CFPS 1 - 1/1000s, interchangeable finder, built-in uncoupled light meter, *automatic stop down, with lenses so equipped.*

R3* $90	£47	DM148	FF460

Edixa Reflex II-D: (WR120); C1957, 35mm SLR, interchangeable Westromat f1.9/50mm lens (among others), CFPS 9 - 1/1000s, interchangeable finder, self timer, *automatic stop down, with lenses so equipped.*

R3* $90	£47	DM148	FF460

Edixamat Reflex-B: (WR121); C1960, 35mm SLR, interchangeable Xenon f1.9/50mm lens (among others), CFPS, 1 - 1/1000s, interchangeable finder, also model BL.

R3* $80	£42	DM132	FF409

Edixamat Reflex-C: (WR122); C1960, 35mm SLR, interchangeable Iscolar f2.8/50mm lens (among others), CFPS 1 -

Edixamat Reflex-C

1/1000s, built-in uncoupled light meter, as (WR121) but for light meter.

| R3* $110 | £58 | DM181 | FF562 |

Edixamat Reflex-D: (WR123); C1960, 35mm SLR, interchangeable Westromat f1.9/50mm lens (among others), CFPS, 9 - 1/1000s, interchangeable finder, self timer, as (WR121) but for slowest speed, and self timer, also model DL.

| R3* $125 | £66 | DM206 | FF639 |

Edixa Standard: (WR124); C1961, 35mm SLR, interchangeable Xenon f1.9/50mm lens, (among others), CFPS 1/2 - 1/500s, interchangeable finder, a cheap version of the then current Edixamat Reflex-B (WR121)

| R3* $60 | £31 | DM99 | FF307 |

Edixa Kadett: (WR125); C1961, 35mm SLR, interchangeable Auto-Casseron f2.8/50mm lens, (among others) , CFPS 1/30 - 1/500s, interchangeable finder, a cheap version of the then current Edixa Standard (WR124) with simplified shutter.

| R3* $60 | £31 | DM99 | FF307 |

Edixa Prismaflex: (WR126); C1967. 35mm SLR, interchangeable Iscotar f2.8/50mm lens, (among others) CFPS 1/4 - 1/1000s, stopped down TTL metering, *non-interchangeable* finder.

| R3* $70 | £37 | DM115 | FF358 |

Edixa Prismat: (WR127); C1970, 35mm SLR, interchangeable Xenon f1.9/50mm lens, (among others), CFPS 1 - 1/1000s, open TTL metering.

| R3* $90 | £47 | DM148 | FF460 |

Edixa Stereo IA: (WR100); C1950, 35mm stereo camera, Steinheil Cassar f3.5/35mm lenses; Vario or Prontor shutter 1/25-1/200s

| R3* $100 | £52 | DM165 | FF511 |

Edixa Stereo IB: (WR104); C1954, 35mm stereo camera; Edinar f3.5/35mm lenses; Velio shutter, speeds 1/10 - 1/200 s.

| R3* $100 | £52 | DM165 | FF511 |

Edixa Stereo IIA: (WR101); C1954 35mm stereo camera with coupled RFR Steinheil Cassar f3.5/35mm lenses; Pronto SVS shutter 1-1/300 s.

| R3* $110 | £58 | DM181 | FF562 |

Edixa Stereo IIIA: (WR102); C1955, 35mm stereo camera with coupled RFR Steinheil Cassar f3.5/35mm lenses; Prontor SVS shutter 1-1/300 s, built-in meter.

| R3* $125 | £66 | DM206 | FF639 |

Edixa 16: (WR103); C1960, subminiature VFR camera Travear or Trinar f2.8/25mm lens. 12 x 16mm exp on 16mm film, coupled meter.available as accessory.

| R3* $70 | £37 | DM115 | FF358 |

Edixa 16MB: (WR128); C1969, subminiature VFR camera Travear or Trinar f2.8/25mm lens. 12 x 16mm exp on 16mm film,coupled meter available as accessory, as (WR103) but for redesigned camera back, and film transport.

| R3* $70 | £37 | DM115 | FF358 |

WITT ILOCA, Hamburg, Germany.

Citascope: (WT200); reflex stereo camera; Tessar lens; 45 x 107mm exp. Lenticular viewing screen.

| R4* $350 | £184 | DM577 | FF1.8k |

Iloca: (WT201); C1950, 35mm VFR camera; Illing Hamburg f3.5/45mm lens; Pronto II shutter 1 - 1/250 s.

| R3* $35 | £18 | DM58 | FF179 |

Iloca I: (WT205): C1950, metal 35mm VFR camera, Ilitar f3.5/45mm lens, Vario or Prontor-S shutter, knob wind.

| R2* $25 | £13 | DM41 | FF128 |

Iloca Ia: (WT206); C1951, metal 35mm VFR camera, Ilitar f2.9/45mm lens, Prontor-S shutter, knob wind, body mounted shutter release.

| R2* $30 | £16 | DM49 | FF153 |

Iloca II: (WT207); C1950, metal 35mm camera, coupled RFR, Ilitar f3.5/45mm lens, Prontor-S shutter, knob wind, no accessory shoe.

| R3* $45 | £24 | DM74 | FF230 |

Iloca IIa: (WT208); C1952, metal 35mm camera, coupled RFR, Ilitar f3.5/45mm lens, Prontor-S shutter, knob wind, no accessory shoe, as (WT207) but for addition of body mounted shutter release, and redesigned top.

| R3* $40 | £21 | DM66 | FF204 |

Iloca Quick A: (WT209); C1954, metal 35mm VFR camera, Ilitar f3.5/45mm lens, Vero shutter, no accessory shoe, knob wind.

| R2* $20 | £10 | DM33 | FF102 |

Iloca Quick B: (WT210); C1954, metal 35mm camera, coupled RFR, Ilitar f2.9 or Ilitar f3.5/45mm lens, Prontor-S shutter, accessory shoe, knob wind, body mounted shutter release.

| R2* $40 | £21 | DM66 | FF204 |

Iloca Quick S: (WT211); C1954, 35mm VFR camera, Ilitar f3.5/45mm lens, Prontor-S shutter, accessory shoe, knob wind, body mounted shutter release.

| R3* $20 | £10 | DM33 | FF102 |

Iloca Quick R: (WT212); C1956, metal 35mm VFR camera, Cassar f2.8/45mm lens, Vero shutter, lever advance, accessory shoe.

| R3* $25 | £13 | DM41 | FF128 |

Iloca Rapid: (WT213); C1956, metal 35mm VFR camera, Ilitar f2.8 or Cassar f2.8/45mm lens, Prontor SV shutter, folding lever advance, accessory shoe.

| H2* $30 | £16 | DM49 | FF153 |

Iloca Rapid B: (WT214); C1956, metal 35mm camera, coupled RFR, Ilitar-Super f2.8, Cassar-S or Cassarit f2.8/45mm lens, Prontor SV shutter, folding lever advance, accessory shoe.

| R2* $55 | £29 | DM91 | FF281 |

Iloca Rapid I: (WT215); C1956, metal 35mm VFR camera, Cassarit f2.8/45mm lens, Compur shutter, lever advance, accessory shoe.

| R3* $30 | £16 | DM49 | FF153 |

Iloca Rapid IL: (WT216); C1956, metal 35mm VFR camera, Ilitar or Cassar f2.8/45mm lens, Prontor SV shutter, lever advance, accessory shoe, as (WT215) but for built-in light meter.

| R3* $30 | £16 | DM49 | FF153 |

Iloca Rapid IIL: (WT217); C1956, metal

35mm camera with coupled RFR, Cassar-S or Cassarit f2.8, or Heligon f2/50mm lens, lever advance, accessory shoe, Gauthier shutter or Compur Rapid shutter with EV settings.

| R3* $55 | £29 | DM91 | FF281 |

Reporter: (WT218); C1953, metal 35mm VFR camera, Reporter 3.5/45mm lens, Prontor-S shutter, accessory shoe, knob wind, body mounted shutter release. Made by Iloca for sale by other retailers.

| R3* $30 | £16 | DM49 | FF153 |

Iloca Stereo: (WT202); C1951, 35mm VFR stereo camera, Jlitar f3.5/45mm individually focused lenses; Prontor S shutter 1-1/300 s.

| R2* $125 | £66 | DM206 | FF639 |

Iloca Stereo II: (WT203); C1954, 35mm VFR stereo camera, Jlitar f3.5/35mm lenses; Prontor S shutter 1-1/300 s.

| R3* $130 | £68 | DM214 | FF664 |

Iloca Stereo Rapid : (WT204); 35mm stereo camera, CRF, lever wind, Steinheil Cassarit f2.8/35mm lenses; Prontor S shutter 1-1/300 s. Also available as the Iloca Stereo Rapid 3.8, a modified version of which was made for Realist Inc, and sold in the USA as the Realist 45 (WT100) C 1955.

| R3* $180 | £94 | DM297 | FF920 |

WITTNAUER INSTRUMENT DIVISION, Longier-Wittnauer.

Wittnauer Cine Twin WD400: (WD100); 8mm movie camera and projector; Zoom f1.6 lens; electric motor drive. Unusual combination of battery driven camera which converts to a 110V projector. C 1955.

| R2* $60 | £31 | DM99 | FF307 |

WOLFGANG-SIMONS & CO., Bern, Switzerland.

Sico: (WS100); C 1923, 35mm miniature camera; Rudersdorf Anastigmat 60mm f3.5 lens; Dial-set Comput shutter 1 - 1/300 s. 25 exp, 30 x 40mm on unperforated 35mm paperbacked roll film. Dark brown wooden body with brass trim. Only pre-Leica 35mm with wooden body.

| R5* $1.5k | £787 | DM2.5k | FF7.7k |

Sico

WOLLENSAK OPTICAL CO., Rochester, New York.

Wollensak Stereo: (WO100); C1950, 35mm stereo camera; Wollensak Amaton f2.7 lens; Rapax shutter 1/2 - 1/300 s, CRF. Similar to Revere design.

| R3* $300 | £157 | DM495 | FF1.5k |

Wonder Trick Camera: (BB286); C1970, toy "camera" with squeaking mouse. Toy mouse squeaks and jumps out of the camera when shutter is tripped. Mfd in Japan.

| R3* $20 | £10 | DM33 | FF102 |

Wonder Trick Camera

WRATTEN AND WAINWRIGHT, London, England.

Wratten and Wainwright Tailboard Camera: (WW100); 13" x 18" tailboard camera; Excelsior 3 Rochester Optical Company brass lens. Shifting stereo lens panel; dark red Russian leather bellows. C 1890's.

| R4* $300 | £157 | DM495 | FF1.5k |

WRAY OPTICAL WORKS, London, England.

Wrayflex: (WZ100); 1950's. Cfps, 1/2 - 1/1000 sec, reflex viewing, key wind on base, interchangeable Wray Unilux F2.8/50mm lens. Early cameras shot 24 x 32mm.

| R2* $275 | £144 | DM453 | FF1.4k |

Wray Stereo Camera: (WZ101); 1950's. Simple 1/50 sec shutter, coated Wray F4.0/35mm lenses, made under license from Graflex Corp. Basically the same camera as the Stereo Graphic.

| R2* $100 | £52 | DM165 | FF511 |

Wrayflex II: (WZ102); 1950. Cfps, 1/2 - 1/1000 sec, prism reflex viewing, interchangeable coated Unilite F2.0/50mm lens. Key wind on base. Very few of these cameras were made.

| R3* $350 | £184 | DM577 | FF1.8k |

Emil WUNSCHE, REICK, Dresden, Germany.

Emil Wunsche's Postage Stamp Camera: (WU100); 12 exp, 25 x 30mm on a 13 x 18cm plate. C 1900.

| R5* $2k+ | £1.1k+ | DM3.3k+ | FF10.2k+ |

Mars Detective Camera: (WU101); mahogany box form camera; Aplanat 130mm f8 lens; rotary shutter. 9 x 12cm exp. C 1893.

| R5* $500 | £262 | DM824 | FF2.6k |

Mars Box camera: (WU102); C1900. leather covered box camera for 8 x 10cm plates, internal plate changing mechanism for 12 plates, external shutter.

| R4* NSR est $350 | £184 | DM577 | FF1.8k |

W

Mars 99: (WU103); C1900, leather covered box camera for 9 x 12cm plates, external shutter.

R4*	NSR est $200	£105	DM330	FF1k

Bosco: (WU104); C1900, leather covered box camera for 9 x 9cm on roll film, external shutter.

R4*	$175	£92	DM288	FF894

Elite stereo: (WU105); C1900, leather covered box camera for 9 x 18cm stereo frames on glass plates, internal plate changing mechanism for 12 plates, two speed shutter.

R4*	$425	£223	DM701	FF2.2k

Sport stereo: (WU106); C1908, leather covered box camera for 8.5 x 17cm stereo frames on glass plates, two speed shutter.

R4*	$400	£210	DM659	FF2k

Victrix stereo: (WU107); C1908, leather covered folding camera for 6 x 13cm stereo frames on glass plates, CFPS 1/25 - 1/200, Rapid-Aplanate lenses.

R4*	NSR est $500	£262	DM824	FF2.6k

Victrix:(WU108); C1908, strut type folding camera for 9 x 12cm plates, Tessar f6.3 135mm lens, CFPS, 1/25 - 1/200s.

R3*	$175	£92	DM288	FF894

Kobold: (WU109); C1904, leather covered box camera for 9 x 12cm plates, internal changing mechanism for 6 glass plates, two speed shutter, meniscus lens.

R3*	$60	£31	DM99	FF307

Nova: (WU110); C1908, leather covered box camera for 9 x 12cm plates, internal changing mechanism for 12 glass plates, Dagor lens, internal pneumatic shutter, automatic frame counting.

R4*	NSR est $125	£66	DM206	FF639

Legion: (WU111); leather covered box camera with nickel plates fittings for 9 x 12cm plates, offered as a "tropical" model in catalogues of the day..........

R4*	NSR est $125	£66	DM206	FF639

Nixe (roll film): (WU112); C1900, leather covered folding camera for roll film only, 8.3 x 10.8cm and 6 x 9cm sizes, many different lens shutter combinations, typically Mars-Anastigmat f6.8 lens, Univers shutter, -50% for simpler less decorative models.

R3*	$60	£31	DM99	FF307

Nixe (roll film & plates): (WU113); C1900, leather covered folding camera for roll film or glass plates, 8.3 x 10.8cm on roll film and 9 x 12cm on glass plates, many different lens shutter combinations, typically Dynar lens, Compound shutter, -50% for simpler less decorative models.

R3*	$90	£47	DM148	FF460

Kolibri: (WU114); C1904, leather covered (including lens standard) horizontal folding camera for 6 x 6cm frames on roll film, Achromat lens, two speed shutter.

R4*	$170	£89	DM280	FF869

Apfi 6 x 9: (WU115); C1900, leather covered folding camera for 9 x 12cm platesn many lens and shutter combinations, typically Extra-Rapid-Aplanat f 8 lens, Automat shutter, camera interior polished Mahogany or Walnut.

R3*	$65	£34	DM107	FF332

Afpi "querformat": (WU116);C1904, leather covered folding camera in 9 x 12cm or 13 x 18 model, square design allows the making of horivontal and vertical photos by simply turning the removable camera back 90 degrees, many lens and shutter combinations, typically Imagonal F6 lens, S.V Automat shutter, double extension bellows, camera interior polished Mahogany or Walnut.

R3*	$70	£37	DM115	FF358

Minimum: (WU117); leather covered folding camera for 9 x 12cm glass plates or film packs, double extension bellows, many lens and shutter combinations, typically Rapid Aplanat f8 lens, Compound shutter.

R3*	$70	£37	DM115	FF358

Nymphe: (WU118); C1904, leather covered scissors type folding camera for 9 x 9cm on roll film, anastigmat lens, two speed shutter.

R4*	$140	£73	DM231	FF716

YASHICA CO., LTD., Tokyo, Japan.

Yashica Atoron Electro:C 1970, (YA101); subminiature detective camera; Yashinon 18mm f2.8 coated lens. Camera flash and right-angle finder.

R2* $80	£42	DM132	FF409

Yashica 44: (YA102); C1956,TLR camera for 4 x 4cm exp on 127 roll film, Yashicor f3.5/60mm lens, Copal SV shutter, 1s - 1/500s, *crank advance*. Usually found in grey.

R2* $85	£45	DM140	FF434

Yashica 44A: (YA105); C1959, TLR camera for 4 x 4cm exp on 127 roll film, Yashicor f3.5/60mm lens, Copal shutter, 1/25 - 1/300s *knob advance*. Usually found in grey.

R3* $80	£42	DM132	FF409

Yashica 44LM: (YA106); C1962, TLR camera for 4 x 4cm exp on 127 roll film, Yashinon f3.5/60mm lens, Copal SV shut-ter, 1s - 1/500s, *knob advance*, built-in light meter. Usually found in grey.

R2* $85	£45	DM140	FF434

Yashica YF: (YA103); C1959, CFPS, 1- 1/1000 sec, FP and X flash synch, seperate Rfr/Vfr windows, diopter adjustment, screw mount Nikkor H F2.0/5cm lens. Completely redesigned top plate. The same as the Nicca IIIL, see (NC103), produced by the Nicca Camera Company Ltd.

R3* $350	£184	DM577	FF1.8k

Yashica YF

Yashica YE: (YA104); 1959 CFPS, 1/2- 1/500 sec, FP and X flash synch, separate Rfr/Vfr windows, diopter adjustment, screw mount Nicca F2.8/50mm lens. The same as the Nicca 33, (NC108).produced by the Nicca Camera Company Ltd.

R2* $350	£184	DM577	FF1.8k

Yashicamat : (YA107); C1959, TLR for 6 x 6cm frames on 120 roll film, Yashicor f3.5/80mm lens, Copal shutter, 1 - 1/500s.

R2* $50	£26	DM82	FF256

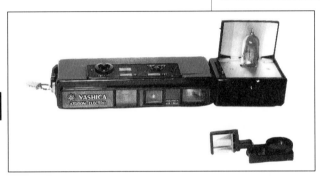

Yashica Atoron Electro

Yashica YE

Yashicamat 635: (YA108); C1959, TLR for 6 x 6cm frames on 120 roll film, or 24 x 36mm on 35mm film with adapter, Yashicor f3.5/80mm lens, Copal shutter, 1 - 1/500s. (price includes 35mm adapter.)

| R2* $90 | £47 | DM148 | FF460 |

Yashica A: (YA109); C1959, TLR for 6 x 6cm frames on 120 roll film, Yashikor f3.5/80mm lens, Copal shutter, 1/25 - 1/300s, knob advance not coupled to shutter, screw mount filters.

| R2* $45 | £24 | DM74 | FF230 |

Yashica C: (YA110); C1960, TLR for 6 x 6cm frames on 120 roll film, Yashikor f3.5/80mm lens, Copal shutter, 1 - 1/300s, knob advance coupled to shutter, bayonette mount filters.

| R2* $50 | £26 | DM82 | FF256 |

Yashica D: (YA111); C1960, TLR for 6 x 6cm frames on 120 roll film, Yashikor f3.5/80mm lens, Copal shutter, 1 - 1/500s, knob advance coupled to shutter, bayonette mount filters. Users pay more than collectors.

| R2* $65 | £34 | DM107 | FF332 |

Yashica LM: (YA112); C1960, TLR for 6 x 6cm frames on 120 roll film, Yashikor f3.5/80mm lens, Copal shutter, 1 - 1/300s, built-in light meter, knob advance coupled to shutter, bayonette mount filters.

| R2* $50 | £26 | DM82 | FF256 |

Rapide: (YA113); C1962, vertically styled 35mm half frame (18 x 24mm) camera, Yashinon f2.8/28mm lens, Copal shutter, 1 - 1/500s, built-in light meter.

| R3* $80 | £42 | DM132 | FF409 |

Sequelle: (YA114); C1962, 35mm half frame (18 x 24mm) camera, looking much like a small movie camera, Yashinon f2.8/28mm lens, Seikosha shutter, 1/30 - 1/250s, built-in light meter.

| R3* $90 | £47 | DM148 | FF460 |

Paul ZEH KAMERAWERK, Dresden, Germany.

Zecaflex: (ZK100); C 1938, folding TLR camera for 12 exp, 2¹/₄" x 2¹/₄" on roll film, Xenar or Tessar f3.5, or f4.5/75mm lens, Compur Rapid shutter 1-1/400 s.

R4* $800	£420	DM1.3k	FF4.1k

Goldi: (ZK101); C1938, folding camera for 3 x 4cm frames on roll film, Zecanar f2.9/

50mm lens, Compur shutter

R3* $45	£24	DM74	FF230

Beltax: (ZK102); C1938, folding camera for 6 x 9cm or 6 x 4.5cm on roll film, Trinar f4.5/105mm lens, Pronto or Compur shutter

R3* $50	£26	DM82	FF256

Zoetrope: (OT100); Early optical toy consisting of a circular drum pierced with slits, usually mounted on a metal base. Paper strips are placed inside the drum, which is then set spinning. The images on the strip seem to move when viewed through the slits of the turning drum. Usually sold with several paper scenes.

R3* $300	£157	DM495	FF1.5k

Two views of the Zecaflex folding twin lens reflex

ZEISS IKON A.G.,
Dresden, Germany.

Zeiss Ikon A.G. was founded at Dresden, Germany in 1926 by the merger of several leading German camera manufacturers, among them: Contessa-Nettel A.G., Stuttgart; Ernemann Werke A.G., Dresden; Optisch-Anstalt C.P. Goerz, Berlin; and Ica A.G., Dresden. Camera production ceased in 1971, although assembly continued into 1972 at Stuttgart.

In a single year (1927) Zeiss offered 104 different models with an average of three formats each with more than three lens and shutter combinations - 936 choices of "stock" models in one catalogue! The camera model with the most variations was the Deckrullo (later called "Nettel") press camera. It could be ordered in five formats (4.5 x 6cm, 6.5 x 9cm, 9 x 12cm, 10 x 15cm and 13 x 18cm). All except the smallest size were available in Tropical models with varnished teak wood construction and brown leather bellows. A selection of 30 different lenses was available for the nine models - 39 possible variations for this single model. This was in the 1927 catalogue, before any of the really famous Zeiss Ikon cameras such as the Contax, Contarex, Kolibri, and Super Ikonta cameras had been introduced.

From the above you can get some idea of the complexity of identifying and pricing all Zeiss Ikon cameras, so please regard this list as covering only the more usual types and those of special interest. Where the Zeiss Ikon model number is likely to be found on the camera it is included in the description. The number is usually expressed as a fraction - 250/7 for a 9 x 2cm Ideal and 250/3 for a 6.5 x 9cm Ideal. The second part of the fraction gives the film size according to the following table. (1) These film size numbers

were used from 1927-1960; decimal numbers were used after 1960. The focal length of the most usual lens for the format is also shown.

Number	Size	Usual lens
none	4.5 x 6cm	75mm
none	22 x 31mm	45 or 50mm
1	4.5 x 10.7cm	twin 65mm
2	6 x 9cm	105mm
3	6.5 x 9cm	105mm
4	6 x 13cm	twin 75mm
5	8.5 x 11.5cm	135mm
6	8 x 14cm	150mm
7	9 x 12cm	135mm
8	9 x 14cm (ICA)	Stereo
9	10 x 15cm	165mm
10	9 x 18cm (ICA)	Stereo
11	13 x 18cm (5" x 7")	210mm
12	4 x 6.5cm	75mm
13	13 x 18cm (ICA)	210mm
14	5 x 7.5cm	90mm
15	6.5 x 11cm	120mm
16	6 x 6cm	80mm
17	8 x 10.5cm	120mm
18	3 x 4cm	50mm
19		
24	24 x 36mm	50mm
27	24 x 24mm	40mm

Baby Box Tengor: small box camera marked "Baby Box" on front or rear. (Z54/18), 3 x 4cm; Frontar f11 lens; plain leather front. C 1931. **$40**
(Z54/18E), 3 x 4cm; Novar f6.3 focusing lens; black metal front plate.
C 1931-1934.

R3* $60	£31	DM99	FF307

Baby Deckrullo: (Z870); 4.5 x 6cm plate camera, 80mm f4.5 or f2.7 lens; FPS. Chrome struts; door closes; focus knob on top. C 1929.

R4* $475	£249	DM783	FF2.4k

Baby Ikonta: (Z520/18); 3 x 4cm roll film camera; Novar 50mm f3.5 lens. C 1936, $80. C 1936, Tessar 50mm f3.5 lens, $100. C 192. Novar f6.3 and Tessar f4.5 lens

Z

R2* $125	£66	DM206	FF639

Box Tengor - 56/2   *Box Tengor - 54/2*   *Box Tengor - 54*   *Box Tengor - 54/18E*

Baldur Box: (Z51); C1938, metal box camera for 6 x 4.5 frames on roll film, named for the leader of the Hitler Youth, and sold to its members!

| R3* $70 | £37 | DM115 | FF358 |

Baldur Box: (Z51/2); C1938, as (Z51) but for 6 x 9 frames.

| R3* $90 | £47 | DM148 | FF460 |

Balilla Box: (Z51a); C1938, metal box camera for 6 x 4.5 frames on roll film, named after the Facist Youth organization in Italy the "Balilla" for children 11 to 13 years old. Only one camera has been recently discovered, where one might expect there to have been many thousands produced. The story of its production still waits to be told.

| R5* $200 | £105 | DM330 | FF1k |

Balilla Box

Bebe: (Z342); 4.5 x 6cm camera with struts and unpleated bellows. Tessar 75mm f4.5 or Triotar f3.5 lens (front cell focus). C 1928. Dial-set Compur, $250. C 1930. Rim-set Compur, $300. (Z342/3), 6.5 x 9cm; Tessar 105mm f4.5 lens, Tessar 105mm f3.5 lens, Rim-set shutter, adds 20% to the price.

| R3* $250 | £131 | DM412 | FF1.3k |

Bob: (Z510) - (Z510/2); 4.5 x 6cm or 6 x 9cm folding camera; Nettar lenses; Inexpensive black camera. C 1934-1941.

| R2* $30 | £16 | DM49 | FF153 |

Bob IV and V: clean up of Ernemann 4 x 6.5cm, 6 x 6cm, 6 x 9cm, 6.5 x 11cm and 7.25 x 12.5cm cameras - 33 different lens/shutter combinations. C 1927. Smaller sizes, **$40**; larger sizes, **$70.**

| R2* | Prices as above |

Bobette I: (Z549); folding roll film camera with struts - 2.2 x 3.1cm format; Frontar 50mm f9 lens. C 1929. Ernoplast 50mm f4.5 and Erid f8 lens add 50% to the price.

| R3* $125 | £66 | DM206 | FF639 |

Bobette II: (Z548); folding roll film camera - 2.2 x 3.1cm format; Ernon 40mm f3.5 or Ernostar 42mm f2 lens. Earliest f2 lens on a miniature roll film camera. C 1929.

| R4* $500 | £262 | DM824 | FF2.6k |

Box Tengor (127 roll film size - 5 x 7.5cm): (Z54/14). Two models, both with Frontar f11 lens. First model (C 1926-1928) had plain leather covered front with the two finder lenses located vertically - upper left; winding knob on left side at bottom Second model (C 1928-1934) is similar, except the two finder lenses are located horizontally across top of front priced 25% less.

R3* $100	£52	DM165	FF511

Box Tengor (half of 120 roll film size - 4.5 x 6cm): (Z54/0); all models had the Frontar f11 lens. Rotating waterhouse stops and close-up lens (controlled front of camera). Diamond shaped winding knob; 2 ruby windows. C 1934-1939.

R3* $60	£31	DM99	FF307

Box Tengor (full 120 roll film size - 6 x 9cm): six models. (Z54/2), C 1926-1928. Frontar f11 lens; plain leatherette front; vf objectives located vertically - one above the other - on the upper left of front; winding knob on left side at bottom.

R3* $40	£21	DM66	FF204

(Z54/2), C 1928-1934. Similar to above, except vf objectives located horizontally across top of front; winding knob on left side at top. Frontar f11 lens with waterhouse stops and close-up lens. **$35**

(Z54/2), C 1934-1938. Frontar f11 lens with waterhouse stops and close-up lens in centre of hexagonal shaped front plate. Black enamel trim around front edge of camera; diamond shaped winding knob located on left side at top. **$40**

(Z54/2), C 1938. Similar to above, except release button moved to top left of camera. **$50**

(Z54/2), C 1939. Similar to above, except serrated round winding knob with leatherette centre; black enamel front trim; double exp interlock coupled to winding knob. **$60**

(Z54/2), C 1948-1956. Chrome trim; lever-type shutter release on lower front. Frontar f9 lens. **$40**

Box Tengor (116 roll film size - 6.5 x 11cm): three models. (Z54/15), C 1926-1928. Vf windows of ground glass - the objectives located one above the other on the left front; winding knob on left side at bottom. **$50**

(Z54/15), C 1928-1933. Mirror on front of shutter; vf objectives located horizontally across top of front; winding knob on left side at top; controls for diaphragm and close-up lens located on top of camera. **$40**

(Z54/15), C 1933-1939. Similar to above, except has elongated hexagonal design on front around lens; brilliant vf with rectangular lenses; control for diaphragm and close-up lens located on front metal plate. This size was discontinued after 1938-1939.

R3* $55	£29	DM91	FF281

Cocarette: roll film folding camera; Frontar, Periskop, Novar, Dominar or Tessar lenses; Derval, Klio or Compur shutters - 64 possible combinations. To load film, the finder and film track are removed from the side of the camera; the back does not open (similar to loading film in a Leica camera). All models were finished in black. (Z514), five sizes, single extension.
(Z519), three sizes, single extension, no vertical lens adjustment, lever focus.
(Z517), two sizes, single extension, vertical lens adjustment, lever focus.
(Z518), two sizes, same as above. A plate model also exists. C 928. All variations.

R2* $55	£29	DM91	FF281

Cocarette Luxus: Covered in brown leather with polished metal fittings, dial-set Compur shutter. Double ext bellows; two sizes. (Z521/12), 6 x 9cm with Dominar 105mm f4.5 lens, **$100**. With Tessar 105mm f4.5 lens, **$250**. (Z522/17), 8 x 10.5cm, Dominar f4.5 lens, **$100**. With Tessar f4.5 lens.

R3* $250	£131	DM412	FF1.3k

Cocarette (1930): black models (Z517), (Z518), and (Z519) were manufactured with Compur rim-set shutters; they are worth $5 to $10 more than models with dial-set shutters. No Cocarettes were offered after 1930.

R3* $50	£26	DM82	FF256

Coloura: (Z10.0641); inexpensive 35mm camera; Novicar 50mm f2.8 lens; Prontar 125 shutter, X synch. Camera is marked "Coloura" on right side of top. The Novicar is an unusual lens. C 1963-1965.

R3* $30	£16	DM49	FF153

Coloura "F": (Z10.0641); similar to above except, accessory shoe (on top) tips back to become reflector for AG-1 flash bulbs; the flash socket is uncovered as the shoe tips back. Flash calculator built into rewind knob. C 1963-1965.

R3* $35	£18	DM58	FF179

Z

ZEISS

Contaflex TLR: 35mm TLR camera; the 80mm viewing lens is not interchangeable; eight interchangeable taking lenses range from 35mm to 135mm focal length. World's first camera with built-in photo-electric exp meter. **$1600** if the condition is mint and the camera is fully operational. It is worth much less if meter is inoperative, if shutter is slow or jammed, or if the Albada finder is discoloured. It is a difficult camera to repair; few repair men will accept the responsibility.

R3* $1.6k	£840	DM2.6k	FF8.2k

Contaflex TLR

Contaflex TLR Lenses

Orthometer or Biogon 35mm lens, with viewfinder, **$800**.
Sonnar 50mm f2, f1.5 or Tessar 50m f2.8 lens, **$500**.
Sonnar 80mm f2 lens, **$650**
Triotar 85mm f4 lens, **$650**.
Sonnar 135mm f4 lens, **$800**.

Contaflex I: (Z861/24); 35mm SLR camera; Tessar 45mm f2.8 lens; Synchro-Compur shutter. No exp meter. C 1953-1958.

R2* $60	£31	DM99	FF307

Contaflex I

Contaflex II: (Z863/24); similar to above except, has built-in exp meter. C 1954-1958.

R2* $75	£39	DM124	FF383

Contaflex III: (Z863/24); 35mm SLR camera; Tessar 50mm lens, interchangeable front element. Last model with knob wind for film advance. No built-in meter. Stereo attachment,**$325**. "O" stereo viewer, **$125** "OO" stereo viewer, **$150** C 1957-1959. camera alone.

R3* $70	£37	DM115	FF358

Contaflex IV: (Z864/24); similar to above, except has LVS settings on shutter, built-in exp meter with hinged door. C 57-1959.

R2* $70	£37	DM115	FF358

Contaflex "Alpha": (Z10.1241); inexpensive version of Contaflex III; Pantar 45mm f2.8 lens, interchangeable front element for Pantar series lenses. C 1958-1959.

R2* $65	£34	DM107	FF332

Contaflex "Beta": (Z10.1251); similar to "Alpha" model, except has exp meter. C 1958-1959.

R2* $85	£45	DM140	FF434

Contaflex "Rapid": (Z10.1261); Tessar 50mm f2.8 lens, interchangeable front element. Three special features first appeared on this camera and succeeding models: rapid film advance lever; accessory shoe on prism housing; and interchangeable magazine backs. C 1959-1961.

R2* $120	£63	DM198	FF613

Contaflex "Prima": (Z10.1291); similar to "Rapid", except has Pantar 45mm f2.8 lens;

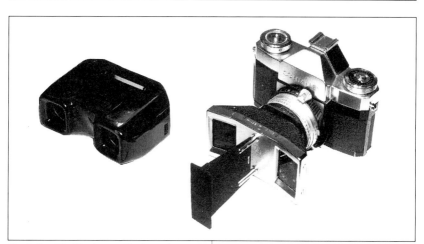

Contaflex III with stereo attachment

uncovered match needle exp meter (right side). C 1959-1965.

| R2* $130 | £68 | DM214 | FF664 |

Contaflex "Super": (Z10.1262); similar to "Rapid" except has coupled exp meter. The uncovered meter window is in the front of the prism housing - meter adjustment wheel is on the right front of the camera (the only Contaflex with external wheel). C 1959-1962.

| R1* $130 | £68 | DM214 | FF664 |

Contaflex "Super" (new style): (Z10.1271); Tessar 50mm f2.8 lens; shutter marked "Synchro-Compur Z". Larger exp meter window marked "Zeiss Ikon": top mount exp meter window shows two red arrows - no numbers; internal RFR images shows small "2x" (visible at top of exp meter slot - right side). No auto exp control. C 1962-1967.

| R1* $130 | £68 | DM214 | FF664 |

Contaflex "Super B": (Z10.1272); similar to above, except shows numbers in top mounted exp meter and in vf. Shutter marked "Synchro-Compur" under lens. Auto exp control. C 1963-1968.

| R1* $150 | £79 | DM247 | FF767 |

Contaflex "Super BC": (Z10.1273); similar to above, except has no external exp meter window. Has through-the-lens CdS

photo-electric meter. Marked "Zeiss Ikon" in rectangle above lens. Battery compartment with door located at 9 o'clock from lens. Was produced in chrome or black finish. C 1967-1970.

| R3* $200 | £105 | DM330 | FF1k |

Contaflex "S" Automatic: (Z10.1273); similar to above, except has no external exp meter window. Has through-the-lens CdS photo-electric meter. Marked "Zeiss Ikon" in rectangle above lens. Battery compartment with door located at 9 o'clock from lens. Produced in chrome or black finish. C 1967-1970.

| R3* $200 | £105 | DM330 | FF1k |

Contaflex "S" Automatic

Lenses for Contaflex SLR (35mm: 24 x 36mm)

(Z11.1203), Teleskop 1.7x (fits models I and II only). Complete with bracket, **$80**.

(Z20.2004), (old 812), Steritar A (stereo prism for Teleskop 1.7x). **$350**.

(Z11.1201), (old 1003), Pro-Tessar 35mm f4-takes filters with 49mm external thread. **$125**.

(Z11.1201), Pro-Tessar 35mm f3.2-takes filters with 60mm external thread. **$150**.

(Z11.1202), (old 1004), Pro-Tessar 85mm f4-takes filters with 60mm external thread. **$135**.

(Z11.1202), Pro-Tessar 85mm f3.2-takes filters with 60mm external thread. **$90**.

(Z11.1205), Pro-Tessar 115mm f4-takes filters with 67mm external thread. **$150**.

(Z11.1204), Pro-Tessar M-1:1 Macro lens. **$120.**

Lenses for Contaflex Alpha, Beta, Primar and Contina III

(Z11.0601), Pantar 30mm f4 lens. **$60**.

(Z11.0601), (old 1002), Pantar 75mm f4 lens. **$70**.

(Z20.2006), (old 814), Steritar "D". **$200**.

Lenses for Contaflex III to "S"

(Z20.2005), (old 813), Steritar "B". **$350**.

Contaflex 126: (Z10.1102); Tessar 45mm f2.8 or Colour Pantar 45mm f2.8 lens; FPS. Automatic exp control; marked "Contaflex 126" on front of camera. 28 x 28mm exp on 26 Instamatic cartridge. Seven interchangeable lenses were available, 25 to 200mm. C 1970-1973.

R3* $150	£79	DM247	FF767

Lenses for Contaflex 126 (28 x 28mm)

(Z11.1113), Distagon 25mm f4. Rare: **$200**.
(Z11.1101), Distagon 32mm f2.8. **$80**
(Z11.1102), Colour Pantar 45mm f2.8. **$45**.
(Z11.1103), Tessar 45mm f2.8. **$50**
(Z11.1104), Sonnar 85mm f2.8. **$100**
(Z11.1105), Tele-Tessar 135mm f4. **$90**
(Z11.1112), Tele-Tessar 200mm f4. **$225**.

Contarex cameras are marked "Contarex"; the microscope version is not marked.

Contarex "Bullseye": (Z10.2401); Planar 50mm f2 (chrome) lens, interchangeable mount. Coupled exp meter - large round window on front of pentaprism. Early models lacked data strip slot at rear of camera. C 1960-1967.

R2* $500	£262	DM824	FF2.6k

Contarex "Special": (Z10.2500 body); script style logo "Contarex"; interchangeable vf - reflex or prism; no meter. C 1960-1966.

R4* $500	£262	DM824	FF2.6k

Contarex "Bullseye"

Contarex "Professional": (Z10.2700 body); fixed prism finder; no meter; logo "Professional" on front at 11 o'clock position from lens.

R4* $800	£420	DM1.3k	FF4.1k

Contarex "Super": (Z10.2600 body); logo "Super" marked on front. C 1968-1972. First model had through-the-lens exp meter on front at 2 o'clock. (Black add 30%). Second model had switch under winding lever.

R3* $600	£315	DM989	FF3.1k

Contarex "Electronic": (Z10.2800 body); marked "Electronic" at 11 o'clock from lens. C 1970-1972. Chrome or black (rare) finish. Seldom offered.

R3* $1k	£525	DM1.6k	FF5.1k

Contarex "Hologon": (Z10.0659 outfit); Hologon 15mm f8 fixed focus (fixed opening) lens; (linear type, not a fisheye). C 1970-1972. Outfit: camera, grip, cable release, special neutral density graduated filter and combination case.

R4* $2k	£1.1k	DM3.3k	FF10.2k

Contarex Microscope Camera: marked "Zeiss Ikon" on top. No lens, vf or exp meter. Takes interchangeable backs.

R4* $650	£341	DM1.1k	FF3.3k

Contarex Lenses: manufactured between 1959 and 1973 by Carl Zeiss, Oberkochen. These lenses have seldom been equalled and never surpassed, even with modern technology. Prior to 1965, lenses with focal length of 135mm and shorter were finished in chrome; those of 180 focal length and longer were finished in black; after 1965 all lenses were finished in black.

(Z11.2442), Distagon Fisheye 16mm f2.8. C 1973. Rare. **$900**
(Z11.2418), Distagon 18mm f4, with adapter ring for B96 filters. C 1967-1973. **$850**
(Z11.2402), Biogon 21mm f4.5, won't work on Contarexes after Bullseye model. C 1960-1963. **$600**
(Z11.2408), Distagon 25mm f2.8. C 1963-1973. Chrome, $400; black, **$500**
(Z11.2403), Distagon 35mm f4.

C 1960-1963. **$200**
(Z11.2413), Blitz Distagon 35mm f4, built-in flash automation.
C 1966-1973. **$275**
(Z11.2414), Distagon 35mm f2.
C 1965-1973. **$425**
(Z11.2501), Tessar 50mm f2.8. Chrome or black, **$125**.
(Z11.2401), Planar 50mm f2. C 1960-1973. Chrome, **$110**
(Z11.2412), Blitz-Planar 50mm f2.
C 1966-1973. Chrome, **$150**
(Z11.2405), S-Planar 50mm f4, for critical closeups to 3". C 1963-1968. **$500**
(Z11.2407), Planar 55mm f1.4,
C 1965-1973. Chrome, $250; black, **$350**.
(Z11.2404), Sonnar 85mm f2. C 1960-1973. Chrome, **$325**; black, **$425**
Planar 85mm f1.4. C 1974. Rare. **$1100**
(Z11.2417), Tessar 115mm f3.5, for use with bellows. C 1960-1973. **$500**
(Z11.2405), Sonnar 135mm f4.
C 1960-1973. Chrome, **$200** black, **$250**.
(Z11.2409), Olympia-Sonnar 135mm f2.8. C 1965-1973. **$325**.
(Z11.2425), Olympia-Sonnar 180mm f2.8. C1967-1973. **$1500**
(Z11.2406), Sonnar 250mm f4, manual pre-set ring focus. C 1960-1963. **$625**
(Z11.2421), Olympia-Sonnar 250mm f4, knob focus auto stop down.
C 1963-1973. **$850**
(Z11.2420), Mirotar 500mm f4.5, Catadioptric. C 1963-1973. **$2500**
(Z11.2422), Mirotar 1000mm f5.6, Catadioptric. C 1964-1970. Rare, only four known to have been offered in last fourteen years, negotiated price, around **$6000**
(Z11.2434), Tele-Tessar 400mm f5.6. C 1970-1973. Rare. **$1300**
(Z11.2423), Vario-Sonnar 40/120mm f2.8. C 1970-1973. Rare. **$2000**
(Z11.2424), Vario-Sonnar 85/250mm f4. C 1970-1973. Rare. **$2600**

Monocular 8 x 30B with 27mm thread at eyepiece to fit Contaflex SLR or Contarex with an adapter. First model (Z 20.1629) had eyepiece focus and line for 140 feet. C 1960. Second model had front end focusing and a distance scale; this was the most

Z

Mirotar
1000mm lens

Contarex lenses

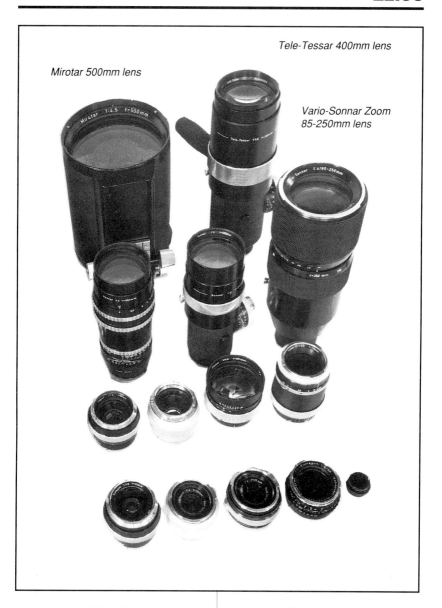

Tele-Tessar 400mm lens

Mirotar 500mm lens

Vario-Sonnar Zoom
85-250mm lens

common type. **$225** C 1963. Third model, (Z 11.1206) had a porroprism and front end focus; the shape is straight, it looks like a small refracting telescope. C 1969. **$350**

Curtagon 35PA f4, (Z 11.2430), automatic stop-down with perspective control by lateral movement of up to 7mm in any of four directions. Mfd by Schneider, mounted and sold by Zeiss Ikon, Stuttgart. C 1973. Rare.

R5* $1k	£525	DM1.6k	FF5.1k

Z

ZEISS

Contax Series

Introduced in 1932, the Contax I was the most advanced 35mm system camera of its time. Early Zeiss literature stresses many competitive advantages: the long base RFR with pivoting gold-plated prism; the MFPS with 1/1000 s top speed; the interchangeable bayonet lens mount; availability of a wide range of lenses and accessories; and the removable back for convenient film loading and cleaning. Production of subsequent models continued (except for the period from 1944 to 1952) until 1961.

Many design changes occurred during the production span of the Contax I (1932-1936). These variations have been grouped into six models, designated: I(a); I(b); I(c); I(d); I(e) and I(f). Dissimilar and yet similar, they shared many features: the rectangular body with removable back finished in black enamel; the logo "CONTAX" was marked on the front, above the lens mount in white letters; the bayonet lens mount; and the combination film wind knob and shutter setting dial located on the front of the body, to the left of the lens mount.

Prices shown below include the value of the correct (period) lens.

Contax I(a): (Z540/24a); no low (below 1/25 s) shutter speeds; no "foot" on tripod socket. Some models had one or more raised "dimples" on the front of the camera (covering ends of shafts). The vf window eyepiece is to the right of the RFR window

Contax I(a)

(looking at the rear). The distance scale around the base of the lens mount is finished in black enamel with white numerals. Serial numbers start with "AU" or "AV".

R4* $850	£446	DM1.4k	FF4.3k

Contax I(b): (Z540/24b); similar to I(a) except front bezel extends across front of camera to vf and RFR window.

R4* $800	£420	DM1.3k	FF4.1k

Contax I(c): (Z540/24c); slow shutter speeds added; pivoting "foot" added to tripod socket. Lens bezel has guard attached which surrounds slow speed setting ring.

R4* $650	£341	DM1.1k	FF3.3k

Note: the preceding models did not have a button to unlock the infinity stop when lenses with an external bayonet were in use.

Contax I(d): (Z540/24d); similar to I(c), except has button to release infinity lock located at 1 o'clock from lens. Distance scale around base of lens mount finished in chrome with black numerals.

R3* $500	£262	DM824	FF2.6k

Contax I(e): (Z540/24e); similar to I(d), except the vf window (viewing body from rear). A shallow vertical groove in the front bezel separates the area containing the logo "CONTAX" and the focus wheel.

R3* $500	£262	DM824	FF2.6k

Contax I(f): (Z540/24f); similar to I(e), except accessory shoe has four screws; the marker for setting the shutter speeds was changed from a slotted screw head to a small pointer.

R3* $500	£262	DM824	FF2.6k

Contax II: (Z543/24); Sonnar 50mm f2 lens; MFPS to 1/1250 s, no synch. Combined range and vf; narrow frame around left RFR window; chrome finish; winding knob with shutter speed dial on top left. C 1936-1942.

R3* $140	£73	DM231	FF716

Contax III: (Z544/24); similar to Contax II, except had uncoupled selenium photo-electric exp meter on top, and higher rewind knob. C 1936-1942.

R3* $150	£79	DM247	FF767

Contax II

Contax D

"No Name" Contax, Contax D and Contax F: several variations of the Contax were produced in East Germany after WWII. The Contax D was the first 35mm camera to use a pentaprism.

R2*	$300	£157	DM495	FF1.5k

Contax IIa: (563/24); a superb 35mm camera produced at Stuttgart. Chrome finish; "CONTAX" logo marked on front; wide frame around left RFR window; film speed and type indicator on rewind knob. C 1950-1961. First model had black numerals on shutter speed dial; the synch connection looks like a flat plunger in socket - a special attachment is required to convert mechanical motion to electrical contact. **$310** Second model similar, except the numbers on the shutter speed dial were in colour - 1 s-1/25 s, black; 1/50 s, yellow; 1/100-1/1250 s, red. Regular P.C. flash connector on rear.

R3*	$400	£210	DM659	FF2k

Contax IIIa: similar to Contax IIa, except has uncoupled selenium photo-electric exp meter on top. First model: black dial, **$225**. Second model: coloured dial, **$325**

R3*	Prices as above

Contax IIIa

Contax Lenses (prewar) Collectors prefer the early Contax lenses with black enamel finish and chrome trim (to the later chrome finished versions); early lenses, therefore, usually bring a higher price. The snr range is approximately 1,350,000 to 2,700,000.

Tessar 28mm f8 non-coupled lens, (ZI001); **$140**.
Biogon 35mm f2.8 lens, will not fit post-war Contaxes. (ZI002); **$150**
Orthometer 35mm f4.5 lens, rare. (ZI003); **$425**
Biotar 40mm and 42.5mm f2 lenses, chrome, (ZI004); **$500**; black, **$700**
Tessar 50mm f3.5 lens, (ZI005); **$65**
Tessar 50mm f2.8 lens, (ZI006); **$65**
Sonnar 50mm f2 lens, (ZI007); **$60**
Sonnar 50mm f1.5 lens, (ZI008); **$90**
Triotar 85mm f4 lens, (ZI009); **$100**
Sonnar 85mm f2 lens, (ZI010); **$125**
Sonnar 135mm f4 lens, (ZI011); **$125**
Tele-Tessar K 180mm f6.3 lens, direct mount. (ZI012); **$900**
Sonnar 180mm f2.8 lens, direct mount. (ZI013); **$1500**
Sonnar 180mm f2.8 lens, in Flektoskop (inverted image) with case. (ZI014); **$1000**
Tele-Tessar K 300mm f8 lens, direct or Flektoskop mount. (ZI015); **$2500**
Fern 500mm f8 lens (distance), in direct or Flektoskop mount. Rare. (ZI016); **$5000+**

Postwar Contax Lenses. Chrome finish, except that the Fern 180mm and 500mm f2 lenses, and the Tessar 115mm f3.5 lens, were offered in black.

(Z563/013), Biogon 21mm f4 lens with finder, **$625**
Topogon 25mm f4 lens. Rare. (ZI017); NSI. Estimate **$800**

Biometer 35mm f2.8 lens, (ZI018); **$250**
(Z563/014), Planar 35mm f3.5 lens, **$250**
(Z563/09), Biogon 35mm f2.8 lens, **$300**
(Z543/00), Tessar 50mm f3.5 lens, **$90**
(Z543/59), Sonnar 50mm f2 lens, **$60**
(Z543/60), Sonnar 50mm f1.5 lens, **$85**
Biotar 75mm f1.5 lens, (ZI019); rare. Estimate: **$1125**
(Z563/05), Sonnar 85mm f2 lens, **$225**
(Z543/02), Triotar 85mm f4 lens, **$125**
(Z5522/01), Panflex Tessar 115mm f3.5 lens, for bellows, rare. **$850**
(Z543/64), Sonnar 135mm f4 lens, **$160**
Sonnar 180mm f2.8 lens, direct or Flektoskop mount, (ZI020); rare. **$1600**
Sonnar 300mm f4 lens, Flektoskop mount, (ZI021); rare, **$2500**. Direct mount, rare, **$3300**
Tele-lens 500mm f8 lens, with Flektoskop or Panflex mount, and case. (ZI022); This lens sold for $835 in October 1952. Rare, estimate, **$4000+**
(Z810/01), (Z20.2000), Stereotar "C" outfit, stereo lens outfit: prism, special vf, closeup lenses and leather case. Rare, estimate **$2250+**

Contessa 35:
(Z533/24);
Tessar 45mm
f2.8 lens;
C o m p u r -
Rapid shutter,
X synch only.
Dual-range
uncoupled
s e l e n i u m
photo-electric
exp meter.
L o g o
"Contessa"   *Contessa 35*
marked in
gold-leaf letters on leather covered lens bed; round RFR window above lens. Film advance coupled to shutter cocking. First version, C 1950-1953: Second version, C 1953-1955: similar except had Synchro-Compur shutter, MX synch. Third version, C 1960-1961: redesigned body with built-in exp meter, Tessar 50mm f2.8 lens in rigid mount; Pronto 1/30-1/250 s shutter; logo "Contessa" on top cover. All three versions have lately been selling around the same price.

R3* $150	£79	DM247	FF767

Contessa LK: (Z10.0637); Tessar 50mm f2.8 lens; Prontor 500 LK shutter. coupled match needle exp meter; no RFR. Marked "Contessa LK" on top cover. C 1963-1965.

R2* $65	£34	DM107	FF332

Contessa LKE: (Z10.0638); similar to LK except had coupled RFR; marked with logo "Contessa LKE" on top cover. C 1963-1965.

R2* $65	£34	DM107	FF332

Contessa S-310: (Z10.0351); Tessar 40mm f2.8 lens, rigid mount. Pronto S500 Electronic shutter coupled to photo-electric exp meter (max exp-8 s). Logo "S-310" marked on front. C 1971.

R1* $80	£42	DM132	FF409

Contessa S-312: (Z10.0354); similar to S-310, except has coupled RFR and marked with logo "S-312" on front.

R2* $150	£79	DM247	FF767

Contessamatic "E": Tessar 50mm f2.8 lens; Prontor SLK "Special" 1 - 1/500 s, MX synch. Coupled RFR; coupled photo-electric exp meter. Marked with logo "Contessa" on front above lens mount; top cover is not marked. C 1960-1963.

R2* $40	£21	DM66	FF204

Contessamatic: similar to "E", except has Prontor SLK shutter and does not have RFR. C 1960-1961.

R1* $65	£34	DM107	FF332

Contessamat: Colour Pantar 45mm f2.8 lens; Prontormatic 1/30-1/125 shutter. Coupled photo-electric exp meter; no RFR; logo "Contessamat" on top cover. C 1964-1965.

R2* $85	£45	DM140	FF434

Contessamat "SE": (Z10.0654); similar to Contessamat (above), except has Prontormatic 1-1/500 s shutter; CRF; logo "Contessamat SE" marked on top cover. C 1964-1965.

R2* $85	£45	DM140	FF434

Contessamat "STE": similar to SE except has Tessar 50mm f2.8 lens; Prontormatic 500 SL 1-1/500 s shutter; logo "Contessamat STE" marked on top cover. C 1965.

R2* $100	£52	DM165	FF511

Contessamat "SBE": (Z10.0652); similar to STE, except top cover has a cover over the flash contacts; is marked "flashmatic" in red letters and "Contessamat SBE" in black letters. Linkage between distance and diaphragm setting provided auto flash exp control. C 1963-1967.

R2* $85	£45	DM140	FF434

Contina I: (Z522/24); 35mm folding camera; Novar 45mm f3.5 lens; Prontor SV shutter, X synch. Also came with Tessar 45mm f2.8 lens; Synchro-Compur shutter X synch. Model number impressed in leather on rear of body near latch. C 1952-1955.

R2* $30	£16	DM49	FF153

Contina I: (526/24); Novicar 45mm f2.8 lens, rigid mount; Prontor SVS 1-1/300 s, MX synch. Came with Pantar 45mm f2.8 ens in 1958. Marked "Contina" under lens and on bezel at 1 o'clock from lens. Model number impressed in leather on rear of body near latch. C 1956-1957.

R2* $40	£21	DM66	FF204

Contina II: (Z524/24); Opton-Tessar 45mm f2.8 lens; Synchro-Compur 1 - 1/500 s, MX synch. Also came with Novar 45mm f3.5 lens and Prontor SV shutter. Uncoupled RFR. Marked "Contina" on leather of lens bed; model number impressed in leather on rear of body near latch. C 1952-1953.

R2* $65	£34	DM107	FF332

Contina IIa: (Z527/24); Novar 45mm f35 lens, rigid mount or Novicar 45mm f2.8 lens; Prontor 1-1/300 s, MX synch. Rapid wind film advance; top mounted uncoupled match-needle exp meter. Marked "Contina" on front under lens; model number on back. C 1956-1958.

R2* $50	£26	DM82	FF256

Contina III: (Z529/24); similar to IIa, except has Pantar 45mm f2.8 convertible lens - uses all lenses of Contaflex "Alpha" series. Marked "Contina" on front bezel at upper left (not under the lens as in IIa); model number on back. C 1956-1958.

R2* $90	£47	DM148	FF460

(ZI023), Pantar 30mm f4 lens, **$80**
(ZI024), Pantar 75mm f4 lens, **$90**
(Z814), Steritar "D", for 3D pictures. **$400**
(Z422), Wide-angle (30mm) finder, **$50**
(Z423), Telephoto finder, **$50**
(Z425), Telephoto rangefinder, (correct field of view for 75mm Pantar), **$90**
(Z426), Universal finder for all above items. **$110**

Contina II Microscope Camera: modified III body used with standard Zeiss Microscope Connecting funnel. No lens; has Ibsor B self-cocking 1 - 1/125 s, X synch. No exp meter; no RFR; no vf. Marked "Zeiss Ikon" in middle of rear - no other markings. Usual shutter release button does not release shutter but must be depressed to advance film.

R4* $350	£184	DM577	FF1.8k

Contina: (Z10.0626); 35mm camera; Colour Pantar 45mm f2.8 lens, rigid mount; Pronto 1-1/250 s, X synch, self-timer. Marked "Contina" on top cover. C 1962-1965.

R2* $50	£26	DM82	FF256

Contina "L": (Z10.0605); similar to Contina, except has built-in uncoupled exp meter. Prontor 1/30-1/250 s. Marked "Contina L" on top cover. C 1964-1965.

R1* $50	£26	DM82	FF256

Contina "LK": (Z10.0637); similar to "L" except has coupled exp meter. Marked "Contina LK" on top cover. C 1963-1965.

R1* $50	£26	DM82	FF256

Continette: (Z10.0625); Lucinar 45mm f2.8 lens, rigid mount; Pronto 1/30-1/250 s, self-timer. The Continette was the only camera by Zeiss Ikon to use the Lucinar lens. Marked "Continette" on front next to vf. C 1960-1961.

R1* $50	£26	DM82	FF256

Citoskop: (Z617/1); 45 x 107mm stereo camera; Tessar 65mm f4.5 lenses; Dial-set Stereo Compur shutter. Reflex vf. C 1929.

R4* $350	£184	DM577	FF1.8k

Z

ZEISS

Donata: (Z227/3); (Z227/7); inexpensive folding plate camera; Tessar f4.5 or Dominar f4.5 lens, Compur shutter. Marked "Donata" on or under handle. 6.5 x 9cm or 9 x 12cm exp on cut film. C 1927-1931.

R3* $65	£34	DM107	FF332

Elegante: (Z816); field camera with square bellows and rigid front. Polished wood finish, brass fittings. C 1927-1934.

R4* $400	£210	DM659	FF2k

Era-Box: inexpensive version of Box Tengor. Marked "ERA-BOX" around lens. Two formats: 16 exp, 4.5 x 6cm or 8 exp, 6 x 9cm exp on 120 roll film. C 1934-1938.

R2* $50	£26	DM82	FF256

Ergo: (Z301); monocular-style detective camera; Tessar 55mm f4.5 lens; self-cocking shutter. C 1927-1931. Rare.

R4* $1.6k	£840	DM2.6k	FF8.2k

Ergo

Ermanox: (Z858); 4.5 x 6cm plate camera; Ernostar 85mm f1.8 lens, rigid mount with helical focus; FPS 1/20-1/200. Model with Ernostar f2 lens is rare. C 1927-1931.

R4* $1.5k	£787	DM2.5k	FF7.7k

Ermanox: (Z858/3), (Z858/7), (Z858/9), (Z858/11). C 1927 (Z858/3), Ernostar f1.8 lens; FPS to 1/1000 s; bellows with struts. 6.5 x 9cm on plates. Rare. **$1500+** (Z858/7), Ernostar 165mm f1.8 lens, 9 x 12cm exp on plates. Two other sizes - 10 x 15cm and 5" x 7" are listed in period catalogues.

R4* NSR $3.5k+	£1.8k+	DM6k+	FF18k+

Ermanox-Reflex: 4.5 x 6cm SLR camera; Ernostar 105mm f1.8 lens, rigid mount with helical focus; FPS 1/20-1/1200 s. C 1927-1929.

R4* $3.5k	£1.8k	DM5.8k	FF17.9k

Erni: (Z27), (Z27/3); box camera with celluloid "ground glass". C 1927-1930. Rare.

R3* $250	£131	DM412	FF1.3k

Favorit: (Z265/3), (Z265/7), (Z265/9), (Z265/11); plate camera; Tessar f4.5 or Dominar f3.5 lens. Usually marked with number or "Favorit" on handle; number usually marked on rear door near hinge. C 1927-1935. 9 x 12cm or 10 x 15cm (rotating back), **$190**. (Z265/11), 5" x 7". Rare. NSI Estimate:

R4* $275	£144	DM453	FF1.4k

Favorit: (Z266), (Z266/7), (Z266/9); tropical plate camera; Tessar or Dominar f4.5 lens; Compur shutter. Polished teak construction. Brown leather handle marked with name "Favorit" and model number. C 1917-1931.

R4* $800	£420	DM1.3k	FF4.1k

Hochtourist, Kosmopolit, Perfekt: view cameras of polished wood with brass fittings; square bellows. Sizes: 5" x 7", 8" x 10", and 10" x 12" exp on plates. Although these cameras are not marked with a model name, they usually have a round metal plate with logo "Zeiss Ikon". These are rare and are seldom offered on the market. Estimate

R4* $250	£131	DM412	FF1.3k

Hologon: refer to Contarex.

Icarette: (Z509), (Z500), (Z512), (Z551/2); Sizes: 4 x 6.5cm, 6 x 6cm, 6 x 9cm, 6.5 x 11cm, 8 x 10.5cm and a combination model which used 6 x 9cm roll film or 6.5 x 9cm plates. There were more than 60 different lens and shutter combinations and four different bodies. Usually marked "Icarette" on handle or impressed in leather of body. C 1927-1936.

R2* $50	£26	DM82	FF256

Icarex 35 (BM): (Z10.2200); colour Pantar 50mm f2.8 lens; interchangeable bayonet mount; CFPS 1/2-1/1000 s, x synch. Interchangeable viewing screens and vf. C 1967-1973. With Colour Pantar 50mm f2.8 lens, **$125**. With Tessar 50mm f2.8 lens,

R2* $160	£84	DM264	FF818

Icarex 35 (TM): marked TM at 1 o'clock position from lens. C 1967-1973. With Tessar 50mm f2.8 lens, or with Ultron 50mm f1.8 lens.

R2* $250	£131	DM412	FF1.3k

Either of the above cameras became an "Icarex CS" with the addition of a pentaprism D vf containing a through-the-lens CdS meter; the finder is marked "Icarex 35-CS". With the vf.

R2* $75	£39	DM124	FF383

Icarex 35S: available in both "TM" and "BM" models, the "35S" differed from the previous two models: the vf and view screens

Icarex 35S with Super Dynarex 200mm f/4

were not interchangeable; the CdS meter is built-in and coupled to the diaphragm by stop-down metering. Four Zeiss lenses were available for the "TM" model; there were nine lenses for the "BM" model. Some of the early black models were marked "PRO". (TM designates 42mm thread mount; BM designates bayonet mount).

(Z10.3600), 35S (TM) or (Z10.3300), 35S (BM), with Pantar, **$125**.
(Z10.3600), 35S (TM) or (Z10.3300), 35S (BM) with Tessar f2.8 lens, **$200**
(Z10.3600), 35S (TM) or (Z10.3300) 35S (BM) with Ultron f1.8 lens, **$150**. Black models are worth additional **$30**

R2*	Prices as above

Icarex SL-706: (Z10.3700); front of body marked "SL-706" at 11 o'clock from lens mount. Open aperture metering with Zeiss lenses. C 1972-1973. With Ultron 50m f1.8 lens:

R3* $325	£171	DM536	FF1.7k

Icarex Lenses - all accept 50mm bayonet or 56mm threaded filters and sunshades.

Bayonet Mount Lenses

(Z11.2003), Skoparex 35mm f3.4 lens, **$50**.
(Z11.2001), Colour Pantar 50mm f2.8 lens, **$50**.
(Z11.2002), Tessar 50mm f2.8 lens, **$60**.

Z

(Z11.2004), Dynarex 90mm f3.4 lens, **$125**.
(Z11.2005), Super Dynarex 135mm f4 lens, **$150.**
(Z11.2008), Super Dynarex 200mm f4 lens, **$300**.
(Z11.2010), Telomar 400mm f5 lens, rare. **$400**
(Z11.2012), Zooman 36-82mm f2.8 lens, **$425**.
(Z11.2014), Ultron 50mm f1.8 lens, **$75**

Thread Mount Lenses

(Z11.3503), Distagon 25mm f2.8 lens, rare. **$300**
(Z11.3510), Skoparex 35mm f3.4 lens, **$150**
(Z11.35), Tessar 50mm f2.8 lens, **$50**
(Z11.3502), Ultron 50mm f1.8 lens, **$75**
(Z11,3511), Super Dynarex 135mm f4 lens, **$175**

Ideal: folding plate camera; Dominar, Tessar or Double Protar lenses. Usually marked with name "Ideal" and model number on leather under the handle. Double ext bellows; removable "pop-off" holders. C 1927-1938. (Z250/3), 6.5x9cm, **$40**. (Z250/7), 9 x 12cm, **$40**. (Z250/9), 10 x 15cm, **$75**. (Z250/11), 13 x 18cm, **$100**.

Ikoflex (Original)

Ikoflex (Original): (Z850/16); Novar 80mm f6.3 or Novar f4.5; Derval, Klio, or Compur-Rapid shutter. Marked "Ikoflex" on shutter above lens. Called the 'coffee can' model by collectors; all black enamel finish on body. Has 2 film counters; one for 120 film, and one for 620 film; lever focus under lens. C 1935-1960.

R3* $150	£79	DM247	FF767

Ikoflex I: (Z851/16b); Tessar 70mm f3.5 or Novar 75mm f3.5 lens; Compur shutter to 1/300 s until 1939; Klio shutter to 1/250 s after 1939. Chrome plate inscribed with "Ikoflex" at top front of camera; models from first production year had lever focus on right side; later models had a knob. C 1936-1950.

R3* $90	£47	DM148	FF460

Ikoflex I(a): (Z865/16c); Novar 75mm f3.5 or Tessar 75mm f3.5 lens; Prontor SV shutter to 1/300 s. No folding shutter release. Marked "Ikoflex" in chrome on black background on front of vf. C 1952-1956.

R2* $90	£47	DM148	FF460

Ikoflex I(b): (Z865/16d); similar to I(a); but improved; Tessar or Novar 75mm f3.5 lens; only Novar was available in 1957-1958; Prontor SVS shutter, folding shutter release. Focusing hood opens and closes with simple action; magnifiers over diaphragm and shutter speed dials; no exp meter. C 1956-1958 - price for Novar lens, Tessar lens 20% more.

R2* $75	£39	DM124	FF383

Ikoflex I(c): (Z886/16e); similar to I(b), except has built-in exp meter needle visible on ground glass inside hood. C 1956-1958.

R2* $110	£58	DM181	FF562

Ikoflex II: (Z851/16f); Tessar 75mm f3.5 lens; Compur Rapid shutter to 1/300 s. Auto film counter; double exp prevention; viewing lens in extended chrome tube (as compared to other models). Marked "Ikoflex" on chrome plate on front. 1937 models had focus lever, 1938 and later had focusing knob. C 1937-1939.

R2* $100	£52	DM165	FF511

Ikoflex II(a): (Z851/16g); similar to II, ex-

Z

cept has flash synch; magnifiers on peep windows over shutter speed and aperture setting dials (these are set by levers below the shutter housing). C 1950-1952.

| R2* $110 | £58 | DM181 | FF562 |

Ikoflex II(a)

Ikoflex II(a): (Z851/16); similar to previous model, except the viewing lens bezel is black; the peep windows are directly over the lens. Shutter and aperture settings are adjusted with wheels. Does not have LVS settings as does the Favorit. C 1953-1956.

| R3* $130 | £68 | DM214 | FF664 |

Ikoflex III: (Z853/16h); Tessar 80mm f2.8 lens; only Ikoflex with huge Albada finder on front of viewing hood (similar to Albada finder on Contaflex TLR). Crank-type film advance coupled to shutter cocking mechanism. C 1939-1940.

| R3* $250 | £131 | DM412 | FF1.3k |

Ikoflex Favorit: (Z887/16i); last model of the Ikoflex line; Tessar 75mm f3.5 lens; Synchro-Compur shutter. Built-in LVS cross-coupled exp meter. Shutter and aperture adjustment set by wheels. C 1956-1960.

| R3* $250 | £131 | DM412 | FF1.3k |

Ikoflex III

Ikomatic "A": (Z10.0552); inexpensive instamatic camera for 126 cartridge film; Colour Citar 45mm f6.3 lens; shutter, 1/90 s for daylight; 1/30 s for flash. Built-in photoelectric exp control; hot shoe. Marked "Ikomatic A" on lower right front of camera. C 1964-1965.

| R2* $30 | £16 | DM49 | FF153 |

Ikomatic "F": (Z10.0551); similar to above except Frontar fixed focus lens; no exp control; built-in pop-up reflector for AG-1 flash bulb (top right of camera). Marked "Ikomatic F" on lower right front of camera. C 1964-1965.

| R2* $30 | £16 | DM49 | FF153 |

Ikonette: (Z504/12); small 127 roll film camera; Frontar 80mm f9 lens; self-cocking shutter. Removable back for film loading. There were at least two variations of the body latch mechanism. C 1929-1931.

| R3* $50 | £26 | DM82 | FF256 |

Ikonette 35: (Z500/24); 35mm camera of gray plastic; Novar 45mm f3.5 lens; Pronto shutter, X synch. Unusual combination film

Z

ZEISS

advance lever and shutter release. Close fitting blue plastic case. Red signal appears in vf when film advance lever is not cocked. C 1958-1960.

R2* $45	£24	DM74	FF230

Ikonta Series. Early model was called "Ikomat". All had lenses with front cell focus. C 1929-1956.

Ikonta: (Z520/14); 5 x 7.5cm folding roll film camera. C 1931. Novar 80mm f6.3 lens and Derval shutter, 40% less. price with Tessar 80mm f4.5 lens and Compur shutter.

R2* $50	£26	DM82	FF256

Ikonta A: (Z520); 1/2 120 film size; Compur shutter. C 1933-1940. Novar 80mm f4.5 lens, 40% less price with Tessar 80mm f3.5 lens.

R2* $80	£42	DM132	FF409

Ikonta A: (Z521); postwar version. Tessar 75mm f3.5 lens and Synchro-Compur shutter, Novar 75mm f4.5 or f3.5 and Prontar shutter, 40% less.

R2* $80	£42	DM132	FF409

Ikonta C: (Z520/2); 6 x 9cm folding roll film camera. C 1930-1940. Tessar 105mm F4.5 lens $40. Novar 105mm f8.3 lens **$35**. C 1936-1937 Tessar 105mm F3.8 lens **$45**. After 1937 Tessar 105mm f3.5 lens.

R2* $60	£31	DM99	FF307

Ikonta C: (Z523/2); 6 x 9cm folding roll film camera, heavy chrome trim on top cover. Novar 105mm f3.5 or f4.5, or Tessar 105mm f3.5 lens. C 1950-1956. **$50** (Z524/2), C 1954-1956. Similar to above, except had built-in CRF.

R2* $150	£79	DM247	FF767

Ikonta D: (Z520/15); early version used 126 film; later version used 616 film. Most Ikomats are of this size. C 1931-1939. Novar 120mm f6.3 lens and Derval shutter, **$35** Tessar 120mm f4.5 lens and Compur shutter.

R2* $50	£26	DM82	FF256

Ikonta B: (Z520/16); 12 exp, 6 x 6cm on 120 film. C 1937-1939. Novar 75mm f3.5 or f4.5 in Compur or Klio shutter, **$50**. Tessar 75mm f3.5 lens and Compur-Rapid shutter.

R2* $80	£42	DM132	FF409

Ikonta B: (Z521/16); similar to above, except had more chrome trim, and chrome lens mount. C 1948-1953 with Tessar lens.

R2* $65	£34	DM107	FF332

Ikonta B: (Z523/16); similar to above, except had chrome top plate and Prontor SV or Synchro-Compur shutter. C 1954-1956.

R2* $80	£42	DM132	FF409

Ikonta B: (Z524/16); 6 x 6cm roll film camera with built-in uncoupled RFR. C 1954-1956. Novar 105mm f3.5 or f4.5 lens and Prontor SV shutter, **$100**. Tessar 105mm f3.5 lens and Synchro-Compur shutter.

R2* $140	£73	DM231	FF716

Ikonta 35: (Z522/24); 35mm folding camera; Novar 45mm f3.5 or Tessar 45mm f2.8 lens; also Xenar 45mm f2.8 lens was supplied during the first two years. Rigid front lens bed - centre of camera. Marked "Ikonta" on leather on rear of camera. C 1949-1953.

R2* $65	£34	DM107	FF332

Juwel: (Z275/7); 9 x 12cm leather covered plate camera of metal; revolving back; rising, falling, shifting and tilting front; removable backs. Triple ext bellows; two rack and pinion knobs on folding bed; one moves back and front, other moves lens stand. Bayonet mount; interchangeable lenses. Marked "Juwel" or "Universal Juwel" on or under handle C 1927-1938. Price depends on condition and lens.

R4* $250	£131	DM412	FF1.3k

Juwel: (Z275/11); 13 x 18cm plate camera; lens interchanges with aluminium board, otherwise similar to above. Tessar or Triple convertible Protar. This was the most expensive camera mfg by Zeiss throughout the pre-war years. Camera used extensively by Ansel Adams. Rare and still usable. C 1927-1939. with Tessar 210mm f4.5 lens, **$500.** with Protar lens.

R3* $650	£341	DM1.1k	FF3.3k

Kolibri: (Z523/18); compact 127 roll film camera; lens extends for picture taking on brightly polished chrome tube. Unique shaped brown or black case; "Kolibri" in leather below lens. Hinge on right side of open case has screw in "foot" to be inserted in lens mount for horizontal still pictures. 16 exp, 4 x 6.5cm on 12 roll film. C 1930-1935. Novar 50mm f3.5 or f4.5 lens and Telma shutter, **$150**. Tessar 50mm f3.5 lens and rimset Compur shutter, common, **$300** Tessar 50mm f2.8 lens and Rim-set Compur shutter, rare, **$550** Microscope version with no lens or shutter, rare,**$350**. Biotar 45mm f2 lens and Rim-set Compur shutter.

R3* $650	£341	DM1.1k	FF3.3k

Kolibri

Kosmopolit: (Z818); 5 x 7; (Z819), 7 x 9.5; field camera; tapered bellow; reversing back; rising and sliding front (no swing). Wood finish, brass fittings. C 1927-1934.

R4* $275	£144	DM453	FF1.4k

Lilliput: (Z361), 4.5 x 6cm; (Z370), 6.5 x 9cm tiny strut-type folding plate camera; f12.5 lens; celluloid "ground glass"; struts inside bellows.
C 1927-1928.

R2* $125	£66	DM206	FF639

Lloyd: (Z510/17); black leather covered folding roll film camera; Tessar 120mm f4.5 lens; Compur shutter; ability to use cut film and ground glass focusing by sliding out back cover plate. Marked "Lloyd" in leather on front of camera. C 1928-1931.

R2* $40	£21	DM66	FF204

Maximar A: (Z207/3); 6.5 x 9cm folding plate camera; Tessar 105mm f4.5 lens; Compur shutter; slide in holders. Marked "Maximar" in leather on rear of camera. C 1927-1939.

R2* $75	£39	DM124	FF383

Maximar B: (Z207/7); 9 x 12cm folding plate camera; similar to above. Tessar 135mm f4.5 lens; Compur shutter. C 1927-1939.

R2* $80	£42	DM132	FF409

Maximar: (Z207/9); 10 x 15cm folding plate camera; similar to above. Tessar 165mm f4.5 lens; Compur shutter. C 1927-1937. Rare.

R* $125	£66	DM206	FF639

Miroflex A: (Z859/3); 6.5 x 9cm folding SLR plate camera; FPS 1/3 - 1/200 s. Reflex viewing; sportsfinder. Marked "Miroflex" in leather on front of camera. C 1927-1936. Tessar 120mm f4.5 lens, **$300**. with Tessar 135mm f3.5 or Bio Tessar 135mm f2.8 lens.

Miroflex A

R4* $400	£210	DM659	FF2k

Miroflex B: (Z859/7); 9 x 12cm film or plates; similar to above. Tessar 165mm f4.5 lens, **$250**. Tessar 165 f3.5 or Bio Tessar 165mm f2.8 lens, more common.

R4* $350	£184	DM577	FF1.8k

Nettar: (Z515); 4.5 x 6cm; (Z515/2), 6 x 9cm; (Z515/16); the Bob camera (Z510); was known as Nettar 510 in England. C 1934-1941. Inexpensive folding roll film camera with Nettar or Novar lens. "Nettar"

Z

ZEISS

Nettax with special Contameter

impressed on leather. Postwar version, C 1949-1957, (Z518/16) and (Z517/2), fancier style with body release and chrome top. Sixteen possible lens/shutter combinations. Novar models, **$30**. Tessar models.

R2* $40	£21	DM66	FF204

Nettax: (Z538/24); 35mm camera looks somewhat like Contax II, except has rotating RFR window attached to interchangeable lens; FPS to 1/1000 s. C 1936-1938. Tessar 50mm f2.8 lens, rare, **$600**. Tessar 50mm f3.5 lens, rare, **$750**. Extra for telephoto (rare), Triotar 105mm f5.6 lens, **$400**.

R4*	Prices as above

Nettax: (Z513/16); 6 x 6cm folding roll film camera; Novar 75mm f4.5 lens; Pronto shutter. Built-in uncoupled exp meter; chrome top cover. C 1955-1957. Rare.

R4* $65	£34	DM107	FF332

Nettel: (Z870), 4.5 x 6cm; (Z870/3), 6.5 x 9cm; (Z870/7) 9 x 12cm, most common; (Z870/9), 10 x 15cm; (Z870/11), 5" x 7". "Nettel" marked on right side of camera - below FPS winding and setting knob; black leather covered; 12 lens/shutter/format combinations. C 1929-1937.

R2* $70	£37	DM115	FF358

Nettel, Tropen: (Z871/3); tropical model; in four larger sizes shown above; focal plane press camera; polished teak wood, brown leather bellows.

R3* $650	£341	DM1.1k	FF3.3k

Nixe: (Z551/17); folding camera; Dominar, Tessar or Double Protar lens; double ext bellows. 8 x 10.5 roll film or 9 x 12cm cut film. Marked "Nixe" on handle or impressed in leather of body. C 1927-1934.

R2* $45	£24	DM74	FF230

Z

Nixe: (Z551/6); similar to above, except 8 x 14cm roll film or 9 x 14cm cut film.

R2* $55	£29	DM91	FF281

Onito: (Z126/3); 6.5 x 9cm; (Z126/7), 9 x 12cm. Inexpensive folding plate camera; Novar f6.3 lens; single ext bellows; lever focus. C 1927-1929.

R2* $30	£16	DM49	FF153

Orix: (Z3081); 10 x 15cm folding plate camera; Tessar 150mm f4.5 lens; Double ext bellows; rack and pinion focusing; was used as press camera; a special model with spring back was available. C 1928-1934.

R2* $60	£31	DM99	FF307

Palmos-O: 4.5 x 6cm plate camera; Tessar 80mm f2.7 (high-speed) lens; FPS 1/50-1/1000 s. Struts: folding door. Sold in Europe (1927) as Minimum Palmos. C 1927-1928.

R3* $450	£236	DM742	FF2.3k

Piccolette: (Z545/12); inexpensive all metal strut-type camera; Achromat 75mm f11, Novar 75mm f6.3 or Tessar 75mm f4.5 lens. Marked "Piccolette" below lens; "Zeiss Ikon" at 11 o'clock from lens; 3 x 4cm exp on 127 roll film. C 1927-1930, in Germany; available until 1932 in U.S.

R3* $60	£31	DM99	FF307

Piccolette-Luxus: (Z546/12); 4 x 6.5cm, top-of-the-line model, with folding bed. Dominar 5mm f4.5 or Tessar 75mm f4.5 lens; Dial-set Compur shutter. Lazy tong struts; brown leather covering, brown bellows. C 1927-1930.

R3* $200	£105	DM330	FF1k

Plaskop: (Z602/1); inexpensive stereo box camera. Marked "Plaskop" on front under left lens. 4.5 x 10.5cm exp. C 1927-1930.

R3* $125	£66	DM206	FF639

Plaskop: (Z603/1); stereo box camera; Novar 60mm f6.8 lenses. Marked "Plaskop" on oval label - left front. 4.5 x 10.5cm exp. C 1927-1930.

R3* $140	£73	DM231	FF716

Plaskop: (Z603/4); stereo box camera, similar to above, except has brilliant finder - top centre. 6 x 13cm exp. C 1927-1930.

R3* $225	£118	DM371	FF1.2k

Polyskop: (Z609/1); precision stereo box camera; tessar 65mm f4.5 lenses; Compur Dial-set stereo shutter. Brilliant finder - top centre; covered with black leather. 12 exp, 4.5 x 10.5cm on plates in septum magazine. C 1927-1930.

R3* $275	£144	DM453	FF1.4k

Polyskop: (Z609/4); similar to above except has Tessar 75mm f4.5 lenses. 6 x 13cm exp on plates. C 1927-1930.

R3* $275	£144	DM453	FF1.4k

Simplex: (Z112/7); inexpensive folding plate camera; for 9 x 12cm plates. Frontar 140mm f9 lens or Novar 135mm f6.3 lens. Marked "Simplex" on leather under handle; "Zeiss Ikon" under lens on front of lens standard. C 1928-1930.

R2* $30	£16	DM49	FF153

Simplex: (Z511/2); brown plastic bodied 6 x 9cm roll film camera; Nettar 105mm f6.5 lens; Telma or Derval shutter. Marked "Simplex". The hardware and struts vary on this model.

R3* $50	£26	DM82	FF256

Simplex

Simplex-Ernoflex: (Z853), 4.5 x 6cm; (Z853/3), 6.5 x 9cm; (Z853/7), 9 x 12cm. SLR focal plane camera; Ernoplast f4.5 or f3.5, Ernon f3.5 or Tessar f4.5 lens; CFPS 1/20-1/1000 s. The early model was marked "Ernemann" - right side and back; "Zeiss Ikon" - on round metal plate. In 1930 it was marked "Simplex Ernoflex" over lens; "Zeiss Ikon" - right side and door of focusing hood. C 1927-1930. NSI.

| R3* | $450+ | £236+ | DM742+ | FF2.3k+ |

Sirene: (Z135/7); inexpensive folding plate camera (9 x 12cm or 6.5 x 9cm); marked "Sirene" under handle. The same model number used later on Volta cameras. C 1927.

| R2* | $30 | £16 | DM49 | FF153 |

Sirene: (Z135/5); similar to above, 3¼" x 4¼" size for American market; Dominar 135mm f4.5 lens; Compur shutter. C 1930-1931. Rare.

| R4* | $50 | £26 | DM82 | FF256 |

Sonnet: (Z303); 4.5 x 6cm tropical folding plate camera; Novar 80mm or 75mm f6.3, Dominar or Tessar 75mm f4.5 lens. Teak wood construction, brown leather door covering and brown bellows. C 1927-1930.

| R3* | $750 | £394 | DM1.2k | FF3.8k |

Sonnet: (Z303/3); tropical 6.5 x 9cm folding plate camera; similar to above, except 6.5 x 9cm size. Novar 105mm f6.3 or Dominar or Tessar 120mm f4.5 lens. C 1927-1930.

| R4* | $700 | £367 | DM1.2k | FF3.6k |

Stereolette-Cupido: (Z611); 4.5 x 10.7cm folding stereo plate camera; black leather covered. Marked "Stereolette-Cupido" on handle; "Stereolette" on outside of door. C 1927-1928.

| R3* | $250 | £131 | DM412 | FF1.3k |

Stereoco: (Z621/1); 4.5 x 10.7cm leather covered stereo box plate camera; tapered shape; Tessar 55mm f6.3 lenses; Derval or Dial-set Compur shutters. Marked "Stereoco" on upper front between lenses; "Zeiss Ikon" below lenses. C 1927-1930.

| R3* | $300 | £157 | DM495 | FF1.5k |

Stereo-Ernoflex: (Z621/1); folding stereo camera; Ernotar 75mm f4.5, Ernon 75mm f3.5 or Tessar 75mm f3.5 lenses; CFPS 1/20-1/1000 s. Full length viewing hood cover. C 1927-1929.

| R4* | $550 | £289 | DM907 | FF2.8k |

Stereo-Simplex-Ernoflex: (Z615/1); non-folding stereo box camera; Ernon 75mm f3.5 or Tessar 75mm or 80mm f4.5 lenses; CFPS. Marked "Ernemann" on front between lenses. Viewing hood cover is on 1/2 of camera top; pop-up frame finder on other half. C 1927-1930.

| R3* | $500 | £262 | DM824 | FF2.6k |

Stereo Ideal: (Z651); 6 x 13cm folding stereo camera; Tessar 90mm f4.5 lenses; Dial-set Compur shutter on 1927 version; Compound shutter on 1928 versions. Marked "Stereo-Ideal-651" on handle; "Zeiss Ikon" inside door. Covered with black leather. C 1927-1928.

| R4* | $300 | £157 | DM495 | FF1.5k |

Stereo Nettel: (Z613/4); 6 x 13cm scissors strut stereo camera; Tessar 90mm f4 lenses; FPS; wire finder; focusing knob on right side (over shutter winding knob). Internal roller blind separates two images (removable for full frame use). C 1927-1930. Black leather, $350. (Z614/4), tropical model: teak wood, brown bellows.

| R4* | $1.2k | £630 | DM2k | FF6.1k |

Stereo Nettel: (Z613/9); similar to above, except 10 x 15cm model. Tessar 120mm f4.5 lenses. C 1927-1930. Black leather, **$350** (Z614/9), tropical model: teak wood and brown bellows.

| R4* | $1k | £525 | DM1.6k | FF5.1k |

Super Ikonta Series

Folding roll film camera: lenses had front cell focusing, coupled to a coincidence type built-in RFR. Post-war models had factory installed flash synch.

Super Ikonta "A": (Z530); 1934-1937.

| R2* | $225 | £118 | DM371 | FF1.2k |

Super Ikonta "A": (Z530); 1937-1950.

| R2* | $250 | £131 | DM412 | FF1.3k |

Super Ikonta "A": (Z531); 1950-1956.

| R2* | $450 | £236 | DM742 | FF2.3k |

Super Ikonta "B": (Z530/16); 1935-1937.

| R2* | $250 | £131 | DM412 | FF1.3k |

Super Ikonta A

Super Ikonta B

Super Ikonta C

Super Ikonta IV

Super Ikonta "B": (Z532/16); 1937-1951.

R2* $300	£157	DM495	FF1.5k

Super Ikonta "B": (Z532/16); 1951-1956.

R2* $350	£184	DM577	FF1.8k

Super Ikonta "BX": (Z533/16); 1937-1952.

R2* $350	£184	DM577	FF1.8k

Super Ikonta "BX": (Z533/16); 1952-1957.

R2* $350	£184	DM577	FF1.8k

Super Ikonta III: (Z531/16); 1954-1958.

R2* $350	£184	DM577	FF1.8k

Super Ikonta IV: (Z534/16); 1956-1960.

R2* $425	£223	DM701	FF2.2k

Super Ikonta "C": (Z530/2); 1934-1936.

R2* $300	£157	DM495	FF1.5k

Super Ikonta "C": (Z531/2); 1936-1950.

R2* $325	£171	DM536	FF1.7k

Super Ikonta "C": (Z531/2); 1950-1955.

R2* $300	£157	DM495	FF1.5k

Super Ikonta BX

Super Ikonta "D": (Z530/15); 1934-1936,.

R3* $250	£131	DM412	FF1.3k

Super Ikonta "D": (Z530/15); 1936-1939.

R4* $300	£157	DM495	FF1.5k

Super Nettel: (Z536/24); 35mm folding bellows camera; Tessar 50mm f3.5 or f2.8 lens. 1935 - Triotar 50mm f3.5 lens offered. The Tessar lens was discontinued in 1936. FPS 1/5-1/1000 s. Black enamel finish with leather covering. Marked "Super Nettel" in

Z

Super Nettel

Super Nettel II

leather on door. C 1934-1937.

R3* $425	£223	DM701	FF2.2k

Super Nettel II: (Z537/24); similar to above, except had polished chrome door, top cover was finished with matte chrome. Tessar 50mm f2.8 lens. C 1936-1938.

R4* $750	£394	DM1.2k	FF3.8k

Symbolica: (Z10.6035); 35mm camera; Tessar 50mm f2.8 lens. Coupled match-needle exp meter; no RFR; lens had front cell focus. Marked "Symbolica" on top. C 1959-1962.

R2* $65	£34	DM107	FF332

Taxo: (Z122/3); 6.5 x 9cm; (Z122/7), 9 x 12cm; inexpensive folding plate camera; Periskop 105mm f11, Novar 105mm or 135mm f6.3 lens (Frontar or Dominar lens later); Derval shutter. Single ext bellows. Marked "Taxo" on body under handle. Lens had slide on track for focusing. C 1927-1931.

R2* $25	£13	DM41	FF128

Taxo: (Z126/3); 6.5 x 9cm; (Z126/7), 9 x 12cm; similar to above, except had radial focusing lever. C 1927-1930.

R2* $25	£13	DM41	FF128

Taxona: post WWII 35mm camera, 24 x 24mm made from captured Tenax I parts; Tessar 37.5mm f3.5 lens. Marked "TAXONA" around lens. See Tenax below. 24 x 24mm exp on 35mm film.

R2* $50	£26	DM82	FF256

Tenax: popular strut folding plate camera; 16 different lenses offered; compound shutter. 4.5 x 6cm, 6.5 x 9cm, 4.5 x 10.7cm (stereo). Clean-up items that were never actually mfd by or marked "Zeiss Ikon". Marked "TENAX" or "Taschen Tenax" on front or top. C 1927.

R3* $150	£79	DM247	FF767

Tenax I: (Z570/37); Novar 35mm f3.5 lens; Compur shutter. Lever on right side advanced film and cocked shutter; no RFR. 35mm film, 50 exp, 24 x 24mm on 36 exp roll. Marked "TENAX" under lens. C 1930-1941.

R2* $100	£52	DM165	FF511

Tenax I: similar to above, except Tessar 37.5mm f3.5 coated lens; flash synch contact on top of shutter. Marked "Zeiss Ikon" above lens; "TENAX" below lens. Possibly East German. C 1948.

R2* $160	£84	DM264	FF818

Tenax II: (Z580/27); 24 x 24mm format; interchangeable lenses; coupled rangefinder; shoe for vf and Contameter (No. 1339). A rare microscope (or X-ray) version exists with dark slide and without lens. C 1938-1941. Tessar 40mm f2.4 lens, **$275**. Sonnar 40mm f2 lens.

R4* $300	£157	DM495	FF1.5k

Accessory lenses for Tenax II:
Sonnar 75mm f4 (telephoto) lens with vf, **$400**
Orthometer 27mm f4.5 (wide angle) lens with vf, **$350**.

Tenax Automatic: (Z10.0651); full frame 35mm camera; Tessar 50mm f2.8 lens; Prontormat shutter. No RFR; front cell focus; auto exp control with selenium photoelectric cell. Marked "Tenax" at 11 o'clock from lens on exp meter window. C 1960-1963.

| R2* $25 | £13 | DM41 | FF128 |

Tengoflex: (Z85/16); box camera; 6 x 6cm exp on 120 film. Large brilliant finder on top gives appearance of TLR. Marked "Tengoflex" on front. C 1941-1942. Rare.

| R4* $600 | £315 | DM989 | FF3.1k |

Tessco: 9 x 12cm folding plate camera; 5 different lenses range from Periskop f11 to Tessar f4.5. Double ext bellows. Marked "Tessco" in leather on handle. C 1927-1928. Rare.

| R4* $60 | £31 | DM99 | FF307 |

Trona: (Z210/3), (Z210/5), (Z210/7); folding plate camera; Dominar or Tessar f4.5 lens. Double ext bellows. (Z210/5), 8.5 x 11cm (3¼" x 4¼") was originally marketed in England and America; today it is hard to find. "TRONA" and model number marked under handle. C 1927-1930. (Z210/3), (Z210/5), **$60** (Z210/7), **$40.**

| R2* | Prices as above |

Trona: (Z214/3), 6.5 x 9cm; (Z214/7), 9 x 12cm; Tessar f3.5 lens; Compur shutter (Rim-set after 1930). The original ground glass back was of aluminium and it is rare today. The camera is usually found with standard back. "TRONA" and model number marked under handle. C 1929-1938. (Z214/3), **$70**. (Z214/7), **$60.**

| R2* $60 | £31 | DM99 | FF307 |

Tropen Adoro

Tropen Adoro: (Z230/3), (Z230/7), (Z230/9); tropical folding plate camera; Tessar 105mm or 120mm f4.5 lens in (Z230/3); Tessar 135mm or 150mm f4.5 lens in (Z230/7), 9 x 12cm; Tessar 165mm or 180mm f4.5 lens (Z230/9) 10 x 15cm. Compur shutter in all models. Double ext bellows. Brown leather covering on door and back; brown

Trona cameras

ZEISS-ZUIHO

bellows. "TROPEN ADORO" and model number marked on leather of door. C 1927-1936.

| R4* $800 | £420 | DM1.3k | FF4.1k |

Tropica: (Z285/7), 9 x 12cm; (Z285/6), 10 x 15cm; (Z285/11), 5" x 7"; folding plate camera. Polished teak wood construction (even the door to the ground glass back is of teak wood) with hardware of German silver. Rotating back. Marked "Zeiss Ikon" between knobs on front standard. 14 different lenses, all in Compur shutter. All sizes are rare today, especially the 5" x 7" size. C 1927-1931 (1935 in foreign catalogues). NSR. Estimate:

| R5* $1.5k+ | £787+ | DM2.5k+ | FF7.7k+ |

Unette: (Z550); leatherette covered wooden box camera; 40mm f12.5 lens. Metal frame finder on top (rear). 22 x 31mm exp on roll film. Marked "UNETTE" on front over lens in leatherette: "Zeiss Ikon" over lens; "Ernemann" on right side. C 1927-1930. Rare, only one sale known.

| R5* est $300 | £157 | DM495 | FF1.5k |

Victrix: (Z101); small folding plate camera; Novar 75mm f6.3, Dominar 75mm f4.5 and Tessar lens; Compur shutter. 4.5 x 6cm exp. Marked "Victrix 101" in leather on top of camera. "Zeiss Ikon" marked on lens, between knobs and on door. C 1927-1931. Rare.

| R4* $100 | £52 | DM165 | FF511 |

Volta: (Z146/3), (146/7); inexpensive folding plate camera; Novar, Dominar or Tessar lenses; Compur or Klio shutters. Single ext bellows; radial arm focusing. C 1927-1931.

| R4* $40 | £21 | DM66 | FF204 |

Volta: (Z135/3), (Z135/7), similar to above but without radial focus. C 1926-1927.

| R4* $40 | £21 | DM66 | FF204 |

Z ZORKI see KRAZNOGORSK MECHNICAL WORKS

ZUIHO PRECISION OPTICAL Company, Japan

Honor SL: (ZU100); 1959 CFPS, 1 - 1/1000 sec, combined RFR/VFR window, lever advance and folding crank rewind. Honor 50mm/f1.9 lens. This camera uses a redesigned top plate, and has lost some of its "Leica copy" looks, more like a Canon VT or Tanack V3. Quite rare.

| R4* $1k | £525 | DM1.6k | FF5.1k |

Honor : (ZU101); 1956 CFPS, 1 - 1/500 sec, seperate RFR/VFR window, knob. Honor or Hexanon 50mm/f1.9 lens or Hexar 50mm/f3.5 lens. Quite Leica like!

| R4* $700 | £367 | DM1.2k | FF3.6k |

E

D

INDEX

MANUFACTURER INDEX

U

V

T

INDEX

INDEX

INDEX

INDEX

CAMERA INDEX

INDEX

C

INDEX

INDEX

CAMERA INDEX

INDEX

E

INDEX

Giroux Daguerreotype Camera; 195
Gitza; 195
Globus Field View Camera; 174
Glock; 195
Gloria; 132
Gloriette B; 131
Gloriette; 131
Glyphos Stereo Camera, Le; 341
Gnu Stereoscopic Magazine Hand Camera; 373
Golda; 199
Goldeck 16; 198
Goldeck 16; 198
Golden Ricoh "16"; 341
Goldi; 402
Goldix; 199
Gousset, Le; 197
Gradosol; 109
Graflex Camera, The; 199
Graflex Fingerprint Camera; 202
Graflex, The 1A; 201
Graflex, The 3A; 202
Grand Photographe Camera; 149
Graph-Check Sequential Camera; 197
Graphic 35; 204
Graphic Camera, The; 199
Graphic Jet; 204
Graphic No.0; 201
Graphic Sr, The; 199
Graphic Twin Lens Special, The; 199
Graphic View Camera; 204
Graphostereochrome, Le; 291
Great Wall DF-2; 205
Great Wall SZ-1; 205
Great Wall SZ-2; 205
Grenaflex; 358
Grundmann Leipzig Detective Camera; 206

Gugo-Knips; 199
Guilford, The; 206
Guilleminot Detective Camera; 206
Guinea Detective or Hand Camera; 206
Gymea Minor; 336

H

Handy, Le; 211
Handy, The; 346
Hanimar; 210
Hanimex Box; 210
Hans Pock Detective Camera; 337
Hapyucc (Narciss); 211
Harvard Camera; 331
Hasselblad 1000F; 212
Hasselblad 1600F; 211
Hasselblad Super Wide Camera; 212
Hawkeye Detective Camera; 126
Hawkeye Detective Camera; 129
Heag I; 174
Heag II; 174
Heag III; 174
Heag IV; 174
Heag V; 174
Heag VII; 174
Heag XI; 174,175
Heag XII; 175
Heag XII; 175
Heidoscop; 184
Hell-Klack; 342
Hensold Reporter; 223
Hermagis Field Camera; 212
Herzog Camera; 212
Hetherington Magazine Camera; 213

INDEX

INDEX

CAMERA INDEX

CAMERA INDEX

INDEX

M

INDEX

CAMERA INDEX

INDEX

CAMERA INDEX

Q

R

INDEX

S

INDEX

INDEX

INDEX

INDEX

INDEX

Y

Z

INDEX

INDEX

◫ HOVE FOTO BOOKS

The Leica Pocket Book – 5th Edition

New edition brought up-to-date with new products and latest production numbers. The guide to all Leica cameras and lenses. Lists variations, military models, serial numbers, production quantities and factory conversions.

7 3/4" x 3 3/4" 144pp Leatherette binding
ISBN 0-906447-88-7

Asahi Pentax Cameras 1951-89

Asahi Optical were responsible more than any other manufacturer for the success of the 35mm format. The author is a collector and authority on Pentax and also appreciates them for their elegant lines and as masterpieces of industrial design.

8 1/2" x 6" 200pp Casebound and dust jacket
(250 illustrations)
ISBN 0-9514392-0-0

NEW

Leica International Price Guide – 5th Edition

Current prices for all items listed in Leica Pocket Book and Leica Accessory Guide. Includes rarity and condition guides. Each item is priced for three different markets: Germany, United Kingdom and United States.

7 1/4" x 3 1/4" 100pp Leatherette binding
ISBN 0-906447-89-5

Spycamera — The Minox Story

Morris Moses is the leading American authority on the history and development of the Minox. Moses tells the story of Walter Zapp and his vision of a high-quality, very small camera. From pre-war production in Latvia to post-war West Germany. As well as technical information there are tales of covert activities and reproductions of pictures taken in this manner.

8 1/2" x 6" 200pp, casebound and dust-jacket
ISBN 0-906447-43-7

My Life With the Leica

Much has been written about the early days of Leica, but here is someone who was actually there as an apprentice at Leitz when it was still very much a family business, when Oskar Barnack was his inspiration and mentor. Walter Benser was to become famous for his Leica slide lectures in America and Europe, as well as his unique style of Leica photography (illustrated).

9 3/4" x 6 3/4" 224pp, casebound and dust-jacket
ISBN 0-906447-58-5

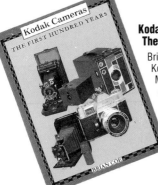

Kodak Cameras – The First Hundred Years

Brian Coe, the editor has collected 100 years worth of everybody's Kodak's. 600 cameras are listed alphabetically, divided by type. Most of them are illustrated, including many of the variations; in all over 760 pictures (including colour). For the collector this is an essential book. For those who remember their Kodak as the faithful recorder of their life and times, it's a lively visit with old friends.

10 1/2" x 8 1/2" 300pp, casebound
and dust- jacket   ISBN 0-906447-58-5

Exakta Cameras

Complete story by Clement Aguila and Michel Rouah documents fully the pioneering SLR roll-film cameras and the world's first successful 35mm SLR. Lists all models, lenses and accessories. A star system gives the comparative rarity of each camera

8 1/2" x 6" 159pp, 144 b&w illustrations
Casebound and dust-jacket
ISBN 0-906447-38-0

Nikon Rangefinder Cameras

An Illustrated History by Robert Rotoloni, from the end of the war to the very last rangefinder model produced. Includes lenses, accessories, etc.

350 b&w illustrations
8 1/2" x 6" 190pp, casebound,dust-jacket
ISBN 0-906447-25-9

Canon Rangefinder Cameras
1933-1968

Peter Dechert's complete history of the Canon Rangefinder camera; its lenses, variations, numbers, types, etc.

200 b&w illustrations
8 1/2" x 6" 200pp, casebound,dust-jacket
ISBN 0-906447-30-5

Leica and Leicaflex Lenses
Second Edition
Gianni Rogliatti

The standard reference on the history of the Leica camera, from the first prototype to the present day, with detailed accounts of all models produced, serial numbers and glossary of code words. Fully illustrated in b&w.

8 1/2" x 6" 180pp
Casebound, dust-jacket
ISBN 0-906447-07-0

Leica Accessory Guide

Comprehensive guide for collectors and dealers to practically all known Leica accessories for screw, M and reflex cameras. Rangefinders, viewfinders, reflex housing and focusing stages with all accessories, winders, motors, stereo, close-up, single exposure housing, copying, technical and medical, meters, flash, as well as a host of minor accessories. 1100 known accessories listed and 500 illustrated

7 3/4" x 3 3/4" 124pp. Leatherette binding
ISBN 0-906447-28-3

Leica — The First 60 Years
Gianni Rogliatti

The standard reference on the history of the Leica camera, from the first prototype to the present day, with detailed accounts of all models produced, serial numbers and glossary of code words. Fully illustrated in b&w.

8 1/2" x 6" 224pp, casebound, dust-jacket
ISBN 0-906447-32-1

Hove Foto Books publish an extensive range of collectors' books and modern Leica books as well as a series of manuals for all the popular modern SLR cameras, also professional guides to Canon and Hasselblad, and video handbooks. Further information can be obtained either direct from Hove Foto Books or any of our worldwide distributors.

Leica General Catalogues & Instruction Books
Reprints of Leitz catalogues for the key years in the history of Leica. Invaluable source of information on cameras, lenses, accessories, projectors, and copying equipment. Ideal for collectors and users of older equipment.

Leica General Catalogue 1931	ISBN 0-906447-13-5
Leica General Catalogue 1933	ISBN 0-906447-14-3
Leica General Catalogue 1936	ISBN 0-906447-15-1
Leica General Catalogue 1955/58	ISBN 0-906447-16-x
Leica General Catalogue 1961	ISBN 0-906447-08-9
Leica General Catalogue 1975	ISBN 0-906447-27-5
Instructions for use of Models Standard, IIIa, 250 and Accessories	ISBN 0-906447-17-8
Instructions for use of Models c, f and g	ISBN 0-906447-10-1
Instructions for use of Models M1, M2, M3 and M4	ISBN 0-906447-18-6
Instructions for use of Models M5, CL, Leicaflex, Leicaflex SL and SL2	ISBN 0-906447-19-4
Instructions for use of Reproduction Devices including Visoflex, Bellows, etc.	ISBN 0-906447-04-6

HOVE FOTO BOOKS

34 Church Road, Hove, Sussex BN3 2GJ ENGLAND
Tel: 0273 822000   Fax: 0273 723504

Dear Reader and Collector;

In the last five (5) years since we have opened a " TRADE & USED DEPARTMENT "
we have concentrated and specialized in trying to procure rare and collectable camera pieces.
Our efforts have rewarded us handsomely, as we now have the largest selection on display
of many rare Cameras, Lenses, Etc. in the New York Area. For example, we have an extensive
selection of CANON, LEICA, NIKON, ZEISS IKON, in range-finder and SLR equipment also
BRONICA, DEARDORF, GRAFLEX, HASSELBLAD, KOWA, LINHOFF, MAMIYA, ROLLEIFLEX, and
many more too numerous to mention. We also have an extensive collection of SUPER 8mm & 16mm
movie cameras & acc. In our store we have on display over 5000 of the most beautiful
and rarest pieces of Camera equipment ever to be displayed in any establishment.

We have our entire collection on computer, which enables us to send you a Catalog of
our entire inventory. Or if you desire or need a specific type of Camera, we can print you
an up-to-date print-out of those cameras. Our success can be measured by the reputation that
we have established world-wide with an extensive list of repeat customers, who are also on our
computer mailing list where we inform them of our latest acquisitions as soon as they become
available. We also have a service where if there is a certain item that you are interested in
obtaining we are constantly on the look-out for it, and when it becomes available we will
inform you about it immediately.

We also have a Trade-in department where we purchase anything, from one item to an
entire Collection or Estate. We can either come to your place or we can have your items
picked-up from your place via UPS at our expense.

Whether you are buying or selling, you can feel confident that you will be treated with
fairness and courtesy. As our motto says *" A SATISFIED CUSTOMER IS A REPEAT CUSTOMER"*

FOTO-CELL
Trade and Used Dept.